SPECTROSCOPIC AND GROUP THEORETICAL METHODS IN PHYSICS

Spectroscopic

RACAH

PUBLISHED UNDER THE AUSPICES OF
THE HEBREW UNIVERSITY OF JERUSALEM
THE ISRAEL ACADEMY OF SCIENCES AND HUMANITIES

and Group Theoretical Methods in Physics

MEMORIAL VOLUME

Edited by: F. BLOCH, S. G. COHEN, A. DE-SHALIT
S. SAMBURSKY, I. TALMI

1968
NORTH-HOLLAND PUBLISHING COMPANY – AMSTERDAM

Library of Congress Catalog Card Number: 68-16558

Publishers:
NORTH-HOLLAND PUBLISHING CO. - AMSTERDAM
SOLE DISTRIBUTORS FOR THE WESTERN HEMISPHERE:
WILEY INTERSCIENCE DIVISION
JOHN WILEY & SONS, INC. – NEW YORK

Printed in The Netherlands

Giulio Racah

9 February 1909 – 28 August 1965

Preface

The sudden death of Giulio Racah in 1965 at the age of 56, was a great loss to theoretical physics. Racah was a profound and original researcher who left his mark on important developments in atomic, nuclear and elementary particle physics. For 26 years, since leaving Italy, Racah worked and taught in Jerusalem at the Hebrew University. During the years of World War II, in relative isolation, he produced some of his most important work; he developed new powerful techniques and group theoretical methods for solving problems of complex atomic spectra, which later were to find wide applications in nuclear theory and elementary particle physics.

The loss to physics in Israel was tremendous. He was essentially the father of theoretical physics in Israel. Single handed, as an inspiring teacher, he had a profound effect on many generations of students at the Hebrew University. Thus, the Racah tradition is carried on in many scientific institutions in Israel.

The present volume contains articles from colleagues, friends and pupils, covering a wide range of topics in physics. For the most part these papers fall under the general heading covered by the title of the volume, "Spectroscopic and Group Theoretical Methods in Physics". These are the methods to which Racah devoted his creative endeavors and which bear his distinct and original mark.

The Editors

F. Bloch, *Stanford University, Stanford, California*
S. G. Cohen, *The Hebrew University of Jerusalem, Jerusalem, Israel*
A. De-Shalit, *The Weizmann Institute of Science, Rehovoth, Israel*
S. Sambursky, *The Hebrew University of Jerusalem, Jerusalem, Israel*
I. Talmi, *The Weizmann Institute of Science, Rehovoth, Israel*

CONTRIBUTORS

CONTENTS

Spectroscopic and group theoretical methods in physics

SEMICLASSICAL LIMIT OF RACAH COEFFICIENTS†

G. PONZANO*

Palmer Physical Laboratory, Princeton University, Princeton, New Jersey, U.S.A.

and

T. REGGE

Institute for Advanced Study, Princeton, New Jersey, U.S.A.

1. Introduction

Almost twenty-five years ago the W-coefficient appeared for the first time in a paper by Racah[1]) as an auxiliary tool for the computation of matrix elements in the theory of complex spectra. Today there is hardly any branch of physics involving angular momenta[2]) where the use of W-coefficients is not needed in order to carry out the simplest computation. Yet we feel that the W-coefficient is something more than an extremely successful computational tool and a beautiful toy for theoretical physicists to play with. In fact, a complete understanding of the properties of this remarkable function may very well yield to a new insight into the theory of angular momenta.

We think, and we know that our view is shared by others[3]), that a complete investigation of the semiclassical limit of W-coefficients and related functions is a prerequisite for a deeper understanding of their properties.

The present paper contains a heuristic derivation of an asymptotic formula, or better, of a set of asymptotic formulae with separate ranges of validity, for the W-coefficient. These formulae are certainly a useful complement to the existing tables of Racah coefficients, since they are remarkably accurate for surprisingly low values of the angular momenta involved.

A similar point of view could be adopted for the Clebsch–Gordan coefficients. However, since their definition depends on the particular labelling

† Work supported in part by EOAR under grant 66–29.

* On leave of absence from Istituto di Fisica, Torino, Italy. N.A.T.O. visiting fellow.

adopted for the vector basis of the representations, and since, moreover, they can be deduced as a particular limit carried on the W-coefficients, we are definitely tempted to regard them as subsidiary quantities in this paper.

Coming back to the W-coefficient or, rather, to the symmetric version of it, i.e. the 6*j*-symbol defined by Wigner[4]), it has been for years a normal practice to associate to it a diagram or graph which exhibits the symmetry properties in a most obvious way. A further advantage of these graphs is that they can be generalized to the higher order 3*nj*-symbols defined by Wigner[4]) and others[5,6]). There are at least three different versions[7]) of these graphical algorithms, all having approximately the same content, the

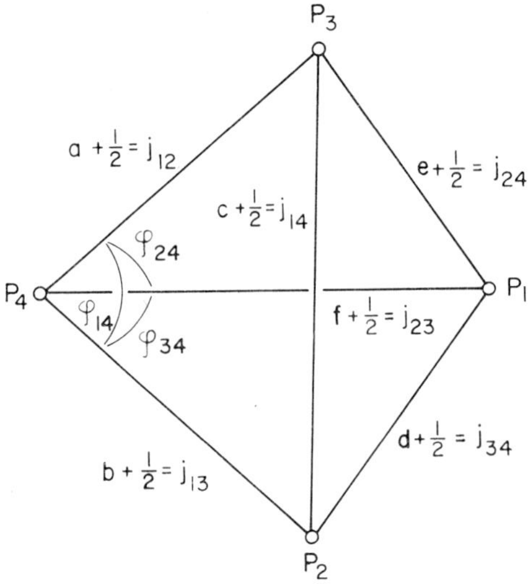

Fig. 1. Three-dimensional representation of the 6*j*-symbol $\begin{Bmatrix} a & b & c \\ d & e & f \end{Bmatrix}$.

translation of one into the others being achieved through some principle of plane or space duality. The reason for choosing any one of them is rather sentimental and largely related to individual habits.

We shall prefer here a three-dimensional representation in which angular momenta appear as vectors satisfying "bona fide" graphical composition rules. In this particular calculus the 6*j*-symbol $\begin{Bmatrix} a & b & c \\ d & e & f \end{Bmatrix}$ is associated to the tetrahedron shown in fig. 1. So far the tetrahedron is just a mnemonical device. However, we may think about a real solid T whose edges are just $a+\frac{1}{2}$, $b+\frac{1}{2}$, etc.[8]). With reference to fig. 1, we shall use also the following notation for the edges: $j_{12}=a+\frac{1}{2}$, $j_{13}=b+\frac{1}{2}$, $j_{14}=c+\frac{1}{2}$, $j_{34}=d+\frac{1}{2}$, $j_{24}=e+\frac{1}{2}$, $j_{23}=f+\frac{1}{2}$, and $j_{hh}=0$, $j_{hk}=j_{kh}(h, k=1, 2, 3, 4)$.

We shall restrict ourselves to values of the angular momenta which satisfy the triangular inequalities, i.e., $|b-c|\leqslant a\leqslant b+c$, etc. for the triads (abc), (aef), (dbf), (dec). Therefore, in each face there must be an even number of half-integer angular momenta. This entails that the sums $q_1=a+b+c$, $q_2=a+e+f$, $q_3=b+d+f$, $q_4=c+d+e$, $p_1=a+b+d+e$, $p_2=a+c+d+f$, $p_3=b+c+e+f$, are all integer. Moreover, because of the triangular inequalities, we have

$$p_h \geqslant q_k\,, \qquad h, k = 1, 2, 3, 4\,. \tag{1.1}$$

While these conditions are in general sufficient to guarantee the existence of a non-vanishing $6j$-symbol, they are not enough to ensure the existence of the tetrahedron T with the given edges. Since the two cases (A) T exists, (B) T does not exist, deserve radically different asymptotic treatments, we must give necessary and sufficient conditions for the existence of T.

It is known since Tartaglia[9]) and Jungius[10]) that the square of the volume of a tetrahedron is given by a polynomial in the square of its edges; in a more symmetrical setting, given by Cayley in his first published paper[11]), we have indeed

$$2^3(3!)^2\,V^2 = \begin{vmatrix} 0 & j_{34}^2 & j_{24}^2 & j_{23}^2 & 1 \\ j_{34}^2 & 0 & j_{14}^2 & j_{13}^2 & 1 \\ j_{24}^2 & j_{14}^2 & 0 & j_{12}^2 & 1 \\ j_{23}^2 & j_{13}^2 & j_{12}^2 & 0 & 1 \\ 1 & 1 & 1 & 1 & 0 \end{vmatrix}. \tag{1.2}$$

Therefore we see that $V^2\geqslant 0$ is a necessary condition. It can be proved to be also sufficient. In fact let us keep all edges fixed but, for instance, j_{12} and let $j_{12}=x$. Then V^2 is a second order polynomial in x^2 which will have two roots $(x_<)^2<(x_>)^2$. Since $\partial^2[V^2(x^2)]/[\partial x^2]^2=-(j_{34})^2/72$, we shall have $V^2(x^2)>0$ if $x_<<x<x_>$. A more elaborate discussion would show, in addition, that $x_<>x_{\mathrm{m}}-\frac{1}{2}$ where x_{m} is the largest between $|b-c|+\frac{1}{2}$ and $|e-f|+\frac{1}{2}$, and that $x_><x_{\mathrm{M}}+\frac{1}{2}$ where x_{M} is the smallest between $b+c+\frac{1}{2}$ and $e+f+\frac{1}{2}$. Therefore the condition $V^2>0$ is stronger than (1.1). We shall accordingly distinguish between the above mentioned cases: (A) $V^2>0$, and (B) $V^2<0$. The third possibility, $V^2=0$, which would correspond to a flat tetrahedron, is purely academical, for it can be proved that if p_h and q_k are all integer then $V^2\neq 0$ (ref. 12). A "tetrahedron" in (B) will be referred to as a hyperflat tetrahedron. Let us start with case:

(A) We expect T to be relevant in describing the properties of $6j$-symbols.

In fact a result due to Wigner[13]) states that for large angular momenta

$$\begin{Bmatrix} a & b & c \\ d & e & f \end{Bmatrix}^2 \sim \frac{1}{24\pi V}, \tag{1.3a}$$

where V is the volume of T. This formula, which has been a guiding principle in the present investigation, is very interesting because it relates the numerical value of the 6*j*-symbol directly to a geometric property of T. However, as stressed in the same ref. 13, Wigner's asymptotic estimate cannot be accepted at face value. Inspection of numerical tables shows in fact that the symbol is a rapidly oscillating function of the indices and that the r.h.s. of (1.3a) more correctly approximates the average of the l.h.s. over several contiguous values of the indices.

A correct statement would be

$$\begin{Bmatrix} a & b & c \\ d & e & f \end{Bmatrix} \simeq \frac{1}{\sqrt{12\pi V}} \mathscr{C}, \tag{1.3b}$$

where $\mathscr{C}$ is a rapidly oscillating function so that the average $\mathscr{C}^2$ over a large enough interval is $\frac{1}{2}$. We claim that

$$\begin{Bmatrix} a & b & c \\ d & e & f \end{Bmatrix} \simeq \frac{1}{\sqrt{12\pi V}} \cos\left(\sum_{h,\,k=1}^{4} j_{hk}\theta_{hk} + \tfrac{1}{4}\pi \right), \tag{1.4}$$

where $\theta_{hk} = \theta_{kh} (k \neq h = 1, 2, 3, 4)$ are the angles between the outer normals of the two faces which belong to j_{hk}. Let A_h be the area of the face opposite to the vertex h (fig. 1); then we have (appendix B)

$$A_h A_k \sin\theta_{hk} = \tfrac{3}{2} V j_{hk}, \qquad h \neq k = 1, 2, 3, 4. \tag{1.5}$$

(B) Wigner's argument yields

$$\begin{Bmatrix} a & b & c \\ d & e & f \end{Bmatrix}^2 \sim 0. \tag{1.6}$$

This result could be loosely described as the impossibility of having six angular momenta forming a non-existing tetrahedral scheme. A closer scrutiny of numerical tables, however, shows that the symbols in (B), although, as a rule, smaller than in (A), are still non-vanishing.

Any attempt to use (1.4) in this region leads to a meaningless result. In fact, relations (1.1) guarantee that A_h are real; since $V^2 < 0$, V is imaginary and (1.5) implies that $\theta_{hk} = n\pi + \mathrm{i}\,\mathrm{Im}\,\theta_{hk}$. However, as it stands, (1.4) bears a strong resemblance with some formulae familiar from the WKB method[14]). Although we know of no differential equation from which in general (1.4) might be deduced, there are particular instances in which this can be done (section 5). This suggests that we may use the connection formulae of the WKB method to go across the transition points $x_<$, $x_>$. We define

$$\Phi = \sum_{h,k=1}^{4} (j_{hk} - \tfrac{1}{2}) \operatorname{Re} \theta_{hk} \tag{1.7}$$

which, for physical values of j_{hk}, is always an integer multiple of π. According to the WKB connection formulae (appendix G), we find for physical angular momenta

$$\begin{Bmatrix} a & b & c \\ d & e & f \end{Bmatrix} \simeq \frac{1}{2\sqrt{12\pi |V|}} \cos \Phi \exp\left(- \left| \sum_{h,k=1}^{4} j_{hk} \operatorname{Im} \theta_{hk} \right| \right), \tag{1.8}$$

where the sign of $\operatorname{Im} \theta_{hk}$ must be chosen according to the rules explained in section 5. Also this formula turns out to be in remarkably satisfactory agreement with numerical tables. The exponential decrease shown by (1.8) clearly describes a quantum tunnel effect into the classically forbidden region (B).

We expect (1.4) and (1.8) to be inaccurate in the neighbourhood of $x_{\gtrless}$. In fact, the error is here considerably large, although not disastrous. Transition formulae involving Airy functions have been worked out for this region (section 5) and found to be accurate.

In spite of these numerical checks, a sound proof of our formulae is still missing. However there are other arguments in favour of (1.4) and (1.8). For instance, (1.4) has the right symmetry properties, including the extra symmetries discovered by one of us[15]) and satisfies asymptotically the recursion relations as well as the identities of the $6j$-symbols. It is also consistent with the previously investigated particular cases of asymptotic behaviours[16]).

Relations (1.4) and (1.8), together with a transition formula, solve completely the analysis of $6j$-symbols when all angular momenta are large. However, it is also interesting to investigate the case in which one or more edges remain constant and finite while the others increase. We may picture the limiting process as one in which one or more vertices of T go to infinity either separately or in clusters. Therefore there are as many ways to carry out the process as decompositions of 4 into sums of natural integers, i.e., $1+1+1+1$ (all edges large), $1+1+2$ (one small edge), $2+2$ (two small edges), $1+3$ (three small edges). The $1+1+2$ case has been widely studied[16]), while we have found no reference to $2+2$ and accordingly we solve this uninteresting case in the present paper. Some examples of the $1+3$ case, which yield a connection between $6j$- and $3j$-symbols, have been discussed by Brussaard and Tolhoek[16]). Our treatment, however, is quite general and shows how the symmetries of the 3j-symbol can be derived from those of the 6j-coefficient. As a by-product of this analysis, we obtain a new asymptotic formula for Clebsch–Gordan coefficients.

2. Asymptotic connection with the Clebsch–Gordan coefficients

Of some interest is the $1+3$ case, which occurs when we take the positive integer R large in $\begin{Bmatrix} a & b & c \\ d+R & e+R & f+R \end{Bmatrix}$. The related limits $\begin{Bmatrix} a & b+R & c+R \\ d+R & e & f \end{Bmatrix}$ etc. can be reduced to it by symmetry. The starting point of our discussion is Racah's formula (A.4), which, using $\xi = x-2R$ as summation variable becomes

$$\begin{Bmatrix} a & b & c \\ d+R & e+R & f+R \end{Bmatrix} = [\Delta(abc)\,\Delta(d+R, e+R, c) \times \times \Delta(e+R, f+R, a)\,\Delta(f+R, d+R, b)]^{\frac{1}{2}} \sum_{\xi} (-1)^{\xi+2R} \times \times (\xi+2R+1)!\,[(a+b+d+e-\xi)!\,(b+c+e+f-\xi)! \times \times (c+a+f+d-\xi)!\,(\xi-a-b-c+2R)! \times \times (\xi-a-e-f)!\,(\xi-d-e-c)!\,(\xi-d-b-f)!]^{-1}. \tag{2.1}$$

From Stirling's formula we find, for instance, that for large R

$$\frac{(\xi+2R+1)!}{(\xi+2R-a-b-c)!} \simeq \xi^{a+b+c+1}, \tag{2.2}$$

which entails for example

$$\Delta(a, e+R, f+R) \simeq (a+e-f)!\,(a-e+f)!\,(2R)^{-2a-1}. \tag{2.3}$$

By means of (2.2), (2.3) and similar relations, (2.1) transforms into

$$\begin{Bmatrix} a & b & c \\ d+R & e+R & f+R \end{Bmatrix} \simeq \left[\frac{\Delta(abc)}{2R}\right]^{\frac{1}{2}} [(a+e-f)!\,(a-e+f)! \times \times (b+f-d)!\,(b-f+d)!\,(c+d-e)!\,(c-d+e)!]^{\frac{1}{2}} \times \times \sum_{\xi} (-1)^{\xi} [(a+b+d+e-\xi)!\,(b+c+e+f-\xi)! \times \times (c+a+f+d-\xi)!\,(\xi-a-e-f)! \times \times (\xi-b-d-f)!\,(\xi-c-d-e)!]^{-1}. \tag{2.4}$$

Looking at (A.1) we realize that the r.h.s. of (2.4) can be written in terms of a $3j$-symbol (this result is quoted by K. Alder et al.[16])):

$$\begin{Bmatrix} a & b & c \\ d+R & e+R & f+R \end{Bmatrix} \simeq (-1)^{a+b+c+2(d+e+f)}(2R)^{-\frac{1}{2}} \begin{pmatrix} a & b & c \\ e-f & f-d & d-e \end{pmatrix} \tag{2.5a}$$

or using the pattern notation of appendix A

$$\begin{vmatrix} a+b-c & b+f-d & a+f-e \\ b+d-f & b+c-a & c+d-e \\ a+e-f & e+c-d & c+a-b \\ e+d-c+2R & e+f-a+2R & d+f-b+2R \end{vmatrix} \simeq$$

$$\simeq (-1)^{a+b+c+2(d+e+f)}(2R)^{-\frac{1}{2}} \begin{vmatrix} b+c-a & c+a-b & a+b-c \\ a-e+f & b-f+d & c-d+e \\ a+e-f & b+f-d & c+d-e \end{vmatrix}. \tag{2.5b}$$

From (2.5b) it is easy to check that the symmetry

$$\begin{Bmatrix} a & b & c \\ d+R & e+R & f+R \end{Bmatrix} = \\ = \begin{Bmatrix} a & \frac{1}{2}(f+c+b-e) & \frac{1}{2}(b+e+c-f) \\ d+R & \frac{1}{2}(f+c+e-b)+R & \frac{1}{2}(b+e+f-c)+R \end{Bmatrix}$$

entails

$$\begin{vmatrix} b+c-a & c+a-b & a+b-c \\ a-e+f & b-f+d & c-d+e \\ a+e-f & b+f-d & c+d-e \end{vmatrix} = \begin{vmatrix} b+c-a & a+e-f & a-e+f \\ a+b-c & c+d-e & c-d+e \\ c+a-b & b+f-d & b-f+d \end{vmatrix},$$

which is one of the extra symmetries of the $3j$-symbol pointed out by one of us[15]). Actually, (2.5b) relates the subgroup of R_1 (see appendix A) formed by all the even 36 symmetries of the $3j$-symbol to the subgroup of R_2 corresponding to permutations of columns and/or of the upper three lines of the pattern in the l.h.s. of (2.5b). The geometrical and physical content of these symmetries is still to be understood and they remain a puzzling feature of the theory of angular momenta. Therefore it is a pleasant result to be able to reduce the problem of their interpretation to the Racah coefficient only.

From (2.5a) we obtain also an expression for the $3j$-symbol for large quantum numbers. Our derivation of this result is rather heuristic as it involves the exchange of different limiting processes. Just as for (1.4) the formula which we are going to present has a rather "a posteriori" validity, for it satisfies all possible consistency checks. We obtain it from (2.5a) by supposing a, b, c, d, e, f large and finite. Using (1.4) in the l.h.s. of (2.5a) and performing the limit $R\to\infty$, we find

$$\begin{pmatrix} a & b & c \\ m_a & m_b & m_c \end{pmatrix} \simeq (2\pi A)^{-\frac{1}{2}} (-1)^{a+b-c+1} \times$$
$$\times \cos\left[(a+\tfrac{1}{2})A + (b+\tfrac{1}{2})B + (c+\tfrac{1}{2})C - m_b D + m_a E + \tfrac{1}{4}\pi\right], \qquad (2.6)$$

where $m_a = e-f$, $m_b = f-d$, $m_c = d-e$ are the third components of a, b, c along the direction in which P_4 was sent to infinity (fig. 2). A is the area of the shaded triangle in fig. 2 which corresponds to the projection of $P_1P_2P_3$ on a plane perpendicular to the z axis. The angles $A,\ldots, D,\ldots,$ defined according to (1.4) are given in terms of m_a, m_b, m_c by

$$\cos A = \frac{2(a+\frac{1}{2})^2 m_c + m_a[(c+\frac{1}{2})^2 + (a+\frac{1}{2})^2 - (b+\frac{1}{2})^2]}{([(a+\frac{1}{2})^2 - m_a^2]\{4(c+\frac{1}{2})^2(a+\frac{1}{2})^2 - [(c+\frac{1}{2})^2 + (a+\frac{1}{2})^2 - (b+\frac{1}{2})^2]^2\})^{\frac{1}{2}}}. \qquad (2.7)$$

$$\cos D = \frac{1}{2}\,\frac{(a+\frac{1}{2})^2 - (b+\frac{1}{2})^2 - (c+\frac{1}{2})^2 - 2m_b m_c}{\{[(b+\frac{1}{2})^2 - m_b^2]\,[(c+\frac{1}{2})^2 - m_c^2]\}^{\frac{1}{2}}}, \qquad (2.8)$$

$\cos B$, $\cos C$ and $\cos E$, $\cos F$ are deduced respectively from (2.7), (2,8) by circular permutations of the labels, a, b, c; note that $D+E+F=2\pi$. When

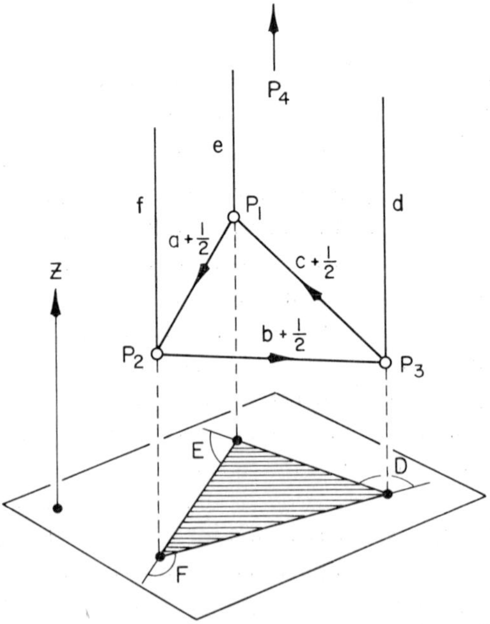

Fig. 2. Limit case in which a 6*j*-symbol degenerates into a 3*j*-symbol.

$m_a = m_b = m_c = 0$, the plane $P_1P_2P_3$ is perpendicular to z and $A = B = C = \frac{1}{2}\pi$; (2.6) reduces to the known[16]) result

$$\begin{pmatrix} a & b & c \\ 0 & 0 & 0 \end{pmatrix} \simeq \tfrac{1}{2}[1 + (-1)^{a+b+c}](-1)^{\frac{1}{2}(a+b+c)}(2\pi A)^{-\frac{1}{2}}. \tag{2.9}$$

The $2+2$ case can be dealt with in much the same way. Using once more $\xi = x - 2R$ as summation variable, from (A.4), (2.2) we obtain

$$\begin{aligned} \begin{Bmatrix} a & b+R & c+R \\ d & e+R & f+R \end{Bmatrix} &\simeq [(a+b-c)!\,(a-b+c)!\,(a+e-f)!\,\times \\ &\times (a-e+f)!\,(d+e-c)!\,(d-e+c)!\,(d+b-f)!\,(d-b+f)!]^{\frac{1}{2}} \times \\ &\times (2R)^{-2a-2d-b-c-e-f-1} \sum_{\xi} (-1)^{\xi} (2R)^{2\xi} [(a+d+b+e-\xi)!\,\times \\ &\times (a+d+c+f-\xi)!\,(\xi-a-b-c)!\,\times \\ &\times (\xi-a-e-f)!\,(\xi-c-d-e)!\,(\xi-b-d-f)!]^{-1}. \end{aligned} \tag{2.10}$$

For R large the main contribution to this summation comes from the largest allowed value of ξ, i.e. from the minimum between $a+d+b+c$ and $a+d+c+f$; therefore

$$\begin{aligned} \begin{Bmatrix} a & b+R & c+R \\ d & e+R & f+R \end{Bmatrix} &\simeq (-1)^{a+d+\min(b+e,\,c+f)} \times \\ &\times \left[\frac{(a-b+c)!\,(a-e+f)!\,(d-e+c)!\,(d-b+f)!}{(a+b-c)!\,(a+e-f)!\,(d+e-c)!\,(d+b-f)!}\right]^{\frac{1}{2}\mathrm{sign}(c+f-b-e)} \times \\ &\times \frac{(2R)^{-|b+e-c-f|-1}}{|b+e-c-f|!}[1 + O(R^{-2})], \end{aligned} \tag{2.11}$$

where $\mathrm{sign}\,(x) = +1, -1$ according to $x \geqslant 0, < 0$. It must be pointed out that unless $b+e = c+f$, the corresponding tetrahedron becomes hyperflat; in fact it turns out that $144\,V^2 = -4(b+c-e-f)^2R^4 + O(R^3)$.

The remaining particular case $2+1+1$ will be discussed in some detail in appendix H.

3. Improvement of Wigner asymptotic formula

According to Wigner[13]), the physical interpretation of the $6j$-symbol is clearly related to its definition as a recoupling coefficient

$$\begin{aligned} |(j_1, (j_2, j_3)j_{23})J\rangle &= \\ &= \sum_{j_{12}} [(2j_{12}+1)(2j_{23}+1)]^{\frac{1}{2}} (-1)^{j_1+j_2+j_3+J} \begin{Bmatrix} j_1 & j_2 & j_{12} \\ j_3 & J & j_{23} \end{Bmatrix} \times \\ &\times |((j_1, j_2)j_{12}, j_3)J\rangle. \end{aligned} \tag{3.1}$$

It follows that

$$(2j_{12}+1)(2j_{23}+1)\begin{Bmatrix} j_1 & j_2 & j_{12} \\ j_3 & J & j_{23} \end{Bmatrix}^2 \mathrm{d}j_{23}, \tag{3.2}$$

is the probability that the sum of the angular momenta $\boldsymbol{j}_2$ and $\boldsymbol{j}_3$ has the length in the interval $j_{23}, j_{33}+\mathrm{d}j_{23}$ whenever $\boldsymbol{j}_1$ and $\boldsymbol{j}_2$ have sum of length j_{12} and $\boldsymbol{j}_{12}=\boldsymbol{j}_1+\boldsymbol{j}_2$ is coupled with $\boldsymbol{j}_3$ to a vector $\boldsymbol{J}$ of length J. As anticipated in the introduction, the mutual relationship of these vectors is best seen on a diagram (fig. 3).

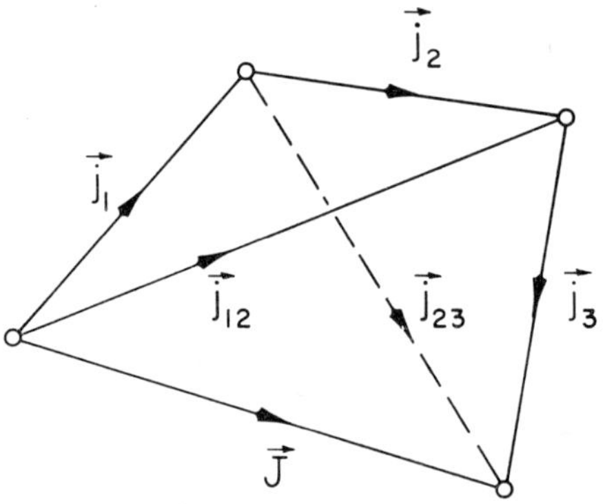

Fig. 3. Recoupling scheme corresponding to (3.1).

Let j_1, j_2, j_3, j_{12}, J (i.e. all the quantum numbers in the l.h.s. of (3.1)) be fixed; then the angle ψ between the plane of the vectors $\boldsymbol{j}_1, \boldsymbol{j}_2$ and the plane of the vectors $\boldsymbol{j}_3, \boldsymbol{J}$ is still undetermined, for both of them can rotate around the common axis $\boldsymbol{j}_{12}$. During this rotation the point P describes a circle; we assume[13]) that every point of this circle has equal probability. Then the probability that the length of $\boldsymbol{j}_{23}$ falls into the interval $j_{23}, j_{23}+\mathrm{d}j_{23}$ is just $\{2|\mathrm{d}\psi/\mathrm{d}j_{23}|/(2\pi)\}\,\mathrm{d}j_{23}$, the factor 2 being needed because there are two configurations corresponding to ψ and $2\pi-\psi$ which yield the same j_{23}. An elementary computation (appendix B) shows that

$$\frac{\mathrm{d}\psi}{\mathrm{d}j_{23}} = \frac{j_{12}j_{23}}{6V}, \tag{3.3}$$

where V is the volume of the tetrahedron in fig. 3. Therefore, for large angular momenta, we obtain Wigner's result (1.3a). If j_{23} is such that $V^2<0$, it is impossible to reach the prescribed value of j_{23} by varying ψ in the real interval $0-2\pi$.

The arguments given so far are clearly heuristic since they assume as granted a uniform probability distribution in ψ. A rigorous justification of this statement would take us too far and would destroy the simplicity of the discussion.

It is, however, interesting to notice that there is a variation to Wigner's argument which seems to have escaped detection so far. Let us suppose that in fig. 3 three of the vertices of the tetrahedron are held fixed, while the remaining one P is allowed to vary. We use J^2, j_{23}^2, j_3^2 as coordinates of P instead of the usual Euclidean coordinates (i.e., for instance, the components of $\boldsymbol{J}$: J_x, J_y, J_z). Notice that there are two points P corresponding to the same set J^2, j_{23}^2, j_3^2. We assume that the "a priori" probability for P to lie in the small volume $\mathrm{d}V = \mathrm{d}J_x\,\mathrm{d}J_y\,\mathrm{d}J_z$ does not depend on P. In this case, the probability that the "tricentrical" coordinates of P: J^2, j_{23}^2, j_3^2 lie in the interval $\mathrm{d}J^2\,\mathrm{d}j_{23}^2\,\mathrm{d}j_3^2$ is

$$2\left|\frac{\partial(J^2, j_{23}^2, j_3^2)}{\partial(J_x, J_y, J_z)}\right|^{-1} \mathrm{d}J^2\,\mathrm{d}j_{23}^2\,\mathrm{d}j_3^2 = 2\mathscr{J}\,\mathrm{d}J^2\,\mathrm{d}j_{23}^2\,\mathrm{d}j_3^2, \tag{3.4}$$

and since

$$\left|\frac{\partial(J^2, j_{23}^2, j_3^2)}{\partial(J_x, J_y, J_z)}\right| = 8\,|\boldsymbol{J}\times\boldsymbol{j}_{23}\cdot\boldsymbol{j}_3| = 48V,$$

using (1.3a) we have

$$\begin{Bmatrix} j_1 & j_2 & j_{12} \\ j_3 & J & j_{23} \end{Bmatrix}^2 \sim 2\frac{\mathscr{J}}{\pi}. \tag{3.5}$$

This second argument has the advantage that it can be formally generalized to higher $3nj$-symbols.

An interesting discussion, which leads to a generalization of Wigner's formula, can be developed by the combined use of the known results[16]) for the 1+1+2 case and of the Biedenharn–Elliott identity[17]). According to Edmonds (eq. (A.2.2) of ref. 16) we have with our conventions of appendix A

$$\begin{Bmatrix} c & a & b \\ f & b+\delta & a+\delta' \end{Bmatrix} \simeq \frac{(-1)^{a+b+c+f+\delta}}{[(2a+1)(2b+1)]^{\frac{1}{2}}}\, d^{(f)}_{\delta,\delta'}(\theta), \tag{3.6}$$

where a, b, c are large in comparison with f, δ, δ' and (see fig. 4)

$$\cos\theta = \frac{a(a+1)+b(b+1)-c(c+1)}{2[a(a+1)\,b(b+1)]^{\frac{1}{2}}}, \qquad 0 \leqslant \theta \leqslant \pi. \tag{3.7}$$

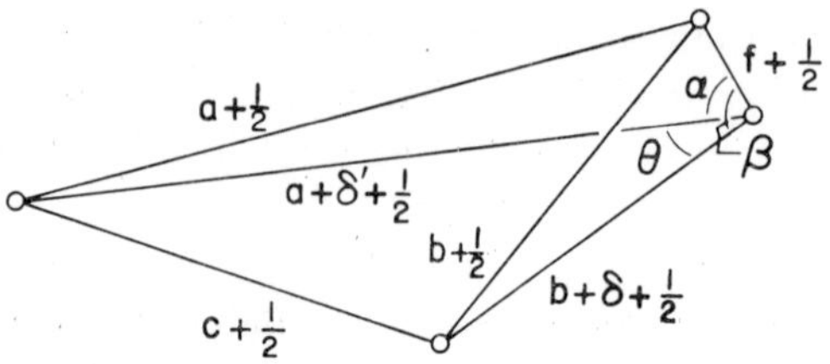

Fig. 4. Particular case in which f is small with respect to the other edges.

Let us recall here the just mentioned identity

$$Y \equiv \begin{Bmatrix} g & h & j \\ e & a & d \end{Bmatrix} \begin{Bmatrix} g & h & j \\ e' & a' & d' \end{Bmatrix} = \sum_x (-1)^{\varphi_x} (2x+1) \begin{Bmatrix} a & a' & x \\ d' & d & g \end{Bmatrix} \begin{Bmatrix} d & d' & x \\ e' & e & h \end{Bmatrix} \begin{Bmatrix} e & e' & x \\ a' & a & j \end{Bmatrix}, \tag{3.8}$$

$$\varphi_x = g + h + j + e + a + d + e' + a' + d' + x .$$

Now we intend to use (3.8) under the following conditions:

i) $g, h, j, e, a, d, e', a', d'$, are large;

ii) $e'-e=\eta$, $a'-a=\alpha$, $d'-d=\delta$ are small with respect to the parameters quoted in i). It follows that the 6j-symbols which appear under summation in (3.8) are of a form suitable for the use of (3.6); we have:

$$\begin{Bmatrix} a & a' & x \\ d' & d & g \end{Bmatrix} \simeq \frac{(-1)^{a+d+g+\delta+x}}{[(2a+1)(2d+1)]^{\frac{1}{2}}} d^{(x)}_{\delta,\alpha}(\gamma),$$

$$\cos\gamma = \frac{a(a+1)+d(d+1)-g(g+1)}{2[a(a+1)d(d+1)]^{\frac{1}{2}}}, \quad 0 \leqslant \gamma \leqslant \pi, \tag{3.9}$$

$$\begin{Bmatrix} d & d' & x \\ e' & e & h \end{Bmatrix} \simeq \frac{(-1)^{d+e+h+\eta+x}}{[(2d+1)(2e+1)]^{\frac{1}{2}}} d^{(x)}_{\eta,\delta}(\chi),$$

$$\cos\chi = \frac{d(d+1)+e(e+1)-h(h+1)}{2[d(d+1)e(e+1)]^{\frac{1}{2}}}, \quad 0 \leqslant \chi \leqslant \pi, \tag{3.10}$$

$$\begin{Bmatrix} e & e' & x \\ a' & a & j \end{Bmatrix} \simeq \frac{(-1)^{e+a+j+\alpha+x}}{[(2e+1)(2a+1)]^{\frac{1}{2}}} d^{(x)}_{\alpha,\eta}(\iota),$$

$$\cos\iota = \frac{e(e+1)+a(a+1)-j(j+1)}{2[e(e+1)a(a+1)]^{\frac{1}{2}}}, \quad 0 \leqslant \iota \leqslant \pi . \tag{3.11}$$

If we now replace (3.9)–(3.11) into (3.8) and assume that we may perform the asymptotic limit under the infinite summation on x, we obtain an expression for the product of symbols in the l.h.s. of (3.8) where *all* angular momenta are large. Clearly this procedure is incorrect, but, nevertheless, it turns out that it is very instructive. We find

$$\begin{Bmatrix} g & h & j \\ e & a & d \end{Bmatrix} \begin{Bmatrix} g & h & j \\ e+\eta & a+\alpha & d+\delta \end{Bmatrix} \sim$$

$$\sim [(2a+1)(2e+1)(2d+1)]^{-1} \sum_{x=0}^{\infty} (2x+1)\, d^{(x)}_{\alpha,\eta}(\iota)\, d^{(x)}_{\eta,\delta}(\chi)\, d^{(x)}_{\delta,\alpha}(\gamma). \tag{3.12}$$

The sum in the r.h.s. can be performed by exploiting the group representation properties of the functions $d^{(x)}_{\alpha,\eta}(\iota)$ as shown in appendix C. The result is

$$\begin{Bmatrix} g & h & j \\ e & a & d \end{Bmatrix} \begin{Bmatrix} g & h & j \\ e+\eta & a+\alpha & d+\delta \end{Bmatrix} \sim \frac{\Theta(V^2)}{24\pi V} \cos(\eta E + \alpha A + \delta D), \tag{3.13}$$

where $\Theta(V^2)=0$ or 1 according to $V^2<0$ or $V^2>0$; V is the volume of the tetrahedron T with edges $g+\frac{1}{2}$, $h+\frac{1}{2}$ etc. The angles E, A, D are defined by

$$\cos E = \frac{\cos\chi \cos\iota - \cos\gamma}{\sin\chi \sin i},$$

$$\cos A = \frac{\cos\iota \cos\gamma - \cos\chi}{\sin i \sin\gamma}, \quad \cos D = \frac{\cos\gamma \cos\chi - \cos\iota}{\sin\gamma \sin\chi} \tag{3.14}$$

and A, for instance, can be interpreted as the angle between outer normals of the two faces of T which have a as common edge. If $\delta=\alpha=\eta=0$, we find once again Wigner's result.

This procedure is in part disappointing because it fails to yield a complete description of the rapidly oscillating term $\mathscr{C}$ in (1.3b). However the result (3.13), when δ, α, $\eta \neq 0$, is very illuminating because the r.h.s. contains the interference term $\cos(\eta E+\alpha A+\delta D)$ which, according to the point of view exposed in section 1, is an average over the product of the two rapidly oscillating factors of the two 6j-symbols.

In order to reconstruct the original expression, let us introduce the function

$$\Omega'(T) \equiv \Omega'\begin{pmatrix} a & b & c \\ d & e & f \end{pmatrix} = \sum_{h,k=1}^{4} j_{hk}\theta_{hk}, \tag{3.15a}$$

with notations defined in section 1. An interesting property of $\Omega'(T)$ is that, with obvious notations[18])

$$\Omega'(T+\delta T) - \Omega'(T) = \sum_{h,k=1}^{4} \delta j_{hk}\theta_{hk} \quad \text{or} \quad \frac{\partial \Omega'}{\partial j_{hk}} = \theta_{hk}, \tag{3.16}$$

i.e. we may vary the parameters in Ω' as if θ_{hk} were constant. Therefore we deduce readily that

$$\delta\Omega' = \Omega'\begin{pmatrix} g & h & j \\ e+\eta & a+\alpha & d+\delta \end{pmatrix} - \Omega'\begin{pmatrix} g & h & j \\ e & a & d \end{pmatrix} = \eta E + \alpha A + \delta D\,,$$

and the r.h.s. is just the argument of the cosine in (3.13). Notice that V and $\delta\Omega'$ are slowly varying functions of the edges as compared to Ω' itself. This result suggests a formula of the following type:

$$\begin{Bmatrix} a & b & c \\ d & e & f \end{Bmatrix} \simeq \frac{1}{\sqrt{12\pi V}} \cos(\Omega' + \omega)\,, \tag{3.17}$$

where ω is a yet unknown constant phase. ω can be determined by matching (3.17) to the particular $1+1+2$ case studied first by Racah[1]):

$$\begin{Bmatrix} a & b & c \\ b & a & f \end{Bmatrix} \simeq \frac{(-1)^{a+b+c+f}}{\sqrt{(2a+1)(2b+1)}} P_f(\cos\theta)\,, \tag{3.18}$$

where $\cos\theta$ is given by (3.7). If f is large, but small with respect to a, b, c, we may replace the Legendre polynomial with its asymptotic behaviour[19]):

$$P_f(\cos\theta) \simeq \left[\frac{2}{\pi(f+\frac{1}{2})\sin\theta}\right]^{\frac{1}{2}} \cos\left[(f+\tfrac{1}{2})\theta - \tfrac{1}{4}\pi\right], \tag{3.19}$$

from which we deduce:

$$\begin{Bmatrix} a & b & c \\ b & a & f \end{Bmatrix} \simeq \frac{(-1)^{a+b+c+f}}{\sqrt{12\pi V}} \cos\left[(f+\tfrac{1}{2})\theta - \tfrac{1}{4}\pi\right], \tag{3.20a}$$

having noticed that $6V \simeq (a+\frac{1}{2})(b+\frac{1}{2})(f+\frac{1}{2})\sin\theta$. On the other hand, in order to work out how Ω' depends on f, we can write $\Omega'(f+\frac{1}{2})$ explicitly for this particular case. We have (fig. 4 with $\delta=\delta'=0$): $\Omega'(0)=\pi(a+b+c+\frac{3}{2})$ and $(\partial\Omega'/\partial f)_{f+\frac{1}{2}=0}=\pi-\theta$. Therefore,

$$\Omega'(f+\tfrac{1}{2}) \simeq \Omega'(0) + \left(\frac{\partial\Omega}{\partial f}\right)_{f+\frac{1}{2}=0}(f+\tfrac{1}{2}) \simeq$$

$$\simeq \pi(a+b+c+\tfrac{3}{2}) + (\pi-\theta)(f+\tfrac{1}{2}). \tag{3.21}$$

Taking into account these results, we see that (3.20a) can be rewritten as

$$\begin{Bmatrix} a & b & c \\ b & a & f \end{Bmatrix} \simeq \frac{1}{(12\pi V)^{\frac{1}{2}}} \cos(\Omega' + \tfrac{1}{4}\pi)\,, \tag{3.20b}$$

which shows not only that (3.1) is compatible with this particular case, but also tells us that $\omega=\frac{1}{4}\pi$. We have reached, therefore, the important general formula

$$\begin{Bmatrix} a & b & c \\ d & e & f \end{Bmatrix} \simeq \frac{1}{(12\pi V)^{\frac{1}{2}}} \cos \Omega, \tag{1.4a}$$

$$\Omega = \sum_{h,k=1}^{4} j_{hk}\theta_{hk} + \tfrac{1}{4}\pi, \tag{3.15b}$$

which must be supplemented with explicit formulae for the angles θ_{hk} (appendix B):

$$\cos \theta_{hk} = -\frac{9}{A_h A_k} \frac{\partial V^2}{\partial (j_{rs}^2)}, \qquad 0 \leqslant \theta_{rs} \leqslant \pi \tag{3.22}$$

where $h \neq k \neq r \neq s = 1, 2, 3, 4$; A_h are defined in (1.5).

TABLE 1

Numerical examples of 6*j*-symbols showing the degree of approximation of our asymptotic formulae. The cases denoted with I, II, III correspond to the use of (1.4), (5.6), or (5.7), (1.8) respectively. The indices *a*, *b*,…, *f* are the same as in fig. 1. The exact values of this table as well as of table 2 are taken from A. F. Nikiforov et al., *Tables of Racah coefficients* (New York, 1965); as usual, .1–01, for instance, means 10^{-2}

a	*b*	*c*	*d*	*e*	*f*	Exact value	Approximate value	
1	1	1	1/2	1/2	1/2	−.33333–00	−.37828–00	I
1	1	1	1	1	1	.16667–00	.16683–00	I
7/2	7	9/2	17/2	5	5/2	−.41785–01	−.41520–01	I
17/2	15/2	10	15/2	15/2	4	.16494–01	.16422–01	I
13/2	8	9/2	13/2	6	15/2	.25518–01	.25506–01	I
5	8	12	9	7	6	−.22441–01	−.22422–01	I
9	9	9	9	9	9	−.15647–01	−.15640–01	I
1/2	1	1/2	1/2	1	1/2	.16667–00	.16026–00	II
7/2	7	9/2	17/2	5	17/2	.19826–01	.18954–01	II
4	13/2	15/2	8	9/2	17/2	−.20120–01	−.19897–01	II
17/2	15/2	9	15/2	15/2	13	−.13801–01	−.13773–01	II
17/2	15/2	10	15/2	13/2	12	.99633–02	.97944–02	II
5	8	10	9	7	10	−.21100–01	−.19971–01	II
8	9	14	9	8	10	.13420–01	.13296–01	II
9/2	5	1/2	11/2	6	3/2	.13222–01	.13549–01	III
17/2	6	9/2	17/2	6	7/2	.10386–02	.10411–02	III
5	8	13	9	7	9	−.19671–02	−.19726–02	III
17/2	15/2	10	15/2	13/2	14	.49191–03	.49301–03	III
5	8	13	9	7	12	−.11052–04	−.10443–04	III
8	9	17	9	8	13	.59756–06	.56161–06	III
8	9	17	9	8	16	.31622–09	.28579–09	III

4. Arguments in favor of the proposed asymptotic formula

We list here some arguments in favour of (1.4).

i) Our formula is numerically accurate, as can be seen from tables 1–4 and figs. 5–7. On the average, the accuracy improves as the values of the angular momenta increase.

TABLE 2

Numerical results for the 6*j*-symbol with $a=7$, $b=8$, $c=9$, $d=6$, $e=9$ as $f\equiv J$ assumes all permissible values

J	Exact value	Approximate value		J	Exact value	Approximate value	
2	.76018–02	.76923–02	III	9	−.20540–01	−.20578–01	I
3	−.22627–01	−.22171–01	II	10	−.31376–02	−.36479–02	I
4	.29469–01	.30474–01	I	11	.20586–01	.20528–01	I
5	−.13704–01	−.13212–01	I	12	.20068–01	.19019–01	II
6	−.13529–01	−.13944–01	I	13	.84777–02	.78298–02	II
7	.20388–01	.20345–01	I	14	.16637–02	.16638–02	III
8	.34782–02	.37774–02	I				

TABLE 3

Case with $a=13$, $b=15$, $c=24$, $d=29/2$, $e=33/2$ and $f\equiv J$ variable. The exact values of this table as well as of table 4 were obtained by means of the recursion formula (4.3)

J	Exact value	Approximate value		J	Exact value	Approximate value	
7/2	−.17136–01	−.18812–01	I	35/2	−.66442–02	−.66033–02	II
9/2	−.94803–02	−.94381–02	I	37/2	−.38116–02	−.37155–02	II
11/2	.59559–02	.60861–02	I	39/2	−.17980–02	−.18980–02	III
13/2	.11188–01	.11222–01	I	41/2	−.70668–03	−.72809–03	III
15/2	.25847–02	.25778–02	I	43/2	−.23231–03	−.23652–03	III
17/2	−.78677–02	−.78773–02	I	45/2	−.63708–04	−.64401–04	III
19/2	−.85291–02	−.85619–02	I	47/2	−.14450–04	−.14536–04	III
21/2	−.13122–03	−.19186–03	I	49/2	−.26704–05	−.26756–05	III
23/2	.77958–02	.77680–02	I	51/2	−.39262–06	−.39197–06	III
25/2	.81257–02	.82093–02	I	53/2	−.44251–07	−.43997–07	III
27/2	.17590–02	.19590–02	I	55/2	−.35949–08	−.35537–08	III
29/2	−.56229–02	−.54326–02	I	57/2	−.18760–09	−.18332–09	III
31/2	−.95185–02	−.94911–02	II	59/2	−.47264–11	−.44115–11	III
33/2	−.92382–02	−.87903–02	II				

TABLE 4

Case with $a=35/2$, $b=39/2$, $c=9$, $d=31/2$, $e=37/2$ and $f\equiv J$ variable

J	Exact value	Approximate value		J	Exact value	Approximate value	
4	.21149–03	.20909–03	III	20	−.66008–02	−.65600–02	I
5	−.69682–03	−.71066–03	III	21	.29687–02	.29011–02	I
6	.16116–02	.16753–02	III	22	.16649–02	.17306–02	I
7	−.30296–02	−.32386–02	III	23	−.57355–02	−.57788–02	I
8	.49034–02	.47498–02	II	24	.76269–02	.76402–02	I
9	−.70293–02	−.70467–02	II	25	−.63213–02	−.63099–02	I
10	.90494–02	.88460–02	II	26	.20313–02	.20080–02	I
11	−.10502–01	−.99536–02	II	27	.34992–02	.35214–02	I
12	.10918–01	.11351–01	I	28	−.73734–02	−.73873–02	I
13	−.99508–02	−.99826–02	I	29	.68216–02	.68250–02	I
14	.75021–02	.73395–02	I	30	−.12056–02	−.11953–02	I
15	−.38167–02	−.35839–02	I	31	−.61644–02	−.61915–02	I
16	−.49920–03	−.72271–03	I	32	−.83350–02	−.83482–02	I
17	.45603–02	.47270–02	I	33	.10743–03	.24555–03	I
18	−.73894–02	−.74789–02	I	34	−.11326–01	−.11727–01	I
19	.81842–02	.81987–02	I	35	−.58537–02	−.56155–02	II

ii) (1.4) is obviously invariant under the exchange of the vertices of T. As stated before, this is only a subgroup of the full symmetry group R_2 of $6j$-symbols (appendix A). We checked, however, in a somewhat laborious way, that both V and Ω are actually invariant under R_2. The proof is sketched in appendix D.

iii) It has been shown [20]) that the identities (A.6), (A.7), (2.8) together with the tetrahedral symmetries, are enough to derive all properties as well as the numerical values of $6j$-symbols, apart from an overall phase. In particular, the Biedenharn–Elliott identity and the recursion relations which follow from it are a distinctive feature of Racah coefficients. Therefore it is a highly significant result that our formula satisfies asymptotically not only these recursion relations, but also the above mentioned identities.

An intuitive understanding of these formulae can be reached by a correspondence principle of the form:

$$\frac{1}{\mathrm{i}}\frac{\partial}{\partial j_{hk}} \sim \theta_{hk},$$

where θ_{hk} are the angles appearing in Ω. By the same token we define the

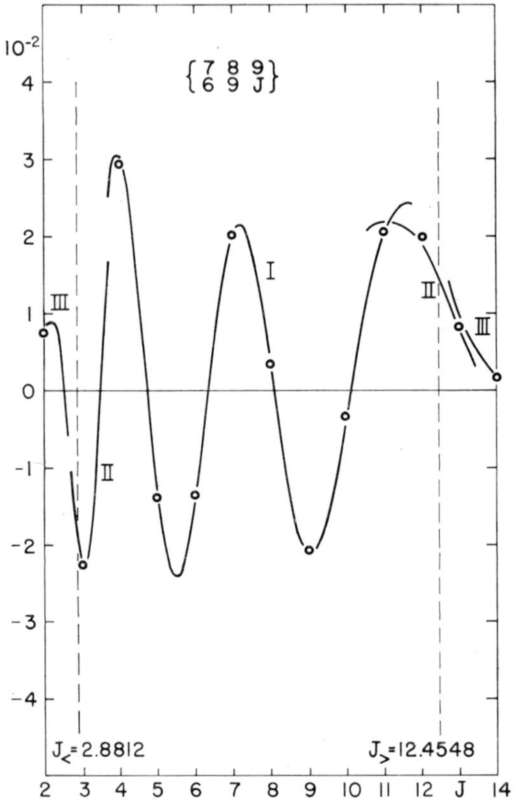

Fig. 5. Here, as well as in figs. 6 and 7, the interpolation between contiguous physical points in the classically forbidden regions is based on (1.8). For numerical values, see table 2. According to the numerical tables, curves labelled with I, II, III correspond to the use of (1.4), (5.6), or (5.7), (1.8) respectively.

operator

$$\mathscr{D}_{j_{hk}} = \exp\left(\frac{1}{2}\frac{\partial}{\partial_{j_{hk}}}\right) \sim \exp\left(\tfrac{1}{2}\mathrm{i}\theta_{hk}\right), \tag{4.1}$$

so that, for instance:

$$\mathscr{D}_a^2 \begin{Bmatrix} a & b & c \\ d & e & f \end{Bmatrix} = \begin{Bmatrix} a+1 & b & c \\ d & e & f \end{Bmatrix}$$

and from (4.1)

$$(\mathscr{D}_a^2 + \mathscr{D}_a^{-2}) \begin{Bmatrix} a & b & c \\ d & e & f \end{Bmatrix} =$$

$$= \begin{Bmatrix} a+1 & b & c \\ d & e & f \end{Bmatrix} + \begin{Bmatrix} a-1 & b & c \\ d & e & f \end{Bmatrix} \sim 2\cos\theta_a \begin{Bmatrix} a & b & c \\ d & e & f \end{Bmatrix}. \tag{4.2}$$

Let us consider[21])

$$a\left[(a+b+c+2)(a-b+c+1)(a+b-c+1)\times\right.$$
$$\times(b+c-a)(a+e+f+2)(a-e+f+1)(a+e-f+1)\times$$
$$\left.\times(e+f-a)\right]^{\frac{1}{2}}\begin{Bmatrix}a+1 & b & c\\ d & e & f\end{Bmatrix}+(a+1)\left[(a+b+c+1)\times\right.$$
$$\times(a-b+c)(a+b-c)(b+c-a+1)(a+e+f+1)\times$$
$$\left.\times(a-e+f)(a+e-f)(e+f-a+1)\right]^{\frac{1}{2}}\begin{Bmatrix}a-1 & b & c\\ d & e & f\end{Bmatrix}=$$
$$=(2a+1)\{2[a(a+1)d(d+1)-b(b+1)e(e+1)-c(c+1)\times$$
$$\times f(f+1)]+[a(a+1)-b(b+1)-c(c+1)][a(a+1)+$$
$$-e(e+1)-f(f+1)]\}\begin{Bmatrix}a & b & c\\ d & e & f\end{Bmatrix}; \qquad (4.3a)$$

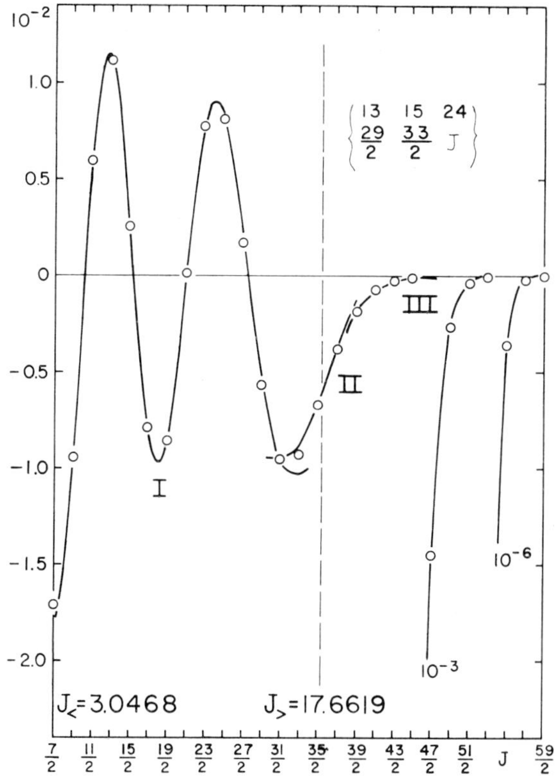

Fig. 6. In this case, which corresponds to table 3, the exponential decrease is particularly emphasized.

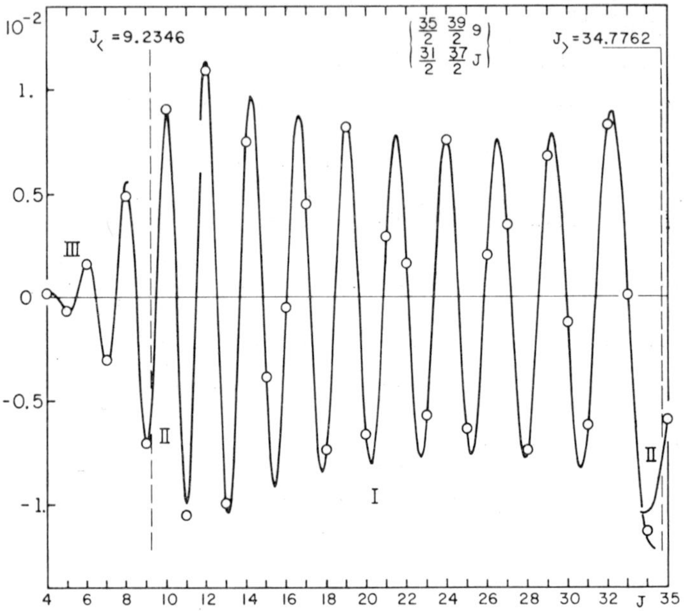

Fig. 7. The corresponding numerical values for physical points are given in table 4.

using notations defined in section 1, we have asymptotically

$$8A_1A_2\left(\begin{Bmatrix} a+1 & b & c \\ d & e & f \end{Bmatrix} + \begin{Bmatrix} a-1 & b & c \\ d & e & f \end{Bmatrix}\right) \simeq [2(j_{12}^2 j_{34}^2 - j_{13}^2 j_{24}^2 - j_{14}^2 j_{23}^2) + \\ + (j_{12}^2 - j_{13}^2 - j_{14}^2)(j_{12}^2 - j_{24}^2 - j_{23}^2)] \begin{Bmatrix} a & b & c \\ d & e & f \end{Bmatrix}.$$

Recalling (B.2) and (4.1) we obtain

$$\begin{Bmatrix} a+1 & b & c \\ d & e & f \end{Bmatrix} + \begin{Bmatrix} a-1 & b & c \\ d & e & f \end{Bmatrix} \simeq 2\cos\theta_{12} \begin{Bmatrix} a & b & c \\ d & e & f \end{Bmatrix}, \tag{4.3b}$$

which is equivalent to the result (4.2) based on the correspondence principle (4.1). Less formally, we want to check that (4.3b) is identically satisfied if we replace the $6j$-symbols of (4.3b) with our asymptotic formula (1.4). Since the volume of T is a slowly varying function of the edges, it can be regarded as constant in the three symbols of (4.3b); in this case (4.3b) transforms into the trivial identity $\cos(\Omega+\theta_{12}) + \cos(\Omega-\theta_{12}) \simeq 2\cos\theta_{12}\cos\Omega$.

In a similar way, the recursion relation

$$[(a+b+c+1)(b+c-a)(c+d+e+1)(c+d-e)]^{\frac{1}{2}}\begin{Bmatrix} a & b & c \\ d & e & f \end{Bmatrix} + \\ -[(a+b-c+1)(a-b+c)(e+d-c+1)(e+c-d)]^{\frac{1}{2}} \times \\ \times \begin{Bmatrix} a & b & c-1 \\ d & e & f \end{Bmatrix} = -2c[(b+d+f+1)(b+d-f)]^{\frac{1}{2}} \times \\ \times \begin{Bmatrix} a & e & f \\ d-\frac{1}{2} & b-\frac{1}{2} & c-\frac{1}{2} \end{Bmatrix}$$

by means of (1.4) becomes asymptotically

$$[(j_{13}+j_{12}+j_{14})(j_{13}+j_{14}-j_{12})(j_{14}+j_{24}+j_{34}) \times \\ \times (j_{14}+j_{34}-j_{24})]^{\frac{1}{2}} e^{\frac{1}{2}i(\theta_{13}+\theta_{14}+\theta_{34})} - [(j_{12}+j_{13}-j_{14}) \times \\ \times (j_{12}+j_{14}-j_{13})(j_{24}+j_{34}-j_{14})(j_{24}+j_{14}-j_{34})]^{\frac{1}{2}} e^{\frac{1}{2}i(\theta_{13}-\theta_{14}+\theta_{34})} \simeq \\ \simeq -2j_{14}[(j_{13}+j_{34}+j_{23})(j_{13}+j_{34}-j_{23})]^{\frac{1}{2}},$$

which, using Delambre's relations[22]), reduces to simple identities.

A much more involved computation is needed to show that also the full Biedenharn–Elliott identity is satisfied asymptotically by (1.4). Introducing (1.4) into the r.h.s. of (3.8), we realize that inside the summation over x there appears a rapidly varying function of x. Its behaviour can be displayed most transparently if we split all cosines into positive and negative frequency parts according to Euler's formula. Let T_j $(j=1, 2, 3)$ be the tetrahedra corresponding to the r.h.s. of (3.8); with obvious notations we have

$$\prod_{j=1}^{3} \cos \Omega_j = 2^{-3} \times \\ \times [e^{i(\Omega_1+\Omega_2+\Omega_3)} + e^{i(\Omega_1+\Omega_2-\Omega_3)} + e^{i(\Omega_1-\Omega_2+\Omega_3)} + e^{i(\Omega_1-\Omega_2-\Omega_3)} + \text{c.c.}]. \tag{4.4}$$

Given the heuristic character of our investigation, it is reasonable to assume that the discrete summation over x can be replaced with an integration whose most important contribution arises from points where the phase $\Gamma(x)=\Omega_1(x)+\Omega_2(x)+\Omega_3(x)$ and its analogs of (4.4) are slowly varying as functions of x. We are led quite naturally to consider, for example

$$\frac{\partial \Gamma(x)}{\partial x} = 0. \tag{4.5}$$

Denoting the supplementary dihedral angles relative to x with θ_x^1, θ_x^2, θ_x^3, a heartening result is that, since in any first order variation of the edges we may consider all angles as constants, we have as necessary condition for (4.5)

$$\theta_x^1 + \theta_x^2 + \theta_x^3 - \pi = 0\,, \tag{4.6}$$

having taken into account the phase $(-1)^{\varphi_x}$ of (3.8). If we consider the other terms in (4.4) as well, we find that the bulk of the contribution to the integral may come only from those values of x such that

$$\pm\,\theta_x^1 \pm \theta_x^2 \pm \theta_x^3 = \pi\,. \tag{4.7}$$

The conditions (4.7) have an immediate geometrical interpretation if we look at the diagram in fig. 8a. There one sees that by leaving out in turn any one of the five points $P_1, \ldots, P_5$, the remaining points form five tetrahedra $T_1, \ldots, T_5$ which are just those appearing in (3.8). Note that there are ten edges connecting five points in all possible ways and in fact there are ten angular momenta appearing in (3.8) including x. As it has been long known, if five points are imbedded into a three dimensional-Euclidean space, their mutual distances are not independent. The explicit form of their dependence was discovered by Cayley[11]) and can be written as

$$-\,2^4 (4!)^2 I^2 \equiv \begin{vmatrix} 0 & j_{12}^2 & j_{13}^2 & j_{14}^2 & j_{15}^2 & 1 \\ j_{12}^2 & 0 & j_{23}^2 & j_{24}^2 & j_{25}^2 & 1 \\ j_{13}^2 & j_{23}^2 & 0 & j_{34}^2 & j_{35}^2 & 1 \\ j_{14}^2 & j_{24}^2 & j_{34}^2 & 0 & j_{45}^2 & 1 \\ j_{15}^2 & j_{25}^2 & j_{35}^2 & j_{45}^2 & 0 & 1 \\ 1 & 1 & 1 & 1 & 1 & 0 \end{vmatrix} = 0\,, \tag{4.8}$$

where j_{hk} is the distance between P_h and P_k. It is crucial to understand that (4.8) is in fact equivalent to (4.7). Indeed (4.7) implies that the sum of the internal dihedral angles $\pi - \theta_x^j$ around the edge x is a multiple of 2π, as expected if the diagram is drawn in three dimensions. The ambiguity in the signs of the angles arises from the different possible orientations of the five involved tetrahedra, as exemplified by fig. 8b.

Therefore, the only asymptotical contribution to the integral comes from the configuration of the diagram in fig. 8a and the like, which are three-dimensional, i.e. from those values of x such that $I(x^2) = 0$. First we notice that the range of summation is restricted to $x > 0$ and, "a fortiori," to $x^2 > 0$. Secondly, $I(x^2)$ is a quadratic polynomial in x^2 and it has therefore two roots $(x_<)^2$ and $(x_>)^2$. There are rigorous arguments showing that, if T_4, T_5 are physical tetrahedra, i.e. $V_4^2, V_5^2 > 0$, then $x_<$ and $x_>$ are real. To us it will be enough to note that, quite obviously, the smaller root $x_<$ corresponds to the configuration in which P_4, P_5 lie on the same side of the plane

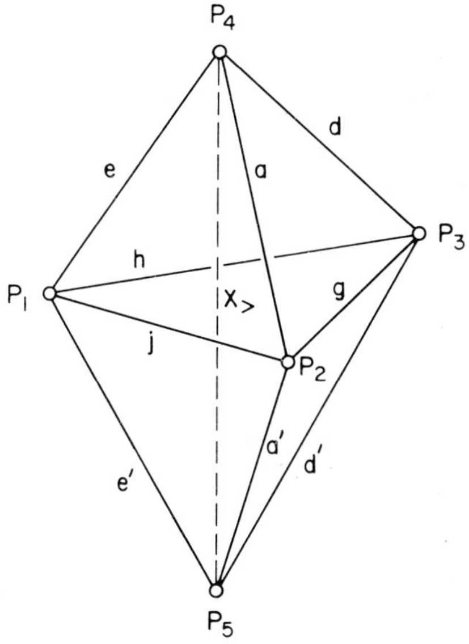

(a)

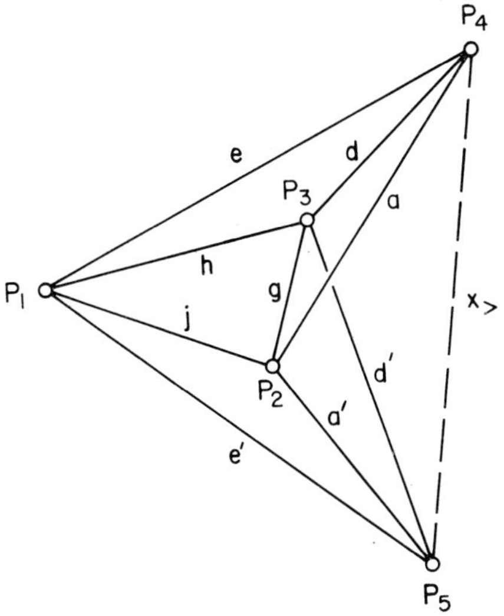

(b)

Fig. 8.

$P_1P_2P_3$ as depicted in fig. 9, while $x_>$ corresponds to P_4,P_5 being on opposite sides as in fig. 8a.

Since in general θ_x^j ($j=1, 2, 3$) are not vanishing, or are equal to some multiple of π, only one of the choices of signs in (4.7) is valid for a given root.

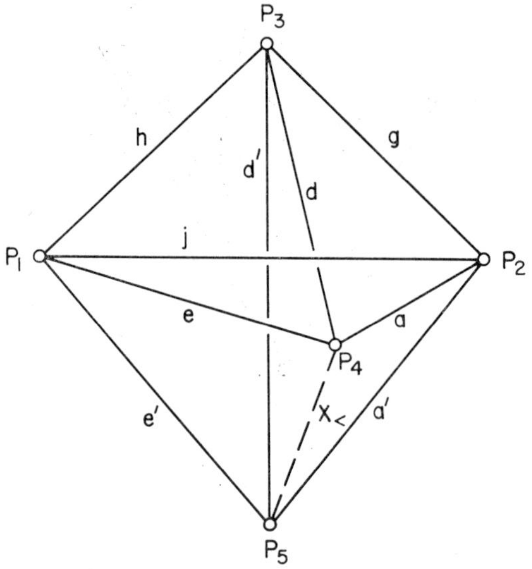

Fig. 9.

It follows that, for $x=x_<$, only one of the eight terms arising from the decomposition (4.4), together with its complex conjugate, does actually contribute to the integral. We cannot decide here which term contributes, because this will depend on the values of the other fixed angular momenta. Let us suppose they are such that for both roots $\theta_x^1+\theta_x^2+\theta_x^3=\pi$.

From (3.8) we have

$$Y \simeq \sum_x \frac{\pi^{-\frac{3}{2}}}{96\sqrt{3}} \mathrm{e}^{\mathrm{i}\pi(\omega+x)} x \left[V_1(x)\, V_2(x)\, V_3(x)\right]^{-\frac{1}{2}} \left[\mathrm{e}^{\mathrm{i}\Gamma(x)} + \mathrm{e}^{-\mathrm{i}\Gamma(x)}\right], \qquad (4.9)$$

where $\omega=a+e+d+a'+e'+d'+g+j+h$. Let us write now

$$x+\tfrac{1}{2}=R\xi;\; a+\tfrac{1}{2}=R\alpha,\;\; e+\tfrac{1}{2}=R\eta,\;\; d+\tfrac{1}{2}=R\delta,\;\; \ldots,\;\; d'+\tfrac{1}{2}=R\delta' \qquad (4.10)$$

with R large and ξ, α, η, δ, α', η', δ' finite; note that the angles θ_{hk} of the five tetrahedra are independent of R. The spacing in the summation on ξ is now

R^{-1} and, as anticipated, we may replace the summation with an integral on ξ

$$Y \simeq \frac{\pi^{-\frac{3}{2}}}{96\sqrt{3}} e^{-i\pi(\omega-\frac{3}{4})} R^2 \int_{\Xi} d\xi\, \xi [V_1(\xi)\, V_2(\xi)\, V_3(\xi)]^{-\frac{1}{2}} e^{iR[\tilde{\Gamma}(\xi)-\pi\xi]} + \text{c.c.} \tag{4.11}$$

having used the fact that $\omega+x$ is integer; here $\Gamma(x)=R\tilde{\Gamma}(\xi)+\frac{1}{4}\pi$. In the limit $R\to\infty$ this integral can be computed with the steepest descent method [23], which yields for an integral of the form

$$\mathscr{I} = \int_{\alpha}^{\beta} g(\xi)\, e^{iRf(\xi)}\, d\xi\,, \tag{4.12}$$

with f and g real, the approximate result

$$\mathscr{I}_{R\to\infty} \cong \sum_j \left(\frac{2\pi}{R\,|f''(\xi_j)|}\right)^{\frac{1}{2}} g(\xi_j)\, e^{i[Rf(\xi_j)\pm\frac{1}{4}\pi]}\,; \tag{4.13}$$

here ξ_j are such that $f'(\xi_j)=0$ and $\alpha<\xi_j<\beta$. In (4.13) the phases $\pm\frac{1}{4}\pi$ must be chosen according to $f''(\xi_j)\gtrless 0$. If $\xi_\gtrless$ correspond to $x_\gtrless$, since we have supposed

$$\left[\frac{\partial[\tilde{\Gamma}(\xi)-\pi\xi]}{\partial\xi}\right]_{\xi=\xi_\gtrless} = [\theta_x^1+\theta_x^2+\theta_x^3-\pi]_{x=x_\gtrless} = 0\,, \tag{4.14}$$

we find in our case

$$f(\xi) = \tilde{\Gamma}(\xi) - \pi\xi; \quad g(\xi) = \xi[V_1(\xi)\, V_2(\xi)\, V_3(\xi)]^{-\frac{1}{2}},$$
$$f''(\xi) = \frac{\partial(\theta_x^1+\theta_x^2+\theta_x^3-\pi)}{\partial\xi}. \tag{4.15}$$

A naive computation of $f''(\xi)$ is out of question because of the lengthy and uninspiring algebra involved. We rather take $I^2(x^2)$, defined in (4.8) as independent variable and write

$$f''(\xi_\gtrless) = \lim_{\xi\to\xi_\gtrless}\left[\frac{\partial(\theta_x^1+\theta_x^2+\theta_x^3-\pi)}{\partial I^2(x^2)}\frac{\partial I^2(x^2)}{\partial\xi}\right]; \tag{4.16}$$

some manipulation of determinants (appendix D) shows that

$$f''(\xi_\gtrless) = \mp\tfrac{1}{6}R^3(\xi_\gtrless)^2\left[\frac{V_4V_5}{V_1V_2V_3}\right]_{\xi=\xi_\gtrless}. \tag{4.17}$$

The evaluation of $f(\xi_{\gtrless})$ is straightforward and yields

$$Rf(\xi_{\gtrless}) \mp \tfrac{1}{4}\pi = \Omega_4 \pm \Omega_5 + \pi(\omega - \tfrac{3}{4}). \tag{4.18}$$

From (4.11)–(4.18) we obtain

$$Y \simeq \frac{1}{4}\frac{1}{12\pi(V_4V_5)^{\frac{1}{2}}}\left[e^{i(\Omega_4+\Omega_5)} + e^{i(\Omega_4-\Omega_5)} + \text{c.c.}\right] \tag{4.19}$$

$$Y \simeq \frac{1}{(12\pi V_4)^{\frac{1}{2}}}\cos\Omega_4 \frac{1}{(12\pi V_5)^{\frac{1}{2}}}\cos\Omega_5\,,$$

which is in obvious agreement with the straightforward use of (1.4) in the l.h.s.

We indulged somewhat more than strictly necessary on the proof of the Biedenharn–Elliott identity in the asymptotic limit, because we felt that the mechanism involved is illuminating and more general than shown by this case. We do not discuss whether the other identities of Racah coefficients: (A.6), (A.7) are satisfied by (1.4), since these proofs follow quite easily from the stationary-phase method. The same procedure can be extended in principle to the computation of asymptotic 9*j*-symbols.

5. A formal analogy with the WKB method

In the previous section we strived to provide as many as possible independent checks and counterchecks for the validity of (1.4) in the region $A(V^2>0)$. As stated in our Introduction, a complete description of the behaviour of a 6*j*-symbol for large angular momenta must include of necessity a similar formula for the region $B(V^2<0)$ and makes it highly desirable to have one for the transitional region $V^2 \simeq 0$ as well.

The guiding idea in this section is a formal analogy with a WKB approximation for the solution of a differential equation. This analogy was prompted by the actual existence of a differential equation at least in the $1+1+2$ case, where in fact the symbol can be expressed as a Jacobi polynomial.

Unfortunately we have not been able to derive a single differential equation valid for unrestricted large parameters, with the possible exception of the transitional region. Our disappointment is somehow mitigated by noticing that, after all, we need a differential equation only in order to fix unambiguously the prosecution of (1.4) through a transition point. This we have achieved and the resulting formulae satisfy properties which are similar to the ones listed under i, ii, iii in section 4. However, it must be stated that the WKB analogy is just a formal device which cannot be accepted as a proof.

Before proceeding further along this analogy, a more detailed investigation of the region B is necessary. From (B.3) we see that if $V^2=0$ and $\prod_{h=1}^{4} A_h \neq 0$, then the angles θ_{hk} are all multiple of π. Since we always choose $0 \leqslant \theta_{hk} \leqslant \pi$, we have that either $\theta_{hk}=0$ or $\theta_{hk}=\pi$; the ambiguity can be settled by means of (3.22). Here, as in the following, we always assume that the areas A_h are represented by positive square roots of radicands like (B.1). Because of the conditions satisfied by angular momenta and taking into account our definition of j_{hk}, it is easy to see that these radicands are indeed always non-negative and may vanish only if $V^2=0$, in which case (see footnote 12), at least one angular momentum assumes a non-physical value.

If $V^2=0$, the four vertices of T lie in the same plane; Let Q be the convex plane set generated by the four vertices. Depending on their relative position, Q may have three or four edges (see figs. 10 and 1). As the reader can

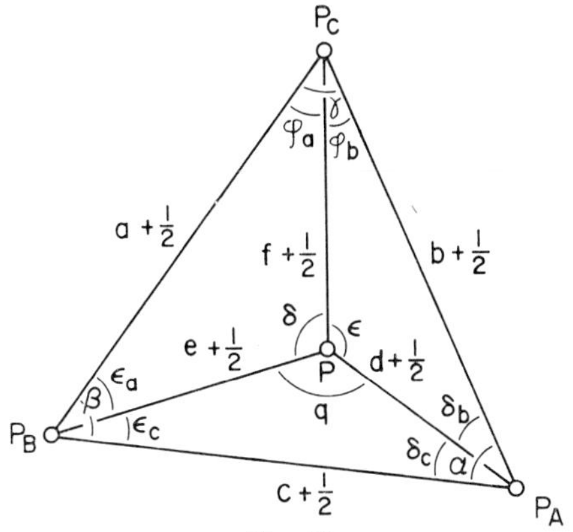

Fig. 10.

easily check, the rule is then: $\theta_{hk}=\pi$ for the edges of Q and $\theta_{hk}=0$ for the others. We may use the symbol $\begin{Bmatrix}\pi & \pi & \pi\\ 0 & 0 & 0\end{Bmatrix}$ to denote the set $\theta_{12}=\theta_{13}=\theta_{14}=\pi$, $\theta_{34}=\theta_{24}=\theta_{23}=0$. The only possibilities are $\begin{Bmatrix}\pi & \pi & \pi\\ 0 & 0 & 0\end{Bmatrix}$, $\begin{Bmatrix}\pi & 0 & 0\\ 0 & \pi & \pi\end{Bmatrix}$, $\begin{Bmatrix}0 & 0 & \pi\\ \pi & \pi & 0\end{Bmatrix}$, $\begin{Bmatrix}0 & \pi & 0\\ \pi & 0 & \pi\end{Bmatrix}$, $\begin{Bmatrix}\pi & \pi & 0\\ \pi & \pi & 0\end{Bmatrix}$, $\begin{Bmatrix}\pi & 0 & \pi\\ \pi & 0 & \pi\end{Bmatrix}$, $\begin{Bmatrix}0 & \pi & \pi\\ 0 & \pi & \pi\end{Bmatrix}$. The subsets with some $A_h=0$ lie on the boundary of the above sets. For instance, the case $j_{12}=j_{13}+j_{14}$ is the common boundary of $\begin{Bmatrix}\pi & 0 & 0\\ 0 & \pi & \pi\end{Bmatrix}$, $\begin{Bmatrix}0 & \pi & \pi\\ 0 & \pi & \pi\end{Bmatrix}$ and, in fact, here $\theta_{12}, \theta_{13}, \theta_{14}$ are discontinuous.

If $V^2<0$, then the angles θ_{hk} are all of the form $n\pi+i\xi_{hk}$. Because of continuity, it follows that $\mathrm{Re}\,\theta_{hk}$ are constants in B whenever $\prod_{h=1}^4 A_h\neq 0$. Therefore we may subdivide B into non-overlapping regions, all points in the same region having the same values of $\mathrm{Re}\,\theta_{hk}$. If we let $V\to 0$ and $\prod_{h=1}^4 A_h\neq 0$, we see that $\lim\limits_{V\to 0}\mathrm{Re}\,\theta_{hk}=\theta_{hk}(V=0)$ so the value of $\mathrm{Re}\,\theta_{hk}$ is determined by the limiting process for $V\to 0$ and is the same as listed above. We may subdivide B into regions $B\begin{pmatrix}\pi&\pi&\pi\\0&0&0\end{pmatrix}$, $B\begin{pmatrix}\pi&\pi&0\\\pi&\pi&0\end{pmatrix}$, etc. such that we have, for instance, in $B\begin{pmatrix}\pi&\pi&\pi\\0&0&0\end{pmatrix}$: $\mathrm{Re}\,\theta_{12}=\mathrm{Re}\,\theta_{13}=\mathrm{Re}\,\theta_{14}=\pi$, $\mathrm{Re}\,\theta_{23}=\mathrm{Re}\,\theta_{24}=\mathrm{Re}\,\theta_{34}=0$; it is also convenient to use the following abbreviations:

$$B_3\equiv B\begin{pmatrix}\pi&\pi&\pi\\0&0&0\end{pmatrix}\cup B\begin{pmatrix}\pi&0&0\\0&\pi&\pi\end{pmatrix}\cup B\begin{pmatrix}0&0&\pi\\\pi&\pi&0\end{pmatrix}\cup B\begin{pmatrix}0&\pi&0\\\pi&0&\pi\end{pmatrix},$$

$$B_4\equiv B\begin{pmatrix}\pi&\pi&0\\\pi&\pi&0\end{pmatrix}\cup B\begin{pmatrix}\pi&0&\pi\\\pi&0&\pi\end{pmatrix}\cup B\begin{pmatrix}0&\pi&\pi\\0&\pi&\pi\end{pmatrix}.$$

These regions are not closed, for they have common boundary points in which some A_h's vanish. As anticipated in (1.7), in every such region we define a phase function Φ as follows

$$\Phi=\sum_{h,k=1}^{4}(j_{hk}-\tfrac{1}{2})\,\mathrm{Re}\,\theta_{hk}\,.$$

For physical values of the angular momenta, Φ is always an integer multiple of π.

We fix now the value of all parameters but one. Without loss of generality we may always choose a as variable and, in order to stress this point, we use x instead of a. We do not restrict ourselves to physical values of x and of the remaining parameters in order to retain some, albeit nominal, freedom in the final results. If $V^2(x_{\gtrless})=0$ we have

$$\begin{aligned}\Omega(x_{\gtrless})&=\Phi-\tfrac{1}{4}\pi\quad\text{approaching } B_3\,,\\ \Omega(x_{\gtrless})&=\Phi+\tfrac{1}{4}\pi\quad\text{approaching } B_4\,.\end{aligned}\tag{5.1}$$

In appendix F it is shown that for $x\to x_{\gtrless}$:

$$\Omega-\Omega(x_{\gtrless})=\begin{cases}+\dfrac{9}{2}\dfrac{V^3}{\prod_{h=1}^{4}A_h} & \text{approaching } B_3\,,\\[2ex] -\dfrac{9}{2}\dfrac{V^3}{\prod_{h=1}^{4}A_h} & \text{approaching } B_4\,.\end{cases}\tag{5.2}$$

It follows that in the neighbourhood of a transition point we have

$$\begin{Bmatrix} a & b & c \\ d & e & f \end{Bmatrix} \simeq \frac{1}{\sqrt{12\pi V}} \cos\left(\frac{9}{2}\frac{V^3}{\prod_{h=1}^{4} A_h} + \Phi - \tfrac{1}{4}\pi\right); \tag{5.3}$$

obviously this formula is incorrect if one gets too close to the transition points. We notice however that, as it stands, (5.3) is the WKB asymptotic approximation to the following differential equation (see (G.6)):

$$\frac{\mathrm{d}}{\mathrm{d}(V^2)}\frac{\mathrm{d}}{\mathrm{d}(V^2)}\psi = \left(\frac{27}{4\prod_{h=1}^{4} A_h}\right)^2 V^2\psi, \tag{5.4}$$

where the independent variable is V, $\prod_{h=1}^{4} A_h$ being treated as a constant[24]. The general solution of (5.4) is (appendix G):

$$\psi \sim V\left[c_1 J_{\frac{1}{3}}\left(\frac{9}{2}\frac{V^3}{\prod_{h=1}^{4} A_h}\right) + c_2 J_{-\frac{1}{3}}\left(\frac{9}{2}\frac{V^3}{\prod_{h=1}^{4} A_h}\right)\right] \tag{5.5}$$

and the one which joins smoothly with (5.3) for large values of $V^2 > 0$ is:

$$\begin{Bmatrix} a & b & c \\ d & e & f \end{Bmatrix} \simeq 2^{-\frac{4}{3}}\left(\prod_{h=1}^{4} A_h\right)^{-\frac{1}{6}} \times \\ \times \left\{\cos\Phi \,\mathrm{Ai}\left[-\left(\frac{(3V)^2}{\left(4\prod_{h=1}^{4} A_h\right)^{\frac{2}{3}}}\right)\right] + \sin\Phi \,\mathrm{Bi}\left[-\left(\frac{(3V)^2}{\left(4\prod_{h=1}^{4} A_h\right)^{\frac{2}{3}}}\right)\right]\right\}. \tag{5.6}$$

in terms of Airy functions[25]. We assume (5.6) to be the correct asymptotic form of the Racah coefficient in the transitional region. The soundness of this assumption is of course at this stage purely aesthetical. However, our conjecture is borne out by comparison with published tables (see tables 1–4).

According to the standard procedure, we may continue (5.6) into the region B; here the resulting formula in the neighbourhood of a transition point is:

$$\begin{Bmatrix} a & b & c \\ d & e & f \end{Bmatrix} \simeq 2^{-\frac{4}{3}}\left(\prod_{h=1}^{4} A_h\right)^{-\frac{1}{6}} \times \\ \times \left\{\cos\Phi \,\mathrm{Ai}\left[\frac{(3|V|)^2}{\left(4\prod_{h=1}^{4} A_h\right)^{\frac{2}{3}}}\right] + \sin\Phi \,\mathrm{Bi}\left[\frac{(3|V|)^2}{\left(4\prod_{h=1}^{4} A_h\right)^{\frac{2}{3}}}\right]\right\}. \tag{5.7}$$

For large values of $|V|^2$ this function joins smoothly with

$$\begin{Bmatrix} a & b & c \\ d & e & f \end{Bmatrix} \simeq \frac{1}{2(12\pi|V|)^{\frac{1}{2}}} \{2 \sin \Phi \, \mathrm{e}^{|\mathrm{Im}\,\Omega|} + \cos \Phi \, \mathrm{e}^{-|\mathrm{Im}\,\Omega|}\}, \tag{5.8}$$

where $\mathrm{Im}\,\Omega = \sum_{h,k=1}^{4} \mathrm{Im}\,\theta_{hk}$. Choosing conventionally in region B: $V = \mathrm{i}|V|$, the imaginary part of θ_{hk} can be retrieved by means of the following formulae:

$$\cosh(\mathrm{Im}\,\theta_{hk}) = -\cos(\mathrm{Re}\,\theta_{hk}) \frac{9}{A_h A_k} \frac{\partial V^2}{\partial j_{rs}^2}, \quad h \neq k \neq r \neq s, \tag{3.22a}$$

$$\sinh(\mathrm{Im}\,\theta_{hk}) = \cos(\mathrm{Re}\,\theta_{hk}) \frac{3\, j_{hk}}{2\, A_h A_k} |V|, \quad h \neq k. \tag{1.5a}$$

According to (5.8), the $6j$-symbol would be represented in region B by a superposition of decreasing and increasing exponentials; however, the coefficient $\sin \Phi$ of the increasing exponential vanishes at the physical points, where (5.8) reduces to (1.8). It turns out that (5.8) is numerically accurate when applied to physical angular momenta.

It is worth noticing that the coefficient $\cos \Phi = (-1)^{\Phi/\pi}$ of the decreasing exponential gives instead a determination of the sign of the $6j$-symbol. This sign is in complete agreement with numerical tables, as well as with the one obtained from the limiting case of a stretched tetrahedron where one edge reaches its maximum permissible value. As an example, let $a = b + c$; from (A.4) we have:

$$\text{sign of} \begin{Bmatrix} b + c & b & c \\ d & e & f \end{Bmatrix} = (-1)^{b+c+e+f}. \tag{5.9}$$

Since $b + c > x_> - \frac{1}{2}$, it is a simple exercise to see that if a increases through $x_>$, then we enter either one of the regions $B\begin{pmatrix} 0 & \pi & \pi \\ 0 & \pi & \pi \end{pmatrix}$, $B\begin{pmatrix} \pi & 0 & 0 \\ 0 & \pi & \pi \end{pmatrix}$, $B\begin{pmatrix} \pi & \pi & \pi \\ 0 & 0 & 0 \end{pmatrix}$. The region $B\begin{pmatrix} \pi & \pi & \pi \\ 0 & 0 & 0 \end{pmatrix}$ is exluded because the point $a = b + c$ is almost on the boundary between $B\begin{pmatrix} 0 & \pi & \pi \\ 0 & \pi & \pi \end{pmatrix}$ and $B\begin{pmatrix} \pi & 0 & 0 \\ 0 & \pi & \pi \end{pmatrix}$; actually, it would be exactly on this boundary if: $a + \frac{1}{2} = b + \frac{1}{2} + c + \frac{1}{2}$, or $a - b - c = \frac{1}{2}$ which is prevented by selection rules. Therefore our phase is $\Phi = \pi(b + c + e + f) = \pi(a + e + f)$ and it agrees with (5.9).

Further evidence in favour of (5.6), (5.8) is offered by the discussion of the particular case: $2 + 1 + 1$; this analysis is carried out in appendix H where it is shown that the behaviour of (3.6) in region A as well as in B is in agreement with (5.8). We notice also that the arguments of the Airy functions in (5.6), (5.7) as well as Φ are invariant under R_2.

We have now a complete set of conjectured asymptotic formulae valid for every range of large *physical* angular momenta. Numerical examples deduced from these formulae are shown in tables 1–4 and in figs. 5–7.

6. The 3*nj*-symbols

The problem of extending our results to higher 3*nj*-symbols is certainly very difficult and we were not able to reach a solution within the frame of this paper. Yet some of the intuitive arguments presented here provide fairly interesting information about the general problem.

In dealing with 3*nj*-symbols where *n* is large the use of diagrams becomes imperative. At first the diagrams, as in the current literature[7]), are just a mnemonical device in order to keep track of the growing complexities of the symbols. They provide an information, which is purely combinatorial, on how angular momenta are coupled in a given scheme. In this sense a very natural language for diagrams is provided by combinatorial topology.

A diagram is essentially a shorthand notation for the expansion of a 3*nj*-symbol in terms of 3*j*-symbols. Let [D] be the 3*nj*-symbol corresponding to the diagram D. [D] can be expressed as:

$$[\mathrm{D}] = \sum_{\text{all } m} \begin{pmatrix} l_1 & l_2 & l_3 \\ m_1 & m_2 & m_3 \end{pmatrix} \cdots \begin{pmatrix} l_i & l_j & l_k \\ m_i & m_j & m_k \end{pmatrix} \begin{pmatrix} & l_k & \\ m_k & & m'_k \end{pmatrix} \begin{pmatrix} l_k & l_p & l_q \\ m'_k & m_p & m_q \end{pmatrix} \cdots, \tag{6.1}$$

where[4]):

$$\begin{pmatrix} & l_k & \\ m_k & & m'_k \end{pmatrix} = (-1)^{l_k - m_k} \delta_{m_k, -m'_k}. \tag{6.2}$$

D can be retrieved from (6.1) by means of the following rules:

a) D is a 2-dimensional combinatorial manifold.

b) There is a one-to-one correspondence between 1-simplexes (edges) of D and angular momenta in the r.h.s. of (6.1).

c) There is a one-to-one correspondence between 3*j*-symbols in (6.1) and 2-simplexes (faces) of D.

d) The boundary of a face is the sum of the three edges appearing as angular momenta in the corresponding 3*j*-symbol.

e) We work for the time being with homology modulo 2, i.e. we forget about the orientation of the simplexes.

From the general structure of [D] we see that there are $2n$ faces and $3n$ edges in D. We have no "a priori" conditions on 0-simplexes (vertices) and in fact they have no physical meaning. This brings in a certain amount of arbitrariness in the construction of D which is lacking in the customary definition of diagrams[6]) (figs. 12a, b). We regard as equivalent diagrams those which yield the same symbol. Since D is a manifold, we may define its Euler characteristic:

$$M = -f + e - v + 2 = n - v + 2,$$

where f, e, v are the number of faces, edges, vertices respectively. Since $M \geqslant 0$, we have $v \leqslant n+2$. For a $6j$-symbol, $M=0$, while in the case of a $9j$-symbol we have: $n=3$, $v=4$ and $M=1$ according to the example sketched in fig. 11. When $M=1$ the diagram is the triangulation of a one-sided surface,

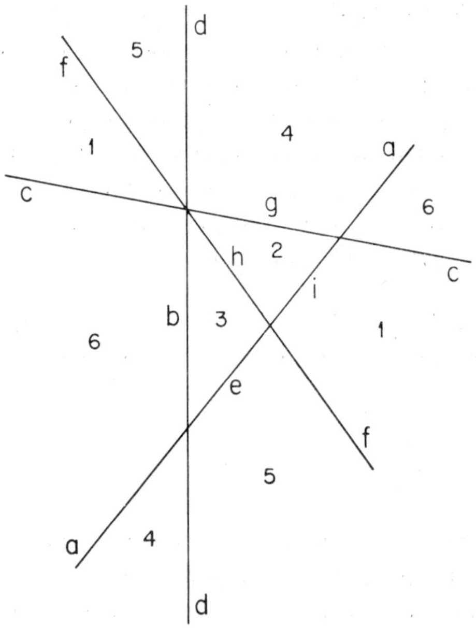

Fig. 11. Planar graphical representation of the $9j$-symbol with triads (abc), (def), (ghi). (adg), (beh), (cfi).

in our case the real projective plane. Since the sphere where opposite points are identified is a homeomorph of the projective plane, it is possible to exhibit the $9j$-symbol as a double hexagonal pyramid as shown in fig. 12a; here each edge and face are repeated twice and the whole diagram has a centre of symmetry. We shall prefer this representation to the one given in fig. 11.

In fact, in dealing with the asymptotic behaviour and with the semiclassical limit of $3nj$-symbols, we expect that it will be possible to represent angular momenta as vectors and the coupling of angular momenta as the addition of classical vectors. It follows that it will be convenient to think of a diagram as a polyhedron imbedded into a 3-dimensional Euclidean space. If one

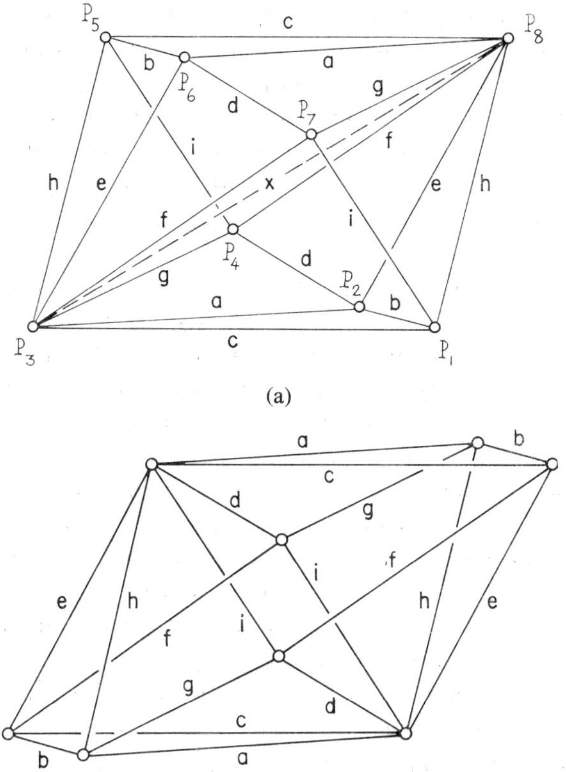

(a)

(b)

Fig. 12. Different three-dimensional diagrams for the $9j$ of fig. 11; note that the edges in case a have the same length and direction as in b.

such a construction exists with prescribed lengths of the edges, we shall speak of a configuration of the diagram.

An interesting phenomenon is that there are several different configurations with identical edges for the same diagram. This ambiguity is connected with the fact that there is uniqueness for a given polyhedron of given topology and given edges only if the polyhedron is convex. A trivial example is a pair of mirror-like right-handed and left-handed tetrahedra. A less trivial example arises already with the $9j$-symbol and we expect it to become more and more important for higher symbols. The technical reasons of this multiplicity can be best seen in the $9j$-symbols. Here the geometrical shape of the object would be completely determined if we knew all the relative angles of all the edges of the diagram. Elementary theorems tell us that this can be achieved if the angle we are looking for is the internal angle of some triangle of which all edges are known; this is true in particular for all faces in the diagram. A similar attempt to compute, for instance, the angle between b and f (fig. 12a) fails unless we know the length of the diagonal x. In the particular case of the $9j$-symbol it turns out that all angles can be computed, provided we know this only missing length x; as we shall see, there may be in principle as much as four different configurations with the same topology.

Since the classification and the discussion of these configurations is relevant to the asymptotic behaviour of the symbol, it is convenient to refine the so far used language. We shall introduce the word diagram when only the topological properties are considered and in doing so we identify equivalent diagrams. Configuration is instead a diagram with the additional information about the angles needed in order to remove the above ambiguities. We may introduce the additional word orientation if a distinction between left-handed and right-handed configurations is desired.

For complicated $3nj$-symbols the number of different configurations for the same diagram grows very rapidly. From our discussion it is clear that if one gives the distance between any pair of vertices in the diagram, then the configuration is completely determined. We cannot give here a general set of rules which would allow one to compute the missing lengths. We found, however, that in the simplest cases it is enough to exploit the relations among squared edges which can be obtained as follows:

a) the diagram may contain quadrilaterals with opposite equal edges; in this case the sum of the squared diagonals is twice the sum of the two different squared edges, a known and elementary relation;

b) since the diagram is imbedded into a 3-dimensional space, one can write for any choice of five vertices the Cayley identity (4.8).

Not all these relations are actually independent. Once a complete and consistent set of identities has been written, one finds a set of algebraic equations for the missing lengths; to each solution of these equations we associate a configuration.

We come now to the general problem of computing the $3nj$-symbols.

In the available literature[7]) explicit formulae are written for any symbol with the aid of diagrams in terms of lower order coefficients. The diagrams used in these previous works are not the same as ours; however it is not difficult to translate one language into the other.

To this purpose we introduce another diagram $\mathscr{D}(\mathrm{D})$ which corresponds to the familiar procedure of dissecting the interior of the polyhedron into tetrahedra; more formally, $\mathscr{D}(\mathrm{D})$ can be conveniently defined as a 3-dimensional combinatorial manifold with boundary D. We name cells the 3-simplexes of $\mathscr{D}$. The edges, faces and vertices of $\mathscr{D}$ will be named external if they belong to D, else internal. Let the set of cells be labelled by T_k, $k=1, 2, \ldots, p$.

From the definition of the symbol [D], we know that it is a function of as many variables as different edges of D. These variables take up integer or half-integer values with the selection rule that the sum of the variables along the boundary of any 2-cycle is always integer. We assume the function [D] to be given by the usual Racah formula (A.4) when D is a tetrahedron. In what follows we shall give a sketchy account of a set of rules which allow the computation of [D] for any D.

In order to evaluate [D], we first construct a given $\mathscr{D}(\mathrm{D})$. We associate variables x_i, $i=1, 2, \ldots, q$ to all internal edges of $\mathscr{D}(\mathrm{D})$ and variables l_j, $j=1, 2, \ldots r$ to the external ones. In this way, to each cell T_k, considered as a diagram, we may associate $[\mathrm{T}_k]$ which is clearly a function of the internal and, possibly, of the external edges of $\mathscr{D}(\mathrm{D})$. Then we form the product:

$$A(x_1, \ldots, x_q) = \prod_{k=1}^{p} [\mathrm{T}_k]\cdot(-1)^{\chi} \prod_{i=1}^{q} (2x_i + 1). \tag{6.3}$$

We found so far no combinatorial rule to construct χ, which applies to any diagram. If D and $\mathscr{D}(\mathrm{D})$ are homeomorphs of a 2-sphere and of a 3-ball, then we have in general:

$$\chi = \sum_{j=1}^{q} (n_j - 2)\, x_j + \chi_0\,,$$

where n_j is the number of tetrahedra belonging to x_j and χ_0 is a fixed phase chosen in order to make χ integer. For simplicity we shall limit ourselves to this case. Let us now consider the sum over all internal variables

$$S = \sum_{x_1} \ldots \sum_{x_q} A(x_1, \ldots, x_q)\,. \tag{6.4}$$

If there are no internal vertices, the sum is finite and $S=[\mathrm{D}]$. On the contrary, if there are internal vertices, the sum is infinite but it is still possible to renormalize it in such a way to obtain [D]. When the immediate goal is just the computation of [D] with the simplest possible method, then there is no need to introduce this additional complication, for one can always find a $\mathscr{D}$(D) with no internal vertices. However the more general case is relevant in suggesting a formal analogy with the Feynman summation over histories[26]) in connection with the theory of relativity; we shall discuss this point later.

Coming back to (6.3), (6.4) and supposing that there are no internal vertices, we may attempt to evaluate the summation in (6.4) using the same methods already tested for the Biedenharn–Elliott identity (section 4). In this case we shall replace each $[\mathrm{T}_k]$ with its asymptotic behaviour according to (1.4). Moreover, we shall split each cosine according to Euler's formula. The function A will then appear as the sum of 2^p pairwise conjugate terms. It is also convenient to replace each factor $(-1)^{n_j x_j}$ with $\exp\left[\pm \mathrm{i}\,\pi(n_j-2)\,x_j\right]$. This procedure, which is clearly correct only for integer x_j, can be easily extended also to half-integer summation indices. Therefore A will contain, among the others, a term of the form

$$\prod_{j=1}^{q} (2x_j+1)\exp\left\{\mathrm{i}\left[\left(\sum_{k=1}^{p_j}\theta_j^k\right)-\pi p_j+2\pi\right]x_j\right\}. \qquad (6.5)$$

As before, we may try to replace the summation with an integral; we expect that the most important contributions to the integral will arise from the points where the phase is stationary with respect to the q variables x_j. Imposing the stationary phase condition, we find:

$$\sum_{k=1}^{p_j}(\pi-\theta_j^k)=2\pi, \qquad (6.6)$$

which means that the sum of internal angles around x_j is just 2π. A discussion similar to the one carried out in section 4 brings to the conclusion that (6.6) implies the existence of a configuration, in the sense defined above, imbedded in a 3-dimensional Euclidean space, where the internal and external lengths are well specified. Because of the lack of internal vertices, the internal edges connect external vertices of the diagram and in fact they are sufficient to specify the configuration completely. A similar discussion can be carried out for the other 2^p-1 terms. In this way we see that the final result will be a sum of contributions from each configuration. We do not know of any simple rule to compute the general form of the partial second derivatives:

$$\partial\left[\sum_{k=1}^{p_j}\theta_j^k\right]/\partial x_j \qquad (6.7)$$

needed in order to carry out, up to the end, the evaluation of (6.4). This lack of knowledge stops us here short of the final result. However the above discussion shows already that the study of configurations is certainly relevant to a complete understanding of the semiclassical limit of the $3nj$-symbols.

As anticipated, we point out a curious connection between our asymptotic formulae and a simplified quantization "à la Feynman" occurring in a 3-dimensional Euclidean theory of gravitation. The classical counterpart of this theory is trivial because the Einstein field equation for empty space

$$R_{\mu\nu} - \tfrac{1}{2}g_{\mu\nu}R = 0 \tag{6.8}$$

implies that the complete Riemann tensor vanishes, i.e., the space is flat. However, the connection we point out may be relevant for further generalizations to less academical cases.

We begin by discussing the sum (6.4) when there are internal vertices. As stated, this sum is infinite, but it is rather interesting to see how this infinity actually arises. For simplicity we restrict ourselves to the case when D is a tetrahedron and there is only one internal vertex P_5 (fig. 13). In this case (6.4) reads:

$$S = \sum_{xyzt} (2x+1)(2y+1)(2z+1)(2t+1)(-1)^{x+y+z+t+a+b+c+d+e+f} \times$$
$$\times \begin{Bmatrix} a & b & c \\ x & y & z \end{Bmatrix} \begin{Bmatrix} f & e & a \\ y & z & t \end{Bmatrix} \begin{Bmatrix} d & b & f \\ z & t & x \end{Bmatrix} \begin{Bmatrix} c & e & d \\ t & x & y \end{Bmatrix} \tag{6.9}$$

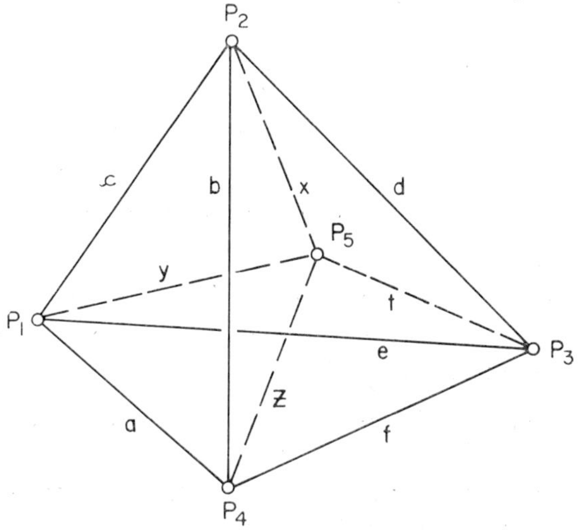

Fig. 13.

having chosen $\chi_0=a+b+c+d+e+f$; the summation is carried out on all x, y, z, t which are compatible with the selection rules. Without loss of generality we may suppose x integer; using (3.8) the summation over t yields:

$$S=\begin{Bmatrix} a & b & c \\ d & e & f \end{Bmatrix} \sum_{xyz} (2x+1)(2y+1)(2z+1) \begin{Bmatrix} a & b & c \\ x & y & z \end{Bmatrix}^2, \tag{6.10}$$

and from (A.6):

$$S=\begin{Bmatrix} a & b & c \\ d & e & f \end{Bmatrix} \sum_{xy} \frac{\delta_{xyc}}{2c+1}(2x+1)(2y+1), \tag{6.11}$$

where δ_{xyc} is a triangular delta which is equal to unity if x, y, c satisfy triangular inequalities and zero otherwise. Since

$$\sum_{y=|x-c|}^{x+c} (2y+1)=(2x+1)(2c+1),$$

we have

$$S=\begin{Bmatrix} a & b & c \\ d & e & f \end{Bmatrix} \sum_{x=0}^{\infty} (2x+1)^2, \tag{6.12}$$

which is infinite and correspondingly meaningless. Let us limit the summation on x up to $x=R$, with R large; in this case we find

$$\mathscr{R}(R) \equiv \sum_{x=0}^{R} (2x+1)^2 \simeq \frac{1}{\pi}\frac{4\pi R^3}{3}. \tag{6.13}$$

This result hints that we may write:

$$[\mathrm{D}] \equiv \begin{Bmatrix} a & b & c \\ d & e & f \end{Bmatrix} = \lim_{R\to\infty} (\mathscr{R}(R))^{-1} \sum_{x,y,z,t<R} (-1)^{a+b+c+d+e+f+x+y+z+t} \times$$
$$\times (2x+1)(2y+1)(2z+1)(2t+1) \times$$
$$\times \begin{Bmatrix} a & b & c \\ x & y & z \end{Bmatrix} \begin{Bmatrix} f & e & a \\ y & z & t \end{Bmatrix} \begin{Bmatrix} d & b & f \\ z & t & x \end{Bmatrix} \begin{Bmatrix} c & e & d \\ t & x & y \end{Bmatrix}. \tag{6.14}$$

In fact we have that, for fixed x, the summand vanishes if $z>x+b$, $y>x+c$, $t>x+d$ so that for $x<\min(R-b, R-c, R-d)$ the limitations $y, z, t<R$ have no weight. Therefore we assume that the above limit is correct and expect that in general [D] is given by:

$$[\mathrm{D}] = \lim_{R\to\infty} (\mathscr{R}(R))^{-P} \sum_{x_1<R} \cdots \sum_{x_q<R} A(x_1, \ldots, x_q) \tag{6.15}$$

where P is the number of internal vertices and A is defined by (6.3).

Now let us suppose that the number of vertices and edges in D and in $\mathscr{D}$(D) is very high. Let also the complex $\mathscr{D}$(D) approach a differentiable manifold $\mathscr{M}$ with boundary D. According to a discussion carried out in a previous paper by one of us[27]), the sum $\sum_{j=1}^{q}[\sum_{k=1}^{p_j}(\pi-\theta_j^k)]x_j$ approaches the integral $8\pi\mathscr{L}(\mathscr{M})=\frac{1}{2}\int_{\mathscr{M}}R\,\mathrm{d}V$, where $\mathrm{d}V$ is the volume element on $\mathscr{M}$ and R the scalar Riemann curvature of $\mathscr{M}$. We see therefore that the positive frequency part S^+ of S in some sense looks like:

$$S^+ = \frac{1}{\mathscr{R}^P}\int_{\partial\mathscr{M}=\mathrm{D}} \mathrm{e}^{\mathrm{i}\mathscr{L}(\mathscr{M})}\,\mathrm{d}\mu(\mathscr{M}), \tag{6.16}$$

where the summations over the variables x_j have been interpreted as an integration over all the manifolds $\mathscr{M}$ with fixed boundary D. The measure $\mathrm{d}\mu$ is here not defined in any precise mathematical sense since all the discussion carried out so far is clearly heuristic in character. In this form, S^+ strongly resembles a Feynman summation over histories with density of Lagrangian $\mathscr{L}$ as in a 3-dimensional Einstein theory. In a more conventional 4-dimensional theory with pseudo Euclidean metric, the corresponding summation would be[28]):

$$S(\Sigma_1, \Sigma_2) = \int \mathrm{d}\mu \exp\left(\mathrm{i}\int_{\Sigma_1}^{\Sigma_2} R\,\mathrm{d}^4x\sqrt{-g}\right), \tag{6.17}$$

the integral on the coordinates being performed in the slab between the space-like hypersurfaces Σ_1, Σ_2. The other terms, other than the positive frequency part, are related to different orientations of the tetrahedra T_j and have a similar interpretation, although their precise meaning is still unclear. It is plausible that in the transition to a smooth manifold $\mathscr{M}$, they will give no essential contribution to the final result.

Finally we report an interesting conjecture over possible extensions of Wigner's result for the 6*j*-symbol. For simplicity we limit ourselves to the 9*j*-symbol, further generalizations being obvious. In the diagram of fig. 12a we keep the vertices P_1, P_2, P_3 of one face fixed; in this way we fix also a, b, c. It can be easily realized that to determine D completely it is enough to give the points P_4 and P_5; in fact, from P_1, P_5 we deduce the symmetry centre $\frac{1}{2}(\mathrm{P}_1+\mathrm{P}_5)$ of D and from it all the remaining vertices. We may use as coordinates for P_4, P_5 either their six Euclidean coordinates $\boldsymbol{r}_4$, $\boldsymbol{r}_5$ or the six remaining lengths d, e, f, g, h, i. Our conjecture, suggested by (3.5), is that:

$$\begin{Bmatrix} a & b & c \\ d & e & f \\ g & h & i \end{Bmatrix}^2 \sim C\sum_{k=1}^{M}\left|\frac{\partial(\boldsymbol{r}_4, \boldsymbol{r}_5)}{\partial(d^2, e^2, f^2, g^2, h^2, i^2)}\right|_{\boldsymbol{r}_4=\boldsymbol{r}_4(k),\ \boldsymbol{r}_5=\boldsymbol{r}_5(k)}, \tag{6.18}$$

where the summation is carried on all the M different configurations $\boldsymbol{r}_4^{(k)}$,

$\boldsymbol{r}_5^{(k)}$ labelled by k, which correspond to the same values of the lengths appearing in the symbol. Cayley identity (4.8) when applied, for instance, to $\mathrm{P}_3, \mathrm{P}_5, \mathrm{P}_6, \mathrm{P}_7, \mathrm{P}_8$, yields a fourth order equation in x^2, which means that, in general, there are four different contributions to (6.18). The constant C can be determined by evaluating

$$\mathfrak{N} = \sum_{a,b,c,d,e,f<R} (2a+1)(2b+1)(2c+1)(2d+1) \times \times (2e+1)(2f+1) \begin{Bmatrix} a & b & c \\ d & e & f \\ g & h & i \end{Bmatrix}^2 \tag{6.19}$$

by means of the orthogonality of $9j$-symbols[6]; following a procedure similar to the one which led to (6.12), we obtain $\mathfrak{N} = (\frac{4}{3}R^3)^2$. On the other hand, we have by means of (6.18)

$$\mathfrak{N} \simeq \int_{a,b,\dots,f<R} \mathrm{d}(a^2)\,\mathrm{d}(b^2)\dots\mathrm{d}(f^2) \begin{Bmatrix} a & b & c \\ d & e & f \\ g & h & i \end{Bmatrix}^2 \simeq \simeq \tfrac{1}{2}C \int_{|\boldsymbol{r}_4|<R} \mathrm{d}^3\boldsymbol{r}_4 \int_{|\boldsymbol{r}_5|<R} \mathrm{d}^3\boldsymbol{r}_5 \simeq \tfrac{1}{2}C\,(\tfrac{4}{3}\pi R^3)^2, \tag{6.20}$$

from which is follows: $C = 2(\pi)^{-2}$. The inverse of the Jacobian appearing in (6.18) can be evaluated easily in terms of volumes of tetrahedra; we hope to present elsewhere more detailed results for this as well as for higher order symbols.

Acknowledgments

The authors are indebted to Prof. E. P. Wigner, Prof. F. J. Dyson, Dr. S. Adler and Dr. J. Lascoux for many interesting discussions.

Appendix A. Racah algebra "in nuce" for SU(2)

This appendix will be devoted to a brief summary of formulae and properties of coupling and recoupling coefficients, as well as of matrix representations for the unitary unimodular group in two dimensions[29]).

The $3j$-symbol is defined by[4]):

$$\begin{pmatrix} a & b & c \\ \alpha & \beta & \gamma \end{pmatrix} \equiv \begin{vmatrix} b+c-a & c+a-b & a+b-c \\ a-\alpha & b-\beta & c-\gamma \\ a+\alpha & b+\beta & c+\gamma \end{vmatrix} =$$

$$= (-1)^{a-b-\gamma} [\Delta(abc)\,(a+\alpha)!\,(a-\alpha)!\,(b+\beta)!\,(b-\beta)!\,(c+\gamma)! \times \times (c-\gamma)!]^{\frac{1}{2}} \sum_x (-1)^x [x!\,(c-b+\alpha+x)!\,(c-a-\beta+x)! \times \times (a+b-c-x)!\,(a-\alpha-x)!\,(b+\beta-x)!]^{-1}, \tag{A.1}$$

with

$$\Delta(abc) = \frac{(a+b-c)!\,(b+c-a)!\,(c+a-b)!}{(a+b+c+1)!}. \tag{A.2}$$

The positive integers or half-integers a, b, c satisfy triangular inequalities: $|a-b| \leqslant c \leqslant a+b$ etc. and $\alpha+\beta+\gamma=0$; $a-|\alpha|$ etc. must be natural integers. If anyone of these conditions is not fulfilled, the value of the symbol is assumed to be zero. The 72 elements[15]) of the symmetry group R_1 of this coefficient are the permutations of lines and/or columns of the square symbol in (A.1) (which yield the phase $(P)^S$ with $S=a+b+c$ and $P=+1,-1$ according to even, odd permutations), and the exchange of lines with columns. For unitarity and orthogonality of 3j-symbols, see Edmonds[16]).

From the definition (3.1) it turns out[4]) that the 6j-symbol is given in terms of 3j-coefficients by:

$$\begin{Bmatrix} a & b & c \\ d & e & f \end{Bmatrix} = \sum_{\substack{\alpha\beta\gamma \\ \delta\varepsilon\varphi}} (-1)^{d+e+f+\delta+\varepsilon+\varphi} \times$$
$$\times \begin{pmatrix} d & e & c \\ \delta & -\varepsilon & \gamma \end{pmatrix} \begin{pmatrix} e & f & a \\ \varepsilon & -\varphi & \alpha \end{pmatrix} \begin{pmatrix} f & d & b \\ \varphi & -\delta & \beta \end{pmatrix} \begin{pmatrix} a & b & c \\ \alpha & \beta & \gamma \end{pmatrix}. \tag{A.3}$$

Racah's treatment of this formula[1]) yields:

$$\begin{Bmatrix} a & b & c \\ d & e & f \end{Bmatrix} = [\Delta(abc)\,\Delta(aef)\,\Delta(cde)\,\Delta(bdf)]^{\frac{1}{2}} \times$$
$$\times \sum_x (-1)^x (x+1)!\,[(a+b+d+e-x)!\,(a+c+d+f-x)! \times$$
$$\times (b+c+e+f-x)!\,(x-a-b-c)!\,(x-a-e-f)! \times$$
$$\times (x-c-d-e)!\,(x-b-d-f)!]^{-1}. \tag{A.4}$$

The symbol is assumed to vanish if anyone of the triads (abc), (cde), (aef), (bdf) does not satisfy triangular inequalities. In addition to the well known symmetries of the associated tetrahedron (fig. 1), the 6j-symbol has also the less evident symmetry[15]):

$$\begin{Bmatrix} a & b & c \\ d & e & f \end{Bmatrix} \equiv \begin{vmatrix} a+b-c & b+f-d & f+a-e \\ d+b-f & b+c-a & c+d-e \\ a+e-f & e+c-d & c+a-b \\ d+e-c & e+f-a & f+d-b \end{vmatrix} =$$
$$= \begin{Bmatrix} a & \frac{1}{2}(c+f+e-b) & \frac{1}{2}(b+e+f-c) \\ d & \frac{1}{2}(c+f+b-e) & \frac{1}{2}(b+e+c-f) \end{Bmatrix}, \tag{A.5}$$

which entails that this coefficient is invariant under the 144 elements of a group R_2 which correspond to the permutations of lines and/or columns of the 3×4 pattern in (A.5). In addition to the Biedenharn–Elliott identity (3.8), the $6j$-symbol satisfies also the following relations[30]):

$$\sum_x (2x+1) \begin{Bmatrix} a & b & x \\ d & e & f \end{Bmatrix} \begin{Bmatrix} a & b & x \\ d & e & f' \end{Bmatrix} = \frac{\delta_{ff'}}{2f+1}, \tag{A.6}$$

$$\sum_x (-1)^{f+g+x} (2x+1) \begin{Bmatrix} a & b & x \\ d & e & f \end{Bmatrix} \begin{Bmatrix} d & e & x \\ b & a & g \end{Bmatrix} = \begin{Bmatrix} a & e & f \\ b & d & g \end{Bmatrix}. \tag{A.7}$$

Wigner's $9j$-symbol[4]), which is proportional to the transformation matrix between different coupling schemes of four angular momenta, is given in terms of $6j$-coefficients by:

$$\begin{Bmatrix} a & b & c \\ d & e & f \\ g & h & i \end{Bmatrix} = \sum_x (-1)^{2x} (2x+1) \begin{Bmatrix} a & i & x \\ f & b & c \end{Bmatrix} \begin{Bmatrix} f & b & x \\ h & d & e \end{Bmatrix} \begin{Bmatrix} h & d & x \\ a & i & g \end{Bmatrix}. \tag{A.8}$$

Its known symmetries are formally the same as those mentioned above for the $3j$-symbol, with $S=a+b+c+d+e+f+g+h+i$. For a more comprehensive account of relations involving these coefficients, see ref. 6.

According to the conventions and notations of ref. 30 for basis vectors, angular momentum operators and Euler angles, the rotation operator

$$\hat{D}(\alpha\beta\gamma) = e^{-i\alpha\hat{Y}_Z}\, e^{-i\beta\hat{Y}_Y}\, e^{-i\gamma\hat{Y}_Z} \tag{A.9}$$

has matrix elements in the $2J+1$ dimensional representation which can be written as

$$D^{(J)}_{MM'}(\alpha\beta\gamma) \equiv \langle JM|\hat{D}(\alpha\beta\gamma)|JM'\rangle = e^{-i\alpha M}\, d^{(J)}_{MM'}(\beta)\, e^{-i\gamma M'} \tag{A.10}$$

in terms of the real matrix: $d^{(J)}_{MM'}(\beta) = D^{(J)}_{MM'}(0\beta 0)$, The following properties hold

$$[D^{(J)}(\alpha\beta\gamma)]^{+} = [D^{(J)}(\alpha\beta\gamma)]^{-1} = D^{(J)}(-\gamma, -\beta, -\alpha), \tag{A.11}$$

$$\sum_M D^{(J)}_{MM'}\, D^{(J)*}_{MM''} = \delta_{M'M''}; \qquad \sum_M D^{(J)}_{M'M}\, D^{(J)*}_{M''M} = \delta_{M'M''}, \tag{A.12}$$

$$\frac{1}{8\pi^2} \int_0^{2\pi} d\alpha \int_0^{2\pi} d\gamma \int_0^{\pi} d\beta \sin\beta\, D^{(J)*}_{M_1M_2}(\alpha\beta\gamma)\, D^{(J')}_{M_1'M_2'}(\alpha\beta\gamma) = \frac{\delta_{JJ'}\,\delta_{M_1M_1'}\,\delta_{M_2M_2'}}{2J+1}, \tag{A.13}$$

in addition to the symmetry

$$D^{(J)*}_{MM'} = (-1)^{M-M'}\, D^{(J)}_{-M,-M'}. \tag{A.14}$$

In general [4])

$$d^{(J)}_{-M,M'}(\beta) = \sum_x (-1)^x \frac{[(J-M)!\,(J+M)!\,(J-M')!\,(J+M')!]^{\frac{1}{2}}}{(J-M-x)!\,(J-M'-x)\,x!\,(x+M+M')!} \times$$
$$\times (\cos \tfrac{1}{2}\beta)^{2J-M-M'-2x} (\sin \tfrac{1}{2}\beta)^{2x+M+M'}, \qquad \text{(A.15)}$$

which leads in particular to

$$d^{(L)}_{M,0}(\beta) = (-1)^M \left[\frac{(L-M)!}{(L+M)!}\right]^{\frac{1}{2}} P^M_L(\cos\beta); \qquad \text{(A.16)}$$

the following symmetries are very useful

$$d^{(J)}_{M,M'}(\beta) = (-1)^{M-M'} d^{(J)}_{-M,-M'}(\beta) =$$
$$= (-1)^{M-M'} d^{(J)}_{M',M}(\beta) = (-1)^{J-M'} d^{(J)}_{-M',M}(\pi-\beta). \qquad \text{(A.17)}$$

The connection with Jacobi polynomials is given by

$$d^{(J)}_{MM'}(\beta) = (-1)^{M-M'} \left[\frac{(J+M)!\,(J-M)!}{(J+M')!\,(J-M')!}\right]^{\frac{1}{2}} \times$$
$$\times (\cos \tfrac{1}{2}\beta)^{M+M'} (\sin \tfrac{1}{2}\beta)^{M-M'} P^{(M-M',\,M+M')}_{J-M}(\cos\beta). \qquad \text{(A.18)}$$

Appendix B. Elementary geometry of tetrahedra

Heron's formula for the content A of a triangle of edges j_1, j_2, j_3 can be written as

$$A^2 = \tfrac{1}{16}(j_1+j_2+j_3)(j_1+j_2-j_3)(j_1-j_2+j_3)(-j_1+j_2+j_3) =$$
$$= -\tfrac{1}{16}\begin{vmatrix} 0 & j_1^2 & j_2^2 & 1 \\ j_1^2 & 0 & j_3^2 & 1 \\ j_2^2 & j_3^2 & 0 & 1 \\ 1 & 1 & 1 & 0 \end{vmatrix}. \qquad \text{(B.1)}$$

We have already given in (1.2) Cayley's form for the content V of a tetrahedron. Performing in (1.2) the derivation of V^2 with respect to $(j_{rs})^2$ and denoting the (r, s) algebraic minor of the Cayley determinant with C_{rs}, the relation [31])

$$-C_{rs} = 16 A_h A_k \cos\theta_{hk}, \qquad r \neq s \neq h \neq k \qquad \text{(B.2)}$$

yields (3.22); in (B.2) h, k, r, s are any permutation of 1, 2, 3, 4. Using (3.22) and the obvious identity

$$A_h A_k \sin\theta_{hk} = \tfrac{3}{2} V j_{hk} \qquad \text{(B.3)}$$

we obtain the differentiation formulae

$$-\frac{d\theta_{hk}}{dj_{rs}}=\frac{j_{hk}j_{rs}}{6V}, \qquad h\neq k\neq r\neq s \tag{B.4}$$

Looking at fig. 1 we see that

$$V=\tfrac{1}{6}j_{12}j_{23}j_{13}\sin\varphi_{14}\sin\varphi_{24}\sin\theta_{12} \tag{B.5}$$

or

$$V=\tfrac{1}{6}j_{12}j_{13}j_{23}\begin{vmatrix}1 & \cos\varphi_{14} & \cos\varphi_{24}\\ \cos\varphi_{14} & 1 & \cos\varphi_{34}\\ \cos\varphi_{24} & \cos\varphi_{34} & 1\end{vmatrix}^{\frac{1}{2}} \tag{B.6}$$

since $\cos\varphi_{34}=\cos\varphi_{14}\cos\varphi_{24}-\sin\varphi_{14}\sin\varphi_{24}\cos\theta_{12}$. Now, if we define with reference to P_4:

$$2\sigma_4=\theta_{12}+\theta_{13}+\theta_{23}, \tag{B.7}$$

$$\Sigma_4=[\sin\sigma_4\sin(\sigma_4-\theta_{12})\sin(\sigma_4-\theta_{13})\sin(\sigma_4-\theta_{23})]^{\frac{1}{2}}, \tag{B.8}$$

then it follows[22]:

$$2\Sigma_4=\sin\theta_{12}\sin\theta_{23}\sin\varphi_{24}=\sin\theta_{13}\sin\theta_{23}\sin\varphi_{34}=$$
$$=\sin\theta_{12}\sin\theta_{13}\sin\varphi_{14}, \tag{B.9}$$

and

$$\begin{aligned}\Sigma_4\operatorname{tg}\tfrac{1}{2}\varphi_{14}&=\sin\sigma_4\sin(\sigma_4-\theta_{23}),\\ \Sigma_4\operatorname{tg}\tfrac{1}{2}\varphi_{24}&=\sin\sigma_4\sin(\sigma_4-\theta_{13}),\\ \Sigma_4\operatorname{tg}\tfrac{1}{2}\varphi_{34}&=\sin\sigma_4\sin(\sigma_4-\theta_{12}).\end{aligned} \tag{B.10}$$

It turns out that $K=\Sigma_h/A_h$ is independent of h; therefore, from (B.5), (B.9):

$$V=\tfrac{2}{3}\left(\prod_{h=1}^{4}A_h\right)^{\frac{1}{2}}K^{\frac{1}{2}}. \tag{B.11}$$

Appendix C. A summation property of Jacobi polynomials

The purpose of this appendix is to prove the relation

$$\sum_{L=0}^{\infty}(2L+1)\,d^{(L)}_{M_1M_2}(\beta_3)\,d^{(L)}_{M_2M_3}(\beta_1)\,d^{(L)}_{M_3M_1}(\beta_2)=$$
$$=\frac{2\Theta(\mathscr{B})}{\pi[\mathscr{B}]^{\frac{1}{2}}}\cos\left(\sum_{i=1}^{3}M_i\delta_i\right), \tag{C.1}$$

where Θ is the step function used in (3.13), while the angles β_i, δ_i $(i=1, 2, 3)$

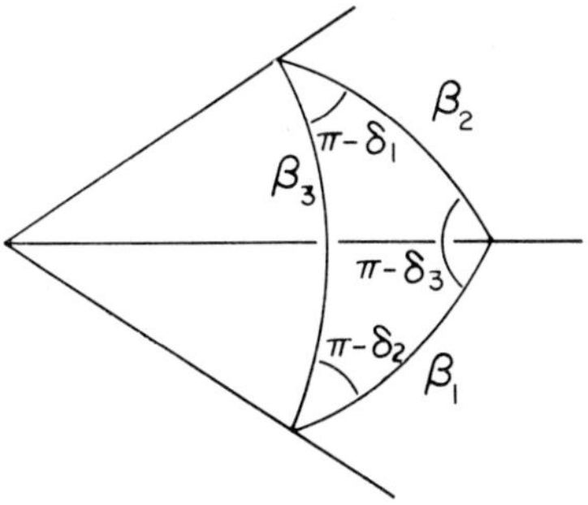

Fig. C1.

are shown in fig. C1 and

$$\mathscr{B} = \begin{vmatrix} 1 & \cos\beta_3 & \cos\beta_2 \\ \cos\beta_3 & 1 & \cos\beta_1 \\ \cos\beta_2 & \cos\beta_1 & 1 \end{vmatrix}. \tag{C.2}$$

The addition property of the rotation group yields:

$$D^{(L)}_{M_1M_2}(\alpha_3\beta_3\gamma_3) = \sum_{M_3} D^{(L)}_{M_1M_3}(\alpha_2\beta_2\gamma_2)\, D^{(L)}_{M_3M_2}(\alpha_1\beta_1\gamma_1), \tag{C.3}$$

from which, using unitarity

$$D^{(L)}_{M_3M_2}(\alpha_1\beta_1\gamma_1) = \sum_{M_1} D^{(L)}_{M_1M_2}(\alpha_3\beta_3\gamma_3)\, D^{(L)*}_{M_1M_3}(\alpha_2\beta_2\gamma_2), \tag{C.4}$$

$$D^{(L)}_{M_1M_3}(\alpha_2\beta_2\gamma_2) = \sum_{M_2} D^{(L)*}_{M_3M_2}(\alpha_1\beta_1\gamma_1)\, D^{(L)}_{M_1M_2}(\alpha_3\beta_3\gamma_3). \tag{C.5}$$

By exploiting (C.3)–(C.5) for low values of L, we obtain

$$\cos\beta_i = \cos\beta_j \cos\beta_k - \sin\beta_j \sin\beta_k \cos\delta_i, \quad i \neq j \neq k = 1, 2, 3 \tag{C.6}$$

$$\sin\beta_i/\sin\delta_i = \sin\beta_j/\sin\delta_j, \quad i \neq j \tag{C.7}$$

where

$$\delta_1 = \alpha_2 - \alpha_3 + \pi, \quad \delta_2 = \gamma_1 - \gamma_3 - \pi, \quad \delta_3 = \alpha_1 + \gamma_2. \tag{C.8}$$

By means of (A.13) and (C.3) we find

$$\int_0^{2\pi} d\alpha_2 \int_0^{2\pi} d\gamma_2 \int_0^{\pi} d\beta_2 \sin\beta_2\, D^{(L')*}_{M_1'M_3'}(\alpha_2\beta_2\gamma_2)\, D^{(L)}_{M_1M_2}(\alpha_3\beta_3\gamma_3) =$$

$$= \frac{8\pi^2}{2L+1}\, \delta_{LL'}\, \delta_{M_1M_1'}\, \delta_{M_3M_3'}\, D^{(L)}_{M_3M_2}(\alpha_1\beta_1\gamma_1); \tag{C.9a}$$

(A.10) and the reality of functions $d^{(L)}_{MM'}$ give

$$\int_0^{2\pi} \mathrm{d}\alpha_2 \int_0^{2\pi} \mathrm{d}\gamma_2 \int_0^{\pi} \mathrm{d}\beta_2 \sin\beta_2 \cos\left(\sum_{j=1}^{3} M_j\delta_j\right) d^{(L)}_{M_1M_3}(\beta_2)\, d^{(L)}_{M_1M_2}(\beta_3) = \\ = \frac{8\pi^2}{2L+1}(-1)^{M_1-M_2}\, d^{(L)}_{M_3M_2}(\beta_1). \tag{C.9b}$$

We notice that, once $\alpha_1, \beta_1, \gamma_1, \beta_2, \gamma_2$ have been fixed, β_3 and δ_i $(i=1, 2, 3)$ are independent of α_2; therefore:

$$\int_0^{2\pi} \mathrm{d}\gamma_2 \int_0^{\pi} \mathrm{d}\beta_2 \sin\beta_2 \cos\left(\sum_{j=1}^{3} M_j\delta_j\right) d^{(L)}_{M_1M_3}(\beta_2)\, d^{(L)}_{M_1M_2}(\beta_3) = \\ = \frac{4\pi}{2L+1}(-1)^{M_1-M_2}\, d^{(L)}_{M_3M_2}(\beta_1). \tag{C.10}$$

Going from the integration variables β_2, γ_2 to $\cos\beta_2, \cos\beta_3$, we find:

$$\frac{\partial(\beta_2, \gamma_2)}{\partial(\cos\beta_2, \cos\beta_3)} = (\sin\beta_2)^{-1}\, \mathscr{B}^{-\frac{1}{2}} \tag{C.11}$$

and

$$\int_{-1}^{+1} \mathrm{d}(\cos\beta_2) \int_{-1}^{+1} \mathrm{d}(\cos\beta_3)\, \frac{\Theta(\mathscr{B})}{\mathscr{B}^{\frac{1}{2}}} \cos\left(\sum_{j=1}^{3} M_j\delta_j\right) d^{(L)}_{M_1M_3}(\beta_2) \times \\ \times d^{(L)}_{M_1M_2}(\beta_3) = \frac{2\pi}{2L+1}(-1)^{M_1-M_2}\, d^{(L)}_{M_3M_2}(\beta_1), \tag{C.12}$$

having noticed that a given point of the integration domain in (C.12) corresponds to two different points in (C.10). Since by means of the orthogonal polynomials $d^{(L)}_{MM'}$ we can define the following expansions:

$$f_{M_1M_2M_1'M_2'}(\beta, \beta') = \sum_{L, L'} \frac{2L+1}{2}\, \frac{2L'+1}{2}\, f_{LL'}^{M_1M_2M_1'M_2'}\, d^{(L)}_{M_1M_2}(\beta)\, d^{(L')}_{M_1'M_2'}(\beta'), \tag{C.13}$$

with coefficients:

$$f_{LL'}^{M_1M_2M_1'M_2'} = \int_{-1}^{+1} \mathrm{d}(\cos\beta) \int_{-1}^{+1} \mathrm{d}(\cos\beta')\, f_{M_1M_2M_1'M_2'}(\beta, \beta') \times \\ \times d^{(L)}_{M_1M_2}(\beta)\, d^{(L)}_{M_1'M_2'}(\beta'), \tag{C.14}$$

which are non-vanishing only if $L \geqslant \max(|M_1|, M_2|)$, $L' \geqslant \max(|M_1'|, |M_2'|)$, we have from (C.12)

$$\frac{\Theta(\mathscr{B})}{\mathscr{B}^{\frac{1}{2}}} \cos\left(\sum_{j=1}^{3} M_j \delta_j\right) (-1)^{M_1 - M_2} =$$

$$= \tfrac{1}{2}\pi \sum_{L=0}^{\infty} (2L+1)\, d^{(L)}_{M_3 M_2}(\beta_1)\, d^{(L)}_{M_1 M_3}(\beta_2)\, d^{(L)}_{M_1 M_2}(\beta_3).$$

The symmetries (A.17) lead us to (C.1).

In order to complete the proof of (3.13), we have just to recall (B.6).

Appendix D. Invariance of Ω under R_2

It is straightforward, though very tedious, to verify that the volume of T is invariant also under the symmetry (A.5). This can be worked out by expanding (1.2) and replacing j_{13} with $\frac{1}{2}(j_{14}+j_{24}+j_{23}-j_{13})$ etc. Incidentally, we note that in the same way one can check also the invariance of $\prod_{h=1}^{4} A_h$ under R_2. Here we prefer to sketch how the symmetry of Ω can be proved.

Let us multiply eqs. (B.10) among themselves. We have for instance

$$(\sin \sigma_4)^2 = \Sigma_4 \operatorname{tg} \tfrac{1}{2}\varphi_{14} \operatorname{tg} \tfrac{1}{2}\varphi_{24} \operatorname{tg} \tfrac{1}{2}\varphi_{34}\,; \qquad \text{(D.1)}$$

then choosing for example the first of (B.10), we have

$$[\sin \tfrac{1}{2}(\theta_{12} + \theta_{13} - \theta_{23})]^2 = \Sigma_4 \operatorname{tg} \tfrac{1}{2}\varphi_{14} \operatorname{cotg} \tfrac{1}{2}\varphi_{24} \operatorname{cotg} \tfrac{1}{2}\varphi_{34}\,. \qquad \text{(D.2)}$$

In order to compute the r.h.s. of (D.2) it is convenient to introduce, with reference to fig. D1, the following notations

$$q_1 = j_{12} + j_{13} + j_{14}, \quad q_2 = j_{12} + j_{23} + j_{24},$$
$$q_3 = j_{13} + j_{23} + j_{34}, \quad q_4 = j_{14} + j_{24} + j_{34}\,; \qquad \text{(D.3)}$$

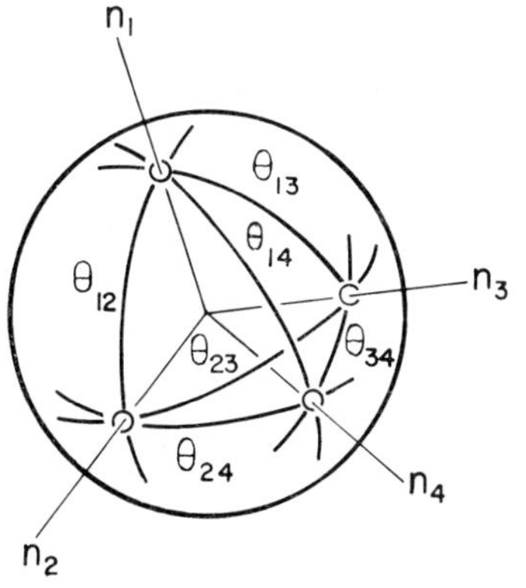

Fig. D1.

$$p_{14}=p_{23}=j_{12}+j_{13}+j_{34}+j_{24},\quad p_{13}=p_{24}=j_{12}+j_{34}+j_{14}+j_{23},$$
$$p_{12}=p_{34}=j_{13}+j_{24}+j_{14}+j_{23}; \tag{D.4}$$

as well as the two patterns

$$r_{st}\equiv\begin{bmatrix} p_{14}-q_1 & p_{13}-q_1 & p_{12}-q_1 & q_1\\ p_{14}-q_2 & p_{13}-q_2 & p_{12}-q_2 & q_2\\ p_{14}-q_3 & p_{13}-q_3 & p_{12}-q_3 & q_3\\ p_{14}-q_4 & p_{13}-q_4 & p_{12}-q_4 & q_4\end{bmatrix};$$
$$\tfrac{1}{2}\vartheta_{st}\equiv\begin{bmatrix} \sigma_4-\theta_{23} & \sigma_3-\theta_{24} & \sigma_2-\theta_{34} & \sigma_1\\ \sigma_3-\theta_{14} & \sigma_4-\theta_{13} & \sigma_1-\theta_{34} & \sigma_2\\ \sigma_2-\theta_{14} & \sigma_1-\theta_{24} & \sigma_4-\theta_{12} & \sigma_3\\ \sigma_1-\theta_{23} & \sigma_2-\theta_{13} & \sigma_3-\theta_{12} & \sigma_4\end{bmatrix}. \tag{D.5}$$

We note that from (B.11)

$$K=\frac{\Sigma_4}{A_4}=\frac{9}{4}\frac{V^2}{\prod_{h=1}^{4}A_h}. \tag{D.6}$$

Since, for example

$$\operatorname{tg}\tfrac{1}{2}\varphi_{14}=\left[\frac{(p_{13}-q_3)(p_{12}-q_2)}{q_1(p_{14}-q_4)}\right]^{\frac{1}{2}},$$

(D.2) becomes

$$\cos(\theta_{12}+\theta_{13}-\theta_{23})=1-2^5 3^2 V^2\,[(p_{13}-q_1)\times$$
$$\times(p_{12}-q_1)q_1(p_{14}-q_2)(p_{14}-q_3)(p_{14}-q_4)]^{-1}$$

and generally for $s\neq t=1, 2, 3, 4$

$$\cos\vartheta_{st}=1-2^3(3!)^2V^2\left\{\left(\prod_{n=1}^{4}r_{sn}\right)\left(\prod_{n=1}^{4}r_{nt}\right)\right\}^{-1}(r_{st})^2, \tag{D.7}$$

which gives, correctly, for a flat tetrahedron, $\vartheta_{st}=0$ or $\vartheta_{st}=2\pi$.

It is easy to check that, under the symmetry (A.5)

$$q'_1=q_2,\quad q'_2=q_1,\quad q'_3=q_4,\quad q'_4=q_3;$$
$$p'_{14}=p_{13},\quad p'_{13}=p_{14},\quad p'_{12}=p_{12}, \tag{D.8}$$

which, taking into account (D.5), (D.7), entails for instance

$$\cos(\theta'_{12}+\theta'_{13}-\theta'_{23})=\cos(\theta_{12}+\theta_{13}-\theta_{23}),$$
$$\cos(\theta'_{13}+\theta'_{23}-\theta'_{12})=\cos(\theta_{14}+\theta_{24}-\theta_{12}), \tag{D.9}$$
$$\cos(\theta'_{12}+\theta'_{23}-\theta'_{13})=\cos(\theta_{12}+\theta_{13}-\theta_{23}).$$

Let us suppose the tetrahedron to be almost regular; asymptotically, this property is not destroyed by the symmetry (A.5); in this case: $0 \leqslant \theta_{hk} \leqslant \frac{1}{2}\pi$ and similarly for the transformed θ'_{hk}. Moreover, looking at fig. D1 we see for example that θ_{12}, θ_{13}, θ_{23} satisfy spherical triangular inequalities; therefore $0 \leqslant \vartheta_{st} < \pi$, $0 \leqslant \vartheta'_{st} < \pi$. Then from (D.9) and similar relations, we obtain

$$\begin{aligned} \theta'_{13} &= \tfrac{1}{2}(\theta_{14}+\theta_{24}+\theta_{23}-\theta_{13}), \\ \theta'_{14} &= \tfrac{1}{2}(\theta_{13}+\theta_{23}+\theta_{24}-\theta_{14}), \qquad \theta'_{12}=\theta_{12}, \\ \theta'_{24} &= \tfrac{1}{2}(\theta_{13}+\theta_{23}+\theta_{14}-\theta_{24}), \\ \theta'_{23} &= \tfrac{1}{2}(\theta_{14}+\theta_{24}+\theta_{13}-\theta_{23}), \qquad \theta'_{34}=\theta_{34}. \end{aligned} \tag{D.10}$$

We conclude that (A.5) induces the same linear transformation on j_{hk} as well as on θ_{hk}; the unitarity of this transformation entails the invariance of $\Omega = \sum_{h,k} j_{hk}\,\theta_{hk} + \frac{1}{4}\pi$ under R_2. Finally, the constraint $\theta_{hk} < \frac{1}{2}\pi$ can be dropped by invoking analytical continuation in θ_{hk}.

Appendix E. Evaluation of $[\partial(\theta_x^1+\theta_x^2+\theta_x^3)/\partial(x^2)]_{x^2=(x_\gtrless)^2}$

According to (4.16), first let us calculate $\partial I^2(x^2)/\partial(x^2)|_{x^2=(x_\gtrless)^2}$. Write (4.8) as follows:

$$C = c_2(x^2)^2 + c_1(x^2) + c_0 = 0, \tag{E.1}$$

where $-2^4(4!)^2 I^2(x^2) = C$; then the solutions of (E.1) are obviously

$$(x_\gtrless)^2 = \frac{\pm\sqrt{c_1^2 - 4c_0c_2} - c_1}{2c_2}, \tag{E.2}$$

where c_0, c_1, c_2 are determinants extracted from C which, for the sake of brevity, we do not write explicitly. Since the tetrahedra T_4, T_5 are supposed to be physical, it follows $(x_\gtrless)^2 > 0$. Then

$$\left[\frac{\partial C}{\partial(x^2)}\right]_{x^2=(x_\gtrless)^2} = \pm\sqrt{c_1^2 - 4c_0c_2}\,. \tag{E.3}$$

From known properties of determinants[32]), it turns out that

$$\tfrac{1}{4}(c_1^2 - 4c_0c_2) = 2^6(3!)^4 V_4^2 V_5^2\,, \tag{E.4}$$

therefore

$$\left[\frac{\partial I^2(x^2)}{\partial(x^2)}\right]_{x^2=(x_\gtrless)^2} = \mp\frac{V_4V_5}{16}. \tag{E.5}$$

In order to evaluate $\partial^2 I^2(x^2)/\partial(\theta_x^1+\theta_x^2+\theta_x^3)|_{x^2=(x_\gtrless)^2}$, suppose to imbed the simplex P_1, P_2, P_3, P_4, P_5 of fig. 8a into a 4-dimensional Euclidean space.

The content I of this simplex is

$$(4!)^2 I^2 = \begin{vmatrix} x & 0 & 0 & 0 \\ 0 & h_{11} & h_{12} & h_{13} \\ 0 & h_{21} & h_{22} & h_{23} \\ 0 & h_{31} & h_{32} & h_{33} \end{vmatrix}^2 \tag{E.6}$$

where $h_{1j}, h_{2j}, h_{3j} (j=1, 2, 3)$ are the components of the distances from P_1, P_2, P_3 to x. The direction of x has been chosen as the first axis of refer-

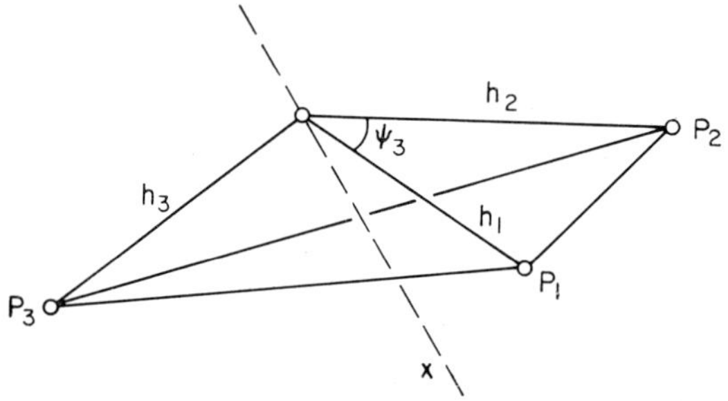

Fig. E1.

ence in this hyperspace. Let H be the volume of the tetrahedron defined by h_1, h_2, h_3 (see fig. E1). Then we are led to the simple formula

$$I = \tfrac{1}{4} x H . \tag{E.7}$$

Now we notice that the angle between, for instance, h_1 and h_2 is $\pi - \theta_x^3$. Therefore from (B.6) we have

$$\begin{aligned} \delta(H^2) = \tfrac{1}{18}(h_1 h_2 h_3)^2 [&\sin\theta_x^1 (\cos\theta_x^2 \cos\theta_x^3 + \cos\theta_x^1)\, \delta\theta_x^1 + \\ &+ \sin\theta_x^2 (\cos\theta_x^3 \cos\theta_x^1 + \cos\theta_x^2)\, \delta\theta_x^2 + \\ &+ \sin\theta_x^3 (\cos\theta_x^1 \cos\theta_x^2 + \cos\theta_x^3)\, \delta\theta_x^3] . \end{aligned} \tag{E.8}$$

Since (E.8) must be evaluated when $\theta_x^1 + \theta_x^2 + \theta_x^3 = \pi$, i.e. when h_1, h_2, h_3 are coplanar, we find

$$\left[\frac{\partial(H^2)}{\partial(\theta_x^1 + \theta_x^2 + \theta_x^3)}\right]_{x^2 = (x \gtrless)^2} = \tfrac{1}{18}(h_1 h_2 h_3)^2 \sin\theta_x^1 \sin\theta_x^2 \sin\theta_x^3 . \tag{E.9}$$

Moreover, from (B.5) we obtain

$$V_i = \tfrac{1}{6} h_1 h_2 h_3 x \frac{\sin\theta_x^i}{h_i}, \qquad i = 1, 2, 3 \tag{E.10}$$

and finally, by means of (E.7)

$$\left[\frac{\partial I^2(x^2)}{\partial(\theta_x^1+\theta_x^2+\theta_x^3)}\right]_{x^2=(x_{\gtrless})^2} = \frac{3}{4}\left[\frac{V_1V_2V_3}{x}\right]_{x^2=(x_{\gtrless})^2}. \tag{E.11}$$

Relations (E.5) and (E.11) yield (4.17).

Appendix F. Evaluation of $\lim_{V^2\to 0}\Omega(V^2)$

The behaviour of Ω in the neighbourhood of a transition point deserves a rather careful investigation. To begin with, let us suppose that we approach the region B_3 as $V^2\to 0$. In fig. 10 we show the notations which will be used in the sequel; moreover we indicate with A, B, C the *internal* dihedral angles between faces belonging to $a+\frac{1}{2}$, $b+\frac{1}{2}$, $c+\frac{1}{2}$ and with $\pi-D$, $\pi-E$, $\pi-F$ the corresponding ones relative to $d+\frac{1}{2}$, $e+\frac{1}{2}$, $f+\frac{1}{2}$. Also the following shorthand notation will be convenient:

$$\begin{aligned}\mu_{bc} &= \cos\alpha, & \mu_{bd} &= \cos\delta_b, & \mu_{cd} &= \cos\delta_c,\\ \mu_{ca} &= \cos\beta, & \mu_{ce} &= \cos\varepsilon_c, & \mu_{ae} &= \cos\varepsilon_a,\\ \mu_{ab} &= \cos\gamma, & \mu_{af} &= \cos\varphi_a, & \mu_{bf} &= \cos\varphi_b.\end{aligned} \tag{F.1}$$

When P lies very near to the plane of the triangle $P_AP_BP_C$ and within its boundary we have $\overset{0}{\mu}_{bc}=\cos(\delta_c+\delta_b)$, $\overset{0}{\mu}_{ca}=\cos(\varepsilon_a+\varepsilon_c)$, $\overset{0}{\mu}_{ab}=\cos(\varphi_a+\varphi_b)$ and $A=B=C=D=E=F=0$. Since $a+\frac{1}{2}=(e+\frac{1}{2})\,\mu_{ae}+(f+\frac{1}{2})\,\mu_{af}$ etc., we obtain in general from the definition (3.15b)

$$\Omega = \pi(a+b+c+\tfrac{7}{4}) + (d+\tfrac{1}{2})\,\Psi_A + (e+\tfrac{1}{2})\,\Psi_B + (f+\tfrac{1}{2})\,\Psi_C, \tag{F.2}$$

where

$$\begin{aligned}\Psi_A = D - B\mu_{bd} - C\mu_{cd},\quad \Psi_B = E - C\mu_{ce} - A\mu_{ae},\\ \Psi_C = F - A\mu_{af} - B\mu_{bf}.\end{aligned} \tag{F.3}$$

In order to evaluate Ω when $V^2\sim 0$, it is useful to exploit the following integral representation for Ψ_A:

$$\Psi_A = \int_{\mu_{bc}{}^0}^{\mu_{bc}} (1-\xi^2)^{-1}(1+2\mu_{bd}\mu_{cd}\xi-\mu_{bd}^2-\mu_{cd}^2-\xi^2)^{\frac{1}{2}}\,\mathrm{d}\xi, \tag{F.4}$$

and similar ones for Ψ_B, Ψ_C. Noticing that $\Psi_A(\mu_{bc}=\overset{0}{\mu}_{bc})=0$ and using the relations

$$D = \arc\cos\left\{\frac{\mu_{bd}\mu_{cd}-\mu_{bc}}{[(1-\mu_{bd}^2)(1-\mu_{cd}^2)]^{\frac{1}{2}}}\right\},\quad B = \arc\cos\left\{\frac{\mu_{cd}-\mu_{bd}\mu_{bc}}{[(1-\mu_{bd}^2)(1-\mu_{bc}^2)]^{\frac{1}{2}}}\right\},$$

$$C = \arc\cos\left\{\frac{\mu_{bd}-\mu_{cd}\mu_{bc}}{[(1-\mu_{cd}^2)(1-\mu_{bc}^2)]^{\frac{1}{2}}}\right\}, \tag{F.5}$$

it is easy to verify that the derivatives with respect to μ_{bc} of both sides of (F.4) are equal. Now let us put

$$1 + 2\mu_{bd}\mu_{cd}\xi - \mu_{bd}^2 - \mu_{cd}^2 - \xi^2 = (\xi - \mu_{bc}^0)(\mu_{bc}^1 - \xi), \qquad \text{(F.6)}$$

where μ_{bc}^1 is the value assumed by μ_{bc} when the tetrahedron is flat with P outside $P_A P_B P_C$. In this case $\alpha = |\delta_b - \delta_c|$ and $\mu_{bc}^1 > \mu_{bc}^0$. In the neighbourhood of $\mu_{bc} = \mu_{bc}^0$ we can approximate the integrand of (F.4) as follows:

$$\Psi_A \simeq \int_{\mu_{bc}^0}^{\mu_{bc}} (1 - \xi^2)^{-1} [(\xi - \mu_{bc}^0)(\mu_{bc}^1 - \mu_{bc}^0)]^{\frac{1}{2}} \, d\xi \simeq \frac{2}{3} \frac{(\mu_{bc} - \mu_{bc}^0)^{\frac{3}{2}}}{1 - (\mu_{bc}^0)^2} (\mu_{bc}^1 - \mu_{bc}^0)^{\frac{1}{2}}, \qquad \text{(F.7)}$$

and using (F.6)

$$\Psi_A \simeq \tfrac{2}{3}(\mu_{bc} - \mu_{bc}^0)[1 - (\mu_{bc}^0)^2]^{-1}(1 + 2\mu_{bd}\mu_{cd}\mu_{bc} - \mu_{bd}^2 - \mu_{cd}^2 - \mu_{bc}^2)^{\frac{1}{2}}. \qquad \text{(F.8)}$$

Since $\mu_{bc} - \mu_{bc}^0 = 2 \sin \frac{1}{2}(\alpha + \delta_b + \delta_c) \sin \frac{1}{2}(-\alpha + \delta_b + \delta_c) \simeq -(\alpha - \delta_b - \delta_c) \sin \alpha$, we obtain from (F.8), (B.6), (B.5)

$$\begin{aligned} \Psi_A &\simeq \tfrac{2}{3} \sin \alpha (\delta_b + \delta_c - \alpha) \frac{6V}{(b + \frac{1}{2})(c + \frac{1}{2})(d + \frac{1}{2})} (\sin \alpha)^{-2} \simeq \\ &\simeq \tfrac{2}{3}(\delta_b + \delta_c - \alpha) \sin \delta_c \sin C. \end{aligned} \qquad \text{(F.9)}$$

If h is the distance of P from the plane $P_A P_B P_C$ we have also

$$(d + \tfrac{1}{2})\Psi_A \simeq \tfrac{2}{3} h(\delta_b + \delta_c - \alpha). \qquad \text{(F.10)}$$

Therefore from (F.10) and similar relations for Ψ_B, Ψ_C we find

$$\Omega \simeq \pi(a + b + c - \tfrac{1}{4}) + \tfrac{2}{3} h(2\pi - \delta - \varepsilon - \varphi). \qquad \text{(F.11)}$$

Our result (E.9) yields in the neighbourhood of $V^2 = 0$

$$V^2 = \tfrac{1}{18}[(d + \tfrac{1}{2})(e + \tfrac{1}{2})(f + \tfrac{1}{2})]^2 \sin \delta \sin \varepsilon \sin \varphi \, (2\pi - \delta - \varepsilon - \varphi), \qquad \text{(F.12)}$$

having taken into account the different definition of δ, ε, φ. Using the proportionality between h and V, we obtain finally from (F.11), (F. 12)

$$\Omega \simeq \pi(a + b + c - \tfrac{1}{4}) + \tfrac{9}{2} V^3 \left(\prod_{k=1}^{4} A_k\right)^{-1}. \qquad \text{(F.13)}$$

In a similar way, when we approach B_4 as $V^2 \to 0$, we find in the case corresponding to fig. 1

$$\Omega \simeq \pi(a + b + d + e + \tfrac{1}{4}) - \tfrac{9}{2} V^3 \left(\prod_{k=1}^{4} A_k\right)^{-1}. \qquad \text{(F.14)}$$

Appendix G. WKB approximation for $d^{(f)}_{\delta\delta'}(\theta)$

Let us recall here the main features of the WKB solutions of

$$\frac{d^2g}{dz^2} + Q^2(z)\,g = 0, \tag{G.1}$$

without discussing their degree of approximation[33]); in (G.1) $Q^2(z) = \mathcal{Q}^2(z)(z-z_1)(z_2-z)$ with $z_1<z_2$ and $\mathcal{Q}^2>0$. We know that the function

$$z \leqslant z_1, \quad g_1(z) = \frac{2}{\pi}\left(\frac{|\mathrm{Im}\, t_1|}{|Q|}\right)^{\frac{1}{2}} \times$$
$$\times \{\pi \sin\eta_1\, I_{\frac{1}{3}}(|\mathrm{Im}\, t_1|) + \cos(\tfrac{1}{3}\pi - \eta_1)\, K_{\frac{1}{3}}(|\mathrm{Im}\, t_1|)\} \tag{G.2}$$

joins smoothly with

$$z_1 < z \leqslant z_2 \begin{cases} g_2(z) = \left(\dfrac{4t_1}{3Q}\right)^{\frac{1}{2}} \{\cos(\tfrac{1}{3}\pi + \eta_1)\, J_{\frac{1}{3}}(t_1) + \cos(\tfrac{1}{3}\pi - \eta_1)\, J_{-\frac{1}{3}}(t_1)\}, & \text{(G.3)} \\[2ex] t_1(z) = \displaystyle\int_{z_1}^{z} Q(\xi)\, d\xi, \quad Q(\xi) = +[Q^2(z)]^{\frac{1}{2}}, & \text{(G.4)} \end{cases}$$

if we choose for $z \leqslant z_1$: $Q(z) = \mathrm{i}|Q(z)|$, $|\mathrm{Im}\, t_1| = \int_z^{z_1} |Q(\xi)|\, d\xi$; far from z_1 we have

$$g_1(z) \simeq (2\pi|Q|)^{-\frac{1}{2}} \{2 \sin\eta_1\, e^{|\mathrm{Im}\, t_1|} + \cos\eta_1\, e^{-|\mathrm{Im}\, t_1|}\}, \tag{G.5}$$

$$g_2(z) \simeq \left(\frac{2}{\pi Q}\right)^{\frac{1}{2}} \cos(t_1 + \eta_1 - \tfrac{1}{4}\pi). \tag{G.6}$$

Similarly, continuity through z_2 can be achieved by means of

$$z_1 < z \leqslant z_2 \begin{cases} g_2'(z) = \left(\dfrac{4t_2}{3Q}\right)^{\frac{1}{2}} \{\cos(\tfrac{1}{3}\pi + \eta_2)\, J_{\frac{1}{3}}(t_2) + \cos(\tfrac{1}{3}\pi - \eta_2)\, J_{-\frac{1}{3}}(t_2)\}, & \text{(G.7)} \\[2ex] t_2(z) = \displaystyle\int_{z}^{z_2} Q(\xi)\, d\xi, \quad Q(\xi) = +[Q^2(\xi)]^{\frac{1}{2}}, & \text{(G.8)} \end{cases}$$

$$z_2 < z, \quad g_3(z) = \frac{2}{\pi}\left(\frac{|\mathrm{Im}\, t_2|}{|Q|}\right)^{\frac{1}{2}} \times$$
$$\times \{\pi \sin\eta_2\, I_{\frac{1}{3}}(|\mathrm{Im}\, t_2|) + \cos(\tfrac{1}{3}\pi - \eta_2)\, K_{\frac{1}{3}}(|\mathrm{Im}\, t_2|)\}, \tag{G.9}$$

choosing for

$$z_2 < z: \quad Q(z) = \mathrm{i}\,|Q(z)|, \quad |\mathrm{Im}\, t_2| = \int\limits_{z_2}^{z} |Q(\xi)|\, \mathrm{d}\xi\,;$$

for large $|z - z_2|$ these solutions behave according to (G.6), (G.5) with the obvious replacements: $t_1 \to t_2$, $\eta_1 \to \eta_2$. We note incidentally that, for instance $g_2(z)$ can be written in terms of Airy functions [25]):

$$g_2(z) = \left(\frac{3t_1}{Qy}\right)^{\frac{1}{2}} \{\cos \eta_1 \,\mathrm{Ai}(-y) + \sin \eta_1 \,\mathrm{Bi}(-y)\} \tag{G.10}$$

$$\mathrm{Ai}(-y) = \tfrac{1}{3} y^{\frac{1}{2}} \left[J_{-\frac{1}{3}}(t_1) + J_{\frac{1}{3}}(t_1)\right], \quad \mathrm{Bi}(-y) = (\tfrac{1}{3} y)^{\frac{1}{2}} \left[J_{-\frac{1}{3}}(t_1) - J_{\frac{1}{3}}(t_1)\right], \tag{G.11}$$

where $y = (\frac{3}{2} t_1)^{\frac{2}{3}}$. We see from (G.6) that the consistency condition $g_2(z) = g_2'(z)$ can be fulfilled for $z_1 \ll z \ll z_2$ if

$$\int\limits_{z_1}^{z_2} Q(\xi)\, \mathrm{d}\xi = -\eta_1 - \eta_2 + (2N + \tfrac{1}{2})\pi\,, \quad N \gg 1 \tag{G.12}$$

which provides a relation between η_1 and η_2.

We know (Brussaard and Tolhoek [16])) that, for large f, $d^{(f)}_{\delta\delta'}(\theta)$ satisfies

$$\left\{\frac{\mathrm{d}}{\mathrm{d}(\cos\theta)} \sin^2\theta \frac{\mathrm{d}}{\mathrm{d}(\cos\theta)} + (f + \tfrac{1}{2})^2 \sin^2\theta \left[(1 - \mu^2) \times \right.\right.$$
$$\left.\left. \times (1 - \nu^2) - (\cos\theta - \mu\nu)^2\right]\right\} d^{(f)}_{\delta\delta'}(\theta) = 0\,, \tag{G.13}$$

where $(f + \frac{1}{2})\,\mu = \delta'$, $(f + \frac{1}{2})\,\nu = \delta$; we shall consider only the domain $|\cos\theta| \leqslant 1$. If we put $\cos\theta = \mathrm{tgh}\, z$, $d^{(f)}_{\delta\delta'}(\theta) = g(z)$, then we obtain (G.1) with

$$Q^2(z) = (f + \tfrac{1}{2})^2 \left[(1 - \mu^2)(1 - \nu^2) - (\mathrm{tgh}\, z - \mu\nu)^2\right], \tag{G.14}$$

and transition points

$$\cos\theta_{1,2} \equiv \mathrm{tgh}\, z_{1,2} = \mu\nu \mp \sqrt{(1 - \mu^2)(1 - \nu^2)}\,; \tag{G.15}$$

when $\mu = \nu$, z_2 corresponds to $\cos\theta_2 = 1$; therefore we shall limit ourselves to $\delta \neq \delta'$.

In order to apply (G.2)–(G.9), we must provide t_1, t_2, η_1 and η_2 explicitly. From (G.4), (G.14) and (F.4) we have

$$\int\limits^{z} (f + \tfrac{1}{2}) \left[1 - \mu^2 - \nu^2 + 2\mu\nu\, \mathrm{tgh}\, z - (\mathrm{tgh}\, z)^2\right]^{\frac{1}{2}} \mathrm{d}z =$$
$$= (f + \tfrac{1}{2}) \left[F(z) - \mu A(z) - \nu B(z)\right], \tag{G.16}$$

where $\pi-F$, A, B are the *internal* dihedral angles between the planes belonging respectively to f, $a+\delta'$, $b+\delta$ (fig. 4 with $\mu=\cos\alpha$, $\nu=\cos\beta$). We notice from (G.15) that z_1 corresponds to $\theta_1=\alpha+\beta$, $A=B=F=0$. On the other hand z_2 is associated to the case $\theta_2=|\alpha-\beta|$; we have for $\alpha>\beta$: $B=F=\pi$, $A=0$ and for $\alpha<\beta$: $A=F=\pi$, $B=0$. Therefore[34]):

$$t_1(\theta) \equiv t = (f+\tfrac{1}{2})(F - A\mu - B\nu),$$
$$F = \arc\cos\left(\frac{\mu\nu-\cos\theta}{|\sin\alpha\sin\beta|}\right), \quad A = \arc\cos\left(\frac{\nu-\mu\cos\theta}{|\sin\alpha\sin\theta|}\right), \tag{G.17}$$
$$B = \arc\cos\left(\frac{\mu-\nu\cos\theta}{|\sin\beta\sin\theta|}\right),$$

and similarly for t_2. Furthermore (G.12) yields now:

$$-\eta_1-\eta_2+(2M+\tfrac{1}{2})\pi = \int_{z_1}^{z_2} Q(\xi)\,\mathrm{d}\xi =$$
$$= \begin{cases}(f+\tfrac{1}{2})(\pi-\pi\nu), & \alpha>\beta, \quad (\delta>\delta'),\\ (f+\tfrac{1}{2})(\pi-\pi\mu), & \alpha<\beta, \quad (\delta<\delta').\end{cases} \tag{G.18}$$

From the asymptotic behaviour of Jacobi polynomials[19]) and relation (A.18) it is easy to obtain:

$$d^{(f)}_{\delta\delta'}(\theta) \simeq \left[\frac{2}{\pi(f+\frac{1}{2})\sin\theta}\right]^{\frac{1}{2}} \cos\left\{(f+\tfrac{1}{2})\theta + \tfrac{1}{2}\pi(\delta-\delta') - \tfrac{1}{4}\pi\right\}, \tag{G.19}$$

valid when f is large and $|\delta|$, $|\delta'| \ll f$; performing this limit in (G.17), we have: $A\simeq B\simeq\frac{1}{2}\pi$, $F\simeq\pi-\theta$ and consequently $t_1(\theta)\simeq(f+\frac{1}{2})(\pi-\theta)-\frac{1}{2}\pi(\delta+\delta')$. Using this result and identifying the arguments of the cosines in (G.6) and (G.19), we obtain

$$\eta_1 = \pi(\delta'-f). \tag{G.20}$$

Therefore from (G.18)

$$\eta_2 = \begin{cases}\pi(\delta-\delta') & \delta>\delta',\\ 0 & \delta<\delta';\end{cases} \tag{G.21}$$

obviously η_1 and η_2 are determined modulo $2N\pi$. It must be stressed that only for "physical" values of δ, δ' the phases η_1, η_2 (except when $\delta<\delta'$) are integer multiples of π; in this case the exponentially increasing term in (G.5) is ruled out.

The overall normalization in (G.2), (G.3) and (G.9) has been chosen in agreement with (A.15).

Appendix H. The 1 + 1 + 2 case

In this last appendix we want to show that (3.6) is in agreement with our asymptotic formulae (1.4), (1.8). To this end we consider the limiting case in which f, δ, δ', though large, are still small with respect to a, b, c; therefore we may use in (3.6) our results of appendix G.

In the oscillatory region we deduce from (3.6), (G.6), (G.17), (G.20)

$$\begin{Bmatrix} c & a & b \\ f & b+\delta & a+\delta' \end{Bmatrix} \simeq \frac{(-1)^{a+b+c+f+\delta}}{[(2a+1)(2b+1)]^{\frac{1}{2}}} \left[\frac{2}{\pi(f+\frac{1}{2})}\right]^{\frac{1}{2}} \times$$
$$\times [(1-\mu^2)(1-\nu^2)-(\cos\theta-\mu\nu)^2]^{-\frac{1}{4}} \cos\{t+\pi(\delta'-f)-\tfrac{1}{4}\pi\}$$

and recalling (B.6):

$$\begin{Bmatrix} c & a & b \\ f & b+\delta & a+\delta' \end{Bmatrix} \simeq \frac{(-1)^{a+b+c+\delta+\delta'}}{[12\pi V]^{\frac{1}{2}}} \cos(t-\tfrac{1}{4}\pi). \tag{H.1}$$

On the other hand we note that as a, b, c increase in the tetrahedron of fig. 4, the two faces belonging to c become almost parallel; therefore: $\theta_c \simeq \pi$, $\theta_a \equiv A \simeq \pi - \theta_{a+\delta'}$, $\theta_b \equiv B \simeq \pi - \theta_{b+\delta}$ and from the definition (3.15b) we obtain

$$\begin{aligned} \Omega &= (a+b+c+\delta+\delta'-\tfrac{1}{4})\pi + (f+\tfrac{1}{2})F - \delta' A - \delta B = \\ &= t + (a+b+c+\delta+\delta'-\tfrac{1}{4})\pi, \end{aligned} \tag{H.2}$$

which, when introduced into (1.4a) leads to (H.1).

Let us now consider the classically forbidden regions. First we notice that the transition points $z_{1,2}$ relative to $d^{(f)}_{\delta\delta'}(\theta)$ discussed in appendix G correspond to configurations in which the tetrahedron of fig. 4 becomes flat; this can be checked by means of (G.14) and (B.6). More precisely, since in z_1: $\theta=\alpha+\beta$, the tetrahedron enters the region B_3 with

$$z_1) \quad \Phi = (a+b+c+\delta+\delta')\pi, \tag{H.3}$$

while in z_2, $\theta=|\alpha-\beta|$ and it enters B_4 in either one of the two ways

$$z_2) \quad \Phi = \begin{cases} (a+b+c+f+\delta')\pi & \delta > \delta', \\ (a+b+c+f+\delta)\pi & \delta < \delta'. \end{cases} \tag{H.4}$$

On the other hand, from (G.5) and (3.6) we have for the forbidden region relative to z_1

$$\begin{Bmatrix} c & a & b \\ f & b+\delta & a+\delta' \end{Bmatrix} \simeq \frac{(-1)^{a+b+c+f+\delta}}{2[12\pi|V|]^{\frac{1}{2}}} \times$$
$$\times \{2\sin\pi(\delta'-f)\,e^{|\mathrm{Im}\,t|} + \cos\pi(\delta'-f)\,e^{-|\mathrm{Im}\,t|}\}. \tag{H.5}$$

Noticing that $|\text{Im}\, t| = |\text{Im}\, \Omega|$, we see from (5.8), (H.2), (H.3) and (H.5) that for physical values of the angular momenta (H.5) and (5.8) become identical even in sign. The same holds also for the forbidden region relative to z_2; in fact we have from (G.21):

$$(-1)^{\eta_2/\pi+a+b+c+f+\delta} = \begin{cases} (-1)^{a+b+c+f+\delta'} & \delta > \delta' \\ (-1)^{a+b+c+f+\delta} & \delta < \delta' \end{cases}$$

in agreement with (H.4).

References and footnotes

1) G. Racah, Phys. Rev. **61**, 186 (1942); **62**, 438 (1942); **63**, 367 (1943); **76**, 1352 (1949).
2) See the exhaustive bibliography in L. C. Biedenharn and H. Van Dam, *Quantum Theory of Angular Momentum* (Academic Press, New York, 1965).
3) L. C. Biedenharn, private communication to one of us (T.R.), 1958.
4) E. P. Wigner, Am. J. Math. **63**, 57 (1941); On the Matrices which Reduce the Kronecker Products of Representations of S. R. Groups (unpublished, 1940); hectographed paper (Princeton, 1951) (see ref. 2).
5) W. T. Sharp, Some Formal Properties of the 12*j*-symbol, Chalk River Report, TPJ-81, Ontario, 1955.
6) A. P. Yutsis, I. B. Levinson and V. V. Vanagas, *The Mathematical Apparatus of the Theory of Angular Momentum* (translated from Russian) (Jerusalem, 1962); A. P. Yutsis and A. A. Bandzaitis, *Teoria Momenta Kolichestva Dvizheniya Kvantovoi Mekhanike* (Vilnius, 1965) (in Russian).
7) In addition to the three-dimensional representation which will be used in this paper, we recall the graphical techniques developed by A. Yutsis and coworkers[6]) as well as its dual, exemplified by U. Fano and G. Racah, *Irreducible Tensorial Sets* (Academic Press, New York, 1959) appendices.
8) We introduce $a+\frac{1}{2}$ rather than a...as length of the edge corresponding to a...because, for high quantum numbers, the length $[a(a+1)]^{\frac{1}{2}}$ of the angular momentum vector is closer to $a+\frac{1}{2}$ in the semiclassical limit; it turns out that any other choice is inconsistent with numerical results and with existing formulae.
9) N. F. Tartaglia, *General trattato de numeri et misure* (Venezia, 1560).
10) See the footnote 142 of ref. 22.
11) A. Cayley, Cambridge Math. J. **2**, 267 (1841).
12) S. Adler has kindly pointed out to us that:

$$2^9(3!)^2V^2 \equiv -(2\alpha+1)(2\gamma+1)(2\varepsilon+1) - 2[2q_4+1]_2[2q_2+1]_2[2q_1+1]_2+1, \text{ mod. } 8$$

where q_1, q_2, q_4 are defined above and $[A]_2 = 0$, 1 if A is even, odd;

$$\alpha = [2a+1]_2[2q_4+1]_2, \quad \gamma = [2c+1]_2[2q_2+1]_2, \quad \varepsilon = [2e+1]_2[2q_1+1]_2.$$

It follows that if all the q's are integer and $\alpha, \gamma, \varepsilon = 0$, or 1:

$$2^9(3!)^2V^2 \equiv -(2\alpha+1)(2\gamma+1)(2\varepsilon+1) - 1 \equiv -2, -4 \text{ mod. } 8;$$

therefore $V^2 \neq 0$.

13) E. P. Wigner, *Group Theory* (Academic Press, New York, 1959).
14) W. Pauli, in: *Handbuch der Physik*, Band 24/1 (Springer-Verlag, Berlin, 1933) p. 170.
15) T. Regge, Nuovo Cimento **10**, 296 (1958); **11**, 116 (1959).
16) G. Racah, Phys. Rev. **84**, 910 (1951); *Lectures on Group Theory* (Institute for Advanced Study, Princeton, 1951); L. C. Biedenharn, J. Math. Phys. **31**, 287 (1953); K. Alder, A. Bohr, T. Huus, B. Mottelson and A. Winther, Rev. Mod. Phys. **28**, 432 (1956); P. J. Brussaard and H. A. Tolhoek, Physica **23**, 955 (1957); A. R. Edmonds, *Angular Momentum in Quantum Mechanics* (Princeton University Press, 1957).
17) L. C. Biedenharn, ref. 16, and J. P. Elliott, Proc. Royal Soc. (London) A **218**, 370 (1953).
18) This property stems from a particular case of a theorem by Schläfli on elliptic tetrahedra; see H. S. M. Coxeter, *Non-Euclidean Geometry* (Toronto, 1957).
19) G. Szegö, *Orthogonal Polynomials* (American Mathematical Society, New York, 1959).
20) A discussion of this theorem, due originally to G. Racah, can be found in the appendix to the book by U. Fano and G. Racah, ref. 7.
21) See for instance eq. (16.8) ref. 6.
22) E. Hammer, *Trigonometrie* (Stuttgart, 1923).
23) A. Erdélyi, *Asymptotic Expansions* (Dover Publications, New York, 1956).
24) We do not expect to be true in general that the 6*j*-symbol is a function of the variables V and $\Pi_{h=1}{}^{4} A_h$ only.
25) J. C. P. Miller, *The Airy Integral* (Cambridge, 1946).
26) R. P. Feynman and A. R. Hibbs, *Quantum Mechanics and Path Integrals* (McGraw-Hill, New York, 1965).
27) T. Regge, Nuovo Cimento **19**, 551 (1961).
28) J. A. Wheeler, Geometrodynamics and the Issue of the Final State (1963), in: *Relativity, Groups and Topology*, Eds. C. and B. DeWitt (Gordon and Breach, New York, 1964).
29) B. L. Van der Waerden, *Die gruppentheoretische Methode in der Quantenmechanik* (Springer-Verlag, Berlin, 1932).
30) A. Messiah, *Quantum Mechanics* (North-Holland Publ. Co., Amsterdam, 1964) appendix C.
31) R. F. Scott, *The Theory of Determinants* (Cambridge, 1904) chapter XVII.
32) T. Regge and G. Barucchi, Nuovo Cimento **34**, 106 (1964).
33) R. E. Langer, Phys. Rev. **51**, 669 (1937).
34) The discussion which is carried out here as well as in appendix H corresponds actually to $\delta > 0$, $\delta' > 0$; however, it can be easily extended to the other cases yielding slight modifications in t_1, t_2, η_1, η_2. For instance, when $\delta < 0$, $\delta' < 0$ one would find $\theta_1 = 2\pi - \alpha - \beta$, $t_1(\theta) = (f + \frac{1}{2}) [F - (A - \pi)\mu - (B - \pi)\nu]$, $\eta_1 = -\pi(f + \delta)$, while η_2 would be the same as in (G.21) for "physical" values of δ, δ'.

Spectroscopic and group theoretical methods in physics
© North-Holland Publ. Co., Amsterdam, 1968

ON RACAH COEFFICIENTS AS COUPLING COEFFICIENTS FOR THE VECTOR SPACE OF WIGNER OPERATORS

L. C. BIEDENHARN*
Duke University, Durham, North Carolina 27706, U.S.A.

1. Introduction and summary

One of the most important contributions made by Giulio Racah to theoretical physics was the systematic development of the theory of tensor operators for angular momentum; the results of this development – called, in honor of its principal creators, the Racah–Wigner calculus –, and its application, are now part of the equipment of every working physicist[1]).

There are two quite distinct reasons that underlie the success of this work. The first is the fundamental nature of angular momentum in quantum mechanics, and this stems ultimately from symmetry (isotropy) of space-time (Poincaré group) which is the deepest presently known foundation for quantum mechanics. This may be termed the 'physical reason' for the importance of the Racah–Wigner calculus. The second reason is mathematical, and provides the ultimate source for the very existence of the Racah–Wigner calculus: the angular momentum group (SU_2) has the property of being *simply reducible*[2]). This is the property which guarantees that the Racah–Wigner calculus is uniquely defined by the group and contains no inherent ambiguities. The really essential part of Wigner's definition of simple reducibility is that in reducing the Kronecker product of two irreducible representations ('irreps'), a given irrep occurs either once or not at all. One is forced by the structure of quantum mechanics (tensor operators acting on states) to 'multiply' irreps; if this 'product' upon being reduced into elements (irreps) has a given irrep occurring more than once, an inherent ambiguity may occur which is not decideable within the original symmetry group.

* Supported in part by the U.S. Army Research Office (Durham) and the National Science Foundation.

The Racah–Wigner calculus is the true prototype of a successful application of symmetry to physics, and it is essential to probe the reasons for its success in order to prepare the way for generalizations. From this point of view – in which an *arbitrary* symmetry, either exact or approximate, is deemed of physical interest – the property of simple reducibility becomes the central issue. Is it possible to develop a 'Racah–Wigner calculus' for an arbitrary symmetry group, in particular one which is *not* simple reducible? Although the problem is not well posed (no criterion as to what constitutes a 'solution' has been stated), it is nonetheless intuitively interesting. Much of Racah's later work – which he characterized as 'the search for new quantum numbers' – may be viewed as bearing directly on this problem.

No general answer is known to this 'problem of simple reducibility' for an arbitrary group, although the relevant literature for particular results is vast. In these studies the family of (unimodular) unitary groups, SU_n, plays a very basic rôle: physically, because of the special importance of SU_2 (angular momentum) and SU_3 (Gell-Mann and Ne'eman's 'Eight-fold way' $SU(3)/Z_3$); mathematically, because all finitely generated compact Lie groups are subgroups of SU_n. If we limit ourselves to SU_n, the answer to our query on simple reducibility is, in the light of recent results [3]) very likely to be *yes*.

It is not our purpose to investigate or even discuss these recent developments here. Rather we propose to re-examine the work of Racah on SU_2, trying to re-phrase the ideas in such a way as to suggest new points of view and new elements of structure. It is always a difficult task to perceive new features in an object so familiar that we scarcely look at it. Necessarily such a task requires many statements of what is in fact obvious (but perhaps not perceived), and apologies are offered in advance if the reader sees these features rather more quickly than the writer.

Let us summarize the results of this re-survey. We shall show that the three basic sets of elements of the Racah–Wigner calculus for SU_2, namely the rotation matrices, the Wigner coefficients and the Racah coefficients are *all isomorphic structures and are but different realizations of the same abstract idea.* We shall demonstrate that, correspondingly, the basic product laws for these three sets are but different realizations of a single abstract product law. The distinction between these realizations, as we shall show, disappears in the classical limit; this provides a natural explanation for the asymptotic relations well known to exist among these three sets.

From the point of view of this isomorphy of structure it follows that the Racah coefficients function as vector coupling coefficients in the vector space of Wigner coefficients, an 'obvious' statement which we shall endeavor to explain in detail!

It is the purpose of this re-phrasing of known results to prepare the way for the general treatment of SU_n, and the relevance of these ideas is discussed briefly in the concluding section.

2. Digression on notation

Eddington has said "Nature is tolerant of invention but she is a stickler for good form". Nowhere is the necessity for 'good form' more evident than in devising a good notation, which if really well done, has even what may appear as a life of its own. (Dirac's bra-ket notation is a beautiful example.)

These remarks are offered in partial justification for the 'adventures in notation' which follow. No claim is made that the proposed notation is optimal or even very good, but to anyone who has waded through some formidable, but basically trivial, Racah–Wigner calculus matrix computations, the need to try is apparent.

The first notational change concerns the state vectors of SU_2. We shall adopt the *Gelfand pattern* as labels for these states. For the state vector $|JM\rangle$ having the quantum numbers: $J^2_{\text{op}} \to J(J+1)$, $(J_z)_{\text{op}} \to M$ the Gelfand pattern, (m), is the triangular array:

$$\begin{pmatrix} 2J & & 0 \\ & J+M & \end{pmatrix} \equiv \begin{pmatrix} m_{12} & & m_{22} \\ & m_{11} & \end{pmatrix} \equiv (m), \tag{1}$$

in which the m_{ij} are positive integers (including 0) that obey the 'betweenness' condition:

$$m_{i+1,\,j+1} \leqslant m_{ij} \leqslant m_{i,\,j+1} \,. \tag{2}$$

To determine J, M from the Gelfand labels we use the relations:

$$J = \tfrac{1}{2}(m_{12} - m_{22}), \qquad M = m_{11} - \tfrac{1}{2}(m_{12} + m_{22}). \tag{3}$$

(The unimodular condition is that $m_{22} = 0$; hence the Gelfand pattern is a bit excessive for SU_2, though essential for higher SU_n.) The state vectors are denoted: $|(m)\rangle$.

For the Wigner coefficients the most frequent notations are: $\langle j_1 j_2 m_1 m_2 | j_1 j_2 JM\rangle$ and $C^{j_1\, j_2\, J}_{m_1\, m_2\, M}$, each of which has many merits. For the purposes to follow, however, we wish to conceive of a *set* of such coefficients as an entity in its own right, and are much less interested in any particular coefficient. As a first step in this direction, we may re-supply the basis for these coefficients and write the *Wigner operator*,

$$\sum |JM\rangle\, C^{j_1\ j_2\ J}_{m_1\ m_2\ M}\, \langle j_1 m_1|\,, \tag{4}$$

where the sum is over all j_1, m_1; J, M, with $J-j_1=$fixed.

As a second step we may introduce Gelfand patterns. Before we do this, however, let us note that the entity considered here is a *tensor operator* which transforms under rotations similarly to the state vector $|j_2 m_2\rangle$. (This is another 'obvious' result, which we shall discuss more fully in section 3.) The labels j_2 and m_2 do not, however, adequately describe this Wigner operator – there is an extra degree of freedom which we may specify as $J-j_1 \equiv \Delta J$, the *change* in the initial angular momentum (j_1) *induced* by the Wigner operator. If we note further that $M-m_1=m_2\equiv\Delta M$, the *change* in the initial component of angular momentum (m_1) *induced* by the Wigner operator, then we see that ΔJ and ΔM play very similar rôles. To make this property a 'triviality' of the notation we write the Wigner operator in the form:

$$\left\langle 2j_2 \begin{matrix} j_2+\Delta J \\ j_2+\Delta M \end{matrix} 0 \right\rangle \equiv \sum |JM\rangle\, C^{j_1\ j_2\ J}_{m_1\ m_2\ M}\, \langle j_1 m_1|\,, \tag{5}$$

where the sum is over j_1, m_1 and J, M subject to the conditions: $m_2=M-m_1=\Delta M$ and $J-j_1=\Delta J$.

Next we introduce the more general Gelfand pattern labels:

$$\left\langle 2j_2 \begin{matrix} j_2+\Delta J \\ j_2+\Delta M \end{matrix} 0 \right\rangle \equiv \left\langle m_{12} \begin{matrix} \mu_{11} \\ m_{11} \end{matrix} m_{22} \right\rangle, \tag{6}$$

and then relinquish the unimodular condition so that now:

$$\begin{aligned} \Delta J &= \mu_{11} - \tfrac{1}{2}(m_{12}+m_{22}), \\ \Delta M &= m_{11} - \tfrac{1}{2}(m_{12}+m_{22}), \end{aligned} \tag{7}$$

and the symmetry between ΔJ and ΔM is clearly in evidence. (Note that μ_{11} obeys the betweenness relation, a non-trivial property of the set of Wigner operators.)

One further development in the notation is to note that the Wigner operator

$$\left\langle m_{12} \begin{matrix} \mu_{11} \\ m_{11} \end{matrix} m_{22} \right\rangle$$

when acting on a general (U_2) state vector $|(m^{\mathrm{i}})\rangle$ carries it into the state vector $\#\,|(m^{\mathrm{f}})\rangle$ where

$$(m^{\mathrm{f}}) = (m^{\mathrm{i}}) + \Delta\,, \quad \text{with} \quad \Delta \equiv \begin{pmatrix} \mu_{11} & & m_{12}+m_{22}-\mu_{11} \\ & m_{11} & \end{pmatrix}. \tag{7a}$$

The numerical factor, #, is then the (numerical) Wigner coefficient.

This notation – besides focusing attention on the Wigner operator as an entity (as designed) – has several additional merits:
(a) By suppressing the labels referring to the initial and final state vectors in the Wigner coefficient we have dismissed as uninteresting 'accidents' those cases where the Wigner coefficient vanishes for special reasons. In particular the Wigner operator *always* has its full complement of μ_{11} and m_{11} indices (e.g., the vector operator has $\Delta J = 1, 0, -1$ even though when acting on $j_{\text{init}} = \frac{1}{2}$ some coefficients vanish).
(b) It suggests that the indices μ_{11} and m_{11} play an equivalent rôle. In particular, the index μ_{11} (as mentioned earlier) satisfies the betweenness relation $m_{22} \leqslant \mu_{11} \leqslant m_{12}$; the notation *implies* this by the position of μ_{11} in the *operator pattern* (generalized Gelfand pattern).
(c) The equivalence of the rôles of μ_{11} and m_{11} suggests strongly that there exists a *transformation group* changing the μ_{11} index just as the SU_2 group itself acts on the m_{11} index. But if the rôles are indeed equivalent then this group, if it exists!, must be isomorphic to SU_2. We discuss this in section 3.

These hints from the notation are all correct, and moreover generalize[4]) to all U_n. Simple as they appear to be, they are non-trivial and must be discussed elsewhere.

Let us note that though equivalent the spaces of μ_{11} and m_{11} are not the same. We distinguish 'upper pattern operator space' with Greek letters and 'lower pattern operator space' with Latin letters.

A notation for the Racah coefficients will be given after these ideas are developed further.

3. The isomorphic structure

We shall demonstrate in this section the isomorphic structure of the three sets of objects that enter into the quantum theory of angular momentum: (a) the rotation matrices, (b) the Wigner coefficients and (c) the Racah coefficients. In order to do this it is necessary first to recall briefly the elements of the representation theory of the angular momentum group SU_2, using the algebraic methods familiar from Racah's work.

The algebraic method starts with the angular momentum operators $\{J_i\}$ which are the (infinitesimal) generators of the group SU_2 and obey the commutation relations: $[J_i, J_j] = i\varepsilon_{ijk}J_k$. The complete set of Hermitean commuting operators is the Casimir invariant $(J^2)_{\text{op}} \equiv J_1^2 + J_2^2 + J_3^2$ and $(J_3)_{\text{op}}$; both $(J^2)_{\text{op}}$ and $(J_3)_{\text{op}}$ take on eigenvalues when acting on the eigenkets $|(J^2)', (J_3)'\rangle$. *From the algebra* (commutation relations) *alone*, it follows that $(J_3)'$ is integral or half integral, $-J' \leqslant J_3' \leqslant J$; $(J^2)' = J(J+1)$. These conclusions are economically expressed by the eigenkets in the Gelfand notation:

$$\left| \begin{pmatrix} m_{12} & & 0 \\ & m_{11} & \end{pmatrix} \right\rangle .$$

To determine the matrices of rotation, we first integrate the infinitesimal operator for a general element $\boldsymbol{p}(g)\cdot\boldsymbol{J}$ by exponentiation: $R(g) \equiv e^{-i\boldsymbol{p}(g)\cdot\boldsymbol{J}}$ and then take matrix elements: $D^J_{M'M}(g) \equiv \langle JM' | R(g) | JM \rangle$.

Now let us repeat these familiar results using, however, a more abstract language. One considers the group of transformations that leaves invariant the Hermitean form: $|x_1|^2 + |x_2|^2$. The infinitesimal generators of these 2×2 transformations are the Pauli matrices $\frac{1}{2}\boldsymbol{\sigma}$. From this defining (2×2) instance of the group SU_2 we seek to find *all unitary representations.* To be very precise, we note that the idea of a representation only involves the *single property of a mapping that preserves products.*

Let the mapping α be defined as $\alpha : g \to h$, that is to every element g of the group we associate another object h. The mapping α defines a representation if the association $\alpha : g \to h$ is such that:

$$\begin{array}{ll} \text{if:} & g_1 \cdot g_2 = g_{12} \\ & \downarrow \quad \downarrow \quad\; \downarrow \\ \text{then:} & h_1 \cdot h_2 = h_{12} \, . \end{array} \tag{8}$$

Let us emphasize that the concept of a representation makes no assertions as to *what* the representing objects are. (Nor is the Hermitean nature of the operators necessarily preserved under the mapping). The $\{h\}$ may belong to another group, the same group, etc. – but by far the most frequent special choice is to choose as the representative objects the set of linear transformations in a vector space. For this we have the fundamental theorem [5]) that the representations by linear transformations in a vector space are isomorphic to the ring of $n \times n$ matrices. We have thus returned to precisely the rotation matrices, $D^J(g)$, defined in the algebraic method.

But this means that the freedom of choice in representation by linear transformations does not lie in the result – the rotation matrices – but rather in the *specific realization* employed in setting up the linear operations.

An example will make this clear: Let us define the linear transformation (operator) associated with the abstract generator $\boldsymbol{p}\cdot\boldsymbol{J}$ to be $\mathcal{O}_{\boldsymbol{p}\cdot\boldsymbol{J}}(\ldots)$. Let the vector space be the eigenkets $\{|(m)\rangle\}$. Then the linear operation $\mathcal{O}_{J_i}(|(m)\rangle)$ is just J_i operating on $|(m)\rangle$, i.e.,

$$\mathcal{O}_{J_i}(|JM\rangle) \equiv J_i |JM\rangle = \sum_{M'} \langle JM' | J_i | JM \rangle \, |JM'\rangle \, . \tag{9}$$

The integrated (finite) operation is then just the exponential:

$$\mathcal{O}_{\text{finite}} = \sum \frac{1}{n!} \underbrace{\mathcal{O}(\mathcal{O}(\ldots))}_{n \text{ repetitions}} \tag{10}$$

or:

$$\mathcal{O}_g(|(m)\rangle) = \mathrm{e}^{-\mathrm{i}\boldsymbol{p}(g)\cdot\boldsymbol{J}}\,|(m)\rangle = \sum_{m'} D^{(J)}_{m'm}(g)\,|(m')\rangle\,, \tag{11}$$

just the rotation matrix as asserted by the theorem, and hardly a surprise.

A more interesting result obtains if we use tensor operators as the vector space, that is the set of Wigner operators $\{\langle(m)\rangle\}$, suppressing the upper pattern label for the moment. The linear operation is now the *commutator product*:

$$\mathcal{O}_{\boldsymbol{p}\cdot\boldsymbol{J}}(\langle(m)\rangle) \equiv [\boldsymbol{p}(g)\cdot\boldsymbol{J}, \langle(m)\rangle]\,. \tag{13}$$

The finite transformations are the exponentiated operation:

$$\mathcal{O}_g(\cdots) \equiv \sum_{n=0}^{\infty} \frac{1}{n!} \underbrace{\mathcal{O}_{\boldsymbol{p}\cdot\boldsymbol{J}}(\mathcal{O}_{\boldsymbol{p}\cdot\boldsymbol{J}}(\cdots))}_{n \text{ repetitions}}, \tag{14}$$

which is now the multiple commutator operation:

$$\mathcal{O}_g(\cdots) = \sum \frac{1}{n!} \underbrace{[\boldsymbol{p}\cdot\boldsymbol{J}, \ldots\ [\boldsymbol{p}\cdot\boldsymbol{J}, \cdots]\ \ldots]}_{n \text{ times}}. \tag{15}$$

By the Baker–Campbell–Hausdorff identity we have:

$$\mathcal{O}_g(\langle(m)\rangle) = \mathrm{e}^{-\mathrm{i}\boldsymbol{p}(g)\cdot\boldsymbol{J}}\langle(m)\rangle\,\mathrm{e}^{+\mathrm{i}\boldsymbol{p}(g)\cdot\boldsymbol{J}}\,, \tag{16}$$

but by the fundamental theorem this is just:

$$\mathcal{O}_g(\langle(m)\rangle) = \sum_{m'} D^{J}_{m'm}(g)\,\langle(m)'\rangle\,, \tag{17}$$

which is once again a familiar result from the quantum theory of angular momentum.

One sees, however, that these two results, eqs. (9)–(11) and (13)–(17), are abstractly equivalent and differ only in the specific realization of the linear operation.

Let us now return to the task at hand: to interpret the meaning of the upper pattern index μ_{11} in the Wigner operator. It is clear from the results above, that this index is completely independent of any transformations involving the lower space index m_{11}. To proceed further, we simply *define* the upper pattern space to be a vector space over the index μ_{11}, i.e., $\{\langle\mu_{11}\rangle\}$, and define a new linear operation (presuming it to exist):

$$\mathcal{O}_{J_i}(\langle\mu_{11}\rangle) \equiv \sum_{\mu'_{11}} \langle\mu'_{11}|\, J_i \,|\mu_{11}\rangle \, \langle\mu'_{11}\rangle . \tag{18}$$

It follows that the transformations of this vector space are isomorphic to the rotation matrices and that the underlying group is SU(2).

We see, moreover, that these upper pattern transformations commute with lower pattern transformations, and hence the composite group is $G = SU_2 \times SU_2$, with the additional condition that the irrep labels agree, hence the group G is the 'orbital group' of R_4. We denote this group by the symbol: $G \equiv SU_2 * SU_2$, "$*$" denoting the restriction to the orbital group of $SU_2 \times SU_2$.

The Wigner operators then, considered as a vector space, are irreps of the group $SU_2 * SU_2$; the space associated with μ_{11} (the "ΔJ" index) and m_{11} (the "ΔM" index) are structurally isomorphic. These were the assertions we set out to justify.

Now at this point the reader may well feel that he has been tricked, that this is but a play upon subtle distinctions. What *content* does our assertion have?

The unease suggested by this question stems from the fact that the real problem is yet to be treated: we must demonstrate in detail precisely *what* the linear operation of eq. (18) is, thereby verifying its existence. The abstract point of view lies precisely in suppressing such particularities.

We shall return to this task in section 5.

4. The calculus of boson operators and the factorization lemma

We have reached the point now where it is valuable to get quite specific and discuss detailed results. The most elegant procedure to recapitulate the desired results of QTAM employs a mapping of SU_2 into the boson operators. This procedure was originally suggested by Pascual Jordan[6]) in 1935 (in fact even more generally – Jordan considered also fermion mappings), but it has been Schwinger[7]) and Bargmann[8]) who have developed the technique most fully.

Consider then the set of boson operators $\{a_i\}$, $i = 1, 2$, satisfying the commutation relations:

$$[\bar{a}_i, a_{i'}] = \delta_{i,i'}; \quad [a_i, a_{i'}] = [\bar{a}_i, \bar{a}_{i'}] = 0 . \tag{19}$$

We map the generators onto[9]):

$$\tfrac{1}{2}J_+ \equiv E_{12} \rightarrow \tfrac{1}{2}a_1\bar{a}_2 , \tag{20}$$

$$(\tfrac{1}{2}J_+)^\dagger = \tfrac{1}{2}J_- \equiv E_{21} \rightarrow \tfrac{1}{2}a_2\bar{a}_1 , \tag{21}$$

$$\frac{1}{\sqrt{2}} J_z \equiv H_1 \to \frac{1}{2\sqrt{2}} (a_1 \bar{a}_1 - a_2 \bar{a}_2). \tag{22}$$

The (unimodular) state vectors $|(m)\rangle$ are determined by this mapping to be:

$$\left| \begin{pmatrix} m_{12} & & 0 \\ & m_{11} & \end{pmatrix} \right\rangle \to M^{-\frac{1}{2}} (a_1)^{m_{11}} (a_2)^{m_{12}-m_{11}} |0\rangle, \tag{23}$$

where $M \equiv m_{11}!\,(m_{12}-m_{11})!$, and $|0\rangle$ is the 'vacuum' ket.

We could proceed to determine the specific matrices of the angular momentum and (by Schwinger's method) the Wigner coefficients. Instead of this customary technique, let us proceed more generally.

First consider U_2 rather than SU_2; this means that we consider *boson pairs* whose angular momenta are coupled to zero. Thus we introduce a (kinematically) independent copy of the set $\{a_i\}$; call the two sets: $\{a_i^j\}$, $i=1, 2$; $j=1, 2$, with the commutation relations: $[\bar{a}_i^j, a_{i'}^{j'}] = \delta_{ii'}\,\delta_{jj'}$, all others zero. The generators map into:

$$\begin{aligned} E_{12} &\to \tfrac{1}{2}(a_1^1 \bar{a}_2^1 + a_1^2 \bar{a}_2^2), \\ E_{21} &\to \tfrac{1}{2}(a_2^1 \bar{a}_1^1 + a_2^2 \bar{a}_1^2), \\ H &\to \frac{1}{2\sqrt{2}}(a_1^1 \bar{a}_1^1 + a_1^2 \bar{a}_1^2 - a_2^1 \bar{a}_2^1 - a_2^2 \bar{a}_2^2). \end{aligned} \tag{24}$$

The state vectors of U_2 are now given by[10]:

$$\left| \begin{pmatrix} m_{12} & & m_{22} \\ & m_{11} & \end{pmatrix} \right\rangle = M^{-\frac{1}{2}} (a_{12})^{m_{22}} (a_1^1)^{m_{11}-m_{22}} (a_2^1)^{m_{12}-m_{11}} |0\rangle, \tag{25}$$

where:

$$\begin{aligned} a_{12} &\equiv a_1^1 a_2^2 - a_2^1 a_1^2, \\ M(m) \equiv M &= \frac{(m_{12}+1)!\,(m_{22})!}{(m_{12}-m_{22}+1)!}(m_{11}-m_{22})!\,(m_{12}-m_{11})!. \end{aligned} \tag{26}$$

The fundamental Wigner coefficients can now be determined by considering the a_i^j as *operators* acting on the states above. One readily finds the two matrix elements (labelled conveniently by the shift pattern Δ of eq. (7a)):

$$\Delta = \begin{pmatrix} 1 & & 0 \\ & 1 & \end{pmatrix}:$$

$$\langle (m')|\, a_1^1 \,|(m)\rangle = \left[\frac{M(m')}{M(m)}\right]^{\frac{1}{2}} = \left[\frac{(m_{12}+2)(m_{12}-m_{11}+1)}{(m_{12}-m_{22}+2)}\right]^{\frac{1}{2}}, \tag{27}$$

with

$$(m') \equiv (m) + \Delta = \begin{pmatrix} m_{12}+1 & & m_{22} \\ & m_{12}+1 & \end{pmatrix},$$

$\Delta = \begin{pmatrix} 1 & & 0 \\ & 0 & \end{pmatrix}$:

$$\langle (m')|\, a_2^1 \,|(m)\rangle = \left[\frac{M(m')}{M(m)}\right]^{\frac{1}{2}} = \left[\frac{(m_{12}+2)(m_{12}-m_{11}+1)}{(m_{12}-m_{22}+2)}\right]^{\frac{1}{2}}, \tag{28}$$

with

$$(m') \equiv (m) + \Delta = \begin{pmatrix} m_{12}+1 & & m_{22} \\ & m_{11} & \end{pmatrix}.$$

For the matrix elements of a_i^2 one uses the conjugate $\bar{a}_i^2$ and takes the transpose, obtaining [as above $(m') \equiv (m) + \Delta$]:

$\Delta = \begin{pmatrix} 0 & & 1 \\ & 1 & \end{pmatrix}$:

$$\langle (m')|\, a_1^2 \,|(m)\rangle = (-)\left[\frac{M(m)}{M(m+\Delta)}\right]^{\frac{1}{2}} (m_{22}+1) =$$

$$= (-)\left[\frac{(m_{12}-m_{11})(m_{22}+1)}{(m_{12}-m_{22})}\right]^{\frac{1}{2}}, \tag{29}$$

$\Delta = \begin{pmatrix} 0 & & 1 \\ & 0 & \end{pmatrix}$:

$$\langle (m')|\, a_2^2 \,|(m)\rangle = +\left[\frac{M(m)}{M(m+\Delta)}\right]^{\frac{1}{2}} (m_{22}+1) =$$

$$= \left[\frac{(m_{11}-m_{22})(m_{22}+1)}{(m_{12}-m_{22})}\right]^{\frac{1}{2}}. \tag{30}$$

From the transformation properties of the a_i^j under the generators (E_{12}, E_{21}, H) of the group SU_2 we know that both $\{a_i^1\}$ and $\{a_i^2\}$ behave as spinors; it follows that – *to within a normalization* (a 'reduced matrix element') – the matrix elements above are the Wigner coefficients for spin $\frac{1}{2}$.

The correct normalization is found to effect two changes: (a) replace every denominator above by the factor $(m_{12}-m_{22}+1)$ and (b) delete all non-unimodular factors (factors in which a single m_{ij} appears, rather than a difference).

Rather than re-write this result, let us introduce yet another notation, that of *the partial hooks* (p_{ij}), which allows one to understand immediately the *structure* of the result. Define then the partial hook:

$$p_{ij} \equiv m_{ij} + j - i\,. \tag{31}$$

In this notation, the desired Wigner operator for spin $\frac{1}{2}$, denoted by $\left\langle \begin{matrix} 1 & \mu & 0 \\ & m & \end{matrix} \right\rangle$, is given by the matrix element table below.

TABLE 1

The fundamental Wigner operator $\left\langle \begin{matrix} 1 & \mu & 0 \\ & m & \end{matrix} \right\rangle$ expressed in terms of partial hooks, p_{ij}

$m \backslash \mu$	1	0
1	$\left[\frac{p_{11}-p_{22}+1}{p_{12}-p_{22}}\right]^{\frac{1}{2}}$	$-\left[\frac{p_{11}-p_{12}+1}{p_{22}-p_{12}}\right]^{\frac{1}{2}}$
0	$\left[\frac{p_{12}-p_{11}}{p_{12}-p_{22}}\right]^{\frac{1}{2}}$	$\left[\frac{p_{22}-p_{11}}{p_{22}-p_{12}}\right]^{\frac{1}{2}}$

To appreciate the elementary nature of the structure of this result let us note that each entry in the table is correlated with the Δ-pattern in eqs. (27)–(30) which specified the *changes* induced by the operator $\left\langle \begin{matrix} 1 & \mu & 0 \\ & m & \end{matrix} \right\rangle$ when acting on a generic state vector $|(m)\rangle$. We assert: *the specific entry in the table may be read off directly from this Δ-pattern.*

An example will suffice: Consider $\left\langle \begin{matrix} 1 & 1 & 0 \\ & 0 & \end{matrix} \right\rangle$. The associated Δ-pattern is $\begin{pmatrix} 1 & & 0 \\ & 0 & \end{pmatrix}$, from eq. (7a). Construct a new triangular pattern by drawing an arrow *from* each 1 in Δ *to* each 0. We get then:

$$\Delta = \begin{pmatrix} 1 & & 0 \\ & 0 & \end{pmatrix} \Rightarrow$$

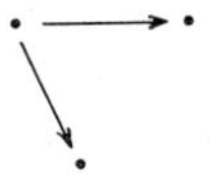

To each arrow associate an algebraic factor:

$[p_{ij}\,(\text{tail of arrow}) - p_{ij}(\text{head of arrow}) + 1\,(\text{if the arrow has its tail on } p_{11})]$,

where the dots in the arrow pattern now correspond to the p_{ij} values of the initial state vector.

Arrows *between* rows imply factors in the numerator; arrows not between rows supply denominator factors. This then determines the (square of the) Wigner coefficient explicitly. For the sign (a convention, recall) we introduce a minus sign for arrows going up to the left.

Hence in this example we get:

$$\Delta = \begin{pmatrix} 1 & & 0 \\ & 0 & \end{pmatrix} \Rightarrow \begin{array}{ccc} \overset{p_{12}}{\bullet} & \longrightarrow & \overset{p_{22}}{\bullet} \\ & \searrow & \\ & & \underset{p_{11}}{\bullet} \end{array} \Rightarrow \left\langle \begin{matrix} 1 & 1 & 0 \\ & 0 & \end{matrix} \right\rangle = + \left[\frac{p_{12} - p_{11}}{p_{12} - p_{22}} \right]^{\frac{1}{2}}. \tag{32}$$

It is easily checked that this reproduces the complete table for the operator $\left\langle \begin{matrix} 1 & \mu & 0 \\ & m & \end{matrix} \right\rangle$. What is even more interesting is that *every Wigner operator in* U_n *of the form* $\langle 11 \ldots 10 \ldots 0 \rangle$ *follows correctly from this same basic rule!*

Let us return to the problem at hand. The fact that the boson operators $\{a_i^j\}$ were *not* a realization of the Wigner operator $\left\langle \begin{matrix} 1 & \mu & 0 \\ & m & \end{matrix} \right\rangle$ is important, and suggests that our viewpoint is still, somehow, unnecessarily restricted. A more general view is to recognize that: *the* $\{a_i^j\}$ *suffice to realize the group* U_4. That is clear if we let the U_4 boson operator $\{a_\alpha\}$ stand for the set $\{a_i^j\}$, re-indexed by $(ij) \leftrightarrow \alpha = 1, 2, 3, 4$. But not every representation of U_4 can be constructed with $\{a_\alpha\}$, only the totally symmetric irreps $[k000]$, k = integer. In other words, the fundamental system for discussing SU_2 and its Wigner operators is the group U_4 restricted to totally symmetric representations alone.

To recover the group U_2 we need only note that the indexing $\{a_i^j\}$ corresponds to reducing U_4 by the sub-group $\mathrm{U}_2 \times \mathrm{U}_2$, where one U_2 refers to the 'physical' angular momentum group (the lower index of a_i^j). The other U_2 group is an isomorphic structure on the upper index. But we go further and note that both U_2 groups share the labels $[m_{12}, m_{22}]$, that is, we really have $\mathrm{U}_2 * \mathrm{U}_2$.

The next point is essential, but not difficult to show: *The irrep* $[k000]$ *of* U_4 *restricted to* $\mathrm{U}_2 * \mathrm{U}_2$ *contains every* $[m_{12}, m_{22}]$ *with* $m_{12} + m_{22} = k$ *exactly once*[11]. This result reinforces the view that totally symmetric irreps of U_4 are the proper framework in which to 'imbed' angular momentum structures.

To apply this result we observe that a state vector of $[k000]$ of U_4 can be labelled by four quantum numbers: two labels $[m_{12}, m_{22}]$ specifying the common U_2 irrep labels (where $k = m_{12} + m_{22}$) and the two labels m_{11} and m'_{11} of the two distinct U_2 groups. We may denote this state vector by: $\left| \begin{matrix} m_{12} & m'_{11} & m_{22} \\ & m_{11} & \end{matrix} \right\rangle$, or more usefully as an operator acting on the vacuum ket:

$$\left| \begin{matrix} m_{12} & m'_{11} & m_{22} \\ & m_{11} & \end{matrix} \right\rangle \equiv A \begin{pmatrix} m_{12} & m'_{11} & m_{22} \\ & m_{11} & \end{pmatrix} |0\rangle . \tag{33}$$

This operator is, however, a *tensor operator* belonging to the subgroup $\mathrm{U}_2 * \mathrm{U}_2$, and is well-defined in *each* U_2. Thus we may represent $A(\ldots)$ as a sum of U_2 tensor operators, that is to say, Wigner operators defined symmetrically in both U_2 subgroups. This makes plausible the *factorization lemma*, a special case of the general U_n result proved in ref. 3.

Factorization Lemma: *The boson operator* $A\begin{pmatrix} & m'_{11} & \\ m_{12} & & m_{22} \\ & m_{11} & \end{pmatrix}$ *may be uniquely factorized into a product of* U_2 *Wigner operators:*

$$A\begin{pmatrix} & m'_{11} & \\ m_{12} & & m_{22} \\ & m_{11} & \end{pmatrix} = \sum_{\mu_{11}} \#(\Delta)\left\langle \begin{matrix} & \mu_{11} & \\ m_{12} & & m_{22} \\ & m_{11} & \end{matrix}\right\rangle \left\langle \begin{matrix} & \mu_{11} & \\ m_{12} & & m_{22} \\ & m'_{11} & \end{matrix}\right\rangle,$$

where:

$$\#(\Delta) = [N\ p_{\text{initial}})/N(p_{\text{final}})]^{\frac{1}{2}}, \tag{35}$$

$$N(p) \equiv \frac{\prod_{i=1}^{2} (p_{i2})!}{\dim[(p)]},$$

and

$$\begin{aligned} (p_{ij})_{\text{final}} &\equiv (p_{ij})_{\text{initial}} + \Delta_{ij}, \\ \dim[(p)] &\equiv \text{dimension of the irrep } [(p)] \\ &= (p_{12} - p_{22}). \end{aligned} \tag{36}$$

Since the significance of this result may not be immediately clear, let us discuss it further. One sees first off that the operator $A(\ldots)$ has been brought to diagonal form – the term denoted $\#(\Delta)$ plays the rôle of an *eigenvalue* and the Wigner operators $\left\langle \begin{matrix} & \mu_{11} & \\ m_{12} & & m_{22} \\ & m_{11} & \end{matrix}\right\rangle$ the rôle of *eigenvectors*. The original operator $A(\ldots)$ was, however, constructed entirely from the two equivalent pairs of boson operators, (a_1^1, a_2^1) and (a_1^2, a_2^2). Thus we see that the boson operator $A(\ldots)$ has been *factorized* into *elementary operators* – the Wigner operators – and hence the significance of the lemma. Recalling that the operator a_i^j was unsatisfactory as a realization of the Wigner operator $\left\langle \begin{matrix} & \mu & \\ 1 & & 0 \\ & m & \end{matrix}\right\rangle$, we can now see why: a_i^j is not really an elementary structure but actually composite, linking upper and lower spaces.

The state vectors of U_2 constructed in the (generalized) Schwinger realization, eq. (25), are now seen to be very special – they involve the maximal state of the 'other U_2 group'. Thus if we use (a_i^j) as an operator acting on these special states (as we did in constructing the matrix elements in eqs. (27), (28)) then we have, for the 'other U_2 group', a maximal Wigner coefficient, i.e., 1. The eigenvalue $\#(\Delta)$ in this case supplies precisely the correct factor to renormalize the matrix elements so obtained into the desired Wigner operator.

We shall reconsider the factorization lemma once again (in section 7) after developing the 'isomorphic structure' of the Wigner operator further.

5. Wigner operators as a vector space

It has been established that the Wigner coefficients are the carrier space of the group $U_2 * U_2$, although the precise realization of the linear operations on 'upper operator space' has yet to be given. That is the purpose of the present section.

Transformations in lower pattern space are easy – these are achieved by commutation with the generators E_{12}, E_{21}, H_1 – this is the familiar tensor operator mapping. It is natural to enquire as to whether operators can be constructed which, by commutation, perform the same task for upper pattern spaces. The answer is, surprisingly perhaps: No. Operators $\mathscr{E}_{12}$, $\mathscr{E}_{21}, \mathscr{H}_1$ such that, for example,

$$\left[\mathscr{E}_{21}, \left\langle 1 \begin{matrix} 1 \\ m \end{matrix} 0 \right\rangle\right] = 0$$

$$\left[\mathscr{E}_{12}, \left\langle 1 \begin{matrix} 0 \\ m \end{matrix} 0 \right\rangle\right] = \tfrac{1}{2} \left\langle 1 \begin{matrix} 1 \\ m \end{matrix} 0 \right\rangle, \quad \text{etc.},$$

do not exist.

In carrying out this fruitless attempt one notices, however, that if we were to *re-normalize* the Wigner operators $\left\langle 1 \begin{matrix} \mu \\ m \end{matrix} 0 \right\rangle$ by removing all denominator factors, than it *is* possible to define suitable operators for the renormalized basis.

The denominators are functions of $(m_{12}-m_{22})$ and do not affect the 'physical' U_2 transformation properties. But for the 'operator space' U_2 these factors are all important, as we shall see more in detail subsequently. Simply renormalizing, as such, turns out to be an unsatisfactory procedure.

One can see this, partly, from examining the commutation relations of the set $\left\{\left\langle 1 \begin{matrix} \mu \\ m \end{matrix} 0 \right\rangle\right\}$ among themselves. The results are:

$$\left[\left\langle 1 \begin{matrix} 1 \\ 1 \end{matrix} 0 \right\rangle, \left\langle 1 \begin{matrix} 1 \\ 0 \end{matrix} 0 \right\rangle\right] = 0, \tag{37a}$$

$$\left[\left\langle 1 \begin{matrix} 0 \\ 1 \end{matrix} 0 \right\rangle, \left\langle 1 \begin{matrix} 0 \\ 0 \end{matrix} 0 \right\rangle\right] = 0, \tag{37b}$$

$$\left[\left\langle\begin{matrix} & 1 & \\ 1 & & 0 \\ & 1 & \end{matrix}\right\rangle, \left\langle\begin{matrix} & 0 & \\ 1 & & 0 \\ & 0 & \end{matrix}\right\rangle\right] = \frac{(p_{22}-p_{11})}{[(p_{12}-p_{22})(p_{12}-p_{22}-1)]^{\frac{1}{2}}} - \frac{(p_{11}-p_{22}+1)}{[(p_{12}-p_{22})(p_{12}-p_{22}+1)]^{\frac{1}{2}}}, \tag{37c}$$

$$\left[\left\langle\begin{matrix} & 1 & \\ 1 & & 0 \\ & 1 & \end{matrix}\right\rangle, \left\langle\begin{matrix} & 0 & \\ 1 & & 0 \\ & 1 & \end{matrix}\right\rangle\right] = \left[\frac{(p_{12}-p_{11}-1)(p_{11}-p_{22}+1)}{(p_{12}-p_{22})(p_{12}-p_{22}+1)}\right]^{\frac{1}{2}} - \left[\frac{(p_{12}-p_{11}-1)(p_{11}-p_{22}+1)}{(p_{12}-p_{22})(p_{12}-p_{22}-1)}\right]^{\frac{1}{2}}, \tag{37d}$$

$$\left[\left\langle\begin{matrix} & 1 & \\ 1 & & 0 \\ & 0 & \end{matrix}\right\rangle, \left\langle\begin{matrix} & 0 & \\ 1 & & 0 \\ & 1 & \end{matrix}\right\rangle\right] = \frac{(p_{11}-p_{12})}{[(p_{12}-p_{22})(p_{12}-p_{22}+1)]^{\frac{1}{2}}} - \frac{(p_{12}-p_{11}-1)}{[(p_{12}-p_{22})(p_{12}-p_{22}-1)]^{\frac{1}{2}}}, \tag{37e}$$

$$\left[\left\langle\begin{matrix} & 1 & \\ 1 & & 0 \\ & 0 & \end{matrix}\right\rangle, \left\langle\begin{matrix} & 0 & \\ 1 & & 0 \\ & 0 & \end{matrix}\right\rangle\right] = \left[\frac{(p_{11}-p_{22})(p_{12}-p_{11})}{(p_{12}-p_{22})(p_{12}-p_{22}-1)}\right]^{\frac{1}{2}} - \left[\frac{(p_{11}-p_{22})(p_{12}-p_{11})}{(p_{12}-p_{22})(p_{12}-p_{22}+1)}\right]^{\frac{1}{2}}. \tag{37f}$$

[Some idea of the importance of the normalization can be seen from the fact that the separate terms on the right hand sides of eqs. (37), essentially are Racah coefficients. The proper normalization and the Racah coefficients are thus intimately related and this relation restricts our freedom of choice.]

If, however, we nonetheless remove the denominators, then the commutators all vanish, except for (37c) and (37e) for which the right side is unity. These results may be summarized by saying that the mapping:

$$\begin{aligned} &\left\langle\begin{matrix} & 1 & \\ 1 & & 0 \\ & 1 & \end{matrix}\right\rangle_{\mathrm{R}} \to a_1, \quad &&\left\langle\begin{matrix} & 0 & \\ 1 & & 0 \\ & 0 & \end{matrix}\right\rangle_{\mathrm{R}} \to \bar{a}_1, \\ &\left\langle\begin{matrix} & 1 & \\ 1 & & 0 \\ & 0 & \end{matrix}\right\rangle_{\mathrm{R}} \to a_2, \quad &&\left\langle\begin{matrix} & 0 & \\ 1 & & 0 \\ & 1 & \end{matrix}\right\rangle_{\mathrm{R}} \to \bar{a}_2, \end{aligned} \tag{38}$$

represents the commutation properties of the *renormalized* operators $\left\{\left\langle\begin{matrix} & \mu & \\ 1 & & 0 \\ & m & \end{matrix}\right\rangle\right\}_{\mathrm{R}}$ among themselves.

Consider next the explicit operator realization defined by the mapping:

$$\begin{aligned} \mathscr{E}_{12} &\to \tfrac{1}{2}a_1 a_2\,, \\ \mathscr{E}_{21} &\to -\tfrac{1}{2}\bar{a}_2\bar{a}_1\,, \\ \mathscr{H}_1 &\to \frac{1}{2\sqrt{2}}(a_1\bar{a}_1 + \bar{a}_2 a_2)\,. \end{aligned} \tag{39}$$

This mapping defines a set of operators, $\{\mathscr{E}_{12}, \mathscr{E}_{21}, \mathscr{H}_1\}$, which are infinitesimal generators of SU_2 as can be verified directly. [Note that this realization is *non-Hermitean* and infinite dimensional.] The existence of the explicit mapping of eqs. (38) and (39) demonstrates that we can in fact define linear transformations, generating SU_2, for the renormalized $\left\langle 1 \begin{smallmatrix} \mu \\ m \end{smallmatrix} 0 \right\rangle_R$ as a basis.

As we will see in a moment the situation is a bit delicate, and we must make our argument here fully explicit in order to be convincing. Our goal is to demonstrate that abstract operators isomorphic to SU_2 generators exist which transform the (upper pattern labels of) the Wigner operators as a vector space. To prove the existence we gave the explicit realization, eq. (38),

$$\left\langle 1 \begin{matrix} \mu \\ m \end{matrix} 0 \right\rangle_R \to \{a_1, \bar{a}_1, a_2, -\bar{a}_2\}\,,$$

and for the abstract operators the realization, eq. (39), for the set $\{\mathscr{E}_{12}, \mathscr{E}_{21}, \mathscr{H}_1\}$ as explicit boson operators. This realization satisfies the requirement of isomorphy with SU_2.

But we must also verify that there exists a 'compatible' realization for the lower pattern space (the 'physical' SU_2). This is not hard to find: Using the same mapping for the $\left\langle 1 \begin{smallmatrix} \mu \\ m \end{smallmatrix} 0 \right\rangle_R$, eq. (38), and the operator realization:

$$\begin{aligned} E_{12} &\to \tfrac{1}{2}a_1\bar{a}_2\,, \\ E_{21} &\to \tfrac{1}{2}a_2\bar{a}_1\,, \\ H_1 &\to \frac{1}{2\sqrt{2}}(a_1\bar{a}_1 - a_2\bar{a}_2)\,, \end{aligned} \tag{40}$$

we recognize at once that the $\{E_{12}, E_{21}, H_1\}$ obey the commutation rules of the generators of SU_2.

At first glance these results appear satisfactory, *but they really are quite unacceptable*. One difficulty is immediate, the two sets of generators, eq. (39) and eq. (40) do *not* commute.

More disturbing is this fact: The realizations are *incompatible* (contradictory). To see this, we must be very careful about phases. Consider first the generators of eq. (40); the explicit basis vectors of the fundamental (defining) irrep are the two (abstractly equivalent) sets:

		Set 1	Set 2
$J=\frac{1}{2}$	$M=\frac{1}{2}$	a_1	$-\bar{a}_2$
	$M=-\frac{1}{2}$	a_2	$\bar{a}_1$

(A)

Note that the relative phases between $M=\frac{1}{2}$ and $M=-\frac{1}{2}$ are fixed and not arbitrary. We assign the mapping for the $\left\langle 1 \begin{smallmatrix}\mu\\ m\end{smallmatrix} 0 \right\rangle_{\mathrm{R}}$ then exactly as in eq. (38), noting that the relative signs are important.

Now consider the generators defined in eq. (39). The state vectors for the two (abstractly equivalent) fundamental irreps are found to be:

		Set 1	Set 2
$J=\frac{1}{2}$	$M=\frac{1}{2}$	a_1	a_2
	$M=-\frac{1}{2}$	$-\bar{a}_2$	$-\bar{a}_1$

(B)

Note the additional minus sign for $\bar{a}_1$ which shows that the realizations A and B are incompatible.

We conclude that there is no consistent one-to-one assignment of the set $\left\{\left\langle 1 \begin{smallmatrix}\mu\\ m\end{smallmatrix} 0 \right\rangle_{\mathrm{R}}\right\}$ onto the set $\{a_1, a_2, \bar{a}_1, \bar{a}_2\}$ such that we get the carrier space of two independent SU_2 groups.

We seem to face a dilemma: The phase and normalization we assert are essential, yet the same normalization and phase prevents a realization of the desired linear transformations!

We can avoid the dilemma, however, if we use a more general realization than commutation for linear operations. The procedure is simple enough: A linear operation will consist of, first, a *scale transformation* (re-normalization and re-phasing of all elements of the vector space), then secondly a commutation, and lastly the inverse scaling transformation. Calling the *fixed* scale transformation S we have in symbols:

$$\mathcal{O}_X(v) \equiv S^{-1}[X, v]\, S\,, \tag{41}$$

where $\mathcal{O}_X(\ldots)$ is the linear operation associated with the generator X, and v is a vector of the space. Lest this appear trivial (it is obvious that this is linear) let us note that the transformation S is a *similarity* transformation but not a unitary transformation[12]).

To be fully explicit we must now supply all details on the scaling transformation S. Let us see what this entails.

Consider the Wigner operator $\left\langle 1 \begin{smallmatrix} \mu \\ m \end{smallmatrix} 0 \right\rangle$. The scaling required is in effect to remove the denominator, i.e., to multiply by the common factor $[p_{12}-p_{22}]^{\frac{1}{2}}$, and supply an extra minus sign for $\left\langle 1 \begin{smallmatrix} 0 \\ 0 \end{smallmatrix} 0 \right\rangle$. The operator S is then diagonal with the matrix elements:

$$S\left(1 \begin{smallmatrix} \mu \\ m \end{smallmatrix} 0\right) = [p_{12} - p_{22}]^{\frac{1}{2}} \begin{cases} -1 & \mu = m = 0\,, \\ +1 & \text{all others}\,. \end{cases} \tag{42}$$

Using the realization given in eqs. (38) and (39) for the mapping onto boson operators, and the abstract operator realization of eq. (41) we see that we have realized an SU_2 group for upper pattern space. Similarly the realization of eqs. (38) and (40) provide an SU_2 realization for lower pattern space transformations. These two realizations are compatible and it follows moreover (by direct calculation) that the operations *commute*. This explicit realization demonstrates therefore that abstract generators exist for the Wigner operators as a vector space, and that the abstract group so generated is isomorphic to $SU_2 * SU_2$.

For the general Wigner operator the determination of S is not so simple. We may proceed this way: The product of any sequence of operators,

$$\left\langle 1 \begin{smallmatrix} \mu_1 \\ 1 \end{smallmatrix} 0 \right\rangle \left\langle 1 \begin{smallmatrix} \mu_2 \\ 1 \end{smallmatrix} 0 \right\rangle \ldots \left\langle 1 \begin{smallmatrix} \mu_n \\ 1 \end{smallmatrix} 0 \right\rangle$$

is (maximal case!) clearly – to within factors involving the 'scale' $(m_{12}-m_{22})$ – the Wigner operator $\left\langle n \begin{smallmatrix} \sum\mu_i \\ n \end{smallmatrix} 0 \right\rangle$. This remains true if we replace every $\left\langle 1 \begin{smallmatrix} \mu_i \\ 1 \end{smallmatrix} 0 \right\rangle$ by the renormalized operator. Hence the scale factor for $\left\langle k \begin{smallmatrix} \mu \\ k \end{smallmatrix} 0 \right\rangle$ is the factor in the matrix elements of $\left\langle k \begin{smallmatrix} \mu \\ k \end{smallmatrix} 0 \right\rangle$ explicitly independent of μ.

To determine this factor we can employ the factorization lemma and construct directly the desired result. (The details are given in the appendix.) To summarize: One finds that the scaling transformation is diagonal, and that the diagonal elements of S are given by:

$$S\begin{pmatrix} m_{12} & \mu_{11} \\ & m_{12} \end{pmatrix} m_{22} = \left| \frac{(p_{12} - p_{22} - m_{12} + 2\mu_{11} - m_{22} - 1)!}{(p_{12} - p_{22} - m_{12} + \mu_{11} - 1)!} \cdot \frac{(p_{22} - p_{12} - 2\mu_{11} + m_{12} + m_{22} - 1)!}{(p_{22} - p_{12} - \mu_{11} + m_{22} - 1)!} \right|^{\frac{1}{2}} . \quad (42a)$$

This seemingly complicated result becomes very much simpler – and its structure intelligible – if we 'diagram' it using partial hooks and arrows. (See appendix.)

It is necessary to point out that we have restricted our attention to the matrix elements of S for those Wigner operators having maximum m_{11}. However, if we know all such 'maximal' operators the general operator follows directly from the physical SU_2 'lowering' operator, E_{21}. Thus it is no restriction to proceed in this way.

6. Racah coefficients as coupling coefficients in the vector space of Wigner operators

It has been the purpose of the previous sections to demonstrate that the Wigner operators are the carrier space of the group $U_2 * U_2$, and that the upper and lower pattern space (μ_{11} and m_{11} respectively) are formally isomorphic. Let us now recall that the Wigner coefficients played a dual rôle in QTAM. On the one hand (by the Wigner–Eckart theorem) they are an orthonormal and complete basis for tensor operators; on the other hand, the Wigner coefficients appear as the coupling coefficients for the coupling of two vector spaces (addition of angular momenta), provided only that the generators of the two spaces are independent[13]) (equivalent to the 'derivation property' for Lie algebras.)

The great advantage of the coupling aspect is that it enables one to construct all irreps of SU_2 out of the fundamental (two dimensional) irrep.

In view of the isomorphism between upper and lower pattern spaces, it is natural to pose the question: Can one define 'Wigner coefficients' that similarly effect the coupling of upper pattern vector spaces? One can, indeed (in fact the isomorphism guarantees it) – the coupling coefficients so-defined are the *Racah coefficients*. It is the thesis of the present paper that such a view[14]) of the Racah coefficients is of basic importance and illustrates most clearly the abstract structure underlying the Racah–Wigner angular momentum calculus.

It is not difficult to demonstrate the validity of our assertion concerning the coupling aspects of the Racah coefficients; one has only to re-interpret Racah's original defining relation. Racah defined $W(abed; cf)$ by the relation:

$$\sum_{\beta} C^{abc}_{\alpha\beta}\, C^{cde}_{\alpha+\beta\,\phi-\beta}\, C^{bdf}_{\beta\,\varphi-\beta} \equiv C^{afe}_{\alpha\,\phi}\, \sqrt{(2c+1)(2f+1)}\, W(abed; cf). \qquad (43)$$

(Note that we have introduced explicitly the delta function relating the three magnetic quantum members in a given Wigner coefficient, and omitted the redundant index.)

Let us transcribe this into the notation of section 2 (noting that the initial state is $|a, \alpha\rangle$ and the final state $|e, \varepsilon = \alpha + \varphi\rangle$ so that the natural matrix element ordering is just the *reverse* of the ordering in both the Wigner coefficients and the relation above). We obtain:

$$\sum_{\beta} C^{bdf}_{\beta\varphi-\beta} \left[\left\langle 2d \begin{matrix} d+e-c \\ d+\varphi-\beta \end{matrix} 0 \right\rangle \left\langle 2b \begin{matrix} b+c-a \\ b+\beta \end{matrix} 0 \right\rangle\right] =$$
$$= \sqrt{(2c+1)(2f+1)}\; W(abed; cf) \left\langle 2f \begin{matrix} e+f-a \\ f+\varphi \end{matrix} 0 \right\rangle. \qquad (44)$$

Let us state the conventions employed here: (1) The specific initial state ($|a, \alpha\rangle$) is suppressed (we must discuss this further, see below). (2) The Wigner operator $\left\langle 2b \begin{matrix} b+c-a \\ b+\beta \end{matrix} 0 \right\rangle$ carries $|a, \alpha\rangle$ into $|c, \alpha+\beta\rangle$ – where c is specified by a and μ_{11} – with the state $|c, \alpha+\beta\rangle$ being multiplied by the numerical quantity $C^{abc}_{\alpha\beta}$. (3) The Wigner operator $\left\langle 2d \begin{matrix} d+e-c \\ d+\varphi-\beta \end{matrix} 0 \right\rangle$ carries the state $|c, \alpha+\beta\rangle$ into $C^{cde}_{\alpha+\beta\,\varphi-\beta}\, |e, \alpha+\varphi\rangle$ – e being specified by c and μ_{11}. On the right hand side, the operator $\left\langle 2f \begin{matrix} e+f-a \\ f+\varphi \end{matrix} 0 \right\rangle$ specifies the same transformation of $|a, \alpha\rangle$ into $|e, \alpha+\beta\rangle$.

It is clear in this form, however, that the coefficient $C^{bdf}_{\beta\,\varphi-\beta}$, and the sum over β is *just the coupling of the two Wigner operators* $\left\langle 2b \begin{matrix} b+c-a \\ b+\beta \end{matrix} 0 \right\rangle$ and $\left\langle 2d \begin{matrix} d+e-c \\ d+\varphi-\beta \end{matrix} 0 \right\rangle$ *into* $\left\langle 2f \begin{matrix} e+f-a \\ f+\varphi \end{matrix} 0 \right\rangle$. If we express this coupling by Ⓦ – W for 'Wigner' – and suppress the m_{11} index we get the suggestive form:

$$\left[\left\langle 2d \; \overset{d+e-c}{\cdot} \; 0 \right\rangle_{\text{Ⓦ}} \left\langle 2b \; \overset{b+c-a}{\cdot} \; 0 \right\rangle\right] =$$

$$= \sqrt{(2c+1)(2f+1)}\, W(abed; cf) \left\langle 2f \; \overset{e+f-a}{\cdot} \; 0 \right\rangle. \tag{45}$$

This equation can be inverted using the orthonormal properties of $\sqrt{\ldots}\, W(\ldots)$; one multiplies both sides by $\sqrt{\ldots}\, W(\ldots)$ and sums over c. Denoting this operation as *Racah coupling*, Ⓡ, we obtain our desired transcription of Racah's definition:

$$\left[\left\langle 2d \; \vdots \; 0 \right\rangle \overset{\text{Ⓡ}}{\underset{\text{Ⓦ}}{}} \left\langle 2b \; \vdots \; 0 \right\rangle\right] = \left\langle 2f \; \vdots \; 0 \right\rangle, \tag{46}$$

(the dots denote dummy indices which are summed over in the coupling on the left side, and are related by delta functions to the indices represented by dots on the right. This saves cluttering up the formulas and obscuring the structure.)

Expressing this transcription of Racah's result in words: *Wigner coupling lower pattern space and Racah coupling upper pattern space effect a vector coupling operation in the vector space of Wigner operators.*

(The reader may convince himself that no slip has occurred in getting this result, by directly transforming Racah's relation in the usual notation[15]). We remark that if we relinquish the unimodular restriction the result becomes even more elegant in appearance.)

But we must point out one significant feature of this result: Unlike the Wigner coupling in eq. (44), the Racah coupling depends *explicitly* on the (suppressed) initial state angular momentum, a, (and accounts for the 'extra' index in the W coefficient). This difference seemingly spoils the isomorphism between Wigner and Racah coupling, until one realizes that this is an essential and necessary aspect stemming from the *scale transformations* required in realizing the isomorphism.

We can make this intimate relationship between the Racah coefficients and the scale transformations clearer by examining, not the general $W(\ldots)$ as above, but the more elementary Racah coefficients belonging to spin-$\frac{1}{2}$.

In order to determine the fundamental (spin-$\frac{1}{2}$) Racah coefficients most expeditiously let us note the following points: (1) If it were not for the scaling transformations the desired result would be precisely the known Wigner coefficients – hence, in essence, our problem is only to put in the changes caused by the scaling; (2) Since transformations in u- and l-space commute, we can simplify our work by considering the vector coupling of maximal (in l-space) Wigner coefficients. (3) We can further simplify the work by taking $m_{22}=0$.

Thus we consider the explicit Wigner operators given by the relation:

$$\left\langle m_{12} \begin{matrix} \mu_{11} \\ m_{12} \end{matrix} 0 \right\rangle = [\mu_{11}!(m_{12}-\mu_{11})!]^{-\frac{1}{2}} \cdot F \cdot \left(\left\langle 1 \begin{matrix} 1 \\ 1 \end{matrix} 0 \right\rangle_{\mathrm{R}} \right)^{\mu_{11}} \left(\left\langle 1 \begin{matrix} 0 \\ 1 \end{matrix} 0 \right\rangle_{\mathrm{R}} \right)^{m_{12}-\mu_{11}},$$

$$F \equiv \left| \frac{(p_{12}-p_{22}-m_{12}+2\mu_{11}-1)!}{(p_{12}-p_{22}-m_{12}+\mu_{11}-1)!} \; \frac{(p_{22}-p_{12}-2\mu_{11}+m_{12}-1)!}{(p_{22}-p_{12}-\mu_{11}-1)!} \right|^{-\frac{1}{2}}. \tag{47}$$

To interpret this result note that, aside from F, this is just the form for the state vector $\left| \begin{pmatrix} m_{12} & & 0 \\ & \mu_{11} & \end{pmatrix} \right\rangle$. The factor F arises from the scale transformations and is in fact just S^{-1}, using eq. (42).

The procedure for determining the fundamental (spin-$\frac{1}{2}$) Racah coefficients is the direct analogon to the derivation given earlier for the fundamental Wigner coefficients. We must be very careful though to take full account of the operator properties implicit in the notation.

Let us couple the Wigner coefficient in eq. (47) above to the operator $\left\langle 1 \begin{matrix} 1 \\ 1 \end{matrix} 0 \right\rangle$, *coupling in this operator on the right so that it acts first*. (This implies that the underlying quantum numbers (p_{ij}) in eq. (47) are *shifted* by the Δ-pattern $\Delta = \begin{pmatrix} 1 & & 0 \\ & 1 & \end{pmatrix}$ resulting from the operator $\left\langle 1 \begin{matrix} 1 \\ 1 \end{matrix} 0 \right\rangle$.) The result is – to within a renormalization, call it N – the Wigner operator $\left\langle m_{12}+1 \begin{matrix} \mu_{11}+1 \\ m_{12}+1 \end{matrix} 0 \right\rangle$. The renormalization is found to be:

$$N = (\mu_{11}+1)^{\frac{1}{2}} \cdot \left[F\begin{pmatrix} & \mu_{11}+1 & \\ m_{12}+1 & & 0 \end{pmatrix} \Big/ F\begin{pmatrix} & \mu_{11} & \\ m_{12} & & 0 \end{pmatrix}; p_{ij} \to p_{ij}+\Delta \right] \cdot F\begin{pmatrix} & 1 & \\ 1 & & 0 \end{pmatrix}, \tag{48}$$

where $F(\ldots)$ denotes the factor in eq. (47) with parameters as indicated.

Recalling the argument which led to the Wigner operators $\left\langle 1 \begin{matrix} \mu \\ m \end{matrix} 0 \right\rangle$ we see that $(\mu_{11}+1)^{\frac{1}{2}}$ corresponds to the operator $\left\langle 1 \begin{matrix} 1 \\ 1 \end{matrix} 0 \right\rangle$. Replacing then $(\mu_{11}+1)^{\frac{1}{2}}$ by $\left\langle 1 \begin{matrix} 1 \\ 1 \end{matrix} 0 \right\rangle$, and removing the unimodular restriction, we get the desired result:

$$\left[\text{Racah coefficient for upper pattern shifts } \Delta_{\mathrm{u}} = \begin{pmatrix} & 1 & \\ 1 & & 0 \end{pmatrix}\right] =$$

$$= \left[\frac{\mu_{11} - m_{22} + 1}{m_{12} - m_{22} + 1} \cdot \frac{p_{12} - p_{22} + \mu_{11} - m_{12}}{p_{12} - p_{22}}\right]^{\frac{1}{2}}. \tag{49}$$

Let us now attempt to devise a notation that puts the *structure* of the Racah coefficient above more in evidence. The Racah coefficient, as determined above, has the property of coupling $\left\langle m_{12} \begin{matrix} \mu_{11} \\ m_{12} \end{matrix} m_{22} \right\rangle$ to $\left\langle 1 \begin{matrix} 1 \\ 1 \end{matrix} 0 \right\rangle$ on the right to produce $\left\langle m_{12}+1 \begin{matrix} \mu_{11}+1 \\ m_{12}+1 \end{matrix} m_{22} \right\rangle$ – in other words to shift the complete operator pattern labels by $\begin{pmatrix} 1 & \begin{matrix} 1 \\ 1 \end{matrix} & 0 \end{pmatrix}$. Since however, the shift in m_{11} is accomplished by a Wigner coupling ($\rightarrow 1$ for maximal states) we see that only the shift $\Delta_{\mathrm{u}} = \begin{pmatrix} & 1 & \\ 1 & & 0 \end{pmatrix}$ is significant. By analogy to the Wigner coefficients, we designate this in a *Racah operator notation*:

$$\left\{1 \begin{matrix} 1 \\ 1 \end{matrix} 0\right\} \leftrightarrow \left[\frac{\mu_{11} - m_{22} + 1}{m_{12} - m_{22} + 1}\right]^{\frac{1}{2}} \cdot \left[\frac{p_{12} - p_{22} + \mu_{11} - m_{12}}{p_{12} - p_{22}}\right]^{\frac{1}{2}}, \tag{50}$$

where:

(1) The p_{ij} refer to the underlying vector space $|(m)^{\text{initial}}\rangle$ (with values agreeing with the state vector on the right).

(2) The values μ_{11}, m_{12}, m_{22} refer to the operator $\left\langle m_{12} \begin{matrix} \mu_{11} \\ \cdot \end{matrix} m_{22} \right\rangle$ coupled to $\left\langle 1 \begin{matrix} 1 \\ \cdot \end{matrix} 0 \right\rangle$ (the latter on the right).

(3) The notation $\left\{1 \begin{matrix} 1 \\ 1 \end{matrix} 0\right\}$ is chosen such that

(a) The bottom '1' implies $\mu_{11} \rightarrow \mu_{11}+1$.

(b) The pattern $\begin{pmatrix} & 1 & \\ 1 & & 0 \end{pmatrix}$ implies $\Delta_{\mathrm{u}} = \begin{pmatrix} 1 & 0 \\ & \cdot & \end{pmatrix}$ so that the change in the irrep labels is: $[m_{12}\, m_{22}] \rightarrow [m_{12}+1\, m_{22}]$, (just as for interpreting the upper pattern in the Wigner operators $\langle \ldots \rangle$).

In order to be fully explicit let us note that $\left\{1 \begin{matrix} i \\ j \end{matrix} 0\right\}$ is precisely an (orthonormalized) Racah coefficient upon taking matrix elements; that is [from the *definition* eq. (46)]:

$$\left\{1 \begin{smallmatrix} i \\ \cdot \\ j \end{smallmatrix} 0\right\} \to (-)^{\frac{1}{2}+j_{\mathrm{f}}-j_{\mathrm{int}}-J}[(2j_{\mathrm{int}}+1)(2J+1)]^{\frac{1}{2}} W(j_{\mathrm{i}}j_{\mathrm{int}}JJ'; \tfrac{1}{2}j_{\mathrm{f}}), \quad (51)$$

where we have defined the variables to be:

$$J = \frac{m_{12}-m_{22}}{2}$$

$$J' = \begin{cases} J+\frac{1}{2} & i=1 \\ J-\frac{1}{2} & i=0 \end{cases}$$

$$j_{\mathrm{i}} = \frac{p_{12}-p_{22}-1}{2}$$

(j_i is the angular momentum of the initial basis state)

$$j_{\mathrm{int}} = \begin{cases} j_{\mathrm{i}}+\frac{1}{2} & j=1 \\ j_{\mathrm{i}}-\frac{1}{2} & j=0 \end{cases}$$

(j_{int} is the intermediate state angular momentum), and,

$$j_{\mathrm{f}} = j_{\mathrm{int}} + \left(\mu_{11} - \frac{m_{12}+m_{22}}{2}\right),$$

that is, j_{int} is shifted by the action of the Wigner operator $\left\langle m_{12} \begin{smallmatrix} \mu_{11} \\ \cdot \end{smallmatrix} m_{22} \right\rangle$. In a manner exactly analogous to the determination of the fundamental Wigner operators given earlier, we determine the 2×2 table of Racah coefficients $\left\{1 \begin{smallmatrix} i \\ \cdot \\ j \end{smallmatrix} 0\right\}$; see table 2.

TABLE 2

The fundamental Racah coefficients $\left\{1 \begin{smallmatrix} i \\ \cdot \\ j \end{smallmatrix} 0\right\}$

$j \backslash i$	1	0
1	$\left[\frac{m_{11}-m_{22}+1}{m_{12}-m_{22}+1} \cdot \frac{p_{12}-p_{22}+m_{11}-m_{12}}{p_{12}-p_{22}}\right]^{\frac{1}{2}}$	$-\left[\frac{m_{12}-m_{11}}{m_{12}-m_{22}+1} \cdot \frac{p_{12}-p_{22}+m_{11}-m_{22}+1}{p_{12}-p_{22}}\right]^{\frac{1}{2}}$
0	$\left[\frac{m_{12}-m_{11}+1}{m_{12}-m_{22}+1} \cdot \frac{p_{12}-p_{22}+m_{11}-m_{22}}{p_{12}-p_{22}}\right]^{\frac{1}{2}}$	$\left[\frac{m_{11}-m_{22}}{m_{12}-m_{22}+1} \cdot \frac{p_{12}-p_{22}+m_{11}-m_{12}-1}{p_{12}-p_{22}}\right]^{\frac{1}{2}}$

The results given in this table are, of course, completely equivalent to the well known algebraic tables for spin-$\frac{1}{2}$ Racah coefficients, but several interesting points are brought out more clearly in the present form. Firstly we see that these spin-$\frac{1}{2}$ Racah coefficients *factor* into two parts: The first part is exactly the Wigner coefficient for the accomplishing the same shift Δ, that is, $\left\langle 1 \begin{smallmatrix} i \\ \cdot \\ j \end{smallmatrix} 0 \right\rangle$. The second factor, as is clear from our derivation, is a direct consequence of the *scale transformations* implied by the particular realizations used for upper pattern operations. It is very clear from this that the bothersome question of 'proper normalization' in our discussion of Wigner operators is in fact an essential consideration.

Let us note also that the *order* of the coupling effected by $\left\langle 1 \begin{smallmatrix} i \\ \cdot \\ j \end{smallmatrix} 0 \right\rangle$, namely $\left\langle 1 \begin{smallmatrix} 1 \\ \cdot \\ \cdot \end{smallmatrix} 0 \right\rangle$ is coupled on the right, is very essential. One could, of course, couple in the opposite order. From the Wigner coefficients, one is familiar with the fact that the coupling order is important, but the difference between the two orders is at most a phase (plus or minus sign). For the Racah coupling the difference is more pronounced, one obtains not only a possible sign difference but a change in *scale*. This is understandable in view of the rôle of scale transformations in the operator realizations used above.

Lastly it is immediately evident from this formulation that in the limit of large quantum numbers, more exactly $p_{12}-p_{22} \gg 1$, we obtain the known asymptotic relation between the Racah and Wigner coefficients[16]; for the case at hand this is simply:

$$\left\{ 1 \begin{smallmatrix} i \\ \cdot \\ j \end{smallmatrix} 0 \right\} \sim \left\langle 1 \begin{smallmatrix} i \\ \cdot \\ j \end{smallmatrix} 0 \right\rangle, \qquad p_{12} - p_{22} \gg 1 . \tag{52}$$

The next section discusses this result in more generality.

7. Concluding remarks

We have asserted that the three structures in QTAM – the representation matrices (D), the Wigner coefficients $\langle \ldots \rangle$ and the Racah coefficients $\{\ldots\}$ – are formally isomorphic structures if each is considered as the carrier (vector) space of an abstract $SU_2 * SU_2$ group. Moreover, in the last section we have seen how the rôle of vector coupling coefficients is played both by Wigner and by Racah coefficients. Let us discuss further some of the implications of these viewpoints.

Each of the three objects – D, $\langle \ldots \rangle$, $\{\ldots\}$ – carries two sets of 'magnetic quantum number' labels. In the case of the rotation matrices we realize both magnetic quantum numbers by similar operators: J_z (space fixed) and J_z'

(body fixed) using the convenient language of symmetric tops. For the Wigner coefficients, the two spaces differ – one is simply the ordinary J_z, the other the space of ΔJ. Finally in the Racah coefficients both spaces are again the same, but now both are the 'ΔJ' type.

Our discussion in the paragraph above has been rather imprecise and intuitive, but it does suffice to show that there are really only three types of objects in QTAM, in the sense that there are two 'types of space' and an 'object' consists of taking two spaces at a time.

Moreover we can couple these vector spaces together; in particular the invariant coupling of two upper pattern spaces for Wigner coefficients yields an object having two distinct J_z spaces. It is in this way that we can understand the structure of the factorization lemma.

The vector coupling coefficients of QTAM were introduced by Wigner as the matrices which diagonalize the Kronecker product of rotation matrices; in symbols:

$$D^J_{m\bar{m}}(\alpha\beta\gamma) \times D^{J'}_{m'\bar{m}'}(\alpha\beta\gamma) = \sum_{\substack{J'' \\ m'',\bar{m}''}} C^{J\ J'\ J''}_{m\ m'\ m''}\, D^{J''}_{m''\bar{m}''}(\alpha\beta\gamma)\, C^{J\ J'\ J''}_{\bar{m}\ \bar{m}'\ \bar{m}''}. \tag{53}$$

If we invert this equation we find:

$$\sum_{\substack{mm' \\ \bar{m}\bar{m}'}} C^{J\ J'\ J''}_{m\ m'\ m''}\, D^J_{m\bar{m}}(\alpha\beta\gamma)\, D^{J'}_{m'\bar{m}'}(\alpha\beta\gamma)\, C^{J\ J'\ J''}_{\bar{m}\ \bar{m}'\ \bar{m}''} = D_{m''\ \bar{m}''}^{\ \ J''}(\alpha\beta\gamma), \tag{54}$$

or expressed more compactly:

$$\left[\boldsymbol{D}^J \overset{Ⓦ}{\underset{Ⓦ}{}} \boldsymbol{D}^{J'}\right] = \boldsymbol{D}^{J''} \tag{$\star$}$$

that is, in words: *Wigner coupling of the two* SU_2 *spaces in the D matrix produces a new D matrix.*

Very familiar, without a doubt. But let us now look at the re-interpreted Racah definition of the Racah coefficient:

$$\left[\left\langle m_{12} \ \vdots\ m_{22} \right\rangle \overset{Ⓡ}{\underset{Ⓦ}{}} \left\langle m'_{12} \ \vdots\ m'_{22} \right\rangle\right] = \left\langle m''_{12} \ \vdots\ m''_{22} \right\rangle. \tag{$\star\star$}$$

Obviously these two results ($\star$) and ($\star\star$) are but different realizations of the *same abstract relation.*

But we can go further – we can 'Racah couple' *twice*. That is, we can guess that there must exist a formal relation:

$$\left[\left\{ m_{12} \ \vdots\ m_{22} \right\} \overset{Ⓡ}{\underset{Ⓡ}{}} \left\{ m'_{12} \ \vdots\ m'_{22} \right\}\right] = \left\{ m''_{12} \ \vdots\ m''_{22} \right\}. \tag{$\star\star\star$}$$

Indeed there does exist such a relation; (★★★) is equivalent to a transcription of the identity introduced by the writer[17]) and independently by Elliott[18]).

We conclude that the three product laws of QTAM, relations (★), (★★), and (★★★) are all abstractly equivalent. Moreover we see that in the limit where the *scale* is irrelevant ($p_{12}-p_{22} \gg 1$) the linear operator realizations necessarily become not only equivalent but identical; this is the ultimate source of the asymptotic relations which link the Racah, Wigner, and rotation matrices[19]). These relations have all been known for many years; in very direct sense, it was to 'explain' the deeper origins of this result that led to the ideas presented here[20]).

One bonus occurs from this development. All of the abstract properties of the relations developed here seem to be quite independent of the group SU_2 and (although the proof is not fully complete) seem to generalize directly to SU_n. This is indeed true for SU_3 (see ref. 3), the case of most physical interest, and could (except for excessive length) have been developed in parallel to the work above on SU_2. One sees from this that very likely the solution of the multiplicity problem for SU_n is abstractly implied by the Weyl branching law for SU_n – in other words, there must exist a generalized Weyl branching law for operator structures! Again this is known to be true for SU_3 (and of course SU_2), but at this stage our inference has only the status of a conjecture.

Acknowledgements

The preparation of this paper has been greatly helped by the past collaboration of the author with Drs. Gordon Baird and Alberto Giovannini on related problems. I am even more indebted to Dr. James Louck who has contributed in a major way to the work in this paper, in particular, to the interpretation of the factorization lemma.

But most of all, would I like to express my deep indebtedness to Professor Giulio Racah. His generous help and encouragement over the years gave evidence of a warmth of personality fully as outstanding as his intellectual gifts.

Appendix

It is desired to derive the scale transformation matrix elements, and it has been shown that this matrix element is the μ_{11}-independent factor in the maximal m_{11} Wigner coefficient $\left\langle m_{12} \begin{matrix} \mu_{11} \\ m_{12} \end{matrix} m_{22} \right\rangle$. Hence we must determine this Wigner coefficient.

To do this, we make use of the factorization lemma. According to this result, we need only determine the eigenvector form of the boson operator product:

$$A\begin{pmatrix} & m_{12} & \\ m_{12} & & 0 \\ & m_{12} & \end{pmatrix} = (a_1^1)^{m_{12}} =$$

$$= \sum_{\mu_{11}} \#(\mu_{11}) \left\langle \begin{matrix} & \mu_{11} & \\ m_{12} & & 0 \\ & m_{12} & \end{matrix} \right\rangle \left\langle \begin{matrix} & \mu_{11} & \\ m_{12} & & 0 \\ & m_{12} & \end{matrix} \right\rangle, \qquad \text{(A-1)}$$

where the two $\langle \ldots \rangle$ operators in eq. (A-1) are in different spaces.

But we know already the fundamental Wigner coefficients from:

$$a_1^1 = \sum_{\mu_{11}=1,0} \#(\mu_{11}) \left\langle \begin{matrix} & \mu_{11} & \\ 1 & & 0 \\ & 1 & \end{matrix} \right\rangle \left\langle \begin{matrix} & \mu_{11} & \\ 1 & & 0 \\ & 1 & \end{matrix} \right\rangle. \qquad \text{(A-2)}$$

Hence we may insert (A-2) in (A-1) and choose the desired terms out of the product, which involves $2^{m_{12}}$ terms. The difficulty is that the various objects involved in this product do not commute.

One difficulty is easily eliminated. The functions $\#(\ldots)$ are multiplicative and depend only on the initial and final states. Hence we may effectively drop these from consideration.

The second simplification is to recognize that re-normalizing the Wigner operators, i.e., $\langle \ldots \rangle \to \langle \ldots \rangle_R$, allows these renormalized elements to commute. Note that the Wigner coefficients in the two spaces share the same normalization factors, so that square roots do not enter.

Finally we note that the commuting factors $\langle \ldots \rangle_R$ are very simply related to the desired scale factor, S^{-1}. That is:

$$\left\langle \begin{matrix} & \mu_{11} & \\ m_{12} & & 0 \\ & m_{12} & \end{matrix} \right\rangle = S \cdot [\mu_{11}!(m_{12}-\mu_{11})!]^{-\frac{1}{2}} \times$$

$$\times \left(\left\langle \begin{matrix} & 1 & \\ 1 & & 0 \\ & 1 & \end{matrix} \right\rangle_R \right)^{\mu_{11}} \left(\left\langle \begin{matrix} & 0 & \\ 1 & & 0 \\ & 1 & \end{matrix} \right\rangle_R \right)^{m_{12}-\mu_{11}}.$$

Calling $S(i)$ the factor (which we must not forget is an operator) that renormalizes $\left\langle \begin{matrix} & i & \\ 1 & & 0 \\ & \cdot & \end{matrix} \right\rangle$ we see that the square of the desired factor S is *the sum of all possible distinct arrangements of the* μ_{11} *factors* $(S(1))^2$ *and* $(m_{12}-\mu_{11})$ *factors* $(S(0))^2$, *divided by the number of such arrangements*. The summation can be carried out to yield eq. (42a), after removing the unimodular condition.

The final answer has a very elegant 'representation' in terms of arrows and partial hooks. Consider the factor:

$$S\begin{pmatrix} & \mu_{11} & \\ m_{12} & & 0 \\ & m_{12} & \end{pmatrix}.$$

These quantum numbers correspond to the Δ-pattern:

$$\Delta = \begin{pmatrix} \mu_{11} & & m_{12}-\mu_{11} \\ & m_{12} & \end{pmatrix}.$$

Now write this Δ-pattern as the sum of two special Δ-patterns: $\Delta = \Delta_1 + \Delta_2$, with

$$\Delta_1 = \begin{pmatrix} \mu_{11} & & 0 \\ & \mu_{11} & \end{pmatrix} \quad \text{and} \quad \Delta_2 = \begin{pmatrix} 0 & & m_{12}-\mu_{11} \\ & m_{12}-\mu_{11} & \end{pmatrix}.$$

(This corresponds to writing the original Wigner operator as a product of operators.)

Represent the initial state pattern (p_{ij}) by dots for each case, Δ_1 and Δ_2, letting the two operators *act on each other* (i.e. shifting the p_{ij}). For Δ_1 we get a pattern with μ_{11} arrows, *which we interpret as a factorial*, thus:

Δ_1:

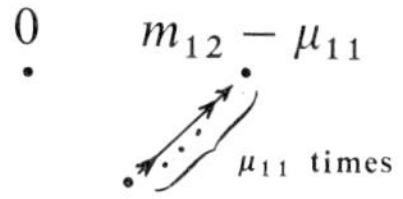

$$\Rightarrow \frac{[p_{11} - \overbrace{(p_{22} - (m_{12}-\mu_{11}))}^{\text{shift in } p_{22}} + \mu_{11} - 1]!}{[p_{11} - p_{22} - (m_{12}-\mu_{11}) - 1]!}.$$

Similarly for Δ_2 we get:

Δ_2:

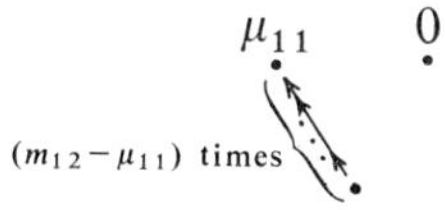

$$\Rightarrow \frac{[p_{11} - \overbrace{(p_{12}+\mu_{11})}^{\text{shift in } p_{12}} + m_{12} - \mu_{11}]!}{[p_{11} - (p_{12}+\mu_{11})]!}$$

The product of the magnitude of these two factors is the square of the desired factor $S\begin{pmatrix} m_{12} & \mu_{11} & 0 \\ & m_{12} & \end{pmatrix}$.

References and footnotes

1) Racah's contributions were published in the Physical Review principally during the decade beginning around 1942. Many texts now survey and incorporate his results; it would be idle for me to attempt here a satisfactory referencing. The monograph by Racah and Fano [G. Racah and U. Fano, *Irreducible Tensorial Sets* (Academic Press, New York, 1959)] is especially to be recommended as providing a comprehensive view of this work. The basic papers by Racah, and by Wigner, Schwinger, Bargmann and others are collected in the book *The Quantum Theory of Angular Momentum*, Eds. L. C. Biedenharn and H. Van Dam (Academic Press, New York, 1965); an extensive bibliography is also attempted there. We denote this book as "QTAM".

2) The term stems from E. P. Wigner, Am. J. Math. **63**, 57 (1941); see also the paper "On the Matrices which Reduce the Kronecker Products of Representations of S.R. Groups"; both papers are in "QTAM", ref. 1.

3) L. C. Biedenharn, A. Giovannini and J. D. Louck, J. Math. Phys. **8**, 691 (1967). A proof is given for SU(3).

4) G. E. Baird and L. C. Biedenharn, "Operator Structures in SU_3 with an Application to Triplets", given at *Symmetry Principles at High Energy, Conference held at the University of Miami, Coral Gables, Florida, 1964* (W. H. Freeman and Co., San Francisco, California, 1965); see also J. Math. Phys. **5**, 1730 (1964).
5) E. Artin, *Geometric Algebra* (Interscience, New York, 1957) p. 13. The theorem is very familiar and given in many places, but Artin elucidates the essence of the result marvellously.
6) P. Jordan, Z. Physik **94**, 531 (1935).
7) J. Schwinger, "On Angular Momentum", manuscript (1952), published in "QTAM", ref. 1.
8) V. Bargmann, Rev. Mod. Phys. **34**, 829 (1952). Reprinted in "QTAM", ref. 1.
9) The normalization is chosen to coincide with Racah's Princeton Lectures, Ergeb. Exakt. Naturw. **37**, 28 (1965). The notation E_{ij}, H stems from Weyl, and is used here since it suggests (correctly) the generalization to U_n.
10) Strictly this is a mapping, but using the equality sign is easier and causes no problem. The normalization, M, has an interesting interpretation in terms of *hooks* (see ref. 4).
11) This is a special case of the general U_n result proved in ref. 3.
12) Recall also that the class of canonical transformations in quantum mechanics is similarly larger than the class of unitary transformations.
13) This proviso is non-trivial and to be fully precise one must prove that the direct product of upper pattern spaces satisfies the derivation property. We shall neglect this technical nicety and argue that by the success of a direct construction [see eq. (46) and footnote 15 below] the desired property must necessarily hold.
14) L. C. Biedenharn, Phys. Letters **14**, 254 (1965).
15) It is the existence of this general result which verifies that the direct product of upper pattern spaces, in the specific realization employed in the present paper, has the desired derivation property.
16) In the classical limit, ($\hbar \to 0$), or equivalently the limit of large angular momenta, both the Wigner and Racah coefficients approach the rotation matrices $D(0\beta 0)$, with $\cos\beta \sim J_z/J$. (These results stem originally from Wigner and from Racah; references to this and later work appear in the bibliography of ref. 1.) There is an intermediate limit in which the Racah coefficients approach the Wigner coefficients; cf. ref. 17.
17) L. C. Biedenharn, J. Math. Phys. (M.I.T.) **31**, 287 (1953).
18) J. P. Elliott, Proc. Roy. Soc. (London) A **218**, 370 (1953).
19) Detailed references are given in "QTAM", ref. 1.
20) The fact that two "ΔJ" spaces are involved in the Racah coefficient makes it intuitively obvious now why there exist two limiting forms, the Wigner coefficient (one asymptotic "ΔJ" space) and the rotation matrix (both "ΔJ" spaces asymptotic).
The reader might be puzzled as to why these asymptotic relations involve only one angle, (β), and not the three Euler angles of the D matrix. The answer is that we are relating vectors in two vector spaces and the two angles (α and γ) supply only a phase to the vectors, which drops out. The phase conventions on the W and C coefficients also require that the comparison be made to the specific Euler angle formulation $D(0\beta 0)$, which is real.

Spectroscopic and group theoretical methods in physics
© North-Holland Publ. Co., Amsterdam, 1968

ON ALGEBRAIC STRUCTURES ASSOCIATED WITH THE 3-j AND 6-j SYMBOLS

A. GIOVANNINI*
Department of Physics, Duke University, Durham, N.C. 27706, U.S.A.

and

D. A. SMITH**
Department of Mathematics, Duke University, Durham, N.C. 27706, U.S.A.

1. The 3-j and 6-j symbols as magic squares

Regge[1]) has shown that each 3-j symbol $\begin{pmatrix} j_1 & j_2 & j_3 \\ m_1 & m_2 & m_3 \end{pmatrix}$ may be associated with a square symbol

$$\boxed{\begin{matrix} -j_1+j_2+j_3 & j_1-j_2+j_3 & j_1+j_2-j_3 \\ j_1-m_1 & j_2-m_2 & j_3-m_3 \\ j_1+m_1 & j_2+m_2 & j_3+m_3 \end{matrix}} \tag{1}$$

in which each of the entries is a non-negative integer, and the row sums and column sums are all equal to $s=j_1+j_2+j_3$. This form displays conveniently the 72 symmetries of the 3-j symbols as combinations of permutations of rows and columns and transposition of (1), i.e. two such arrays that differ only by a symmetry correspond to the same numerical value for the associated 3-j symbol.

Extending Regge's work, Shelepin[2,3]) has associated each 6-j symbol

* Supported in part by U.S. Army Research Office (Durham) and the National Science Foundation. Permanent address: Istituto di Fisica dell' Universita di Torino, Torino, Italy.

** Supported in part by National Science Foundation grant number GP-4473.

$\begin{Bmatrix} j_1 j_2 j_{12} \\ j_3 j \ j_{23} \end{Bmatrix}$ with a 3 by 4 symbol

$$\begin{array}{|llll|} j_1 + j - j_{23} & j_2 + j_3 - j_{23} & j_1 + j_2 - j_{12} & j + j_3 - j_{12} \\ j_1 + j_{12} - j_2 & j_3 + j_{12} - j & j_1 + j_{23} - j & j_3 + j_{23} - j_2 \\ j + j_{12} - j_3 & j_2 + j_{12} - j_1 & j_2 + j_{23} - j_3 & j + j_{23} - j_1 \end{array} \tag{2}$$

which conveniently displays the 144 symmetries of the 6-j symbols. By rearranging the entries of (2) and adding four redundant entries, Shelepin[3]) has also associated with the 6-j symbol a 4 by 4 symbol

$$\begin{array}{|cccc|} j + j_3 - j_{12} & j_1 + j_{23} - j & j + j_{12} - j_3 & j_2 + j_3 + j_{12} + \frac{1}{2}J \\ j_1 + j_{12} - j_2 & j_2 + j_3 - j_{23} & j_3 + j + j_{23} + \frac{1}{2}J & j_2 + j_{23} - j_3 \\ j_2 + j_{12} - j_1 & j_1 + j_{12} + j + \frac{1}{2}J & j_1 + j_2 - j_{12} & j_3 + j_{23} - j_2 \\ j_1 + j_2 + j_{23} + \frac{1}{2}J & j + j_{23} - j_1 & j_3 + j_{12} - j & j_1 + j - j_{23} \end{array} \tag{3}$$

where $J=2(j_1+j_2+j_3+j+j_{12}+j_{23})$. The entries of (3) are non-negative integers, and the row sums and column sums of (3) are all equal to J.

We wish to consider the arrays (1) and (3) as matrices of non-negative integers, and study the natural ordered algebraic structure which they form. We will use the term *magic square* (borrowed from recreational mathematics) for a square matrix of non-negative integers, all of whose row sums and column sums are equal. Let $\mathbf{M}_n$ denote the set of n by n magic squares. If $R=(r_{ij})$ is in $\mathbf{M}_n$, then

$$s_R = \sum_{i=1}^{n} r_{ij} = \sum_{j=1}^{n} r_{ij}$$

will be called the *rank* of R. The cases of n equal to 3 and 4 are of particular interest because of the association with the Regge and Shelepin symbols, but the algebraic structure is the same for all n.

$\mathbf{M}_n$ is closed under the operations of matrix addition and multiplication. Indeed, one can verify easily that if A and B are magic squares of ranks s_A, s_B, then $A+B$ and AB are magic squares, and furthermore

$$s_{A+B} = s_A + s_B\,, \tag{4}$$

$$s_{AB} = s_A s_B\,. \tag{5}$$

An algebraic structure $(\mathbf{A}, +, \cdot)$ with two associative compositions, in which multiplication distributes over addition, is called a *semiring*. The separate structures $(\mathbf{A}, +)$ and $(\mathbf{A}, \cdot)$ are *semigroups*. Thus $(\mathbf{M}_n, +, \cdot)$ is a semiring in which $+$ is commutative, both compositions have identity elements, and the additive cancellation law holds. Furthermore, formulas (4), (5) say that the mapping $A \to s_A$ is a homomorphism from the semiring $\mathbf{M}_n$ onto the semiring of non-negative integers. Since there is only one magic square of rank 0, (5) also implies that there are no (multiplicative) zero-divisors in $\mathbf{M}_n$.

$\mathbf{M}_n$ has a natural partial ordering, namely $A \leqslant B$ if and only if $a_{ij} \leqslant b_{ij}$ for all i, j. In contrast to the same ordering on the set of all n by n matrices of non-negative integers, this is not a lattice ordering; that is, the least upper bound of two magic squares, as matrices, may not be a magic square. However, it is easy to see that both $(\mathbf{M}_n, +)$ and $(\mathbf{M}_n, \cdot)$ are *ordered semigroups*, i.e. $A \leqslant B$ implies $A + C \leqslant B + C$ and $AC \leqslant BC$ for any C in $\mathbf{M}_n$. Furthermore, the ordering is *locally finite* in the sense that $A \leqslant B$ implies there are only finitely many C such that $A \leqslant C \leqslant B$.

There are a number of challenging combinatorial problems associated with $\mathbf{M}_n$, the most important of which is to determine the number $H(s, n)$ of n by n magic squares of a given rank s. This problem has recently been solved by Anand, Dumir and Gupta[4]) for $n=3$:

$$H(s, 3) = \binom{s+2}{2} + 3\binom{s+3}{4}. \tag{6}$$

Furthermore, they give strong evidence to support their conjecture that

$$H(s, 4) = \binom{s+3}{3} + 20\binom{s+4}{5} + 152\binom{s+5}{7} + 352\binom{s+6}{9}. \tag{7}$$

In particular, they have verified (7) for $0 \leqslant s \leqslant 5$. It is of interest to note that, since $H(s, 3)$ is a fourth degree polynomial in s,

$$\lim_{s \to \infty} H(s+1, 3)/H(s, 3) = 1 .$$

A similar statement is probably true for $H(s, n)$ for all n. For $n=4$, it would follow in the same way from (7).

2. The special role of the magic squares of rank 1

A magic square of rank 1 has the entry 1 exactly once in each row and column, and all the other entries 0. These are just the n by n permutation matrices, and hence form a group under multiplication isomorphic to the symmetric group S_n.

Furthermore, these $n!$ elements form a set of generators for the semigroup

$(\mathbf{M}_n, +)$, i.e. every magic square is a sum of magic squares of rank 1. This may be seen by induction as follows: If A has rank $s_A > 1$, then A has entries $a_{1,\sigma(1)}, a_{2,\sigma(2)}, \ldots, a_{n,\sigma(n)}$ all $\geqslant 1$, where σ is some permutation of 1, 2,..., n. (This only means that no row or column of A is entirely zero.) Then $A = B + C$, where B is the matrix of the permutation σ (1 in each of the positions $(1, \sigma(1))$, $(2, \sigma(2)), \ldots, (n, \sigma(n))$, and 0 elsewhere) and C is a magic square of rank $s_A - 1$. By the induction hypothesis, C is a sum of magic squares of rank 1, and therefore A is also.

In view of (4), we may say a little more precisely that *every magic square A is the sum of exactly s_A magic squares of rank* 1.

3. Imbedding the semiring of magic squares in a ring

As observed in section 1, $(\mathbf{M}_n, +)$ is a commutative semigroup with cancellation. It is a well-known theorem of algebra[5]) that $(\mathbf{M}_n, +)$ may be imbedded isomorphically in a commutative group $(\mathbf{R}_n, +)$ whose elements are just differences $A - B$ of elements of $\mathbf{M}_n$, subject to $A - B = C - D$ if and only if $A + D = B + C$ in $\mathbf{M}_n$. Furthermore, multiplication in $\mathbf{M}_n$ can be extended to $\mathbf{R}_n$ in the obvious way:

$$(A - B)(C - D) = (AC + BD) - (AD + BC).$$

It is easy to see that this agrees with matrix multiplication, and as such is associative and distributes over addition. Therefore we have *a natural imbedding of the semiring* $(\mathbf{M}_n, +, \cdot)$ *into a ring with unity*, $(\mathbf{R}_n, +, \cdot)$.

Differences of magic squares still satisfy the condition that all row sums and column sums are equal. Indeed,

$$s_{A-B} = s_A - s_B. \tag{8}$$

Thus $\mathbf{R}_n$ is the set of all n by n matrices of integers satisfying this condition. These are sometimes called *semimagic squares* (over the integers).

Several other observations made above about $\mathbf{M}_n$ extend in a natural way to $\mathbf{R}_n$. For example, the mapping $A \to s_A$ is a ring homomorphism from $\mathbf{R}_n$ onto the integers. The kernel, which is an ideal in $\mathbf{R}_n$, is the set of the semimagic squares of rank 0 (only one element of which is in $\mathbf{M}_n$). The elements of $\mathbf{M}_n$ of rank 1 generate $\mathbf{R}_n$ as a ring (indeed, as an additive group) and form a subgroup of the group of invertible elements, isomorphic to the symmetric group S_n. Thus we see that $\mathbf{R}_n$ *is a homomorphic image of the group ring of* S_n. It is not isomorphic to the group ring, because the permutation matrices are linearly dependent: the sum of the matrices of even permutations minus the sum of the matrices of odd permutations is 0. While $\mathbf{M}_n$ has no zero-divisors, $\mathbf{R}_n$ clearly does, and hence cannot be imbedded in a field. For example,

$$\begin{bmatrix} 1 & 1 & 1 \\ 1 & 1 & 1 \\ 1 & 1 & 1 \end{bmatrix} \left(\begin{bmatrix} 1 & 0 & 0 \\ 0 & 1 & 0 \\ 0 & 0 & 1 \end{bmatrix} - \begin{bmatrix} 0 & 1 & 0 \\ 0 & 0 & 1 \\ 1 & 0 & 0 \end{bmatrix} \right) = 0 .$$

The ordering of $\mathbf{M}_n$ extends in an obvious way to $\mathbf{R}_n$, and $\mathbf{R}_n$ becomes *a locally finite partially ordered ring*. (The last three words mean that if $A \leqslant B$, then $A+C \leqslant B+C$ for arbitrary C, and $AC \leqslant BC$ for $C \geqslant 0$.)

4. Imbedding the magic squares in a semisimple algebra

The semimagic squares with integer entries may be thought of as a subset of the set $\mathbf{Q}_n$ of semimagic squares with entries which are rational numbers, i.e. n by n matrices with rational entries all of whose row sums and column sums are equal. $\mathbf{Q}_n$ is not only a ring, but an algebra over the rationals. Since it is generated, as an algebra, by the permutation matrices, it is a representation algebra for the symmetric group S_n, and hence is semisimple[6]). Moreover, we can describe its simple components very concisely, which is one reason why it is useful to consider this further extension of $\mathbf{M}_n$.

The rank mapping $A \to s_A$ is an algebra homomorphism from $\mathbf{Q}_n$ onto the rationals. The kernel is of course the set K_n of semimagic squares of rank zero. In contrast to the situation with $\mathbf{R}_n$, K_n is a direct summand of $\mathbf{Q}_n$, i.e. there is a one-dimensional subalgebra C_n such that $\mathbf{Q}_n$ is the algebra direct sum $K_n \oplus C_n$. In fact C_n is just the set of constant matrices

$$\begin{bmatrix} c & c & \dots & c \\ c & c & \dots & c \\ & & \dots & \\ c & c & \dots & c \end{bmatrix} \tag{9}$$

where c is rational. Clearly $K_n \cap C_n = 0$, and to see that K_n and C_n generate $\mathbf{Q}_n$, we need only observe that for an arbitrary A in $\mathbf{Q}_n$, A minus the constant matrix (9), with $c = s_A/n$, has rank 0, so A is the sum of a rank 0 matrix and a constant matrix.

K_n and C_n are the simple components of $\mathbf{Q}_n$, because C_n is isomorphic to the rational field, and K_n is easily seen to be isomorphic to the algebra of *all* $(n-1)$ by $(n-1)$ matrices over the rationals. The isomorphism is established by applying a conjugation $A \to PAP^{-1}$ to the elements of K_n with a suitable non-singular matrix P. In particular, for $n=3$ (the general case is similar), we may take

$$P = \begin{bmatrix} 1 & 0 & -1 \\ 0 & 1 & -1 \\ \frac{1}{3} & \frac{1}{3} & \frac{1}{3} \end{bmatrix}, \qquad P^{-1} = \begin{bmatrix} \frac{2}{3} & -\frac{1}{3} & 1 \\ -\frac{1}{3} & \frac{2}{3} & 1 \\ -\frac{1}{3} & -\frac{1}{3} & 1 \end{bmatrix}.$$

If $A=(a_{ij})$ is a 3 by 3 semimagic square of rank 0, then one computes

$$PAP^{-1} = \begin{bmatrix} a_{11}-a_{31} & a_{12}-a_{32} & 0 \\ a_{21}-a_{31} & a_{22}-a_{32} & 0 \\ 0 & 0 & 0 \end{bmatrix}.$$

Deleting the last row and column gives the isomorphism with the algebra of all 2 by 2 matrices.

Note that $\mathbf{Q}_n = \mathrm{K}_n \oplus \mathrm{C}_n$ implies dim $\mathbf{Q}_n = (n-1)^2 + 1 = n^2 - 2n + 2$.

5. A projective geometry associated with the magic squares

The algebra $\mathbf{Q}_n$ is, in particular, a vector space over the rational field. Let $\mathrm{L}(\mathbf{Q}_n)$ denote the set of subspaces of this vector space. It is known that the set of subspaces of a vector space is both a projective geometry and a complemented modular lattice, when the relationships among subspaces are suitably interpreted. We explain this briefly; for a fuller account see references [7, 8, 9]).

A *projective geometry* may be defined to be an abstract set of objects, each assigned a number (*dimension*) 0, 1, 2, etc., with a finite upper bound on the dimensions, and such that the following axioms are satisfied (where "point" means 0-dimensional object, "line" means 1-dimensional object):

P1. Two distinct points are contained in one and only one line.

P2. If A, B, C are points not all on the same line, and D, E are distinct points such that B, C, D are on a line and A, C, E are on a line, then there is a point F such that A, B, F are on a line and also D, E, F are on a line.

P3. Every line contains at least 3 points.

P4. The points on lines through a k-dimensional element and a fixed point not on the element form a $(k+1)$-dimensional element, and every $(k+1)$-dimensional element can be obtained in this way.

It is straightforward to verify that the set of subspaces of a vector space (over a field of more than two elements) satisfies P1–P4, when "k-dimensional object" is taken to mean $(k+1)$-dimensional subspace. (In particular, "point" means one-dimensional subspace and "line" means 2-dimensional subspace.)

Alternatively, under the operations of intersection und sum, the subspaces of a finite dimensional vector space form a complemented modular lattice, ordered by inclusion. *Modular* is defined by the axiom:

M. If $x \leqslant y$, then $x \vee (y \wedge z) = (x \vee z) \wedge y$,
and *complemented* by the axiom:

C. Every x has a complement x' such that $x \wedge x' = 0$ (the smallest element) and $x \vee x' = 1$ (the largest element). For vectors, $\vee$ and $\wedge$ are respectively $+$ and $\cap$.

In any complemented modular lattice, one can define the *dimension* of an element x to be the length of a maximal chain between 0 and x. For subspaces of a vector space, this notion corresponds exactly to the usual notion of dimension. We have the theorem of Birkhoff[8]) that any complemented modular lattice of finite dimensions is isomorphic to the direct product of a finite Boolean algebra and a finite number of projective geometries. Furthermore, the given lattice is *irreducible*, meaning that there is only one nontrivial factor in the direct product (necessarily a projective geometry) if and only if the join $p \wedge q$ of any two points p, q (one-dimensional objects) contains a third point r (i.e. $r \leqslant p \wedge q$, and $r \neq p, q$). This corresponds exactly to axiom P3, and is satisfied for subspaces of a vector space, so we have an alternate way of showing that the set of subspaces of a vector space forms a projective geometry, by observing that it forms an irreducible complemented modular lattice.

Returning now to semimagic squares, we see that $L(\mathbf{Q}_n)$ is a projective geometry in which a typical *point* determined by a given magic square is the set of all semimagic squares proportional to it. In particular, all magic squares proportional to a given one are identified in a single object.

6. Conclusions concerning the 3-j and 6-j symbols

By considering the 3-j symbols, in Regge form (1), as 3 by 3 matrices, we have seen that they form a natural algebraic structure, namely a locally finite partially ordered semiring. This semiring may be imbedded in a locally finite partially ordered ring. By extension of the coefficients to the rational numbers, the ring may be imbedded in a semisimple 5-dimensional algebra. Each of these algebraic structures is generated by the 6 magic squares of rank 1, which are just the permutation matrices representing the elements of the symmetric group S_3. Finally, by considering the vector subspaces of the algebra, we have associated a projective geometry with the 3-j symbols, or equivalently, an irreducible complemented modular lattice.

Similarly, the 6-j symbols, in Shelepin form (3), may be considered as a semiring and imbedded in a locally finite partially ordered ring. This in turn may be imbedded in a 10-dimensional semisimple algebra over the rationals. Each of these structures is generated by the 24 magic squares of rank 1, which represent the elements of the symmetric group S_4. Here too, we have a projective geometry formed by the vector subspaces of the algebra.

There is a difference between the 3-j and 6-j cases which should be noted. Every 3 by 3 magic square can be written in the form (1) and associated with a 3-j symbol. However, for some ranks J, the 4 by 4 magic square (3) does not correspond to a 6-j symbol, or at least not to one which satisfies the conditions for corresponding to a Racah coefficient. Specifically, it is not possible to select, $j_1, j_2, j_3, j_{12}, j_{23}, j$ so that $J=1$, 2, or 5 and at the same time have each of the required triples (j_1, j_2, j_{12}), (j_1, j, j_{23}) (j_1, j_2, j_{23}),(j_3, j, j_{23}) satisfy the triangle inequality and have an integral sum.

We may give an algebraic interpretation to the known limit relationship between the 3-j symbols and the 6-j symbols[10,11]:

$$\lim_{p\to\infty}\begin{Bmatrix} j_1 & j_2 & j_{12} \\ j_3+p & j+p & j_{23}+p \end{Bmatrix} = \begin{pmatrix} j_1 & j_2 & j_{12} \\ j-j_3 & j_{23}-j_3 & j_3-j \end{pmatrix}. \tag{10}$$

If we add p to the appropriate elements in (3), and replace by 0 those elements which become infinite in the limit, (3) is transformed into:

$$\begin{pmatrix} 0 & j_1+j_{23}-j & j+j_{12}-j_3 & 0 \\ j_1+j_{12}-j_2 & j_2+j_3-j_{23} & 0 & j_2+j_{23}-j_3 \\ j_2+j_{12}-j_1 & 0 & j_1+j_2-j_{12} & 0 \\ 0 & 0 & j_3+j_{12}-j & j_1+j-j_{23} \end{pmatrix}. \tag{11}$$

Algebraically, the transformation of (3) into (11) is a projection of the vector space $\mathbf{Q}_4$ onto a certain subspace. The remaining nine entries are precisely the entries of the magic square (1) corresponding to the 3-j symbol $\begin{pmatrix} j_1 & j_2 & j_3 \\ j-j_3 & j_{23}-j_3 & j_3-j \end{pmatrix}$. Thus the image of the projection in $\mathbf{Q}_4$ is a subspace isomorphic to $\mathbf{Q}_3$ as a vector space. (The order of the entries is immaterial.)

The 3 by 4 Shelepin symbol (2) is also useful for interpreting this limiting process. If the same transformation is made, namely adding p to the appropriate elements and removing the elements which become infinite in the limit, this formally erases the last column of (2). The remaining nine elements are the same as those in (11), but they must still be rearranged to form a 3 by 3 magic square.

Acknowledgements

One of the authors (A. G.) wishes to thank Professor L. C. Biedenharn for his kind hospitality at Duke University and for his continuous interest and encouragement during this work. He is also indepted to Professor G. de B. Robinson for some very interesting suggestions.

References

1) T. Regge, Nuovo Cimento **10**, 544 (1958).
2) L. A. Shelepin, Soviet Phys.-JETP **19**, 702 (1964).
3) L. A. Shelepin, Soviet Phys.-JETP **21**, 238 (1965).
4) H. Anand, V. C. Dumir and H. Gupta, Duke Math. J. **33**, 757 (1966).
5) A. G. Kurosh, *Lectures in General Algebra* (Pergamon Press, London, 1965) p. 45.
6) M. Burrow, *Representation Theory of Finite Groups* (Academic Press, New York, 1965) p. 47.
7) M. L. Dubreil-Jacotin, L. Lesieur and R. Croisot, *Leçons sur la Théorie des Treillis des Structures Algébriques Ordonnées et des Treillis Géométriques* (Gauthier-Villars, Paris, 1953).
8) G. Birkhoff, Ann. Math. **36**, 743 (1935).
9) G. Birkhoff, *Lattice Theory*, rev. ed., American Mathematical Society Colloquium Publications, Vol. XXV (1948).
10) L. C. Biedenharn, J. Math. Phys. (M.I.T.) **31**, 287 (1953).
11) G. Ponzano and T. Regge, this book, p. 1.

Spectroscopic and group theoretical methods in physics
© North-Holland Publ. Co., Amsterdam, 1968

RACAH COEFFICIENTS AND STATES WITH PERMUTATIONAL SYMMETRY*

M. MOSHINSKY and E. CHACÓN
Instituto de Fisica, Universidad de México, Mexico City, Mexico

1. Introduction

Racah's fundamental contributions in his series of papers on the "Theory of Complex Spectra" have had so many applications that their mere listing could take a considerable part of this Memorial Volume. Yet, it is the belief of the authors that the applications have by no means been exhausted and, in fact, that no more fitting tribute to the memory of Racah could be given than by presenting new problems in which the Racah coefficients and their generalizations play a fundamental role.

In this paper we shall discuss the construction of n particle states in a three dimensional harmonic oscillator common potential, with the states classified by the irreducible representations (IR) of a physically relevant chain of groups which includes the n dimensional symmetric group S_n.

The importance of these states in many problems of Nuclear Physics, as well as in other fields, has been pointed out in recent publications[1,2,3]), where the explicit construction of these states was attempted. The basic and remaining point in this construction was the application of projection operators of S_n to states classified by the canonical chains of unitary groups $U_n \supset U_{n-1} \supset \cdots \supset U_1$, i.e. Gelfand states[4,5,6]). This requires the knowledge of the matrix elements of the permutations, and basically of the transposition $(n-1, n)$, with respect to Gelfand states. We shall show in this paper that the matrix elements of $(n-1, n)$ can be given in terms of the usual Racah coefficients of SU_2 and their generalizations to unitary unimodular groups of higher order, thus indicating the relevance of these coefficients in the construction of n particle states with permutational symmetry.

* Work supported by Comisión Nacional de Energía Nuclear, México.

In sections 2 and 3, we shall outline our problem first analyzing the procedure by which we could construct the states characterized by the canonical chain of unitary groups $U_n \supset U_{n-1} \supset \cdots \supset U_1$, and then discussing the projection technique for getting out of them states characterized by IR of S_n. In sections 4 and 5, we indicate how the projection operators could be explicitly applied allowing then the detailed determination of states with permutational symmetry.

2. *n* particle states in the harmonic oscillator (h.o.)

We shall take as our Hamiltonian that of *n* particles in the three dimensional harmonic oscillator common potential, i.e.

$$\mathscr{H} = \sum_{s=1}^{n} \sum_{i=1}^{3} \frac{1}{2m} (p_i^s)^2 + \sum_{s=1}^{n} \sum_{i=1}^{3} \tfrac{1}{2} m\omega^2 (x_i^s)^2 . \tag{2.1}$$

We showed in another publication[1,2]) that the case of *n* particles interacting through two body harmonic oscillator forces could easily be reduced to (2.1) when we introduce some simple changes in the interpretation of the transformation properties of x_i^s under permutations.

We now define the usual creation and annihilation operators

$$\eta_i^s = \frac{1}{\sqrt{2}} \left(\sqrt{\frac{m\omega}{\hbar}}\, x_i^s - \frac{i}{\sqrt{m\omega\hbar}}\, p_i^s \right) \tag{2.2a}$$

$$\xi_i^s = \frac{1}{\sqrt{2}} \left(\sqrt{\frac{m\omega}{\hbar}}\, x_i^s + \frac{i}{\sqrt{m\omega\hbar}}\, p_i^s \right) = (\eta_i^s)^\dagger , \tag{2.2b}$$

which satisfy the commutation relations

$$[\eta_i^s, \eta_j^t] = [\xi_i^s, \xi_j^t] = 0 , \qquad [\xi_i^s, \eta_j^t] = \delta_{ij} \delta^{st} , \tag{2.3}$$

and in terms of which the dimensionless Hamiltonian could be written as

$$H = \frac{1}{\hbar\omega} \mathscr{H} - \frac{3n}{2} = \sum_{s=1}^{n} \sum_{i=1}^{3} \eta_i^s \xi_i^s = \sum_{s=1}^{n} \sum_{i=1}^{3} \eta_i^s (\eta_i^s)^\dagger . \tag{2.4}$$

Clearly H is invariant under the $3n$ dimensional arbitrary unitary transformations affecting the vector $\eta_i^s (i=1, 2, 3, s=1, 2, \ldots, n)$ and so the symmetry group of this problem is $\mathbf{U}_{3n}$. It is physically relevant[1,2]) to consider subgroups of this group associated with the unitary group $\mathscr{U}_3$ affecting the component index $i=1,2,3$, and the unitary group U_n affecting the particle index $s=1,\ldots,n$, i.e. to characterize the states by the chain

$$\mathbf{U}_{3n}\supset\mathscr{U}_3\times\mathrm{U}_n\,. \tag{2.5}$$

Furthermore, if we want the states to have definite total orbital angular momentum and projection, they must be classified by the IR of the chain of groups

$$\mathscr{U}_3\supset\mathscr{O}_3\supset\mathscr{O}_2\,, \tag{2.6}$$

where $\mathscr{O}_3$, $\mathscr{O}_2$ are respectively orthogonal groups in three and two dimensions. Finally, our classification scheme would be complete if we also characterized the states by the IR of the mathematically natural chain of subgroups of U_n, i.e.

$$\mathrm{U}_n\supset\mathrm{U}_{n-1}\supset\cdots\supset\mathrm{U}_1\,. \tag{2.7}$$

The n particle states in the h.o. potential can be described in terms of polynomials in the creation operators acting on the ground state, i.e.

$$P(\eta_i^s)\,|0\rangle\,, \tag{2.8a}$$

$$|0\rangle=\left(\frac{m\omega}{\pi\hbar}\right)^{\frac{3}{4}n}\exp\left[-\frac{m\omega}{2\hbar}\sum_{s=1}^{n}\sum_{i=1}^{3}(x_i^s)^2\right]. \tag{2.8b}$$

Because these polynomials are functions of the components of a single $3n$ dimensional vector η_i^s, they can be represented only by the symmetric IR of $\mathbf{U}_{3n}$. In fact, the set of all homogeneous polynomials of degree N, i.e. all N quanta states, correspond to the IR

$$[N\mathrm{O}^{3n-1}]\,, \tag{2.9}$$

of the group $\mathbf{U}_{3n}$.

The IR of $\mathscr{U}_3$ and U_n are given respectively by the partitions $[h_1h_2h_3]$ and $\{k_{1n}\ldots k_{nn}\}$ of N. As the IR (2.9) of $\mathbf{U}_{3n}$ is symmetric, the IR of $\mathscr{U}_3$, U_n must be related by[1])

$$\{k_{1\,n}k_{2\,n}k_{3\,n}k_{4\,n}\ldots k_{n\,n}\}=\{h_1h_2h_30\ldots0\}\,. \tag{2.10}$$

Finally, the IR of the U_m $(m=1,2,\ldots,n-1)$ subgroups of U_n are characterized by the partitions $\{k_{1m}\ldots k_{mm}\}$, but because of (2.10) and the branching rule

$$k_{1\,m}\geqslant k_{1\,m-1}\geqslant k_{2\,m}\geqslant k_{2\,m-1}\geqslant\cdots\geqslant k_{m\,m}\,, \tag{2.11}$$

all k_{lm} with $l>3$ are zero.

Our states can then be described by the ket

$$\left|\begin{matrix} [h_1h_2h_3] & h_1 & h_2 & h_3 & 0\ldots\ldots\ldots 0 \\ ; & k_{1\,n-1} & k_{2\,n-1} & k_{3\,n-1} & 0\ldots 0 \\ & & & \vdots & \\ \Omega LM & & & k_{11} & \end{matrix}\right\rangle \equiv P^{\{k_{lm}\}}_{[h_1h_2h_3]\,\Omega LM}(\eta^s_i)\,|0\rangle\,, \tag{2.12}$$

where the extra quantum number Ω, associated with an appropriate operator[7]), serves to distinguish between repeated IR of $\mathcal{O}_3$ (characterized by L) contained in the same IR of $\mathcal{U}_3$.

A systematic procedure of obtaining explicitly all the polynomials (2.12) was given in refs. 1 and 2. The states thus obtained are not yet physically relevant, as we would like to characterize them by the IR of the chain of groups

$$\mathrm{U}_n \supset \cdots \supset \mathrm{S}_n\,, \tag{2.13a}$$

$$\mathrm{S}_n \supset \mathrm{S}_{n-1} \supset \cdots \supset \mathrm{S}_1\,, \tag{2.13b}$$

rather than by the mathematically natural chain (2.7). The IR of S_n are characterized by the partition of the number n of particles, i.e.

$$f \equiv [f_1 f_2 \cdots f_n]\,, \qquad f_1 + f_2 + \cdots + f_n = n\,, \tag{2.14}$$

while the IR of the groups in the chain (2.13b) determine the Yamanouchi symbol

$$r \equiv (1\, r_2 \ldots r_n)\,, \tag{2.15}$$

associated with the state. In the chain (2.13a) we left space for possible intermediate subgroups[1,2,8]) that could help distinguish between repeated IR of S_n contained in a given IR of U_n.

To include f and r in our classification scheme would be useful if the Hamiltonian we apply to the n particle h.o. states is independent of spin and isospin, as then they would be good quantum numbers. Even if the Hamiltonian does not have this property, the f, r remain useful as we could combine the spatial states with the spin–isospin ones corresponding to the associate partition, and so satisfy the Pauli principle[2]).

We shall discuss in the next section the determination of the states characterized by the IR of the chain (2.13), by the application of the standard projection technique to the explicitly determined states (2.12).

3. Projection operators for states with permutation symmetry

The standard Wigner projection operator[9]) for the symmetric group, associated with the IR of S_n given by the partition f and for a row characterized by the Yamanouchi symbol r, has the form

$$c^f_{rr} \equiv \frac{|f|}{n!} \sum_{p \in S_n} D^{f*}_{rr}(p)\, p\,, \tag{3.1}$$

where p is an arbitrary permutation of S_n, $|f|$ is the dimension of the IR f of S_n, while $D^f_{rr}(p)$ is the diagonal matrix element of the IR f of S_n corresponding to the row r. Extensive tables of $D^f_{rr}(p)$, as well as of the characters $\chi^f(p) = \sum_r D^f_{rr}(p)$ are available[10]).

As S_n is a subgroup of U_n, the application of the operators c^f_{rr} to (2.12) affects only the part of the state characterized by the IR of U_n and its subgroups in the chain (2.7), i.e. the state

$$\left| \begin{matrix} k_{1n} & & k_{2n} & & k_{3n} & & 0 \ldots\ldots\ldots 0 \\ & k_{1n-1} & & k_{2n-1} & & k_{3n-1} & 0 \ldots 0 \\ & & \ldots\ldots & & & & \\ & & & & k_{11} & & \end{matrix} \right\rangle \equiv |k_{l\,m}\rangle\,. \tag{3.2}$$

The states (3.2) are particular cases (particular because the k_{lm} are restricted by $k_{lm}=0$ if $l>3$) of Gelfand states[4,5,6]) of U_n.

Furthermore, again because S_n is a subgroup of U_n, the application of c^f_{rr} to the states $|k_{lm}\rangle$ leads to a linear combination of states of this type corresponding to the same IR of U_n.

If we could construct now the matrix

$$\| \langle k'_{l\,m} |\, c^f_{r\,r}\, | k_{l\,m} \rangle \| \tag{3.3}$$

with

$$\{k'_{l\,n}\} = \{k_{l\,n}\} \tag{3.4}$$

fixed, but taking all allowed values for the other $\{k_{lm}\}$, $\{k'_{lm}\}$ ($l \leqslant m = 1, \ldots, n-1$), then the eigenvalues[1,2,9]) of the matrix (3.3) could only be 1 or 0, and each of the mutually orthogonal eigenstates corresponding to the eigenvalue 1 would be a member of a basis for an IR of S_n with partition f and Yamanouchi symbol r. Designating these eigenstates by $|\alpha f r\rangle$, where α is a short hand notation for all the other quantum numbers or indices in the ket, the diagonalization of (3.3) provides us with the coefficients in the expansion

$$|\alpha f r\rangle = \sum_{k_{l\,m}} A(\alpha f r, \{k_{l\,m}\})\, |k_{l\,m}\rangle\,. \tag{3.5}$$

How can we determine the matrix (3.3) whose dimension, incidentally, is equal to that of the IR $\{k_{ln}\}$ of U_n? As $D^f_{rr}(p)$ is known, we require the knowledge of the matrix elements of the permutations with respect to the Gelfand states $|k_{lm}\rangle$ of (3.2), but as, in turn, any permutation can be expressed as a product of contiguous transpositions $(m-1, m)$, $m=1,\ldots, n$, we require only the matrix elements of the latter. The problem can be further reduced by noting that $(m-1, m)$ is an element of $S_m \subset U_m$, so that its effect on the states (3.2) will go from the mth row downwards and be independent of the IR of the unitary groups $U_{m+1},\ldots, U_n$. Clearly therefore, what we require to determine the matrix (3.3) is the knowledge of the matrix element

$$\langle k'_{l\,m}|(n-1, n)|k_{l\,m}\rangle \tag{3.6}$$

for an arbitrary n, when $|k_{lm}\rangle$ is given by (3.2).

How can we determine from (3.5) the partner states corresponding to the same IR of S_n, i.e. states $|\alpha f r'\rangle$ with all possible values of the Yamanouchi symbol? As is well known, and was discussed explicitly in ref. 1, the states $|\alpha f r'\rangle$ could be obtained from $|\alpha f r\rangle$ by repeated applications of the transpositions $(m-1, m)$, $m=1, 2,\ldots, n$, to the latter state. Because of the expansion (3.5) this implies the application of $(m-1, m)$ to the states (3.2), and this leads us back again to the need of determining the matrices (3.6).

The awareness of what the basic problem was, led the authors to determine first the matrix elements (3.6) for $n=3$ (the case $n=2$ is trivial), showing by direct application that it could be expressed in terms of a Racah coefficient[11]). A later discussion of the problem by one of the authors (M.M.) with Dr. A. Gal and Prof. H. Lipkin at the Weizmann Institute, led to a clear understanding of why the Racah coefficient appeared, thus paving the way to the generalizations to arbitrary n presented in this paper.

Before proceeding with the determination of (3.6), we shall discuss in the next section a method for the determination of the Gelfand states with q-rows, i.e. with $k_{ln}=0$ if $l>q$ in terms of the Wigner coefficients of SU_q, which will be fundamental for our analysis.

4. Construction of Gelfand states of q-rows

In previous publications[5,12]) we have shown how to construct Gelfand states of U_n explicitly by first determining the normalized highest weight state and then applying appropriate lowering operators, together with their corresponding normalization coefficients, to get all other states.

We want in this section to indicate an alternative procedure which may be more convenient if the number of rows of the partition characterizing the IR of U_n is small. For this purpose let us consider that in our creation operators η_i^s, the index s goes, as before, from $s=1, 2,\ldots, n$, while the index i takes the values $i=1,\ldots, q$ with $q\leqslant n$.

By the same reasoning mentioned in section 2, the linearly independent homogeneous polynomials of degree N in the η_i^s would form a basis for the symmetric IR of the $\mathbf{U}_{qn}$ group characterized by the partition

$$[N O^{qn-1}]. \tag{4.1}$$

We furthermore could completely characterize the polynomials by the IR of the following chains of groups[13,14]

$$\mathbf{U}_{qn} \supset \mathscr{U}_q \times \mathbf{U}_n, \tag{4.2a}$$

$$\mathscr{U}_q \supset \mathscr{U}_{q-1} \supset \cdots \supset \mathscr{U}_1, \tag{4.2b}$$

$$\mathbf{U}_n \supset \mathbf{U}_{n-1} \supset \cdots \supset \mathbf{U}_1, \tag{4.2c}$$

which would lead to the states[13,14]

$$\left| \begin{matrix} h_{1q} \quad \cdots\cdots \quad h_{qq} & k_{1n} \quad \cdots\cdots \quad k_{qn} \quad 0 \cdots\cdots 0 \\ h_{1q-1} \cdots h_{q-1q-1}\, ; & k_{1n-1} \cdots k_{q-1n-1} \quad k_{qn-1} \quad 0 \ldots 0 \\ \vdots & \vdots \\ h_{11} & k_{11} \end{matrix} \right\rangle \tag{4.3}$$

where the partitions give the IR of the corresponding groups while, because of the same considerations that lead to (2.10), we have the relation

$$h_{lq} = k_{ln}, \qquad l = 1, 2, \ldots, q. \tag{4.4}$$

Now we could think of a state of the type (4.3) associated only with the first $n-1$ particles, i.e. where the polynomial depends on η_i^s with s restricted to $s = 1, 2, \ldots, n-1$, but corresponding to the same IR of the groups in the chain $\mathbf{U}_{n-1} \supset \cdots \supset \mathbf{U}_1$, i.e. the state

$$\left| \begin{matrix} h'_{1q} \cdots h'_{qq} & k_{1n-1} \cdots k_{qn-1}\, 0 \ldots 0 \\ \vdots \quad ; & \vdots \\ h'_{11} & k_{11} \end{matrix} \right\rangle \tag{4.5}$$

where again

$$h'_{lq} = k_{l\,n-1}, \qquad l = 1, \ldots, q. \tag{4.6}$$

Furthermore, we could construct the state of particle n in a q dimensional harmonic oscillator which corresponds to the one row Gelfand state of $\mathscr{U}_q$, i.e.[2,13]

$$\left| \begin{matrix} h''_{1q} & 0 & 0 \\ h''_{1q-1} & 0 \ldots 0 & \\ \vdots & & \\ h''_{11} & & \end{matrix} \right\rangle =$$

$$= \frac{(\eta_1^n)^{h''_{11}} (\eta_2^n)^{h''_{12} - h''_{11}} \cdots (\eta_q^n)^{h''_{1q} - h''_{1q-1}}}{\{(h''_{11})!\,(h''_{12} - h''_{11})! \ldots (h''_{1q} - h''_{1q-1})!\}^{\frac{1}{2}}} |0\rangle . \tag{4.7}$$

The states (4.5) and (4.7) are both bases for IR of $\mathscr{U}_q$ associated with the partitions $\{h'_{1q}...h'_{qq}\}$ and $\{h''_{1q}0...0\}$ respectively. If we restrict h''_{1q} to the value

$$h''_{1q} = N - N', \quad N = h_{1q} + \cdots + h_{qq}, \quad N' = h'_{1q} + \cdots + h'_{qq}, \qquad (4.8)$$

then, by using the Wigner coefficients of $\mathscr{U}_q$, or what is equivalent of $S\mathscr{U}_q$, we could couple the states (4.5) and (4.7) to give a new state characterized by the partitions $\{h_{lp}\}$, $q \geq p \geq l \geq 1$, of the chain $\mathscr{U}_q \supset \mathscr{U}_{q-1} \supset \cdots \supset \mathscr{U}_1$. This state turns actually to be the state (4.3) for the following reasons:

a) The coupled state is given by an homogeneous polynomial of degree N in the η_i^s, where now $i=1,..., q$ and $s=1,..., n$, so that it is part of the IR $[N0^{qn-1}]$ of U_{qn}. As the coupled state is characterized by the IR $[h_{1q}...h_{qq}]$ of $\mathscr{U}_q$, then by the same reasoning leading to (2.10), it is also characterized by the IR of U_n corresponding to the partition $\{k_{ln}\}$ satisfying (4.4).

b) The state (4.5) is characterized by the IR of the chain $U_{n-1} \supset \cdots \supset U_1$ whose partitions are $\{k_{lm}\}$, $m=n-1,..., 1$. The state (4.7) depending on η_i^n is invariant with respect to this chain. Therefore the coupled state corresponds to the same IR of the chain $U_{n-1} \supset \cdots \supset U_1$ as the state (4.3).

We could repeat the above analysis for the state (4.5) of $n-1$ particles, to decompose it in terms of a state of $n-2$ particles and a single particle state in a q dimensional harmonic oscillator associated with particle $n-1$. Continuing in this way, we see we could construct the state (4.3) in terms of single particle states in a q dimensional harmonic oscillator associated with particles $s=1,2,..., n$, by coupling these single particle states with Wigner coefficients of $S\mathscr{U}_q$.

As the Gelfand states of U_n of q-rows,

$$|k_{lm}\rangle, \qquad 1 \leq l \leq m \leq n, \qquad k_{lm} = 0 \quad \text{if} \quad l > q, \qquad (4.9)$$

are just a particular[13]) case of (4.3) when this state is of highest weight in the $\mathscr{U}_q$ group, i.e.

$$h_{lp} = h_{lq}, \qquad l = 1,..., p, \qquad p = 1,..., q, \qquad (4.10)$$

we conclude that the knowledge of the Wigner coefficients of $S\mathscr{U}_q$ allows us to determine these states by the coupling procedure indicated in the previous paragraph.

We proceed now to illustrate this general technique for the case of one, two and three rows.

4.1. Gelfand states for one row

In this case $q=1$ and the $S\mathscr{U}_q$ group becomes $S\mathscr{U}_1$, which has only the identity element. The states of particle s in a one dimensional harmonic oscillator are given by

$$(n!)^{-\frac{1}{2}}(\eta_1^s)^n|0\rangle, \qquad s=1,\dots,n. \tag{4.11}$$

The coupling of a state of particles 1, 2, ..., $n-1$ with the state (4.11) of particle n, is then just a multiplication. Repeating the analysis for the state of 1, 2, ..., $n-2$ particles and particle $n-1$, etc., we conclude that the one row Gelfand state of U_n could be expressed in terms of products of one dimensional harmonic oscillator states for particle $s=1,2,\dots,n$ as

$$\left|\begin{matrix} k_{1n} & & 0\dots\dots\dots 0 \\ & k_{1n-1} & 0\dots 0 \\ & \vdots & \\ & k_{11} & \end{matrix}\right\rangle =$$

$$= \frac{(\eta_1^1)^{k_{11}}(\eta_1^2)^{k_{12}-k_{11}}\dots(\eta_1^n)^{k_{1n}-k_{1n-1}}}{\{(k_{11})!(k_{12}-k_{11})!\dots(k_{1n}-k_{1n-1})!\}^{\frac{1}{2}}}|0\rangle \tag{4.12}$$

which, incidentally, is an independent derivation of (4.7).

4.2. Gelfand states of two rows

In this case $q=2$, so the group $\mathscr{U}_q$ becomes $\mathscr{U}_2$ and its Gelfand states, characterized by the IR of the groups in the chain $\mathscr{U}_2 \supset \mathscr{U}_1$, take the form

$$\left|\begin{matrix} h_{12} & & h_{22} \\ & h_{11} & \end{matrix}\right\rangle. \tag{4.13}$$

Before proceeding further, let us establish the connection between the partitions in (4.13) and the familiar quantum numbers of the theory of angular momentum.

The generators of the group $\mathscr{U}_2$ are given by[1])

$$\mathscr{C}_{ij} = \sum_{s=1}^{n} \eta_i^s \xi_j^s, \qquad i,j=1,2. \tag{4.14}$$

The trace of $\mathscr{C}_{ij}$, i.e. $\mathscr{C}_{11}+\mathscr{C}_{22}$, commutes with all $\mathscr{C}_{ij}$ and is associated with unitary transformations of the type $e^{i\delta}I$, where I is a 2×2 unit matrix[5]). As any two dimensional unitary matrix can be expressed as a product of $e^{i\delta}I$ by a unitary matrix of determinant 1, we conclude that the remaining linearly independent $\mathscr{C}_{ij}$, i.e.

$$J_+ \equiv \mathscr{C}_{12}, \qquad J_0 \equiv \tfrac{1}{2}(\mathscr{C}_{11}-\mathscr{C}_{22}), \qquad J_- \equiv \mathscr{C}_{21} \tag{4.15}$$

are the generators of $S\mathscr{U}_2$ and satisfy the commutation relations of angular momentum, as can be easily checked.

The state (4.13) is an eigenstate of the operators $\mathscr{C}_{11}, \mathscr{C}_{22}$ with eigenvalues w_1, w_2 given by[12])

$$w_1 = h_{11}, \qquad w_2 = h_{12} + h_{22} - h_{11}. \tag{4.16}$$

Therefore, (4.13) is also an eigenstate of J_0 with eigenvalue given by

$$\rho = h_{11} - \tfrac{1}{2}(h_{12} + h_{22}). \tag{4.17}$$

On the other hand, the application of $J_+ = \mathscr{C}_{12}$ to (4.13) transforms it into a state with $w_1 = h_{11} + 1$ and so, because of (2.11), the highest weight state in (4.13) corresponds to $h_{11} = h_{12}$, for which the corresponding value of ρ, which characterizes the IR κ of $S\mathscr{U}_2$, is

$$\kappa = \tfrac{1}{2}(h_{12} - h_{22}). \tag{4.18}$$

After these preliminaries we can implement for $q=2$ all the steps for the construction of Gelfand states indicated at the beginning of this section. We note first that the state (4.3) of particles $s=1, \ldots, n$, with $q=2$ and satisfying the restriction (4.4), corresponds to the following IR κ_n of $S\mathscr{U}_2$ and row ρ_n

$$\kappa_n = \tfrac{1}{2}(k_{1n} - k_{2n}), \tag{4.19a}$$
$$\rho_n = h_{11} - \tfrac{1}{2}(k_{1n} + k_{2n}). \tag{4.19b}$$

Similarly, for the state (4.5) of particles $s = 1, 2, \ldots, n-1$, the corresponding IR κ_{n-1} of $S\mathscr{U}_2$ and row ρ_{n-1} are

$$\kappa_{n-1} = \tfrac{1}{2}(k_{1n-1} - k_{2n-1}), \tag{4.20a}$$
$$\rho_{n-1} = h'_{11} - \tfrac{1}{2}(k_{1n-1} + k_{2n-1}). \tag{4.20b}$$

Finally, the state (4.7) of particle n in a two dimensional harmonic oscillator corresponds to the IR j_n of $S\mathscr{U}_2$ and row m_n given by

$$j_n = \tfrac{1}{2}h''_{12}, \qquad m_n = h''_{11} - \tfrac{1}{2}h''_{12}, \tag{4.21}$$

where, from (4.8), we have the relation

$$j_n = \tfrac{1}{2}(k_{1n} + k_{2n} - k_{1n-1} - k_{2n-1}). \tag{4.22}$$

To couple the state of particles $s = 1, 2, \ldots, n-1$, and of particle n, we now must use the standard Wigner coefficient[15]) of $S\mathscr{U}_2$

$$\langle \kappa_{n-1} j_n \rho_{n-1} m_n | \kappa_n \rho_n \rangle. \tag{4.23}$$

Repeating the decomposition procedure for the state of particles $s = 1, 2, \ldots,$

$n-1$ etc., we finally write down the two row Gelfand state of U_n as

$$\left|\begin{matrix} k_{1n} & k_{2n} & 0\dots\dots\dots 0 \\ k_{1n-1} & k_{2n-1} & 0\dots 0 \\ & \vdots & \\ & k_{11} & \end{matrix}\right\rangle =$$

$$= [\dots[M^{j_1}(1)\,M^{j_2}(2)]^{\kappa_2}\,M^{j_3}(3)]^{\kappa_3}\dots M^{j_{n-2}}(n-2)]^{\kappa_{n-2}}\times \\ \times M^{j_{n-1}}(n-1)]^{\kappa_{n-1}}\,M^{j_n}(n)]^{\kappa_n}_{\kappa_n}|0\rangle\,, \tag{4.24}$$

where by $M^j_m(s)$ we understand the monomial

$$M^j_m(s) \equiv \frac{(\eta^s_1)^{j+m}(\eta^s_2)^{j-m}}{\{(j+m)!\,(j-m)!\}^{\frac{1}{2}}} \tag{4.25}$$

and the square bracket is the familiar notation for vector coupling, i.e.

$$[M^{j'}(s')\,M^{j''}(s'')]^j_m = \sum_{m'm''} \langle j'j''m'm''|jm\rangle\,M^{j'}_{m'}(s')\,M^{j''}_{m''}(s'')\,. \tag{4.26}$$

The relation between κ_s, j_s and the k_{1s}, k_{2s} are given by (4.19a) and (4.22), when we replace n by s. An ambiguity appears only for the case $s=1$, but it can be resolved if the undefined coefficients k_{10}, k_{20}, k_{21} are taken as zero.

4.3 Gelfand states of three rows

The analysis for three rows parallels step by step the analysis done for two rows, so that the first point is to relate the IR $[h_{13}h_{23}h_{33}]$ of $\mathscr{U}_3$ with the corresponding IR of S$\mathscr{U}_3$. If we follow the notation of Elliott[16]), the IR of S$\mathscr{U}_3$ will be characterized by $(\lambda\mu)$, which are related to the IR of $\mathscr{U}_3$ by

$$\lambda = h_{13} - h_{23}\,, \qquad \mu = h_{23} - h_{33}\,. \tag{4.27}$$

Furthermore, the state of a single particle s in a three dimensional harmonic oscillator potential can be expressed in terms of a monomial of degree l acting on the ground state $|0\rangle$. This monomial is associated with the single row IR $(l0)$ of S$\mathscr{U}_3$ and could be written as

$$M^{(l0)}_{qr}(s) \equiv \frac{(\eta^s_1)^r(\eta^s_2)^{q-r}(\eta^s_3)^{l-q}}{\{r!\,(q-r)!\,(l-q)!\}^{\frac{1}{2}}}, \tag{4.28}$$

where $0\leqslant r\leqslant q\leqslant l$ characterize the row of the IR of S$\mathscr{U}_3$.

Following then the discussion of the previous subsection, we can now write the Gelfand state of U_n of three rows as

$$\left|\begin{matrix} k_{1n} & & k_{2n} & & k_{3n} & & 0\ldots\ldots\ldots 0 \\ & k_{1n-1} & & k_{2n-1} & & k_{3n-1} & & 0\ldots 0 \\ & & & & \vdots & & & \\ & & & & k_{11} & & & \end{matrix}\right\rangle =$$

$$= \{\ldots\{M^{(l_1 0)}(1)\, M^{(l_2 0)}(2)\}^{(\lambda_2\mu_2)}\ldots\}^{(\lambda_{n-2}\mu_{n-2})}\times$$
$$\times M^{(l_{n-1}0)}(n-1)\}^{(\lambda_{n-1}\mu_{n-1})}\, M^{(l_n 0)}(n)\}^{(\lambda_n\mu_n)}_{\text{h.w.}}|0\rangle\,, \qquad (4.29)$$

where the curly brackets { } indicate the coupling of two states associated with IR of $S\mathscr{U}_3$, analogously to the way the square brackets denoted the coupling for IR of $S\mathscr{U}_2$. One of the states in the coupling is always of the type ($l0$), so that the Wigner coefficients of $S\mathscr{U}_3$ required in { } are given explicitly by the algebraic expression of ref. 17, which has been furthermore tabulated by T. A. Brody. The notation h.w. at the end of the last bracket is to indicate coupling to the highest weight state, i.e. the state equivalent for $S\mathscr{U}_3$ of the state with $\rho=\kappa$ in $S\mathscr{U}_2$.

By (4.27) and the previous analysis, we conclude that λ_s, μ_s, l_s are related to k_{1s}, k_{2s}, k_{3s} by

$$\begin{gathered} \lambda_s = k_{1s} - k_{2s}\,, \qquad \mu_s = k_{2s} - k_{3s}\,, \\ l_s = k_{1s} + k_{2s} + k_{3s} - k_{1s-1} - k_{2s-1} - k_{3s-1}\,, \end{gathered} \qquad (4.30)$$

where the ambiguity for $s=2,1$ is eliminated by taking the undefined k_{32}, k_{31}, k_{21}, k_{30}, k_{20}, k_{10} as zero.

We do not elaborate further on the special Wigner coefficients of $S\mathscr{U}_3$ required in (4.29), as the application of the permutation $(n-1, n)$ to (4.29) will give rise to the corresponding Racah coefficients, which we shall discuss in the next section.

5. Matrix elements of the transposition $(n-1, n)$

The transposition $(n-1, n)$ affects only the indices indicated, so that it is an invariant of the subgroup U_{n-2} of U_n. Therefore the only non-vanishing matrix elements of $(n-1, n)$ must be diagonal with respect to the IR of U_{n-2} and its subgroups[18]), i.e. diagonal in $\{k_{lm}\}$, $1\leqslant l\leqslant m\leqslant n-2$, and independent of the IR of U_{n-3} and its subgroups, i.e. independent of $\{k_{lm}\}$, $1\leqslant l\leqslant m\leqslant n-3$. We shall now discuss separately the matrix elements of $(n-1, n)$ with respect to Gelfand states of one, two and three rows.

5.1. Gelfand states of one row

The application of the transposition $(n-1, n)$ to the state (4.12) is trivial, so that we immediately conclude that

$$\left\langle \begin{matrix} k_{1n} & & 0 \ldots\ldots\ldots\ldots 0 \\ & k'_{1n-1} & 0 \ldots\ldots 0 \\ & k_{1n-2} & 0 \ldots 0 \\ & \ldots\ldots\ldots\ldots & \end{matrix} \middle| (n-1, n) \middle| \begin{matrix} k_{1n} & & 0 \ldots\ldots\ldots\ldots 0 \\ & k_{1n-1} & 0 \ldots\ldots 0 \\ & k_{1n-2} & 0 \ldots 0 \\ & \ldots\ldots\ldots\ldots & \end{matrix} \right\rangle =$$

$$= \delta_{k_{1n}-k_{1n-1}, k'_{1n-1}-k_{1n-2}} \delta_{k_{1n-1}-k_{1n-2}, k_{1n}-k'_{1n-1}}, \tag{5.1}$$

where the second Kronecker δ is clearly redundant.

5.2. Gelfand states of two rows

The application of $(n-1, n)$ to (4.24) interchanges the particle indices $n-1$ and n. As the monomials in (4.24) are coupled by Wigner coefficients of $S\mathscr{U}_2$, we see that the evaluation of the matrix elements of $(n-1, n)$ requires only a recoupling of the angular momenta involved, so we get finally

$$\left\langle \begin{matrix} k_{1n} & k_{2n} & & 0 \ldots\ldots\ldots\ldots 0 \\ & k'_{1n-1} & k'_{2n-1} & 0 \ldots\ldots 0 \\ & & k_{1n-2} \quad k_{2n-2} & 0 \ldots 0 \\ & & \ldots\ldots\ldots\ldots\ldots\ldots & \end{matrix} \middle| (n-1, n) \right.$$

$$\left| \begin{matrix} k_{1n} & k_{2n} & & 0 \ldots\ldots 0 \\ & k_{1n-1} & k_{2n-1} & 0 \ldots\ldots 0 \\ & & k_{1n-2} \quad k_{2n-2} & 0 \ldots 0 \\ & & \ldots\ldots\ldots\ldots\ldots\ldots & \end{matrix} \right\rangle =$$

$$= \langle \kappa_{n-2} j'_{n-1} (\kappa'_{n-1}) j'_n \kappa_n | \kappa_{n-2} j_{n-1} (\kappa_{n-1}) j_n \kappa_n \rangle \, \delta_{j_{n-1}, j'_n} \delta_{j_n, j'_{n-1}}, \tag{5.2}$$

where the relation between the primed quantities and k'_{lm} of the bra is the same as that of the unprimed quantities and the k_{lm} of the ket, i.e. they are given by (4.19a), (4.22) with m replacing n. Again the last Kronecker δ in (5.2) is redundant, and because the group involved is $S\mathscr{U}_2$, the recoupling coefficient can be expressed in terms of an ordinary Racah coefficient[19]), i.e.

$$\langle \kappa_{n-2} j_n (\kappa'_{n-1}) j_{n-1} \kappa_n | \kappa_{n-2} j_{n-1} (\kappa_{n-1}) j_n \kappa_n \rangle =$$
$$= [(2\kappa_{n-1}+1)(2\kappa'_{n-1}+1)]^{\frac{1}{2}} \, W(j_n \kappa'_{n-1} \kappa_{n-1} j_{n-1}; \kappa_{n-2} \kappa_n). \tag{5.3}$$

5.3. Gelfand states of three rows

The application of $(n-1, n)$ to (4.29) requires, as in the previous case, a recoupling of the IR, but now of the group $S\mathscr{U}_3$, so we can write in a notation similar to the one used in (5.2) that

$$\left\langle \begin{matrix} k_{1n} & k_{2n} & k_{3n} & 0 \ldots\ldots\ldots\ldots\ldots 0 \\ k'_{1n-1} & k'_{2n-1} & k'_{3n-1} & 0 \ldots\ldots\ldots 0 \\ k_{1n-2} & k_{2n-2} & k_{3n-2} & 0 \ldots 0 \\ \ldots\ldots\ldots\ldots\ldots\ldots\ldots\ldots\ldots\ldots\ldots \end{matrix} \right| (n-1, n) \left| \begin{matrix} k_{1n} & k_{2n} & k_{3n} & 0 \ldots\ldots\ldots\ldots\ldots 0 \\ k_{1n-1} & k_{2n-1} & k_{3n-1} & 0 \ldots\ldots\ldots 0 \\ k_{1n-2} & k_{2n-2} & k_{3n-2} & 0 \ldots 0 \\ \ldots\ldots\ldots\ldots\ldots\ldots\ldots\ldots\ldots\ldots\ldots \end{matrix} \right\rangle =$$

$$= \langle (\lambda_{n-2}\mu_{n-2})\,(l'_{n-1}\,0)\,[(\lambda'_{n-1}\mu'_{n-1})]\,(l'_n\,0)\,(\lambda_n\mu_n) | (\lambda_{n-2}\mu_{n-2})\,(l_{n-1}\,0) \times$$
$$\times [(\lambda_{n-1}\mu_{n-1})]\,(l_n 0)\,(\lambda_n\mu_n)\rangle\, \delta_{l'_n l_{n-1}}\, \delta_{l_n l'_{n-1}}\,. \qquad (5.4)$$

Again the relation of the primed quantities with the k'_{lm} of the bra is the same as the unprimed ones with the k_{lm} of the ket, i.e. (4.30), and the last δ is redundant.

The recoupling transformation bracket in (5.4) is clearly proportional to a special Racah coefficient of $S\mathscr{U}_3$, where the adjective special is due to the fact that some of the IR involved, i.e. $(l_{n-1}\ 0)$, $(l_n 0)$, are of one row only. This special Racah coefficient could be constructed from the Wigner coefficients of $S\mathscr{U}_3$ of ref. 17, but we shall indicate below an independent procedure of deriving both, it and the standard Racah coefficients of $S\mathscr{U}_2$.

5.4. Racah coefficients of $S\mathscr{U}_2$ and $S\mathscr{U}_3$

So far we have discussed the matrix elements of $(n-1, n)$ for Gelfand states of U_n when n is arbitrary. Let us consider the particular case of $n=3$ with two rows, and $n=4$ with three rows. We shall see that these two cases already have the full generality of the two and three row case respectively, and in the appendices we shall evaluate these matrix elements directly, thus leading to the Racah coefficients we require.

For $n=3$ and two rows, our matrix element would be

$$\left\langle \begin{matrix} k_1 & & k_2 & & 0 \\ & q'_1 & & q'_2 & \\ & & r_1 & & \end{matrix} \right| (2,3) \left| \begin{matrix} k_1 & & k_2 & & 0 \\ & q_1 & & q_2 & \\ & & r_1 & & \end{matrix} \right\rangle, \qquad (5.5)$$

where we changed our notation to avoid double indices. Now the matrix element of (5.5) would be given by (5.2) if

$$\kappa_n = \tfrac{1}{2}(k_1 - k_2), \quad \kappa_{n-1} = \tfrac{1}{2}(q_1 - q_2), \quad \kappa'_{n-1} = \tfrac{1}{2}(q'_1 - q'_2), \quad \kappa_{n-2} = \tfrac{1}{2}r_1;$$
$$j_{n-1} = \tfrac{1}{2}(q_1 + q_2 - r_1), \quad j_n = \tfrac{1}{2}(k_1 + k_2 - q_1 - q_2), \qquad (5.6)$$
$$j'_{n-1} = \tfrac{1}{2}(q'_1 + q'_2 - r_1).$$

If we compare (5.6) with the usual definition of the variables indicated, i.e. (4.19a) and (4.21) for arbitrary n, then it is clear that if we evaluate (5.5) in terms of the parameters indicated, we could obtain the most general result if we made the substitution

$$k_i = k_{in} - k_{2\,n-2}, \quad q_i = k_{in-1} - k_{2\,n-2}, \quad r_1 = k_{1\,n-2} - k_{2\,n-2}, \quad i = 1, 2 \tag{5.7}$$

in the matrix element (5.5). The evaluation of (5.5) is carried out in appendix A.

For $n=4$ and three rows, our matrix element would be

$$\left\langle \begin{matrix} k_1 & k_2 & k_3 & 0 \\ & q_1' & q_2' & q_3' \\ & r_1 & r_2 & \\ & & s_1 & \end{matrix} \middle| (3,4) \middle| \begin{matrix} k_1 & k_2 & k_3 & 0 \\ & q_1 & q_2 & q_3 \\ & r_1 & r_2 & \\ & & s_1 & \end{matrix} \right\rangle, \tag{5.8}$$

where again we changed our notation to avoid double indices. Expressing the IR of the $S\mathscr{U}_3$ group involved in the recoupling coefficient (5.4) in terms of the IR of $\mathscr{U}_3$ in (5.8), we conclude by the same reasoning as in the previous paragraph, that we would get the most general result if we make the substitutions

$$\begin{gathered} k_i = k_{in} - k_{3\,n-2}, \qquad q_i = k_{in-1} - k_{3\,n-2}, \qquad i = 1, 2, 3; \\ r_1 = k_{1\,n-2} - k_{3\,n-2}, \qquad r_2 = k_{2\,n-2} - k_{3\,n-2}, \end{gathered} \tag{5.9}$$

in the explicit expression of the matrix element (5.8). The evaluation of (5.8) is discussed in appendix B.

We have determined explicitly the matrix elements of $(n-1, n)$ for Gelfand states of one, two or three rows. For a number of rows larger than three, the problem is no longer of interest in connection with the physical application outlined in section 2, for states in a three dimensional harmonic oscillator potential. The matrix elements are still very important in this case in relation with the finite IR of SU_n, as was indicated by the authors[11]) in their analysis of the particular case $n=3$. It is clear that for the most general case of n rows, this requires the evaluation of special Racah coefficients of SU_n involving again two one rowed IR equivalent to $(l_{n-1}\,0)$, $(l_n\,0)$ for SU_3. This evaluation could be attempted by a number of procedures including the direct one given in the appendices, thus opening the way for the explicit construction of the finite IR of SU_n.

Acknowledgment

The authors are indebted to Dr. A. Gal and Prof. H. Lipkin for the helpful discussions specified at the end of section 3.

Appendix A

RACAH COEFFICIENTS OF SU_2

We shall sketch here the evaluation of the matrix element (5.5) of the transposition (2,3). As indicated in the text, this matrix element can be expressed in terms of a Racah coefficient of SU_2, and so its evaluation gives us an independent procedure for determining the Racah coefficients.

The Gelfand states in (5.5) will be given as polynomials in the creation operators $\eta_i^s (s=1, 2, 3, i=1, 2)$ of section 2, acting on the vacuum. From ref. 5 we have the two alternative expressions

$$\left|\begin{matrix} k_1 & & k_2 & & 0 \\ & q_1 & & q_2 & \\ & & r_1 & & \end{matrix}\right\rangle = N (C^{21})^{q_1 - r_1} (\Delta_1^1)^{q_1 - k_2} (\Delta_1^3)^{k_1 - q_1} (\Delta_{12}^{12})^{q_2} (\Delta_{12}^{13})^{k_2 - q_2} |0\rangle , \tag{A.1}$$

$$\left|\begin{matrix} k_1 & & k_2 & & 0 \\ & q_1 & & q_2 & \\ & & r_1 & & \end{matrix}\right\rangle = N (q_1 - r_1)! \sum_{\nu=0} (-)^\nu \binom{q_1 - q_2 - \nu}{r_1 - q_2} \binom{k_2 - q_2}{\nu} (\Delta_1^1)^{r_1 - k_2} (\Delta_1^2)^{q_1 - r_1 - \nu} \times$$
$$\times (\Delta_1^3)^{k_1 - q_1 + \nu} (\Delta_{12}^{12})^{q_2 + \nu} (\Delta_{12}^{13})^{k_2 - q_2 - \nu} |0\rangle , \tag{A.2}$$

with

$$N = \left[\frac{(k_1 - k_2 + 1)!(r_1 - q_2)!(q_1 - q_2 + 1)}{(k_1 - q_1)!(k_2 - q_2)!(q_1 - k_2)!(k_1 - q_2 + 1)! q_2! (q_1 + 1)!(q_1 - r_1)!} \right]^{\frac{1}{2}} . \tag{A.3}$$

In these formulas $\Delta_i^s = \eta_i^s$, $\Delta_{ij}^{st} = \eta_i^s \eta_j^t - \eta_i^t \eta_j^s$, and C^{21} is one of the nine generators of U_3; the explicit form of these generators being

$$C^{st} = \sum_{i=1}^{2} \eta_i^s \xi_i^t .$$

The commutation relations in (2.3) enable us to write

$$\xi_i^s P(\eta) |0\rangle = \frac{\partial P(\eta)}{\partial \eta_i^s} |0\rangle , \tag{A.4}$$

when $P(\eta)$ is a polynomial. Thus the scalar product of two polynomials

$$(P_1, P_2) = \langle 0| \{P_1(\eta)\}^\dagger P_2(\eta) |0\rangle = \langle 0| P_1(\xi) P_2(\eta) |0\rangle \tag{A.5}$$

can be evaluated by repeated use of (A.4).

For the evaluation of the matrix element

$$\left\langle \begin{matrix} k_1 & k_2 & 0 \\ q_1' & q_2' & \\ r_1 & & \end{matrix} \middle| (2,3) \middle| \begin{matrix} k_1 & k_2 & 0 \\ q_1 & q_2 & \\ r_1 & & \end{matrix} \right\rangle$$

we write the ket in the form (A.2) and apply on it the transposition (2,3) which amounts to the interchange of the upper indices 2 and 3 of the deltas. The remaining part of the calculation consists essentially in the evaluation of a scalar product of two polynomials as in (A.5). In this calculation it is convenient to use some result of similar calculations performed in refs. 17 and 20. In this way we obtain the final result

$$\left\langle \begin{matrix} k_1 & k_2 & 0 \\ q_1' & q_2' & \\ r_1 & & \end{matrix} \middle| (2,3) \middle| \begin{matrix} k_1 & k_2 & 0 \\ q_1 & q_2 & \\ r_1 & & \end{matrix} \right\rangle =$$

$$= \delta_{k_1+k_2-q_1-q_2,\, q_1'+q_2'-r_1} [(q_1'-q_2'+1)(q_1-q_2+1)]^{\frac{1}{2}} \times$$

$$\times \left[\frac{(k_2-q_2)!(q_1-r_1)!(r_1-q_2')!(q_2')!(k_1-q_2'+1)!(k_1-q_1')!(q_1'+1)!(q_1'-k_2)!}{(k_2-q_2')!(q_1'-r_1)!(r_1-q_2)!(q_2)!(k_1-q_2+1)!(k_1-q_1)!(q_1+1)!(q_1-k_2)!}\right]^{\frac{1}{2}} \times$$

$$\times \sum_{\nu=0} (-)^\nu \times$$

$$\times \frac{(k_1-q_1+\nu)!(q_1-q_2-\nu)!(q_2+\nu)!}{\nu!(k_1-q_1-q_1'+r_1+\nu)!(k_1-q_1-q_2'+r_1+1+\nu)!(q_1-r_1-\nu)!(k_2-q_2-\nu)!} . \tag{A.6}$$

If we compare this expression with formula (12′) in the first Racah paper[21], we see that it is equivalent to

$$\delta_{k_1+k_2-q_1-q_2,\, q'_1+q'_2-r_1} [(q_1' - q_2' + 1)(q_1 - q_2 + 1)]^{\frac{1}{2}} \times$$
$$\times W[\tfrac{1}{2}(k_1 - q_1' + k_2 - q_2'), \tfrac{1}{2}(r_1 - q_2 + k_2 - q_2'), \tfrac{1}{2}(q_1' - r_1 + q_1 - k_2),$$
$$\tfrac{1}{2}(q_1' - r_1 + q_2'); \tfrac{1}{2}(k_1 - q_1' + r_1 - q_2), \tfrac{1}{2}(k_1 - q_1 + r_1 - q_2')] . \tag{A.7}$$

This coincides with (5.3) if we make use of some of the Regge symmetries[22] for Racah coefficients.

Appendix B

RACAH COEFFICIENTS OF SU_3

The evaluation of the matrix elements of the transposition (3,4) with respect to Gelfand states of $\mathscr{U}_4$ is very similar to the case discussed in appendix A, but of course the expression for the states is more complicated than in the case of $\mathscr{U}_3$, and the analysis is more lengthy. We omit all the details and quote only the final result.

$$\left\langle \begin{matrix} k_1 & k_2 & k_3 & 0 \\ q'_1 & q'_2 & q'_3 & \\ r_1 & r_2 & & \\ r_1 & & & \end{matrix} \middle| (3,4) \middle| \begin{matrix} k_1 & k_2 & k_3 & 0 \\ q_1 & q_2 & q_3 & \\ r_1 & r_2 & & \\ r_1 & & & \end{matrix} \right\rangle =$$

$$= \delta_{k_1+k_2+k_3-q_1-q_2-q_3,\, q'_1+q'_2+q'_3-r_1-r_2} \times$$
$$\times N[(q_1-q_2+1)(q_1-q_3+2)(q_2-q_3+1)(q'_1-q'_2+1)(q'_1-q'_3+2)(q'_2-q'_3+1)]^{\frac{1}{2}} \times$$
$$\times (k_1-k_2+1)!(k_1-k_3+2)!(k_2-k_3+1)! \times$$
$$\times \sum (-)^{v+\lambda+u+y+z} A_{\lambda\ldots z} \frac{(k_1-q_1+v)!(k_2-q_2-\mu+\lambda)!(q_1-q_2-v)!}{(k_2-q_2-\mu)!(r_2-q_3+\mu-v)!} \times$$
$$\times \frac{(q_2-q_3+\mu-\lambda-v)!(q_1-q_3+1+\mu-v)!}{(k_1-q_1+r_1+r_2-q'_1-q'_2+v+k)!(k_2-q_2-\mu+\lambda-k)!} \times$$
$$\times \frac{(q_3+\lambda-\mu+v)!(r_2-k_3+k+s+u)!(k_2-q_2+\lambda-\mu-k)!}{(q'_1-k_3+q_3-\mu+\lambda+v+2)!(q'_2-k_3+q_3-\mu+\lambda+v+1)!} \times$$
$$\times \frac{(q_2+q_3-r_2+v-s-u)!(v+w+x)!}{(q'_3-k_3+q_3-\mu+\lambda+v)!(k_3-q_3+\mu-\lambda-v)!(q_1-k_2+\mu-v)!} \times$$
$$\times \frac{(q'_1-k_3+p+s+t-v-w-x)!(q_3+\lambda-\mu+v-p-s-t+v-y-z)!}{(r_2-q'_2+k+u+v-y-z)!(k_2+k_3-q_2-q_3-q'_3-k-v+w+y)!} \times$$
$$\times \frac{(w+y)!(k_1-q'_1+x+z)!}{(k_1-q'_1+r_1-q_1+v-u+x+z)!},$$

where

$$N = \left[\frac{(r_2-q'_3)!(q'_1-r_2+1)!(r_1-q'_2)!}{(q_1-r_1)!(q'_1-r_1)!(q_2-r_2)!(q'_2-r_2)!(r_1-q_2)!(r_1-q_3+1)!(q_1-r_2+1)!}\right]^{\frac{1}{2}} \times$$
$$\times \left[\frac{(r_1-q'_3+1)!(r_2-q_3)!}{(k_1-q_1)!(k_1-q'_1)!(k_1-q_2+1)!(k_1-q'_2+1)!(q_1-k_3+1)!(q'_1-k_3+1)!}\right]^{\frac{1}{2}} \times$$
$$\times \left[\frac{(q'_1+2)!(q'_2+1)!(q'_3)!(q_1-k_2)!}{(q_1+2)!(q_2+1)!(q_3)!(q'_1-k_2)!(k_2-q'_2)!(k_3-q'_3)!(q_2-k_3)!}\right]^{\frac{1}{2}} \times$$

$$\times\left[\frac{(k_2-q_2)!(k_3-q_3)!}{(q_2'-k_3)!(k_1-q_3+2)!(k_1-q_3'+2)!(k_2-q_3+1)!(k_2-q_3'+1)!}\right]^{\frac{1}{2}}$$

and

$$\begin{aligned}A_{\lambda\ldots z} = &\binom{q_2-r_2}{\lambda}\binom{\nu}{\mu}\binom{q_1-r_1}{\nu}\binom{q_2'-r_2}{k}\times\\ &\times\binom{q_3+q_3'-k_3+\lambda-\mu+\nu}{p}\binom{k_3-q_3'}{s}\binom{k_3-q_3'-s}{t}\times\\ &\times\binom{q_3+\lambda-\mu+\nu-p-s-t}{u}\binom{q_2'-k_3+s}{v}\binom{p}{w}\binom{k_2-q_2'+t}{x}\times\\ &\times\binom{q_3+q_3'-k_3+\lambda-\mu+\nu-p}{y}\binom{k_3-q_3'-s-t}{z}. \end{aligned} \tag{B.1}$$

The summation is over all indices not appearing in the bra or ket.

References

1) P. Kramer and M. Moshinsky, Nucl. Phys. **82**, 241 (1966).
2) P. Kramer and M. Moshinsky, *Group Theory of Harmonic Oscillators and Nuclear Structure*, in: *Group Theory and Applications*, Ed. E. M. Loebl (Academic Press, New York, 1968).
3) P. Kramer and M. Moshinsky, Phys. Letters **23**, 574 (1966).
4) I. M. Gel'fand and M. L. Zetlin, Dokl. Akad. Nauk SSSR **71**, 825 (1950).
5) M. Moshinsky, J. Math. Phys. **4**, 1128 (1963).
6) G. E. Baird and L. C. Biedenharn, J. Math. Phys. **4**, 1449 (1963).
7) V. Bargmann and M. Moshinsky, Nucl. Phys. **23**, 177 (1961).
8) P. Kramer, J. Math. Phys. (in press).
9) E. P. Wigner, *Group Theory* (Academic Press, New York, 1959) p. 114.
10) M. Hamermesh, *Group Theory* (Addison-Wesley Publ. Co., Reading, Mass., 1962) pp. 224–230, 276–278.
11) E. Chacón and M. Moshinsky, Phys. Letters **23**, 567 (1966).
12) J. Nagel and M. Moshinsky, J. Math. Phys. **6**, 652 (1965).
13) T. A. Brody, M. Moshinsky and I. Renero, J. Math. Phys. **6**, 1540 (1965).
14) J. D. Louck, J. Math. Phys. **6**, 1786 (1965).
15) E. P. Wigner, loc. cit., p. 191.
16) J. P. Elliott, Proc. Roy. Soc. (London) A **245**, 128 (1958).
17) M. Moshinsky, Rev. Mod. Phys. **34**, 813 (1962).
18) E. P. Wigner, loc. cit., p. 115.
19) G. Racah, Phys. Rev. **63**, 367 (1943).
20) T. A. Brody, M. Moshinsky and I. Renero, Rev. Mex. Fís. **15**, 145 (1966).
21) G. Racah, Phys. Rev. **61**, 134 (1942).
22) T. Regge, Nuovo Cimento **11**, 116 (1959).

Spectroscopic and group theoretical methods in physics
© North-Holland Publ. Co., Amsterdam, 1968

U(3) TRANSPOSITIONS AND THE ISOSPIN–U-SPIN TRANSFORMATION

A. GAL and H. J. LIPKIN

The Weizmann Institute of Science, Rehovoth, Israel

"He never lost the physical meaning of whatever he did. He was always amused by those who found after long calculations surprisingly simple results. He never left such miracles unexplained".

– from "Giulio Racah", by I. Talmi[1]).

A "miracle to be explained" was presented by Professor Marcos Moshinsky in a recent seminar in Rehovoth. A Racah coefficient had mysteriously appeared as a "surprisingly simple result" in one of their [2]) recent calculations. Moshinsky suggested that the "explanation of the miracle" might be a suitable exercise for members of the audience of his seminar. He also indicated that their result might be useful in elementary particle physics, and that the "I-spin U-spin" approach might be relevant. This note, dedicated to the memory of Professor Racah is the result of Moshinsky's suggestions.

When the group U(3) is used in physical problems, it is often of interest to consider two classification schemes which differ in the use of different U(2) subgroups in the chain

$$U(3) \supset U(2) \supset U(1). \tag{1}$$

An example is the use of isospin and U-spin eigenstates in the SU(3) classification of elementary particles[3]). The transformation between the two schemes has been considered for a few simple representations[4]). The general transformation has recently been established by Chacón and Moshinsky[2]). They calculate the matrix element of a transposition (2,3) with respect to states of the form

$$\left|\begin{matrix} h_1 & & h_2 & & h_3 \\ & p & & q & \\ & & r & & \end{matrix}\right\rangle, \; h_1 \geqslant p \geqslant h_2 \geqslant q \geqslant h_3 \geqslant 0, \quad p \geqslant r \geqslant q \geqslant 0, \tag{2}$$

where $[h_1, h_2, h_3]$ is the Young pattern of an irreducible representation of U(3) and $[p, q]$ and $[r]$ serve to distinguish between different states of the same U(3) representation, when reduced according to the chain (1). The Chacón-Moshinsky formula is[2])

$$\left\langle\begin{matrix} h_1 & & h_2 & & h_3 \\ & p' & & q' & \\ & & r' & & \end{matrix}\right| (2,3) \left|\begin{matrix} h_1 & & h_2 & & h_3 \\ & p & & q & \\ & & r & & \end{matrix}\right\rangle =$$

$$= (-1)^{h_3} \delta_{r'r} \delta_{p'+q'-r', h_1+h_2+h_3-p-q} \sqrt{(p'-q'+1)(p-q+1)} \times$$
$$\times W(abcd; ef), \tag{3}$$

where

$$a = \tfrac{1}{2}(h_1 - p' + h_2 - q'),\; b = \tfrac{1}{2}(r - q + h_2 - q'),\; c = \tfrac{1}{2}(p' - r + p - h_2),$$
$$d = \tfrac{1}{2}(p' - r + q' - h_3),\quad e = \tfrac{1}{2}(h_1 - p' + r - q),\; f = \tfrac{1}{2}(h_1 - p + r - q'). \tag{4}$$

The Racah coefficient W appears in the derivation simply as a function of the arguments which was identified as a Racah coefficient. There is no apparent significance to the coefficient in terms of coupling of angular momenta.

We present here an alternative derivation of the Chacón–Moshinsky result (3) in which the Racah coefficient appears naturally as the result of decoupling and recoupling of angular momenta which have a direct physical interpretation. We shall also express the result (3) in a form which is directly applicable to the isospin–U-spin transformation used in elementary particle physics.

We construct the representations of U(3) by combining quarks[5]), which are classified in the fundamental triplet representation of U(3), and which have spin one-half. We first consider those representations which have $h_3 = 0$; i.e. they have only two rows in their Young diagram. These include all of the irreducible representations of SU(3). For these representations one can define a spin coupling which is described by the same SU(3) Young diagram, and which combines to give a state which is symmetric in spin and SU(3); i.e. in U(2) × SU(3).

We denote the three members of the quark triplet by p, n and λ. The states p and n constitute a doublet of the isospin SU(2) subgroup, while the λ is a singlet. The states n and λ constitute a doublet of the U-spin SU(2) subgroup, while the p is a singlet[3]). The electric charge Q and the hypercharge $-Y$ are additive quantum numbers and are given in the quark triplet by

$$Q(\mathrm{p}) = \tfrac{2}{3}, \qquad Q(\mathrm{n}) = Q(\lambda) = -\tfrac{1}{3}, \tag{5a}$$

$$Y(\mathrm{p}) = Y(\mathrm{n}) = \tfrac{1}{3}, \qquad Y(\lambda) = -\tfrac{2}{3}. \tag{5b}$$

For a multiquark state we define the total spins $\boldsymbol{S}_\mathrm{p}$, $\boldsymbol{S}_\mathrm{n}$ and $\boldsymbol{S}_\lambda$ of the p, n and λ-quarks respectively, and the total spin

$$\boldsymbol{S} = \boldsymbol{S}_\mathrm{p} + \boldsymbol{S}_\mathrm{n} + \boldsymbol{S}_\lambda. \tag{6}$$

For any irreducible representation $[h_1, h_2, 0]$ of U(3), we can use the SU(3) symbol (λ, μ), where $h_1 = \lambda + \mu$, $h_2 = \mu$. We then see that for the *totally symmetric* U(2) × SU(3) state, the total number of quarks N and the magnitudes of the various spins are given by

$$N = N_\mathrm{p} + N_\mathrm{n} + N_\lambda = h_1 + h_2 \qquad = \lambda + 2\mu, \tag{7a}$$

$$S_\mathrm{p} = \tfrac{1}{2}N_\mathrm{p} \qquad = \tfrac{1}{2}r \qquad = \tfrac{1}{2}[\mu + \tfrac{1}{3}(\lambda - \mu) + Q], \tag{7b}$$

$$S_\mathrm{n} = \tfrac{1}{2}N_\mathrm{n} \qquad = \tfrac{1}{2}(p + q - r) \qquad = \tfrac{1}{2}[\mu + \tfrac{1}{3}(\lambda - \mu) + Y - Q], \tag{7c}$$

$$S_\lambda = \tfrac{1}{2}N_\lambda \qquad = \tfrac{1}{2}(h_1 + h_2 - p - q) = \tfrac{1}{2}[\mu + \tfrac{1}{3}(\lambda - \mu) - Y], \tag{7d}$$

$$S \qquad = \tfrac{1}{2}(h_1 - h_2) \qquad = \tfrac{1}{2}\lambda, \tag{7e}$$

where use was made of (5) and the notation (2).

The spin couplings in any state involve the coupling of three spins, $\boldsymbol{S}_\mathrm{p}$, $\boldsymbol{S}_\mathrm{n}$ and $\boldsymbol{S}_\lambda$ to a total spin $\boldsymbol{S}$. One additional quantum number is required to specify this coupling apart from the projection S_z of the total spin, which is irrelevant for these considerations. Two possibilities relevant for our treatment are the intermediate spins,

$$\boldsymbol{S}_\mathrm{pn} = \boldsymbol{S}_\mathrm{p} + \boldsymbol{S}_\mathrm{n}, \tag{8a}$$

$$\boldsymbol{S}_{\mathrm{n}\lambda} = \boldsymbol{S}_\mathrm{n} + \boldsymbol{S}_\lambda. \tag{8b}$$

These lead to two coupling schemes whose eigenstates we denote by

$$|S_\mathrm{p}, S_\mathrm{n}(S_\mathrm{pn}), S_\lambda; S, S_z\rangle, \tag{9a}$$

$$|S_\mathrm{n}, S_\lambda(S_{\mathrm{n}\lambda}), S_\mathrm{p}; S, S_z\rangle. \tag{9b}$$

Because of the total symmetry in U(2) × SU(3), we see that the U(2) spin coupling scheme defines uniquely the SU(3) coupling scheme. In the S_{pn} scheme, the p and n-quarks are coupled to a state of isospin $I = S_{pn}$. In the $S_{n\lambda}$ scheme the n and λ-quarks are coupled to a state of U-spin $U = S_{n\lambda}$. We can therefore supplement (7) by

$$S_{pn} = I = \tfrac{1}{2}(p - q), \tag{7f}$$

$$S_{n\lambda} = U. \tag{7g}$$

Thus, the transformation between the two bases (9) is also a transformation between isospin and U-spin eigenstates. This transformation is given by[6])

$$\langle S_p, S_n(S_{pn}), S_\lambda; S, S_z | S_n, S_\lambda(S_{n\lambda}), S_p; S, S_z\rangle = \\ = (-1)^{2S - S_{n\lambda} + S_n + S_\lambda} \sqrt{(2S_{pn} + 1)(2S_{n\lambda} + 1)} \begin{Bmatrix} S_p & S_n & S_{pn} \\ S_\lambda & S & S_{n\lambda} \end{Bmatrix}. \tag{10}$$

This result can be expressed in terms of the isospin and U-spin variables by substituting the expressions (7) for the various spins in terms of I, I_z, Y and U, U_z, Q, where

$$I_z = Q - \tfrac{1}{2}Y, \tag{11a}$$

$$U_z = Y - \tfrac{1}{2}Q. \tag{11b}$$

We obtain

$$\langle I, I_z, Y | U, U_z, Q\rangle = (-1)^{\lambda + \mu + \frac{1}{3}(\lambda - \mu) - U - \frac{1}{2}Q} \sqrt{(2I + 1)(2U + 1)} \times \\ \times \begin{Bmatrix} \frac{1}{2}[\mu + \frac{1}{3}(\lambda - \mu) + Q] & \frac{1}{2}[\mu + \frac{1}{3}(\lambda - \mu) + Y - Q] & I \\ \frac{1}{2}[\mu + \frac{1}{3}(\lambda - \mu) - Y] & \frac{1}{2}\lambda & U \end{Bmatrix}. \tag{12}$$

However, the expression (12) defines an inconvenient phase-convention. We should like the transformation bracket to be $+1$ for all non-degenerate values of (Q, Y) where there is only a single state. While (12) yields $+1$ for each transformation bracket within the fundamental (1, 0) triplet, it assumes the value -1 for the $\bar{n}$ and $\bar{\lambda}$ states of the conjugate (0, 1) triplet. For any multiplet, this may be overcome by inserting into (12) an extra phase $(-1)^{\min[(Q - Q_{\min}), \mu]}$, where $Q_{\min} = -\frac{2}{3}\mu - \frac{1}{3}\lambda$. Our final result[7]) is then:

$$\langle(\lambda, \mu)\, I, I_z, Y | (\lambda, \mu)\, U, U_z, Q\rangle = \\ = (-1)^{\lambda + \frac{1}{3}(\lambda - \mu) - U - \frac{1}{2}Q + \min[Q + \frac{1}{3}(\lambda - \mu), 0]} \sqrt{(2I + 1)(2U + 1)} \times \\ \times \begin{Bmatrix} \frac{1}{2}[\mu + \frac{1}{3}(\lambda - \mu) + Q] & \frac{1}{2}[\mu + \frac{1}{3}(\lambda - \mu) + Y - Q] & I \\ \frac{1}{2}[\mu + \frac{1}{3}(\lambda - \mu) - Y] & \frac{1}{2}\lambda & U \end{Bmatrix}. \tag{13}$$

This gives some phases which differ with those in the specific examples of ref. 4.

The matrix (13), where I and U label rows and columns respectively, is manifestly orthogonal. By the usual symmetry properties of the $6j$ symbol it is invariant, except for a phase, under the exchange $I \leftrightarrow U$, $Q \leftrightarrow -Y$. It is also invariant under the R transformation which takes a SU(3) multiplet into its conjugate by changing quarks into antiquarks and vice versa[3]):

$$\lambda \leftrightarrow \mu, \qquad Q \to -Q, \qquad Y \to -Y.$$

Thus

$$\langle(\lambda,\mu)\, I, I_z, Y|(\lambda,\mu)\, U, U_z, Q\rangle = \langle(\mu,\lambda)\, I, -I_z, -Y|(\mu,\lambda)\, U, -U_z, -Q\rangle. \tag{14}$$

The proof of eq. (14) takes advantage of the Regge symmetries[8]) of the $6j$ symbol.

Another useful result follows from the relation[6])

$$\sum_j (-1)^{j_1+j_2+j}(2j+1)\begin{Bmatrix} j_1 & j_1 & j' \\ j_2 & j_2 & j \end{Bmatrix} = \sqrt{(2j_1+1)(2j_2+1)}\,\delta_{j'0}. \tag{15}$$

For self-conjugate SU(3) multiplets and states of $Q = Y = 0$, one can show that the proper combination of isospin eigenstates which is a U-scalar is

$$|(\lambda,\mu)\, U = 0, 0, 0\rangle = \frac{1}{\lambda+1}\sum_I (-1)^I \sqrt{2I+1}\,|(\lambda,\mu)\, I, 0, 0\rangle. \tag{16}$$

In order to prove the Chacón–Moshinsky formula (3), we introduce labels (1), (2) and (3) for the quarks and consider p, n and λ as states which can be occupied by these quarks. The transposition (2, 3) transforms a state in which quarks labeled (1), (2) and (3) are in the states p, n and λ respectively into one in which they are in the states p, λ and n. Thus, the state (9a) $|S_\mathrm{p}(1), S_\mathrm{n}(2)\,(S_\mathrm{pn}), S_\lambda(3); S, S_z\rangle$ is transformed into a state where the (1)-quarks couple their spin S_p with the spin S_n of the (3)-*quarks* to an intermediate spin S_pn. Then, S_pn is coupled with the spin S_λ of the (2)-*quarks* to give a total spin S:

$$\begin{aligned}(2,3)|S_\mathrm{p}(1), S_\mathrm{n}(2)\,(S_\mathrm{pn}), S_\lambda(3); S, S_z\rangle &= \\ &= |S_\mathrm{p}(1), S_\mathrm{n}(3)\,(S_\mathrm{pn}), S_\lambda(2); S, S_z\rangle \\ &= \sum_{S_{\mathrm{p}\lambda}} (-1)^{2S+S_\mathrm{n}-S_\lambda-S_\mathrm{pn}+S_{\mathrm{p}\lambda}}\sqrt{(2S_\mathrm{pn}+1)(2S_{\mathrm{p}\lambda}+1)}\,\times \\ &\times \begin{Bmatrix} S_\mathrm{p} & S_\mathrm{n} & S_\mathrm{pn} \\ S & S_\lambda & S_{\mathrm{p}\lambda} \end{Bmatrix} |S_\mathrm{p}(1), S_\lambda(2)\,(S_{\mathrm{p}\lambda}), S_\mathrm{n}(3); S, S_z\rangle. \end{aligned} \tag{17}$$

Projecting this state on the state $|S'_\mathrm{p}(1), S'_\mathrm{n}(2)\,(S'_\mathrm{pn}), S'_\lambda(3); S, S_z\rangle$ we pick out of the sum (17) just the state with $S_{p\lambda} = S'_{pn}$. The overlap is then equal to

$$\delta_{S_p' S_p}\,\delta_{S_n' S_\lambda}\,\delta_{S_\lambda' S_n}(-1)^{2S+S_n-S_\lambda-S_{pn}+S_{pn}'}\sqrt{(2S_{pn}+1)(2S'_{pn}+1)}\times$$
$$\times\begin{Bmatrix} S_p & S_n & S_{pn} \\ S & S_\lambda & S'_{pn}\end{Bmatrix}. \quad (18)$$

Making use of the relations (7) we can rewrite (18) in terms of h_i $(i = 1, 2)$, p, q and r, for the case $h_3 = 0$. The general case $h_3 \neq 0$ can be included by adding h_3 to all symbols h_i, p, q and r, as well as by inserting an extra phase $(-1)^{h_3}$. We may note that the irreducible bases (2) were constructed [2]) like our quark spins, out of particle-indices only. For this reason we have no further troubles with phases. The final result is then

$$\left\langle \begin{matrix} h_1 & h_2 & h_3 \\ & p' \quad q' & \\ & r' & \end{matrix} \middle| (2,3) \middle| \begin{matrix} h_1 & h_2 & h_3 \\ & p \quad q & \\ & r & \end{matrix} \right\rangle =$$
$$= \delta_{r'r}\,\delta_{p'+q'-r',\,h_1+h_2+h_3-p-q}(-1)^{h_3+h_1-h_2+q-q'}\times$$
$$\times\sqrt{(p-q+1)(p'-q'+1)}\times$$
$$\times\begin{Bmatrix} \tfrac{1}{2}r & \tfrac{1}{2}(p+q-r) & \tfrac{1}{2}(p-q) \\ \tfrac{1}{2}(h_1-h_2) & \tfrac{1}{2}(h_1+h_2-p-q) & \tfrac{1}{2}(p'-q') \end{Bmatrix}. \quad (19)$$

The Chacón–Moshinsky formula (3) is obtainable from our (19) by twice applying to it the Regge symmetries [8]) as well as usual symmetry properties of the $6j$ symbol.

We should like to express our appreciation to Marcos Moshinsky for pointing out this problem and for several illuminating discussions.

Footnotes and references

1) I. Talmi, *Giulio Racah*, Nucl. Phys. **83**, 1 (1966).
2) E. Chacón and M. Moshinsky, Phys. Letters **23**, 567 (1966).
3) See, e.g., H. J. Lipkin, *Lie Groups for Pedestrians* (North-Holland Publ. Co., Amsterdam, 1965) appendix B.
4) H. Harari, Nuovo Cimento **33**, 752 (1964); A. J. Macfarlane, E. C. G. Sudarshan and C. Dullemond, Nuovo Cimento **30**, 845 (1963).
5) M. Gell-Mann, Phys. Letters **8**, 214 (1964); S. Zweig, CERN Report, unpublished.
6) See, e.g., A. de-Shalit and I. Talmi, *Nuclear Shell Theory* (Academic Press, New York, 1963) pp. 517–518.
7) This result could also have been reached by N. Mukunda and L. K. Pandit, J. Math. Phys. **6**, 746 (1965), who obtained a sum on SU(2) Clebsch–Gordan coefficients in their expression for the (I, U) transformation bracket.
8) T. Regge, Nuovo Cimento **10**, 544 (1958).

Spectroscopic and group theoretical methods in physics
© North-Holland Publ. Co., Amsterdam, 1968

IDENTITIES IN THE UNIVERSAL ENVELOPING ALGEBRA OF SU3

YEHIEL LEHRER ILAMED
Soreq Nuclear Research Centre, Israel A.E.C.

1. Introduction

As a basis for the Lie algebra, SU_3, of the three-dimensional unitary unimodular group, we may take[1]) eight linearly independent elements of the set L_h, T_{jk} $(h, j, k=1, 2, 3)$ satisfying relations of the form

$$\begin{aligned}
[L_h, L_j] &= \mathrm{i}\, \varepsilon_{hjk} L_k\,, \\
[L_h, T_{mn}] &= \mathrm{i}\, \varepsilon_{hmk} T_{kn} + \mathrm{i}\, \varepsilon_{hnk} T_{km}\,, \\
[T_{hj}, T_{mn}] &= \mathrm{i}\, (\varepsilon_{hmk}\delta_{jn} + \varepsilon_{hnk}\delta_{jm} + \varepsilon_{jmk}\delta_{hn} + \varepsilon_{jnk}\delta_{hm})\, L_k\,, \\
T_{hj} &= T_{jh}\,, \\
T_{hh} &= 0\,,
\end{aligned} \tag{1}$$

where ε_{hjk} is antisymmetric in all its indices, with $\varepsilon_{123}=1$, and δ_{hk} is equal to 1 or 0 for $h=k$ and $h\neq k$ respectively; the summation convention of repeated indices is assumed. L_1, L_2, and L_3 form a basis for the Lie algebra R_3 of the three-dimensional rotation group. In the universal enveloping algebra of SU_3 we define by contraction the scalars:

$$\begin{aligned}
x &= L_h T_{hk} L_k\,, \qquad & x &= L\cdot T\cdot L\,, \\
y &= L_h T_{hk} T_{kj} L_j\,, \qquad & y &= L\cdot T\cdot T\cdot L\,.
\end{aligned} \tag{2}$$

The universal enveloping algebra of SU_3 is that algebra, generated by the elements of the set L_j, T_{hk}, whose relations are expressed by the laws: 1) associativity, 2) $RS-SR=[R, S]$ for any two elements R, S of the set of generators.

In the present work we give explicit expressions, eqs. (11) and (14), for $[x, [x, y]]$, $[y, [x, y]]$ and $[x, y]^2$. These expressions will be referred to as *the main relations.* They were derived 15 years ago, but only partial results have been communicated[1,2]).

A number of relations between elements of the universal associative enveloping algebra of SU_3 are given here, eqs. (4), (8), (9), (19)–(21), and one of them is calculated as an example in the appendix. These relations may be used to arrive to the main ones. In the course of the derivations we often use an expression, eq. (4), for $T_{hj}T_{jk}T_{km}$ obtained with the help of an obvious generalization of the Cayley–Hamilton identities[3]).

Racah (ref. 1, pp. 31–36) has shown how the main relations may be used to obtain the irreducible representations of SU_3 in a scheme where the representations of R_3 appear in reduced form. A continuation of this work of Racah's will form the subject of a future paper.

2. The Cayley–Hamilton identities

The Cayley–Hamilton identities for an $n \times n$ matrix whose coefficients are elements of an associative commutative algebra form a set of n^2 identically zero homogeneous polynomials of order n in the elements of the matrix. These identities are obtained from the fact that the matrix satisfies its characteristic equation.

The n^2 identities for an $n \times n$ matrix whose coefficients are elements of a free associative algebra are obtained by substitution of its coefficients in the above n^2 homogeneous polynomials followed by complete symmetrization[3]). As an example, for a 3×3 matrix S_{ij} the 9 Cayley–Hamilton identities are

$$\{S_{hi}S_{ij}S_{jk}\} - \{S_{jj}S_{hi}S_{ik}\} - \varepsilon_{jmr}\{S_{1j}S_{2m}S_{3r}\}\,\delta_{hk} + \\ + \{(S_{11}S_{22} + S_{11}S_{33} + S_{22}S_{33} - S_{12}S_{21} - S_{13}S_{31} - S_{23}S_{32})\,S_{hk}\} = 0\,, \tag{3}$$

where the brackets $\{\ \}$ denote that each of the terms enclosed represents the sum of the six terms obtained by the permutations of the factors of that term (complete symmetrization).

Substituting T for S in eq. (3) and using the relations (1), one obtains

$$T^3 = \tfrac{1}{3}t_3\delta + \tfrac{1}{4}(t_2T + Tt_2) + 4T - 3\mathrm{i}(\varepsilon\cdot M)\,, \tag{4}$$

where T^3, t_2, t_3, M and $(\varepsilon\cdot M)$ are defined by

$$(T^r)_{hk} = (T^{r-1})_{hj}T_{jk}\,, \qquad t_r = (T^r)_{jj}\,, \\ M_h = T_{hk}L_k = (T\cdot L)_h\,, \quad (\varepsilon\cdot M)_{hk} = \varepsilon_{hkj}M_j\,. \tag{5}$$

3. The Casimir operators

The Casimir operators constitute a basis of the centre of the universal enveloping algebra. There is an extensive literature[4–15]) on how to construct the Casimir operators. In order to learn about the structure of the SU_3 enveloping algebra we have calculated the commutators of T_{hk} with the scalars t_2, t_3, x and s

$$s = L_j L_j \tag{6}$$

and as a result have obtained the Casimir operators of SU_3.

Let us define $\varepsilon \cdot T$, U and V by

$$\begin{aligned} (\varepsilon \cdot T)_{hjk} &= \varepsilon_{hji} T_{ik}, \\ 2\mathrm{i} U_{hk} &= \varepsilon_{hij}(L_i T_{jk} - T_{ki} L_j), \\ 2\mathrm{i} V_{hk} &= \varepsilon_{hij}(M_i T_{jk} - T_{ki} M_j). \end{aligned} \tag{7}$$

The relations

$$\begin{aligned} (T^2)_{hk} - (T^2)_{kh} &= 5\mathrm{i}(\varepsilon \cdot L)_{hk}, \\ (\varepsilon \cdot T)_{hjk} + (\varepsilon \cdot T)_{jkh} + (\varepsilon \cdot T)_{khj} &= 0, \end{aligned} \tag{8}$$

may be used to derive the expressions for the following commutators

$$\begin{aligned} [s, T_{hk}] &= 2U_{hk} + 2U_{kh}, \\ [t_2, T_{hk}] &= -4U_{hk} - 4U_{kh}, \\ [t_3, T_{hk}] &= 6V_{hk} + 6V_{kh}, \\ [x, T_{hk}] &= 2V_{hk} + 2V_{kh}. \end{aligned} \tag{9}$$

As scalars commute with L_h one obtains from eq. (9) the two Casimir operators g and g_3

$$g = s + \tfrac{1}{2} t_2, \qquad g_3 = x - \tfrac{1}{3} t_3. \tag{10}$$

4. The main relations

The main relations which characterize the structure of the subalgebra of the scalars of the universal enveloping algebra of SU_3 are

$$\begin{aligned} [x, [x, y]] &= -8mx^2 + 24y^2 - 4kg_3 x - 16ny - 8sp, \\ [y, [y, x]] &= 32x^3 - 8m(xy + yx) - 24g_3 x^2 - 4kg_3 y + 16qx + 8sg_3 r, \end{aligned} \tag{11}$$

where

$$\begin{aligned} m &= 2s + g - 18, & p &= (g+3)(s - 4g + 6), \\ k &= 6(3 - s), & q &= sg^2 - g^2 - 7sg - 18s, \\ n &= sg - s^2 + 9s + 3g - 9, & r &= -2sg + 6s + 6g + 9. \end{aligned} \tag{12}$$

The coefficients of x^2 and x in the expression for $[x, [x, y]]$ in eq. (11) are equal to the corresponding coefficients of $xy+yx$ and y in $[y, [y, x]]$, as a necessary condition following from the Jacobi identity

$$[y, [x, [x, y]]] + [x, [[x, y], y]] = 0. \tag{13}$$

We have calculated also

$$[x, y]^2 = 16x^4 - 16g_3x^3 + 16y^3 + c_3(x^2y + yx^2) + c_{11}(xy + yx)g_3 + \\ + c_{20}x^2 + c_{02}y^2 + c_{10}g_3x + c_{01}y + 16s(g+3)c'_{00} + 4sg_3^2c''_{00}, \tag{14}$$

where

$$\begin{aligned} c_3 &= -8(2s + g - 66), \qquad c_{11} = 24(s - 11), \\ c_{02} &= 16(s^2 - sg - 17s - 111), \\ c_{20} &= 16(sg^2 - 39sg - 5g^2 + 126s + 96g - 1152), \\ c_{10} &= -16(2s^2g - 22s^2 - 26sg + 207s + 12g - 576), \\ c_{01} &= 16(12g^2s - s^2g - 131s^2 + 78sg - 8g^2 + 990s + 384g - 1152), \\ c'_{00} &= 3s^2g - 3sg^2 - 15s^2 + 10sg + 4g^2 + 91s - 256g + 384, \\ c''_{00} &= (4s - 3)(s - 12). \end{aligned} \tag{15}$$

These main relations, eqs. (11) and (14), can be obtained by straightforward long calculations.

Let us define the cross product by

$$(L \times M)_j = \varepsilon_{jhk} L_h M_k, \tag{16}$$

and the vectors N, A, B, C, $\bar{M}$, $\bar{N}$ and P by

$$\begin{aligned} N &= T \cdot M, \\ 2\mathrm{i}A &= L \times M - M \times L, \quad 2\mathrm{i}B = L \times N - N \times L, \\ &\qquad\qquad 2\mathrm{i}C = M \times N - N \times M, \\ \bar{M} &= -2N + (g+3)L, \\ \bar{N} &= 2(g-1)N - 2\{x - g_3, M\} + \\ &\qquad + (y + (g+3)s - (g-1)(g+3))L, \\ 2P &= \{1 - s, M\} + (2x + g_3)L, \end{aligned} \tag{17}$$

where the brackets { , } mean the anticommutator, i.e.

$$\{1 - s, M\} = (1 - s)M + M(1 - s). \tag{18}$$

Below we give a number of relations that are useful when deriving eqs. (11) and (14). As an example the derivation of the expression for $[x, N]$ is given in the appendix.

$$L \times M + M \times L = 2\mathrm{i}M, \quad L \times N + N \times L = 2\mathrm{i}N, \quad M \times N + N \times M = 2\mathrm{i}P, \tag{19}$$

$$[s, M] = 2A, \quad [s, N] = 2B, \quad M \times M = \mathrm{i}\bar{M}, \quad N \times N = \mathrm{i}\bar{N},$$

$$\begin{aligned} [x, M] &= -2B, \\ [x, N] &= \{g - s + 4, A\} + 4C, \\ [y, M] &= -2(g+3)A - 4C, \\ [y, N] &= 2\{g_3 - x, A\} + 2(g-1)B. \end{aligned} \tag{20}$$

The relations (20) can also be written in a more symmetric form

$$\begin{aligned} [x, M] &= -\mathrm{i}(M \times A + A \times M), \quad [x, N] = -\mathrm{i}(M \times B + B \times M), \\ [y, M] &= -\mathrm{i}(N \times A + A \times N), \quad [y, N] = -\mathrm{i}(N \times B + B \times N). \end{aligned} \tag{21}$$

Appendix. Derivation of the expression for $[x, N]$

$$[x, N] = [x, T \cdot M] = [x, T] \cdot M + T \cdot [x, M]. \tag{A.1}$$

The expression for $[x, T]$ in eq. (9) and for $[x, M]$ in eq. (20) can be written in the form

$$[x, T] = 2\mathrm{i}(\varepsilon \cdot N) + 4V, \quad [x, M] = 2\mathrm{i}LN + 2N. \tag{A.2}$$

From eqs. (A.1), (A.2) and the relations

$$\begin{aligned} 2V \cdot M &= 2T \cdot N - (g+3)M - \mathrm{i}(M \times N - N \times M), \\ T \cdot (L \times N) &= (T \cdot N) \times L - M \times N + \mathrm{i}T \cdot N, \end{aligned} \tag{A.3}$$

one obtains

$$[x, N] = 4T \cdot N - 2(g+3)M - 4\mathrm{i}M \times N + 2\mathrm{i}(T \cdot N)L. \tag{A.4}$$

The relations (A.4) are derived by using eqs. (8), (19) and

$$\varepsilon_{hij}\varepsilon_{kmr} = \begin{vmatrix} \delta_{hk} & \delta_{hm} & \delta_{hr} \\ \delta_{ik} & \delta_{im} & \delta_{ir} \\ \delta_{jk} & \delta_{jm} & \delta_{jr} \end{vmatrix}. \tag{A.5}$$

Using eqs. (4), (10), (17) and (19) we may derive expressions for $T \cdot N = T^3 \cdot L$, $(T \cdot N) \times L = (T^3 \cdot L) \times L$ and for $M \times N$:

$$\begin{aligned} 2T\cdot N &= 2(x-g_3)L - \{s-g-1, M\} + 6A\,, \\ 2\mathrm{i}(T\cdot N)\times L &= 2(g_3-4x)L - \{s+g-2, A\} + \{4s-g-1, M\}\,, \\ M\times N &= \mathrm{i}(C+P)\,. \end{aligned} \tag{A.6}$$

Substituting for $T\cdot N$, $(T\cdot N)\times L$ and $M\times N$ in eq. (A.4) the corresponding expression obtained in eq. (A.6) and using the definition of P in eq. (17) we obtain the expression for $[x, N]$:

$$[x, N] = \{g-s+4, A\} + 4C\,. \tag{A.7}$$

References

1) G. Racah, Lecture on Lie Groups, in: *Lectures of the Istanbul Summer School of Theoretical Physics, 1962* (Gordon and Breach, New York, 1964).
2) R. N. Sen, *Construction of the Irreducible Representations of* SU_3, Ph.D. Thesis (Hebrew University, Jerusalem, 1963).
3) Y. Lehrer, Bull. Res. Council Israel Sect. A **5**, 197 (1957).
4) G. Racah, Rend. Accad. Naz. Lincei **8**, 108 (1950).
5) I. M. Gelfand, Mat. Sbornik **26**, 103 (1950).
6) G. Racah, *Group Theory and Spectroscopy, Lecture Notes* (Princeton, 1951).
7) V. Bargmann and M. Moshinsky, Nucl. Phys. **23**, 177 (1961).
8) L. C. Biedenharn, J. Math. Phys. **4**, 436 (1963).
9) G. E. Baird and L. C. Biedenharn, J. Math. Phys. **4**, 1449 (1963).
10) M. Umezava, Nucl. Phys. **48**, 111 (1963).
11) M. Micu, Nucl. Phys. **60**, 353 (1964).
12) B. Gruber and L. O'Raifeartaigh, J. Math. Phys. **5**, 1796 (1964).
13) M. C. Pease, J. Math. Phys. **6**, 111, 1134 (1965).
14) T. S. Santhanam, J. Math. Phys. **7**, 1886 (1966).
15) A. M. Perelomov and V. S. Popov, Soviet J. Nucl. Phys. **3**, 676 (1966); Iadernaia Fizika **3**, 1127 (1966).

Spectroscopic and group theoretical methods in physics

CONDITION THAT THE IRREDUCIBLE REPRESENTATIONS OF A GROUP, CONSIDERED AS REPRESENTATIONS OF A SUBGROUP, DO NOT CONTAIN ANY REPRESENTATION OF THE SUBGROUP MORE THAN ONCE

E. P. WIGNER

Palmer Physical Laboratory, Princeton University, Princeton, New Jersey, U.S.A.

Origin of the problem

The interest in the condition contained in the title stems from the desirability to specify a definite form for all irreducible representations of a group, i.e. to specify a particular coordinate system, with some simple properties, in representation space. In order to do this, let us first decompose each representation space into orthogonal subspaces, each such subspace being the representation space of an irreducible representation of a subgroup. If these irreducible representations are all inequivalent, their subspaces are uniquely given and can be characterized by the corresponding irreducible representation of the subgroup. Once this is done, one can proceed in the same way with the subgroup and, if possible, continue until an abelian subgroup of the last group is reached. Hence, if there is a sequence of subgroups $G_1, G_2, \ldots$ of the original group G_0 such that G_{l+1} is a subgroup of G_l of the nature specified in the title, a coordinate axis in the space of an irreducible representation of G_0 can be specified by enumerating the irreducible representations of all the subgroups $G_1, G_2, \ldots$ to the representation spaces of which the vector belongs.

Let us consider, as an example, the symmetric group S_5 of the permutations of 5 letters. Since S_{n-1} is a subgroup of S_n of the nature given in the title, the sequence of $G_1, G_2, \ldots$ can be chosen as S_4, S_3, S_2; the last one being abelian. Let us consider the representation $3+1+1$ of S_5. We then obtain the tree

$$
\begin{array}{lccccccc}
S_5 & & & & 3+1+1 & & & \\
 & & & \swarrow & & \searrow & & \\
S_4 & & 2+1+1 & & & & 3+1 & \\
 & \swarrow & & \searrow & & \swarrow & & \searrow \\
S_3 & 1+1+1 & & 2+1 & & 2+1 & & 3 \\
 & \downarrow & \swarrow & & \searrow \quad \swarrow & & \searrow & \downarrow \\
S_2 & 1+1 & 1+1 & & 2 \quad 1+1 & & 2 & 2
\end{array}
$$

No two arrows issuing from the symbol of any representation end at identical symbols. A vector in the six dimensional space of $3+1+1$ can therefore be characterized uniquely by one of the branches of the tree, such as $2+1+1$, $2+1$, $1+1$.

Many of the classical groups have sequences of subgroups as given in the title so that coordinate systems can be introduced in the spaces of their representations in the manner given above; each axis of these coordinate systems will be labelled by irreducible representations of a sequence of subgroups, each subgroup of the sequence being contained in the preceding subgroup of the sequence.

Establishment of the condition

Denote elements of the subgroup by $p, q, r, \ldots$, elements of the full group by $P, Q, R, \ldots$. Let $\sum_p$ be the summation over all the elements of the subgroup, $\sum_P$ the summation over all the elements of the full group.

Consider vectors a in group space with components $a_E, \ldots, a_R, \ldots$, such that the matrix $\sum_R a_R\, D(R)$ commutes with all $D(s)$ of the subgroup and that this condition be satisfied for all irreducible (and hence also for all) representations D of the whole group. The vectors a form a linear manifold. It will be shown, furthermore, that if a matrix $c^{(0)}$ commutes with all $D^{(0)}(s)$ of a single irreducible representation, $c^{(0)}$ is contained among the matrices $\sum a_R\, D^{(0)}(R)$: the a_R being given by

$$a_R = \frac{l_0}{h} \sum_{ik} c_{ik}^{(0)}\, D^{(0)}\,(R^{-1})_{ki}\,, \tag{1}$$

l_0 is the dimension of $D^{(0)}$ and h the order of the full group. That the a of (1) is in the linear manifold means that

$$\sum_R a_R\, D^{(j)}(R) = \sum_R \frac{l_0}{h} \sum_{ik} c_{ik}^{(0)}\, D^{(0)}(R^{-1})_{ki}\, D^{(j)}(R) \tag{2}$$

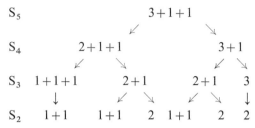

commutes with all $D^{(j)}(s)$ for every j. This is evident since (2) is zero if $D^{(j)}s$ is not equivalent to $D^{(0)}$; it is $c^{(0)}$ if $D^{(j)} = D^{(0)}$. Hence, all matrices which commute with the $D^{(j)}(s)$, for every s but any single j, are contained in the set $\sum a_R \, D(R)$.

Let us determine now the linear manifold of the a. By definition

$$\sum_R a_R \, D(R) \, D(s) = \sum_R a_R \, D(s) \, D(R) \tag{3}$$

or

$$\sum a_R \, D(R) = \sum a_R \, D(sRs^{-1})$$

or

$$\sum_R a_R \, D(R) = \sum_R a_{s^{-1}Rs} \, D(R). \tag{4}$$

Since this must hold for every irreducible representation, and since these (or their matrix elements) form a complete set in group space

$$a_R = a_{s^{-1}Rs} \tag{5}$$

and this holds for every element s of the subgroup. We shall call the complex of elements which can be transformed into each other by an element of the subgroup, a subclass. Hence, the components of a in the direction of the elements which are in the same subclass are equal. A full base for the vectors a has as many members as there are subclasses in the whole group; a vector which has finite components in the direction of the subclass which contains the element Q and zero components in every other direction is

$$a_R = \sum_s \delta(sQs^{-1} R^{-1}) \tag{6}$$

where

$$\delta(P) \begin{cases} = 1 & \text{for } P = E = e, \text{ the unit element}, \\ = 0 & \text{otherwise}. \end{cases} \tag{6a}$$

Evidently, the product of two subclasses consists of full subclasses and every class of the whole group consists of full subclasses. A subclass is either contained in the subgroup or has no element therein.

Let us consider now the vectors b in group space which satisfy two conditions. First $\sum b_R \, D(R)$ commute with all $D(s)$ for every representation (this is the same condition which the vectors a satisfy), second $\sum b_R \, D(R)$ commute with all $\sum a_R \, D(R)$. The vectors b also form a linear manifold and because of the first condition (5) is valid for the b also,

$$b_R = b_{s^{-1}Rs}. \tag{7}$$

Furthermore, if there is a matrix $c^{(0)}$ which commutes with all $D^{(0)}(s)$ of a single representation, and with all matrices in the space of this representation which commute with all matrices commuting with all $D^{(0)}(s)$, it is contained among the $\sum b_R D^{(0)}(R)$. The corresponding b_R is given by the right side of (1) and the proof that the $\sum b_R D(R)$ have the necessary properties for all $D^{(j)}$ follow from eq. (2) as before. If the representation $D^{(0)}$, considered as representation of the subgroup, does not contain any irreducible representation more than once, the matrices which commute with all $D^{(0)}(s)$ also commute with all matrices which commute with all $D^{(0)}(s)$. If this is true for all irreducible representations, $D^{(j)}$, the vectors b are the same as the vectors a and conversely, if every vector a satisfies also the second condition for the b, no irreducible representation of the full group, if considered as representation of the subgroup, contains any representation of the subgroup more than once. Hence, the identity of the linear manifolds a and b is the necessary and sufficient condition for the circumstance given in the title of this note.

The sum $\sum b_T D(T)$ will commute with every $\sum a_R D(R)$ if it commutes with every member of the base (6). Hence

$$\sum_T b_T D(T) \sum_R \sum_s \delta(sQs^{-1}R^{-1})\, D(R) = \sum_R \sum_s \delta(sQs^{-1}R^{-1})\, D(R) \sum_T b_T D(T)$$

is the second condition on the b. Because of (6a), it can be written also

$$\sum_T \sum_s b_T D(TsQs^{-1}) = \sum_T \sum_s b_T\, D(sQs^{-1}T). \tag{8}$$

This second condition will be a consequence of the first, if (8) is satisfied for every vector (6) of the full base of vectors a. Hence we set

$$b_T = \sum_r \delta(rPr^{-1}T^{-1}). \tag{9}$$

Introducing this into (8), one obtains

$$\sum_r \sum_s D(rPr^{-1}\, sQs^{-1}) = \sum_r \sum_s D(sQs^{-1}\, rPr^{-1}). \tag{10}$$

The left side contains the matrices which correspond to the elements of the complex $\mathfrak{P}\mathfrak{Q}$ where $\mathfrak{P}$ is the subclass which contains P and $\mathfrak{Q}$ is the subclass which contains Q, and it contains each equally often. The right side has the same relation with respect to the complex $\mathfrak{Q}\mathfrak{P}$. Since, because of the completeness of the D, eq. (10) can be valid only if the same group elements are present equally often on left and right side, we obtain

$$\mathfrak{P}\mathfrak{Q} = \mathfrak{Q}\mathfrak{P}. \tag{11}$$

The necessary and sufficient condition that no irreducible representation, considered as representation of the subgroup, shall contain any representation of the subgroup more than once, is that the subclasses (with respect to the subgroup) commute.

REMARKS

If the subgroup is the whole group, (11) is the well-known relation of the commutative nature of the multiplication of classes. If, on the other hand, P and Q commute with all elements of the subgroup, $\mathfrak{P}=P$ and $\mathfrak{Q}=Q$ and (11) becomes the condition that the centralizer of the subgroup must be abelian. This is, therefore, a necessary condition for the validity of (11). It can be proved that this necessary condition is satisfied for all maximal subgroups, i.e., each proper subgroup which is not a proper subgroup of a proper subgroup. For, let P and Q be two elements of the centralizer of the subgroup which do not commute, $PQ \neq QP$. This can be the case only if neither is an element of the subgroup since, by definition, both P and Q commute with all elements of the subgroup. If, however, P and Q are not elements of the subgroup – which will be denoted now by S – one can form a new subgroup consisting of S, SP, SP^2,.... This does not contain Q because all its elements commute with P whereas Q does not. Hence, the subgroup S was not maximal. Conversely, if S is maximal, (11) is satisfied for all the subclasses consisting of an element of the centralizer of the subgroup. It may not be satisfied for other subclasses and, indeed, Mackey has constructed a group[1]) which has no subgroup satisfying the condition contained in our title.

Let us observe that, on the other hand, *if all subclasses are ambivalent* (i.e., if all subclasses contain the reciprocal of every element which they contain) *then the subclasses also commute.* The subgroup will then have the property given in the title of this article.

To prove our assertion, let us observe, first, that if the subclasses are ambivalent, one can map each subclass, in a one-to-one fashion, on itself by mapping every element on its reciprocal. Furthermore, if the element R_1 is in the class C_1, and R_2 in the class of C_2, the products of R_1 and R_2 and of their maps R_1^{-1} and R_2^{-1} taken in the opposite order, will be in the same subclass: $R_2^{-1}R_1^{-1}=(R_1R_2)^{-1}$ is in the subclass of R_1R_2. Hence, the complexes C_1C_2 and C_2C_1 will have equally many elements in every subclass. Since both complexes consist of complete subclasses, i.e., contain every element of each subclass equally many times, the two complexes are identical and our assertion is demonstrated.

The group of all permutations of the first $n-1$ elements is a subgroup S_{n-1} of the group S_n of the permutations of all n elements and the subclasses of S_{n-1} are ambivalent. One can see this most easily by decomposing every permutation P into a product of disjoint cycles

$$P = (\alpha_1 \ldots \alpha_\rho)(\alpha_{\rho+1} \cdots \alpha_\sigma) \ldots (\alpha_{\tau+1} \cdots \alpha_{n-1}\, n). \tag{12}$$

The cycle containing n was written as last factor and n was chosen as its last member. The element p of the subgroup S_{n-1} which transforms P into its reciprocal consists of the product of transpositions

$$p = (\alpha_1 \alpha_\rho)(\alpha_2 \alpha_{\rho-1}) \ldots (\alpha_{\rho+1} \alpha_\sigma)(\alpha_{\rho+2} \alpha_{\sigma-1}) \ldots (\alpha_{\tau+1} \alpha_{n-1})(_{\tau+2} \alpha_{n-2}) \ldots . \tag{12a}$$

If the two elements of a transposition in p should be identical (e.g., $\alpha_2 = \alpha_{\rho-1}$), the corresponding transposition can be omitted from (12a). It may be noted that it is not necessary to move the n in the last factor of (12) in order to transform it into its reciprocal.

It follows that the subclasses of the subgroup S_{n-1} of permutations of $1, 2, \ldots, n-1$ are ambivalent and hence that they commute. It then follows that, if an irreducible representation of the full group S_n is considered as a representation of S_{n-1}, it contains each irreducible representation of S_{n-1} once or not at all – a fact which also follows from the standard theory of the representations of the symmetric group S_n developed by Frobenius, Schur and Young[2]).

References

1) G. W. Mackey, personal communication. Dr. Mackey also informed me that he found a shorter and more abstract proof of the principal result of the present paper.

2) See, e.g , M. Hamermesh, *Group Theory* (Addison-Wesley, Reading, Mass., 1962) eq. (7–52), p. 210.

Spectroscopic and group theoretical methods in physics

ON THE ISOTROPIC HARMONIC OSCILLATOR*

M. E. ROSE

University of Virginia, Charlottesville, Virginia, U.S.A.

1. Introduction

It is customary in physics to begin with a physical problem and then to search for the appropriate mathematical apparatus. In this paper we reverse the procedure, unorthodox though that may be. In any event we shall investigate a number of rather interesting properties of the isotropic harmonic oscillator without attempting to apply them directly to the solution of any specific problem. This is done with the expectation that at least some of the results presented here will be useful on more than one occasion in the context of the many physical problems in which the harmonic oscillator plays an important role.

For the most part we restrict our attention to the angular momentum representation for the single particle oscillator problem. It is here that almost all the new results appear. In addition a few remarks will be made in connection with the SU_3 group associated with the oscillator problem.

2. Creation and annihilation operator approach

It is well known that the solution of the Hamiltonian problem

$$\mathscr{H}\psi = \tfrac{1}{2}(\boldsymbol{p}^2 + \boldsymbol{r}^2)\,\psi = E\psi \tag{1}$$

can be compactly represented in terms of creation and annihilation operators, $\boldsymbol{a}^\dagger$ and $\boldsymbol{a}$ respectively:

$$\boldsymbol{a} = \frac{1}{\sqrt{2}}(\boldsymbol{r} + \mathrm{i}\boldsymbol{p}), \tag{2a}$$

$$\boldsymbol{a}^\dagger = \frac{1}{\sqrt{2}}(\boldsymbol{r} - \mathrm{i}\boldsymbol{p}), \tag{2b}$$

* Partially supported by the U.S. Atomic Energy Commission. Document ORO-2915-69.

wherein units are chosen so that $\hbar = m = \omega = 1$, with m and ω the oscillator mass and frequency. Thus, $\mathrm{i}\boldsymbol{p} = \boldsymbol{\nabla}$. The well-known results in the cartesian representation are

$$\mathscr{H} = \boldsymbol{a}^\dagger \cdot \boldsymbol{a} + \tfrac{3}{2} \tag{3a}$$

and

$$E = n + \tfrac{1}{2} \tag{3b}$$

and are readily obtained from the commutation rules

$$(a_j, a_k^\dagger) = \delta_{jk} \tag{4}$$

with all other commutators zero. From (3a) and (4) it follows that

$$(\mathscr{H}, a_k^\dagger) = a_k^\dagger, \tag{5a}$$

and hence

$$(\mathscr{H}, a_k) = -\, a_k, \tag{5b}$$

so that $a_k^\dagger$ and a_k respectively create and annihilate one quantum, in the k direction. The normalized state vectors are

$$|n_1 n_2 n_3\rangle = \Omega_{n_1 n_2 n_3} |000\rangle, \tag{6a}$$

with

$$\Omega_{n_1 n_2 n_3} = \prod_1^3 \frac{a_i^{\dagger n_i}}{\sqrt{(n_i!)}}, \tag{6b}$$

and $\sum_i n_i = n$. The Ω are unitary wherein we note that $\boldsymbol{a}^\dagger = \boldsymbol{a}^*$. Here, and subsequently where no confusion results, the asterisk means hermitian conjugate. Thus,

$$\Omega_{n_1 n_2 n_3}^{-1} = \prod_1^3 \frac{a_i^{n_i}}{\sqrt{(n_i!)}}. \tag{6c}$$

To work in the angular momentum representation with state vectors $|nlm\rangle$ we use the spherical basis

$$a_\pm = \mp \frac{1}{\sqrt{2}} (a_x \pm \mathrm{i} a_y), \qquad a_0 = a_z, \tag{7}$$

and similarly for $a_\mu^\dagger$; $\mu = \pm 1{,}0$. Note that

$$a_\mu^* = (-)^\mu a_{-\mu}^\dagger; \tag{7'}$$

the commutation rules are

$$(a_\mu, a_{\mu'}^\dagger) = (-)^\mu \delta_{\mu, -\mu'}, \tag{8}$$

and all other commutators vanish. In terms of the operators a_μ and $a_\mu^\dagger$ we have

$$\mathscr{H} = \sum_{\mu} (-)^{\mu} a_{\mu}^{\dagger} a_{-\mu} + \tfrac{3}{2}. \tag{3c}$$

The counterpart of (5a, b) is then

$$(\mathscr{H}, a_{\mu}^{\dagger}) = a_{\mu}^{\dagger}, \tag{9a}$$

$$(\mathscr{H}, a_{\mu}) = -\, a_{\mu}, \tag{9b}$$

as is obvious. Also, with $\boldsymbol{L} = \boldsymbol{r} \times \boldsymbol{p}$

$$(L_0, a_{\mu}) = \mu a_{\mu}, \tag{10a}$$

$$(L_0, a_{\mu}^{\dagger}) = \mu a_{\mu}^{\dagger}, \tag{10b}$$

so that $a_{\mu}^{\dagger}$ creates one quantum of energy and μ quanta of angular momentum projection (a.m.p.); a_{μ} annihilates one energy quantum but creates one quantum of a.m.p. However, from

$$\boldsymbol{L} = \boldsymbol{r} \times \boldsymbol{p} = \mathrm{i}\boldsymbol{a} \times \boldsymbol{a}^{\dagger} \tag{11}$$

it is clear that neither a_{μ} or $a_{\mu}^{\dagger}$ commutes with $\boldsymbol{L}^2$. Instead, from the first rank tensor properties of $\boldsymbol{a}$ and $\boldsymbol{a}^{\dagger}$, $a_{\mu}|nlm\rangle$ and $a_{\mu}^{\dagger}|nlm\rangle$ give linear combinations of $|n', l \pm 1, m + \mu\rangle$ with $n' = n - 1$ and $n + 1$ respectively.

To obtain an operator which acting on $|nlm\rangle$ gives $|n+1, l', m' = m + \mu\rangle$, with l' *either* $l + 1$ or $l - 1$, we obviously need to introduce the usual scheme of vector coupling. Thus,

$$|n+1, l', m'\rangle = N_{l'l}^{+} \sum_{\mu} C_{m\,\mu}^{l\,1\,l'}\, a_{\mu}^{\dagger} |nlm\rangle, \tag{12a}$$

where $N_{l'l}^{+}$ is a normalization constant which we will calculate in the following. Similarly,

$$|n-1, l', m'\rangle = N_{l'l}^{-} \sum_{\mu} C_{m\,\mu}^{l\,1\,l'}\, a_{\mu} |nlm\rangle, \tag{12b}$$

and $N_{l'l}^{-}$ is another normalization constant, see eqs. (18) below. Again, in (12a) and (12b), $m' = m + \mu$ and $l' = l \pm 1$. We also note that the energy quantum number n is related to the principal quantum number $\bar{n}$ by

$$n = 2\bar{n} + l - 2\,.$$

The $|nlm\rangle$ are, of course, of the form

$$|nlm\rangle = R_{nl}(r)\, Y_l^m(\hat{r}), \tag{13}$$

where the radial function is labelled with n rather than $\bar{n}$. Obviously $n - l$ is always an even integer.

We can construct a simple diagrammatic representation of the operators in (12a) and (12b) as well as those appearing below by considering the lattice points in an n–l plane with $l \leqslant n$. Then (12a) is represented by the arrows marked a in fig. 1 and (12b) by the arrows marked b. Our present purpose is

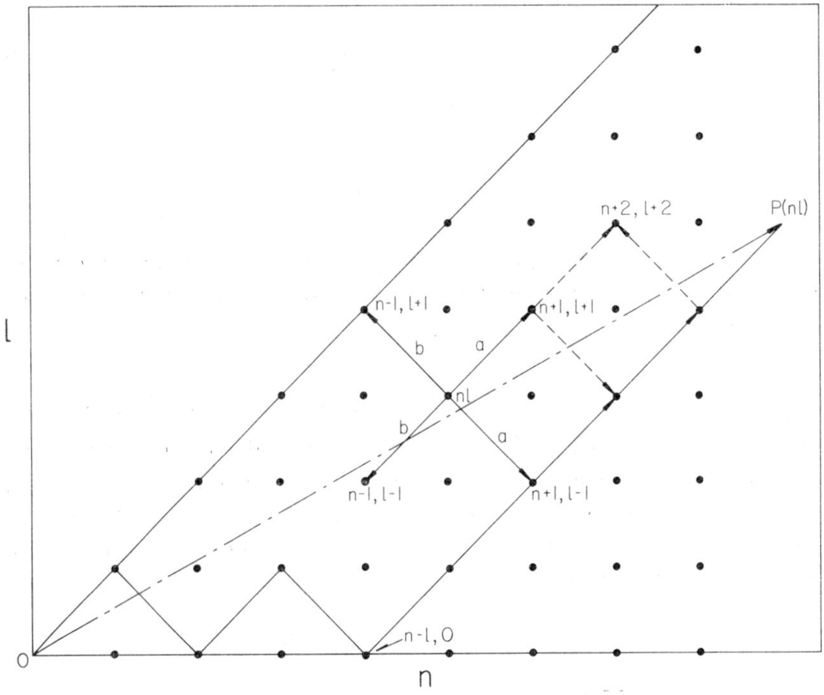

Fig. 1. The n–l diagram with $l \leqslant n$. Each lattice point represents the $2l+1$ states $|nlm\rangle$. The creation and annihilation operators are represented by (in general) broken lines composed of vectors connecting lattice points on a diagonal, such as either of the two vectors a or the two vectors b. The vector OP is not a possible operation but is the resultant of any one which connects the origin, $|000\rangle$, to $|nlm\rangle$ at P.

to construct an operator which creates the state $|nlm\rangle$ from the ground state $|000\rangle$ in analogy with Ω. For clarity the point P in fig. 1 is taken to represent $|nlm\rangle$ and the operator in question corresponds, in some sense, to the arrow from the origin to this point. Clearly, each point in the n–l diagram is $2l+1$-fold degenerate.

The operator which we wish to construct is denoted by χ_{nl}^{m}. Thus,

$$|nlm\rangle = \chi_{nl}^{m}\,|000\rangle\,. \tag{14}$$

Since χ_{nl}^{m} must be a tensor of rank l, with projection along the quantization axis m and since it must be a homogeneous polynomial in the components $a_{\mu}^{\dagger}$ of $\boldsymbol{a}^{\dagger}$, it must have the form

$$\chi_{nl}^{m} = K_{nl}\, a^{\dagger(n-l)}\, \mathscr{Y}_{l}^{m}(\boldsymbol{a}^{\dagger}), \tag{15}$$

where K_{nl} is a normalization factor to be determined. Note that $a^{\dagger(n-l)} = (\boldsymbol{a}^{\dagger}\cdot\boldsymbol{a}^{\dagger})^{\nu}$ with $1\nu = n-l$ and ν is a non-negative integer. That (15) is of the correct form becomes obvious if the operation (12a) is applied successively to $|nlm\rangle$ and then setting $n=l=m=0$. In this way we obtain, with an obvious simplification in notation,

$$K_{nl} = \frac{\sqrt{4\pi}}{\hat{l}_n} \prod_{1}^{n} (N_{l_j l_{j-1}}^{+}\, C_{0\ 0\ 0}^{l_{j-1}\, 1\, l_j}), \tag{16}$$

where $\hat{l}_n = (2l_n + 1)^{\frac{1}{2}}$ and where the sequence of l values is $l_0 l_1 \ldots l_j \ldots l_n$ so that $l_0 = 0$, $l_1 = 1$ and $l_n = l$.

The proof that (15) is correct with K_{nl} given by (16) proceeds by induction. By (15) and (16)

$$
\begin{aligned}
|n+1, l_{n+1}, m_{n+1}\rangle
&= \sqrt{\frac{4\pi}{3}}\, N_{l_{n+1} l_n}^{+} \sum_{m_n} C_{m_n\, m_{n+1}-m_n\, m_{n+1}}^{l_n\ 1\ l_{n+1}}\, \mathscr{Y}_{1}^{m_{n+1}-m_n}(\boldsymbol{a}^{\dagger})\, |nlm\rangle \\
&= \sqrt{\frac{4\pi}{3}} \prod_{1}^{n+1} (N_{l_j l_{j-1}}^{+}\, C_{0\ 0\ 0}^{l_{j-1}\, 1\, l_j}) \sum_{m_n} C_{m_n\, m_{n+1}-m_n}^{l_n\ 1\ l_{n+j}} \times \\
&\quad \times \sum_{\lambda} \frac{\hat{l}_n}{\hat{\lambda}}\, C_{0\ 0}^{l_n\, 1\, \lambda}\, C_{m_n\, m_{n+1}-m_n}^{l_n\ 1\ \lambda}\, a^{\dagger(n-l_n)} \times \\
&\quad \times a^{\dagger(l_n-\lambda+1)}\, \mathscr{Y}_{\lambda}^{m_{n+1}}(\boldsymbol{a}^{\dagger})\, |000\rangle .
\end{aligned}
$$

Carrying out the m_n sum and hence the λ sum we have

$$
\begin{aligned}
|n+1, l_{n+1}, m_{n+1}\rangle = \frac{\sqrt{4\pi}}{\hat{l}_{n+1}} \prod_{1}^{n+1} (N_{l_j l_{j-1}}^{+}\, C_{0\ 0\ 0}^{l_{j-1}\, 1\, l_j}) \times \\
\times\, a^{\dagger(n+1-l_{n+1})}\, \mathscr{Y}_{l_{n+1}}^{m_{n+1}}(\boldsymbol{a}^{\dagger})\, |000\rangle ,
\end{aligned}
$$

which is the required result. Finally, it is readily verified that in any number of special cases, e.g. $n=l=m=0$ and $n=l=1$, (15) is indeed valid with the specific results given by (16) and the normalization constants $N_{l_j l_{j-1}}^{+}$. We give the latter in the following paragraph.

To obtain the normalization constants we apply (12a) using the explicit form of $a_{\mu}^{\dagger}$ given by the counterpart of (7) and (2b). In the notation of (13) we obtain for $l' = l+1$

$$R_{n+1,\,l+1} = -\frac{N^{+}_{l+1,\,l}}{\sqrt{2}}\left(\frac{l+1}{2l+3}\right)^{\frac{1}{2}}\left[\frac{\mathrm{d}}{\mathrm{d}r} - \frac{l}{r} - r\right]R_{nl}\,, \tag{17a}$$

and for $l' = l-1$

$$R_{n+1,\,l-1} = \frac{N^{+}_{l-1,\,l}}{\sqrt{2}}\left(\frac{l}{2l-1}\right)^{\frac{1}{2}}\left[\frac{\mathrm{d}}{\mathrm{d}r} + \frac{l+1}{r} - r\right]R_{nl}\,. \tag{17b}$$

From the fact that

$$\int_0^\infty R^2_{nl}\, r^2\, \mathrm{d}r = 1\,,$$

we obtain, by squaring (17a) and (17b) and using

$$\left[\frac{\mathrm{d}^2}{\mathrm{d}r^2} + 2n + 3 - r^2 = \frac{l(l+1)}{r^2}\right] rR_{nl} = 0\,,$$

the results

$$N^{+}_{l+1,\,l} = \left[\frac{2l+3}{(l+1)\,(n+l+3)}\right]^{\frac{1}{2}}, \tag{18a}$$

$$N^{+}_{l-1,\,l} = \left[\frac{2l-1}{l(n-l+2)}\right]^{\frac{1}{2}}. \tag{18b}$$

Similarly, from (12b), (7) and (2a), we find

$$N^{-}_{l+1,\,l} = \left[\frac{2l+3}{(l+1)\,(n-l)}\right]^{\frac{1}{2}}, \tag{18c}$$

$$N^{-}_{l-1,\,l} = \left[\frac{2l-1}{l(n+l+1)}\right]^{\frac{1}{2}}. \tag{18d}$$

The normalization factor K_{nl} given in (16) can be greatly simplified if it is realized that while, in general, there are many paths in the n–l plane from $|000\rangle$ to $|nlm\rangle$ the latter state is unique and that each path must give the same result. The arbitrariness in phase in $|nlm\rangle$ is of no relevance since by our prescription the phase is completely defined. In this connection, it is recognized, of course, that the vector, in fig. 1 directly from the origin to the point marked P is not a possible path, but the broken line from the origin to the point $(n-l, 0)$ and then directly along the line with unit slope to (n, l) at P is. We refer to this as the "simplest" path.

The verification of uniqueness is interesting in that it is not obvious from the form of (15) and (16). We may first verify that the path from (nl) to $(n+2, l)$ via $(n+1, l+1)$ and alternatively via $(n+1, l-1)$ gives the same results. This is a matter of direct calculation from (15), (16) and (12a) together with (18a) and (18b) and the details need not be given. This result is represented by writing $ab = cd$ in the notation of fig. 2 which represents the

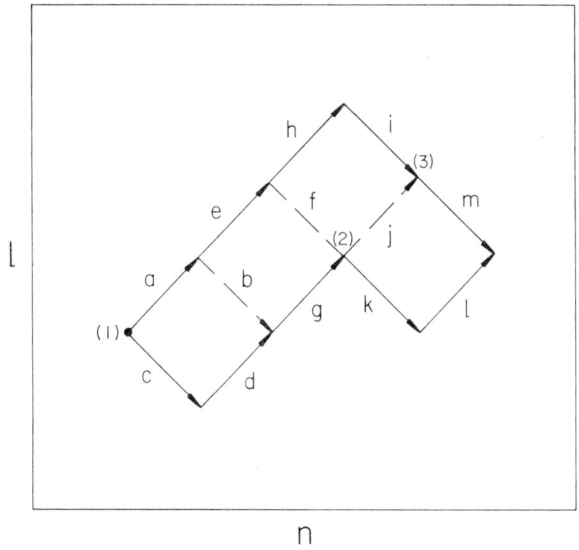

Fig. 2. An illustration of the uniqueness theorem. The state at any lattice point, such as (2) or (3), is independent of the path traversed in arriving to that state.

fact that the product of the operators on the n–l space vectors a and b gives the same result as the product along c and d. Similarly $ef = bg$, $hi = fj$ and $jm = kl$. Note also that each letter, a ... m represents commuting operators. Then from $ab = cd$ and $ef = bg$ we obtain

$$ab(bg)^{-1} = cd(ef)^{-1} \qquad \text{or} \qquad aef = cdg\,.$$

This implies that the state obtained at (2) in fig. 2 from the point (1) is the same for the two paths aef and cdg. In a similar way one can construct equalities for any diagram composed of squares in the n–l plane. Thus, using $ki = fj$ we find for the state at (3) in fig. 2

$$aehi = cdgj$$

and with $jm = kl$ we immediately conclude that $aehim = cdgkl$. To complete the argument, any diagram is composed of a number of contiguous basic squares with vertices at (n, l), $(n+1, l\pm 1)$, $(n+2, l)$. Any path from (n, l) to (n', l') is composed of single traversals of boundary lines (drawn in full in fig. 2) and double traversals of inner lines (dashed in fig. 2). A double traversal makes no contribution since it involves an operator times its inverse. The illustrations given above are sufficient to show that for the outer boundaries of any diagram one gets unique results irrespective of the path.

We make use of this result by calculating K_{nl} for the simplest path. Then from (18) we obtain

$$K_{nl} = (-)^{\nu}\left[\frac{4\pi}{2l+1}\,\frac{(2l+1)!!}{l!}\,\frac{(n-l+1)!!}{(n-l+1)!\,(n+l+1)!!}\right]^{\frac{1}{2}}$$

$$= (-)^{\nu}\left[4\pi\binom{2l}{l}\frac{(l+\nu)!}{\nu!(2\nu+2l+1)!}\right]^{\frac{1}{2}}. \tag{19}$$

With this result and (15) we complete the construction of the χ_{nl}^{m} operator.

3. Properties of the χ_{nl}^{m} operator

We have made use of the inverse operators in the foregoing. These can be obtained explicitly by following the same path as that which led to the results (15) and (19). More simply, we observe that

$$\langle nlm|nlm\rangle = \langle 0|\chi_{nl}^{m*}\,\chi_{nl}^{m}|0\rangle = 1\,.$$

Since

$$[a^{\dagger(n-l)}\mathscr{Y}_l^m(\boldsymbol{a}^{\dagger})]^* = (-)^m a^{n-l}\mathscr{Y}_l^{-m}(\boldsymbol{a})$$

annihilates n units of energy, l units of orbital angular momentum and m units of a.m.p. it follows that $|000\rangle$ is an eigenfunction of $\chi_{nl}^{m*}\,\chi_{nl}^{m}$ and the eigenvalue is unity. In this sense we write

$$\chi_{nl}^{m*}\,\chi_{nl}^{m} = 1\,.$$

Hence, χ_{nl}^{m} is unitary in this restricted sense and

$$(\chi_{nl}^{m})^{-1} = \chi_{nl}^{m*} \tag{20}$$

or

$$(\chi_{nl}^{m})^{-1} = (-)^m K_{nl}\, a^{n-l}\mathscr{Y}_l^{-m}(\boldsymbol{a}), \tag{21}$$

with the normalization factor K_{nl} again given by (19). In a formal way, the operator which connects any two points in the n–l diagram is then

$$\Gamma_{nl,n'l'}^{m,m'} = \chi_{nl}^{m'}(\chi_{n'l'}^{m'})^{-1}$$
$$= \chi_{nl}^{m'}\chi_{n'l'}^{m'*},$$

which converts $|n'l'm'\rangle$ to $|nlm\rangle$. Since χ and χ^* do not commute it is not a simple matter to express this result in a more elementary way. We note that it is possible to express the matrix elements of any operator $\mathcal{O}$ in terms of diagonal matrix elements with the ground state; viz.,

$$\langle n_1 l_1 m_1 | \mathcal{O} | n_2 l_2 m_2 \rangle = \langle 000 | \chi_{n_1 l_1}^{m_1 *} \mathcal{O} \chi_{n_2 l_2}^{m_2} | 000 \rangle .$$

For example, if $\mathcal{O} = \mathcal{Y}_\lambda^m (\boldsymbol{a}^\dagger)$,

$$\langle n_1 l_1 m_1 \mathcal{Y}_\lambda^m (\boldsymbol{a}^\dagger) | n_2 l_2 m_2 \rangle = \frac{(-)^\lambda K_{n_2 l_2}}{\sqrt{4\pi}\, K_{n_1 l_1}} \hat{\lambda} C_{0\ 0}^{l_1\ \lambda\ l_2} C_{m_2\ m}^{l_2\ \lambda\ l_1} \delta_{n_2+\lambda, n_1} \delta_{m+m_2, m_1} ,$$

the corresponding matrix element of $\chi_{n\lambda}^m / K_{n\lambda}$ is obtained simply by replacing $\delta_{n_2+\lambda, n_1}$ with δ_{n_2+n, n_1} in the above result. Similarly the scalar

$$S = \sum_m \chi_{nl}^{m*} \chi_{nl}^m$$

has only diagonal matrix elements given by

$$\langle n_1 l_1 m_1 | S | n_1 l_1 m_1 \rangle = \frac{\hat{l}^2}{4\pi} (K_{nl} K_{n_1 l_1})^2 \sum_\lambda \left(\frac{C_{0\ 0}^{l_1\ l\ \lambda}}{K_{n_1+n,}} \right)^2 ,$$

which is equal to $2l+1$ only for the ground state, $n_1 = l_1 = m_1 = 0$.

A simple interpretation of the factors in χ_{nl}^m can be obtained. If we set $n = l$ in (15) we have

$$|nnm\rangle = K_{nn} \mathcal{Y}_n^m (\boldsymbol{a}^\dagger) |000\rangle ,$$

or

$$|llm\rangle = K_{ll}\, \mathcal{Y}_l^m (\boldsymbol{a}^\dagger) |000\rangle .$$

Since $|nlm\rangle$ can be reached from the origin by the vector from the origin to $|llm\rangle$ and then by a path the resultant of which is the horizontal line segment to $|nlm\rangle$ it follows that

$$\frac{K_{nl}}{K_{ll}} a^{\dagger (n-l)}$$

creates n quanta of energy and nothing else. The product of this with $K_{ll} \mathcal{Y}_l^m (\boldsymbol{a}^\dagger)$ is χ_{nl}^m. So apart from constants the structure of χ_{nl}^m is a product of two operators, one of which creates l units of energy, l units of angular momentum and m units of a.m.p., and another, which creates $n-l$ units of energy and the products can be taken in either order.

We note that

$$\frac{K_{nl}}{K_{ll}} = (-)^{\nu}\left[\frac{(n-l+1)!!}{(n-l+1)!}\,\frac{(2l+1)!!}{(n+l+1)!!}\right]^{\frac{1}{2}}.$$

Also from the horizontal vector operator $\boldsymbol{a}^{\dagger}\cdot\boldsymbol{a}^{\dagger}$, we obtain, as a by product, the recurrence relation

$$R_{nl} = \frac{K_{nl}}{K_{n'l}}\, D^{\frac{1}{2}(n-n')} R_{n'l}, \tag{22}$$

where $n-n'$ is even and D is a radial differential operator given by

$$D = r^2 - n' - 3 - r\frac{\mathrm{d}}{\mathrm{d}r},$$

and R_{nl} is the well-known Laguerre function[1])

$$R_{nl} = \left[\frac{2N!}{(N+l+\frac{1}{2})!}\right]^{\frac{1}{2}} r^l L_N^{l+\frac{1}{2}}(r^2),$$

where $N = \bar{n} - 1$.

4. Unitary transformation from cartesian representation

In a discussion of the Talmi transformation Smirnov[1]) has utilized the unitary transformation between the angular momentum and cartesian representations. We may write this in the form

$$|nlm\rangle = \sum_{n_1n_2n_3} A_{nlm}^{n_1n_2n_3}\,|n_1n_2n_3\rangle, \tag{23}$$

with $\sum_i n_i = n$. In the reference cited explicit numerical results were given for three special cases but no general result for the elements of the matrix A was exhibited. This general result can be obtained by the following procedure. First we note that $|000\rangle$ represents the ground state in both representations. Therefore,

$$A_{nlm}^{n_1n_2n_3} = \langle 000|\,\Omega_{n_1n_2n_3}^{-1}\chi_{nl}^{m}\,|000\rangle. \tag{24}$$

To evaluate the right-hand side of (24) we need to express χ_{nl}^m in terms of the cartesian components of $\boldsymbol{a}^{\dagger}$ and much of this section is devoted to that task.

The first task is to obtain the cartesian expansion of $\mathscr{Y}_l^m(\boldsymbol{c})$ where $\boldsymbol{c}$ is a sum of two non-commuting operators but wherein the components of $\boldsymbol{c}$ commute with each other*. This is done by means of the displacement

* Actually, it will be sufficient to obtain the expansion in terms of monomials involving the spherical components of $\boldsymbol{c}$.

theorem for solid harmonics which was previously[2]) derived for $\boldsymbol{c} = \boldsymbol{a} + \boldsymbol{b}$, where $\boldsymbol{a}$ and $\boldsymbol{b}$ were commuting 3-space vectors. However, the result is also valid if the commutators (a_i, b_j) are c-numbers. To show this and to simplify the proof of the displacement theorem, we proceed as follows. We start with the well-known result

$$\mathrm{e}^{A+B}\,\mathrm{e}^{\frac{1}{2}(A,B)} = \mathrm{e}^{A}\,\mathrm{e}^{B}. \tag{25}$$

We set $A = \mathrm{i}\boldsymbol{k}\cdot\boldsymbol{a}$ and $B = \mathrm{i}\boldsymbol{k}\cdot\boldsymbol{b}$ where $(a_i, b_j) = \alpha\delta_{ij}$, so that $(A, B) = -\alpha k^2$ and α is independent of k.

Using the Rayleigh expansion of the exponentials we have for the left-hand side of (25)

$$\mathrm{e}^{\mathrm{i}\boldsymbol{k}\cdot(\boldsymbol{a}+\boldsymbol{b})} = \mathrm{e}^{\mathrm{i}\boldsymbol{k}\cdot\boldsymbol{c}} = 4\pi \sum_{LM} \mathrm{i}^L j_L(kc)\, Y_L^{M*}(\hat{k})\, Y_L^M(\hat{c}),$$

where we recoqnize that $j_L(kc) = (kc)^L f(kc)$ with f an even function of its argument. Hence only $\mathscr{Y}_L^M(\boldsymbol{c})$ enters as well as even powers of c and $\hat{c}$ need not be defined. Similarly, the right-hand side of (25) is

$$\mathrm{e}^{\mathrm{i}\boldsymbol{k}\cdot\boldsymbol{a}}\,\mathrm{e}^{\mathrm{i}\boldsymbol{k}\cdot\boldsymbol{b}}\,\mathrm{e}^{\frac{1}{2}\alpha k^2} = 16\pi^2 \sum_{ll'} \mathrm{i}^{l+l'}\, j_l(ka)\, j_{l'}(kb)\, \mathrm{e}^{\frac{1}{2}\alpha k^2} \times$$
$$\times \sum_{mm'} Y_l^{m*}(\hat{k})\, Y_{l'}^{m'*}(\hat{k})\, Y_l^m(\hat{a})\, Y_{l'}^{m'}(\hat{b}),$$

and again we interpret $\hat{a}$ and $\hat{b}$ in a fashion similar to $\hat{c}$. Writing the product $[Y_l^m(\hat{k})\, Y_{l'}^{m'}(\hat{k})]^*$ as a sum over λ of $Y_\lambda^{m+m'}(\hat{k})$ and equating coefficients of the spherical harmonics in $\hat{k}$ we find

$$j_L(kc)\, Y_L^M(\hat{c}) = \sqrt{4\pi} \sum_{ll'm} \mathrm{i}^{l+l'-L} j_l(ka)\, j_{l'}(kb)\, \mathrm{e}^{\frac{1}{2}\alpha k^2} \times$$
$$\times \frac{\hat{l}\hat{l}'}{\hat{L}}\, C_{0\,0}^{l\,l'\,L}\, C_{m\,M\,-m}^{l\,l'\,L}\, Y_l^m(\hat{a})\, Y_{l'}^{M-m}(\hat{b}).$$

Since this is an identity in k we can equate coefficients of like powers of k. The term of lowest power has k^L on the left side. The ll' term on the right side has $k^{l+l'}$. Since $l + l' \geqslant L$ it is necessary that $l + l' = L$ and hence,

$$\mathscr{Y}_L^M(\boldsymbol{c}) = \sqrt{4\pi}(2L+1)!! \sum_{lm} \frac{\hat{l}\widehat{(L-l)}}{\hat{L}} \frac{1}{(2l+1)!!\,(2L-2l+1)!!} \times$$
$$\times\, C_{0\,0}^{l\,L-l\,L}\, C_{m\,M\,-m}^{l\,L-l\,L}\, \mathscr{Y}_l^m(\boldsymbol{a})\, \mathscr{Y}_{L-l}^{M-m}(\boldsymbol{b}), \tag{26}$$

and in this result the fact that $\alpha \neq 0$ is immaterial. In summary, this result shows that if $(a_i, b_j) = \alpha\delta_{ij}$ with α a c-number $\mathscr{Y}_L^M(\boldsymbol{a}+\boldsymbol{b})$ can be written as a sum of monomials with $\boldsymbol{a}$ to the left of $\boldsymbol{b}$ or $\boldsymbol{b}$ to the left of $\boldsymbol{a}$ with coefficients independent of α.

We now apply this to the case $\boldsymbol{c} = c_0\,\boldsymbol{e}_0 + \boldsymbol{\rho}$ where $\boldsymbol{e}_0$ is a unit vector in the 0 or z direction and $\boldsymbol{\rho}$ is in the x–y plane. Then, writing (26) in the form

$$\mathscr{Y}_L^M(\boldsymbol{c}) = \sqrt{4\pi}\sum_{lm} \Lambda_{Ll}^{Mm}\,\mathscr{Y}_l^m(\boldsymbol{\rho})\,\mathscr{Y}_{L-l}^{M-m}(c_0\boldsymbol{e}_0),$$

we get $M = m$, $l - M$ even and

$$\mathscr{Y}_L^M(\boldsymbol{0}) = \sum_l (2L-2l+1)^{\frac{1}{2}}\,\Lambda_{Ll}^{MM}\,c_0^{L-l}\,\mathscr{Y}_l^M(\boldsymbol{\rho}).$$

But,

$$\mathscr{Y}_l^M(\boldsymbol{\rho}) = \rho^l\,\mathrm{e}^{\mathrm{i}M\varphi}\,Y_l^M(\tfrac{1}{2}\pi, 0),$$

where

$$\rho^l\,\mathrm{e}^{\mathrm{i}M\varphi} = \rho^l(c_+/\rho)^M = (c_+c_-)^{\frac{1}{2}(l-M)}\,c_+^M,$$

where

$$c_\pm = c_x \pm \mathrm{i}c_y.$$

So,

$$\mathscr{Y}_L^M(\boldsymbol{c}) = \frac{(-)^M}{\sqrt{4\pi}}\sum_l (-)^\lambda\,\hat{l}\,\widehat{(L-l)}\,\Lambda_{Ll}^{MM}\times$$
$$\times\frac{[(l-M)!\,(l+M)!]^{\frac{1}{2}}}{2^l\lambda!\,(l-\lambda)!}\,c_0^{L-l}\,c_+^{\lambda+M}\,c_-^\lambda,$$

where $2\lambda = l - M$. Using eq. (29) of ref. 2, we find

$$\Lambda_{Ll}^{MM} = \frac{1}{(L-l)!}\,\frac{\hat{L}}{\hat{l}\,\widehat{(L-l)}}\left[\frac{(L-M)!\,(L+M)!}{(l-M)!\,(l+M)!}\right]^{\frac{1}{2}},$$

and the simple result

$$\mathscr{Y}_L^M(\boldsymbol{c}) = \frac{(-)^M\hat{L}}{\sqrt{4\pi}}[(L-M)!\,(L+M)!]^{\frac{1}{2}}\sum_l\frac{(-)^\lambda}{2^l\lambda!\,(l-\lambda)!}\,\frac{1}{(L-l)!}\times$$
$$\times\,c_0^{L-l}\,c_+^{\lambda+M}\,c_-^\lambda \tag{27}$$

is obtained. Finally,

$$c^{n-L}\mathscr{Y}_L^M(\boldsymbol{c}) = \frac{(-)^M\hat{L}}{\sqrt{4\pi}}[(L-M)!\,(L+M)!]^{\frac{1}{2}}\times$$
$$\times\sum_{lt}\binom{\nu}{t}\frac{(-)^\lambda 2^{-l}}{\lambda!\,(l-\lambda)!}\,\frac{1}{(L-l)!}\,c_0^{L-l+2t}\,c_+^{\lambda+M+\nu-t}\,c_-^{\lambda+\nu-t}. \tag{28}$$

The matrix element in (24) now becomes

$$A_{nlm}^{n_1n_2n_3} = \mathrm{i}^{n_2}(-)^{\frac{1}{2}(n_1-n_2-m)} \frac{K_{nl}}{\sqrt{4\pi}} \hat{l} \left[\frac{n_3!}{n_1!\, n_2!}(l-m)!\,(l+m)!\right]^{\frac{1}{2}} \times$$
$$\times \left(\frac{n-n_3+m}{2}\right)! \left(\frac{n-n_3-m}{2}\right)! \sum_s (-)^s \binom{n_1}{s} \binom{n_2}{\frac{n-n_3+m}{2}-s} \times$$
$$\times \sum_{l'} \frac{(-)^{\lambda'} 2^{-l'}}{\lambda'!(l'-\lambda')!\,(l-l')!} \binom{\nu}{\frac{n_3+l'-l}{2}}, \tag{29}$$

where now $2\lambda' = l' - m$. The sums are extended over all values for which the arguments of the factorials are non-negative. It will be observed that $\mathrm{i}^{n_2} A_{nlm}^{n_1n_2n_3}$ is symmetrical in n_1 and n_2. Also $n - n_3 \pm m$ and $n_3 + l' - l$ are even integers.

5. Consideration of the Lie algebra

The analysis of the isotropic oscillator from the point of view of the relevant Lie algebra is not new[3]). For the sake of a coherent discussion we shall begin at the beginning and after summarizing some material which does appear in the literature we shall add a few remarks which may be new.

If we consider the nine bilinear operators $a_i^\dagger a_j$ in the cartesian representation, then a classification of the multiplets of the harmonic oscillator can be made on the basis of the associated non-invariance group[4]). It is of interest to consider these nine operators in terms of the spherical basis and we accordingly define

$$b_{\mu\mu'} = a_\mu^\dagger a_{\mu'}, \tag{30}$$

with $\mu = \pm 1, 0$. These operators all leave the energy unchanged. The three operators with $\mu = -\mu'$ play a special role. For instance,

$$b_{\mu\mu'}^* = (-)^{\mu+\mu'} b_{-\mu,-\mu'}, \tag{31}$$

so that the $b_{\mu,-\mu}$ are hermitian. The commutation rules are

$$(b_{\mu_1\mu_2}, b_{\mu_3\mu_4}) = (-)^{\mu_2} \delta_{\mu_3-\mu_2} b_{\mu_1\mu_4} + \\ - (-)^{\mu_1} \delta_{\mu_4-\mu_1} b_{\mu_3\mu_2}. \tag{32}$$

Hence the three $b_{\mu,-\mu}$ commute with each other. Moreover, if $\mu' + \mu'' \neq 0$,

$$(b_{\mu,-\mu}, b_{\mu'\mu''}) = \gamma b_{\mu'\mu''}, \tag{32'}$$

with

$$\gamma = (-)^{\mu'} \delta_{\mu' \mu} - (-)^{\mu} \delta_{\mu'', -\mu} .$$

It follows that $\gamma = \pm 1,0$ so that the six operators other than $b_{\mu,-\mu}$ are raising and lowering operators in terms of the eigenvalues of the $b_{\mu,-\mu}$ operators. The nine $b_{\mu\mu'}$ form the elements of a Lie algebra.

The Hamiltonian is given by

$$\mathscr{H} - \tfrac{3}{2} = \sum_{\mu} (-)^{\mu} b_{\mu, -\mu} , \tag{33}$$

and commutes with all the nine $b_{\mu\mu'}$. Hence we can choose eight linearly independent combinations of the $b_{\mu\mu'}$, other than $\mathscr{H}$, which are associated with a Lie group. For our purposes it is useful to define the eight operators by[3])

$$B_{\lambda}^{m} = -\sqrt{2} \sum_{\mu} C_{\mu\ m-\mu}^{1\ 1\ \lambda}\, b_{\mu, m-\mu} , \tag{34}$$

with $\lambda = 1$ and 2. For $\lambda = 0$ we readily verify that

$$B_0^0 = \sqrt{\tfrac{2}{3}} (\mathscr{H} - \tfrac{3}{2}) .$$

Obviously B_{λ} is a tensor of rank λ. For $\lambda = 1$ the vector is the angular momentum operator

$$\boldsymbol{B} = \boldsymbol{L} = \boldsymbol{r} \times \boldsymbol{p} . \tag{35}$$

In detail

$$B_1^0 = L_0 = b_{-1\,1} - b_{1\,-1} ,$$
$$B_1^{\pm 1} = L_{\pm 1} = \mp (b_{\pm 1\,0} - b_{0\,\pm 1}) ,$$

the other five operators form the components of the "quadrupole" tensor

$$B_2^0 = -\frac{1}{\sqrt{3}} (2b_{0\,0} + b_{1\,-1} + b_{-1\,1})$$
$$= -\frac{1}{\sqrt{3}} (3b_{0\,0} - \mathscr{H} + \tfrac{3}{2}) ,$$
$$B_2^{\pm 1} = -(b_{\pm 1\,0} + b_{0\,\pm 1}) ,$$
$$B_2^{\pm 2} = -\sqrt{2}\, b_{\pm 1\,\pm 1} .$$

It is of interest to point out that the B_{λ}^{m} operators correspond to a vertical displacement in the n–l diagram through 0 or ± 2 units of l. For $\lambda = 0$ and 1, l does not change although, of course, the a.m.p. changes by m for $\lambda = 1$. For $\lambda = 2$ the a.m.p. changes by m and l changes to l' where $l' = l \pm 2, l$.

For application in subsequent considerations we need the commutators of these eight operators. We find

$$(B_\lambda^m, B_{\lambda'}^{m'}) = -\sqrt{2}\sum_{\lambda''} \alpha(\lambda\lambda'\lambda''; mm')\, B_{\lambda''}^{m''}, \tag{36}$$

with $m'' = m + m'$ and

$$\alpha(\lambda\lambda'\lambda''; mm') = 2(-)^{1+\lambda}\hat{\lambda}\hat{\lambda}'\, C_{m\,m'}^{\lambda\,\lambda'\,\lambda''}\, W(\lambda 1 \lambda'' 1; 1\lambda'), \tag{36'}$$

with $\lambda + \lambda' + \lambda''$ odd. Otherwise $\alpha = 0$. In addition $\lambda'' \leqslant 2$. The only vanishing commutators aside from (B_0^0, B_λ^m) and the trivial cases $\lambda = \lambda'$, $m = m'$ are $(B_1^m, B_2^{m'})$ for $|m''| > 2$ and $(B_2^m, B_2^{m'})$ for $|m''| > 1$. In general, the sum in (36) contains only one term. The fact that (B_λ^m, B_2^0) is not proportional to B_λ^m means that the relation analogous to (32′) is not fulfilled.

We also find

$$B_\lambda^{m*} = (-)^m B_\lambda^{-m}$$

as might have been guessed.

In addition to $\mathscr{H}$ two other scalars are to be considered. These are

$$\boldsymbol{L}^2 = \sum_m (-)^m B_1^m B_1^{-m} \tag{37}$$

and the square of the quadrupole tensor

$$\boldsymbol{Q}^2 = \sum_m (-)^m B_2^m B_2^{-m}. \tag{38}$$

From these a Casimir operator can be formed. That is,

$$\mathscr{C} = \beta \boldsymbol{L}^2 + \boldsymbol{Q}^2$$

is to commute with all eight operators B_λ^m. Here β is a constant to be fixed so that $(\mathscr{C}, B_\lambda^m) = 0$. After a lengthy calculation one finds from (36) and (36′) that

$$\beta = -\frac{W(2111; 12)}{W(2121; 11)} = 1,$$

so that

$$\mathscr{C} = \boldsymbol{Q}^2 + \boldsymbol{L}^2. \tag{39}$$

Now, it is clear that $\boldsymbol{L}^2$ commutes with all B_λ^m with $\lambda < 2$. The complete set of commuting operators B_0^0, B_1^0 and $\boldsymbol{L}^2$ is, in fact, the set which is diagonalized in the angular momentum representation. It follows that $\boldsymbol{Q}^2$ must also commute with all B_λ^m with $\lambda < 2$ but not with B_2^m. Consequently $\boldsymbol{Q}^2$ must be a function of $\mathscr{H}$ and $\boldsymbol{L}^2$. It cannot contain the components B_1^m in any other manner since it is a scalar. To determine the relationship between $\boldsymbol{Q}^2$, $\mathscr{H}$

and $\boldsymbol{L}^2$ we calculate the eigenvalue or equivalently the expectation value of $\boldsymbol{Q}^2$ for the state $|nlm\rangle$. Thus,

$$Q_0^2 = \langle nlm|\, Q^2\, |nlm\rangle = \sum_M \langle B_2^M nlm|\, B_2^M nlm\rangle$$

turns out to be

$$Q_0^2 = \tfrac{1}{3}(2n+3)^2 - (l^2 + l + 3)\,.$$

Thus, we conclude that

$$\boldsymbol{Q}^2 = \tfrac{4}{3}\mathscr{H}^2 - \boldsymbol{L}^2 - 3\,, \tag{40}$$

and that the Casimir operator is

$$\mathscr{C} = \tfrac{4}{3}\mathscr{H}^2 - 3\,. \tag{41}$$

One may argue that $\mathscr{C}$ as well as any other Casimir operator which may exist must be diagonal in the angular momentum representation and, since all such operators are scalars, only $\mathscr{H}$ and $\boldsymbol{L}^2$ may be involved. However, since $\boldsymbol{L}^2$ is not a Casimir operator it appears plausible that all such operators may depend on $\mathscr{H}$ only. In the special case considered this result is verified.

Footnotes and references

1) For example, Y. F. Smirnov, Nucl. Phys. **39**, 346 (1962).
2) M. E. Rose, J. Math. Phys. (M.I.T.) **37**, 215 (1958).
3) See for example, H. Lipkin, *Lie Groups for Pedestrians* (North-Holland Publ. Co., Amsterdam, 1965).
4) O. A. Novaro, Bull. Am. Phys. Soc. [2] **11**, 762 (1966). Strictly speaking, the operators $a_i^\dagger a_j^\dagger$ and $a_i a_j$ which create and annihilate two quanta are also involved in this discussion.

Spectroscopic and group theoretical methods in physics

FIELD CONFIGURATIONS AND PARAMETERS THAT IDENTIFY STATES WITH $j=1$

U. FANO

National Bureau of Standards, Washington, D.C. 20234, U.S.A.
and
*University of Chicago, Chicago, Illinois 60637, U.S.A.**

1. Introduction

A particle (e.g., an atom, molecule or nucleus) isolated in space and with nonzero angular momentum in its rest frame has a manifold of states with equal energy. Weak external fields can change these states into one another. A familiar transformation of this kind is the Larmor precession of the orientation of a system, which is induced by a uniform magnetic field. Particles with $j \geqslant 1$ experience, in addition, continuous rearrangements of their charge and current distributions under the influence of weak multipole fields.

Recall, in this connection, that the familiar intrinsic parameters of a particle (its magnetic dipole μ, electric quadrupole q, etc.) represent the nonzero components of its respective multipole moments for the *particular* state with $m=j$ (which is selected by a suitable Stern–Gerlach device). They also describe completely the electric and magnetic properties of any state obtained from the first one by an adiabatic rotation of coordinate axes. However, we consider here a much *greater variety of states* whose magnetic and electric properties must be represented by suitable sets of numerical parameters in addition to μ, q, etc. The classification of such states has attracted little attention, presumably because of the weakness of multipole interactions and of the limited types of field geometries that have been utilized.

Analytical methods of identifying each state of given angular momentum and its transformations are, of course, available. Yet our qualitative understanding is limited, since the parameters utilized for this purpose (e.g., the

* Permanent address.

coefficients a_m of a superposition $\psi = \Sigma_m a_m u_m$) are often obscurely related to physical observables, nor are their ranges of variation easily outlined. Consider, by contrast, the related problem of light polarization where familiarity was acquired long ago with the concepts that identify the types of polarization (linear, circular or elliptical, partial or total) and the classes of active elements (crystals, reflectors, etc.) which produce, modify or detect polarization.

In the search for a more operational and transparent description of states and of their transformations, this author had the benefit of numerous exchanges with Professor Racah. Accordingly, it seems appropriate to return to the problem in this Memorial Volume, even though only fragmentary progress can be reported and its implications and extensions still elude us.

For each pure state of an isolated particle one can find a weak field of suitable characteristics which leaves this state stationary. The most familiar states, namely those identified by a magnetic quantum number m, are stationary in the presence of a uniform magnetic field. Which set of field configurations is required to characterize similarly any other pure state for a given j? Again, a magnetic field changes only the orientation of a non-stationary state. Which field configurations are required to change any given pure state into any other one?

A general state of a particle (whether pure or non-pure) can be characterized by the set of mean values of all components of its multipole moments, that is, by the pattern of static electric and magnetic fields which the particle generates under stationary conditions in the surrounding space or by the radiation pattern which it emits when precessing in a magnetic field. (The detection of magnetic dipole signals in a Bloch induction experiment can in principle be complemented by detecting signals of electric quadrupole and higher multipolarity.) What range of variability have the strengths, relative orientations and other characteristics of the various multipole moments of a system with given values of μ, q, etc.?

The answer to these questions is well known for systems with $j = \frac{1}{2}$, which have only a magnetic dipole of strength μ and whose energy is determined only by the strength H of a uniform magnetic field. Each of their pure states can be identified as the state that would remain stationary, with energy $-\mu H$, for a specific field direction $\hat{H}$. Each non-pure state can be identified by mean ("expectation") values of the direction and strength of its magnetic dipole moment, $P\boldsymbol{\mu}$, where $0 \leqslant P < 1$ indicates the degree of polarization of the state ($P = 1$ for pure states). Corresponding answers to the same questions are given in this paper for $j = 1$ but are apparently unknown for $j > 1$.

2. Pure states with $j=1$

Consider now a system with $j=1$ and with intrinsic dipole and quadrupole moments represented by μ and q. We wish to demonstrate how each of its pure states can be identified as the state that remains stationary with lowest energy under application of weak electric and magnetic fields

$$\boldsymbol{H} = (0, 0, H), \qquad \boldsymbol{E} = (2Kx, -2Ky, 0), \tag{1}$$

for a suitable orientation of the coordinate axes and for a suitable ratio of strengths K/H. An arrangement of coils and condenser plates that produces

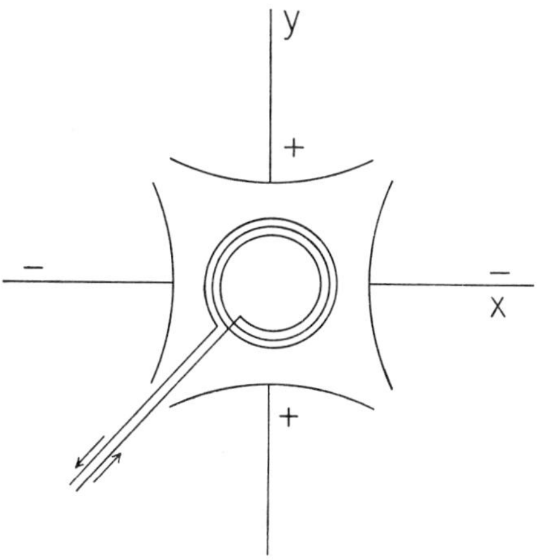

Fig. 1. Cross section of a quadrupole condenser and coils that provide a standard test field configuration.

the field configuration (1) is shown in fig. 1. The energy of the system in this field is represented by

$$W = -\mu H J_z - qK(J_x^2 - J_y^2) = -[(\mu H)^2 + (qK)^2]^{\frac{1}{2}}[\cos 2\lambda\, J_z + \sin 2\lambda\, Q_2], \tag{2}$$

where $\boldsymbol{J}$ is the angular momentum operator in units of $\hbar$,

$$\tan 2\lambda = qK/\mu H, \tag{3}$$

$$Q_2 = J_x^2 - J_y^2. \tag{4}$$

The structure of the electric energy operator is obtained by writing the potential $V = -K(x^2 - y^2)$ and replacing the coordinates by components of $\boldsymbol{J}$. The matrix of W, in the usual representation where J_z is diagonal and in dimensionless units, is

$$\frac{-W}{[(\mu H)^2+(qK)^2]^{\frac{1}{2}}} = \begin{vmatrix} \cos 2\lambda & 0 & \sin 2\lambda \\ 0 & 0 & 0 \\ \sin 2\lambda & 0 & -\cos 2\lambda \end{vmatrix}. \tag{5}$$

The eigenvalues of this matrix are 1, 0 and -1. Its eigenfunction corresponding to the (lowest energy) eigenvalue 1 is, in the same representation,

$$\psi_\lambda = \cos\lambda u_1 + \sin\lambda u_{-1}. \tag{6}$$

A main feature of the state ψ_λ consists of the parameter λ which indicates the relative values of the mean magnetic moment component $\langle\mu_z\rangle = \mu\langle J_z\rangle = \mu\cos 2\lambda$ and of the mean quadrupole component $q\langle Q_2\rangle = q\sin 2\lambda$. (Notice that $\langle\mu_x\rangle = \langle\mu_y\rangle = 0$ for all values of λ.) The state ψ_λ also depends on 3 orientation parameters which identify the intrinsic coordinate axes, i.e., including λ, on a total of 4 parameters. Thus, variations of λ represent changes of the distribution of charges and currents that are unrelated to the particle's orientation with respect to coordinate axes.

For $\lambda = 0$, ψ_λ coincides with u_1 and corresponds to fully cylindrical symmetry of the charge distribution about the intrinsic z axis and to a maximum of the effective mean magnetic moment, i.e., of the current circulation about the z axis. As λ increases up to $\frac{1}{4}\pi$ the effective current circulation decreases, in accordance with admixture of u_{-1} in (6), and an asymmetry of charge distribution in the x and y directions emerges. In the particular case where the system consists of a particle in a p state of a central potential, with wave functions

$$u_{\pm 1} = (3/8\pi)^{\frac{1}{2}} f(r)\,(\pm\sin\vartheta)\exp(\pm i\varphi),$$

(6) becomes

$$\psi_\lambda = -(3/4\pi)^{\frac{1}{2}} f(r)\sin\vartheta\,[\cos(\lambda + \tfrac{1}{4}\pi)\cos\varphi + i\sin(\lambda + \tfrac{1}{4}\pi)\sin\varphi]. \tag{7}$$

For $\lambda = \frac{1}{4}\pi$, (7) reduces to the "p_y" orbital, i.e., $\psi_{\frac{1}{4}\pi}$ coincides with the $m=0$ state pertaining to the quantization axis y.

The usual representation of an arbitrary pure state for $j=1$ is

$$\psi = \sum_{m=-1}^{1} a_m u_m \tag{8}$$

where the coefficients a_m can be regarded as the components of a complex unit vector

$$\hat{a} = \boldsymbol{b} + i\boldsymbol{c} \tag{9}$$

($\boldsymbol{b}$ and $\boldsymbol{c}$ real); for an orbital p state (8) becomes

$$\psi = (3/4\pi)^{\frac{1}{2}} f(r)\,\hat{a}\cdot\hat{r}\,. \tag{10}$$

Since the arbitrary ψ depends on 4 real parameters (i.e., 6 components of $\boldsymbol{b}$ and $\boldsymbol{c}$ subject to the normalization condition and to elimination of an irrelevant phase), it should be possible to reduce it to the form (6) by a suitable choice of coordinate axes ($\hat{x}'$, $\hat{y}'$, $\hat{z}'$) and of λ.

This surmise is verified readily by comparing (10) with (7) or (6). Since (6) does not contain u_0, the $\hat{z}'$ axis should be orthogonal to $\hat{a}$, i.e., parallel to $\hat{a}^* \times \hat{a} = 2\mathrm{i}\,\boldsymbol{b}\times\boldsymbol{c}$. The remaining axes, $\hat{x}'$ and $\hat{y}'$, should be parallel to the axes of the ellipse that has $\boldsymbol{b}$ and $\boldsymbol{c}$ as conjugate diameters*. Indeed, $\hat{y}'$ is the unit vector that maximizes $|\hat{a}\cdot\hat{y}'|^2$, the maximum of this quantity being $\sin^2(\lambda+\frac{1}{4}\pi)$. Thus, the desired orientation of the axes and the value of λ are identified through the operation that finds the axes of the ellipse $|\hat{a}\cdot\boldsymbol{r}|^2=1$.

It seems interesting that the single highly symmetric field geometry (1) suffices to identify the most general type of pure state. It also suffices to transform the λ value of a state at will. (Changes of orientation are performed by a pure Larmor precession in a suitable magnetic field.) For example, suppose that a particle has been prepared in the center of the layout of fig. 1 at zero field and in the state with $\lambda=\frac{1}{4}\pi$ (i.e., in the non-magnetic p_y state). Switching on the magnetic field for a time t such that $\mu Ht/\hbar=\frac{1}{4}\pi-\lambda$ causes the particle to turn adiabatically by an angle $-(\frac{1}{4}\pi-\lambda)$ without introducing any net current circulation, i.e., leaving the mean magnetic moment $\langle\boldsymbol{\mu}\rangle=0$. Subsequent application of the electric field for a time t' such that $qKt'/\hbar=\frac{1}{4}\pi$ does introduce a current circulation represented by $\langle\mu_z\rangle = \mu\cos 2\lambda$ and changes the state of the system to ψ_λ.

3. General states with $j=1$

A general (pure or non-pure) state can be identified by the mean values of its magnetic dipole and electric quadrupole moments. The magnetic dipole moment is represented by

$$\mu\langle\boldsymbol{J}\rangle\,, \tag{11}$$

where $\langle\boldsymbol{J}\rangle$ is the mean value of the vector angular momentum. We represent the mean quadrupole moment by a model set of suitably placed charges, as shown in fig. 2†. The characteristics of this quadrupole can be expressed in

* Multiplication of $\hat{a}$ by $\exp(\mathrm{i}\alpha)$ replaces $\boldsymbol{b}$ and $\boldsymbol{c}$ by another pair of conjugate diameters of the same ellipse.

† The most familiar quadrupole consists of two positive and two negative charges. The pattern of fig. 2 appears convenient for our immediate purpose.

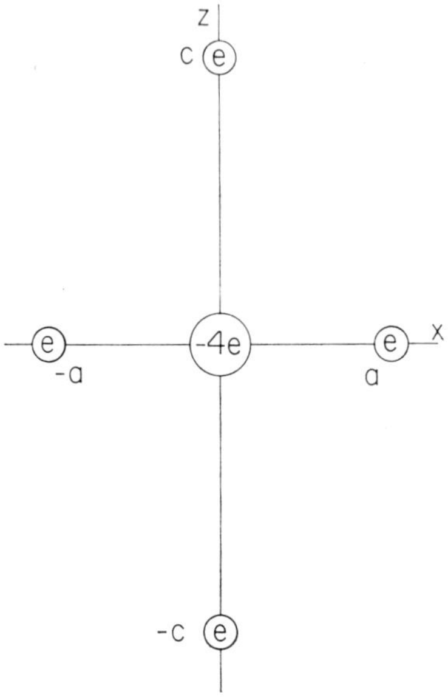

Fig. 2. Diagram of equivalent quadrupole.

terms of the mean values of the operators

$$Q_0 = 3J_z^2 - j(j+1) \tag{12}$$

and Q_2 from (4), provided the coordinate axes are so oriented that the mean values

$$\langle J_xJ_y + J_yJ_x\rangle = \langle J_yJ_z + J_zJ_y\rangle = \langle J_zJ_x + J_xJ_z\rangle = 0\,. \tag{13}$$

Then the charges e and coordinates $(\pm a, 0, 0)$, $(0, 0, \pm c)$ of the quadrupole will be such that

$$2ea^2 = q\,\langle Q_2\rangle\,, \qquad 2ec^2 = q\,\langle Q_0\rangle\,. \tag{14}$$

The coordinate axes can also be labeled so that

$$0 \leqslant \langle Q_2\rangle \leqslant \langle Q_0\rangle \leqslant 1\,. \tag{15}$$

The state ψ_λ of section 2 corresponds to $\langle J_x\rangle = \langle J_y\rangle = 0$, $\langle Q_0\rangle = 1$, and $\langle Q_2\rangle/\langle J_z\rangle = \tan 2\lambda$. Here we have utilized 8 independent parameters to identify the state, namely, the 3 components of $\langle \boldsymbol{J}\rangle$ in (11), the 3 orientation parameters of the coordinate axes, and the 2 quadrupole parameters $\langle Q_0\rangle$ and $\langle Q_2\rangle$. These 8 parameters are just sufficient to define the density matrix which is, in the representation with J_z diagonal,

$$\rho = \tfrac{1}{3} + \tfrac{1}{2}\langle \boldsymbol{J}\rangle\cdot\boldsymbol{J} + \tfrac{1}{6}\langle Q_0\rangle\, Q_0 + \tfrac{1}{2}\langle Q_2\rangle\, Q_2 =$$

$$= \begin{vmatrix} \tfrac{1}{3} + \tfrac{1}{2}\langle J_z\rangle + \tfrac{1}{6}\langle Q_0\rangle & \tfrac{1}{2}\langle J_x - \mathrm{i}J_y\rangle & \tfrac{1}{2}\langle Q_2\rangle \\ \tfrac{1}{2}\langle J_x + \mathrm{i}J_y\rangle & \tfrac{1}{3}(1 - \langle Q_0\rangle) & \tfrac{1}{2}\langle J_x - \mathrm{i}J_y\rangle \\ \tfrac{1}{2}\langle Q_2\rangle & \tfrac{1}{2}\langle J_x + \mathrm{i}J_y\rangle & \tfrac{1}{3} - \tfrac{1}{2}\langle J_z\rangle + \tfrac{1}{6}\langle Q_0\rangle \end{vmatrix}. \quad (16)$$

Let us consider now which restrictions upon the strengths and mutual orientation of the dipole and quadrupole, as well as on the "quadrupole arm ratio" $\langle Q_2\rangle/\langle Q_0\rangle$, derive from the fact that the eigenvalues of the density matrix are non-negative probabilities totaling unity. Minnaert[1]) has expressed these restrictions in terms of the requirement that coefficients c_n of the secular equation

$$\mathrm{Det}\,|\rho_{mm'} - \lambda\delta_{mm'}| = \sum_{n=0}^{3} c_n(-\lambda)^{3-n} = 0 \quad (17)$$

be non-negative

$$c_n \geqslant 0\,, \qquad n = 2, 3\,. \quad (18)$$

The equality obtains in (18) for $n=2$ and 3 in the case of pure states and for $n=3$ only if a single eigenvalue of ρ vanishes. Application of (18) and (17) to the matrix (16), taking into account (15), yields the chain of relations

$$\begin{aligned} 1 - |\langle \boldsymbol{J}\rangle|^2 - \langle Q_2\rangle^2 &\geqslant \\ &\geqslant (1 - \langle Q_0\rangle)\{(\tfrac{1}{3}\langle Q_0\rangle + \tfrac{2}{3})^2 - |\langle \boldsymbol{J}\rangle|^2 - \langle Q_2\rangle^2\} \geqslant \\ &\geqslant \langle Q_0\rangle(\langle J_x\rangle^2 + \langle J_y\rangle^2) - \langle Q_2\rangle(\langle J_x\rangle^2 - \langle J_y\rangle^2) \geqslant \\ &\geqslant 0 \geqslant -\tfrac{1}{3}(1 - \langle Q_0\rangle^2)\,. \end{aligned} \quad (19)$$

The implications of (19) can be described as follows. The quadrupole moment, as defined by fig. 2 and eq. (14), is subject only to the limitation (15). Once $\langle Q_0\rangle$ and $\langle Q_2\rangle$ are fixed, the second inequality in (19) (which expresses the condition $c_3 \geqslant 0$) can be cast in the form

$$\begin{aligned} (1 - \langle Q_2\rangle)\langle J_x\rangle^2 + (1 + \langle Q_2\rangle)\langle J_y\rangle^2 + (1 - \langle Q_0\rangle)\langle J_z\rangle^2 &\leqslant \\ \leqslant (1 - \langle Q_0\rangle)\,[(\tfrac{1}{3}\langle Q_0\rangle + \tfrac{2}{3})^2 - \langle Q_2\rangle^2]\,. \end{aligned} \quad (20)$$

This equation confines the tip of the vector $\langle \boldsymbol{J}\rangle$ within an ellipsoid whose axes lie along the coordinates. The tip reaches the surface of the ellipsoid when $c_3=0$, i.e., when one eigenvalue of ρ vanishes. The ellipsoid reduces to a sphere with radius $\tfrac{2}{3}$ when the quadrupole moment vanishes. On the other hand it becomes increasingly prolate as $\langle Q_0\rangle$ increases and it shrinks to the z axis when $\langle Q_0\rangle=1$, which also implies $c_3=0$. All pure states belong to the subset $\langle Q_0 \rangle = 1$. The states of this subset are in one-to-one correspondence with the states of elliptical light polarization, partial in general and complete for pure states.

Acknowledgement

I wish to thank V. L. Telegdi for extensive discussions and for reading the manuscript. I also thank Murray Peshkin for reading an earlier draft.

Reference

[1]) P. Minnaert, Phys. Rev. **151**, 1306 (1966).

Spectroscopic and group theoretical methods in physics

OPTICAL DOUBLE RESONANCE STUDIES OF EXCITED STATES OF Tm I WITH MICROSECOND LIFETIMES

B. BUDICK and A. SIMIEVIC
Department of Physics, The Hebrew University, Jerusalem, Israel

1. Introduction

Despite their complexity, the first spectra of the rare earth metals are gradually yielding to analysis. In particular, Racah techniques have been successfully applied in a study of the low lying even configurations of thulium[1]). Of special importance for this work has been a remark of Racah's concerning the coupling of angular momenta in configurations of the type $(4f)^n 6s6p$ (ref. 2). For Tm, for example, the coupling most nearly approximates to $|(f)^{13} J_1, (sp) S_2 L_2 J_2, J\rangle$. We have sought and found further striking confirmation for this coupling scheme in the lifetimes, τ, of excited states belonging to $(4f)^{13} 6s6p$. Transitions to the ground $(4f)^{13}(6s)^2\,{}^2F$ levels from excited states based on $(6s)(6p)\,{}^3P$ should be forbidden in first approximation. Optical pumping techniques have been used to observe three such transitions. The lifetime of the excited state in each case is of the order of microseconds.

We have exploited this phenomenon to make precise measurements of the hyperfine structure (hfs) and Landé g factors of two of the excited states in question. Our work indicates that forbidden transitions should be present in other heavy rare earth metals where the coupling scheme suggested by Racah is valid. These forbidden transitions, in conjunction with optical pumping techniques, can be used to identify hitherto unclassified levels. They may also be used to make precise measurements of the hfs anomaly[3]) when two isotopes are available (Dy, Lu and Yb) (ref. 4).

2. Experimental technique and apparatus

We have used the optical double resonance method first developed by Brossel and Bitter[5]). An atomic vapor of thulium atoms is illuminated with thulium resonance radiation from a hollow cathode light source. The incident radiation is linearly polarized such that only $\Delta m=0$ transitions occur in the excitation process. This is indicated by the vertical arrows pointing upward in fig. 1, which displays the Zeeman sublevels of the ground $F=3$

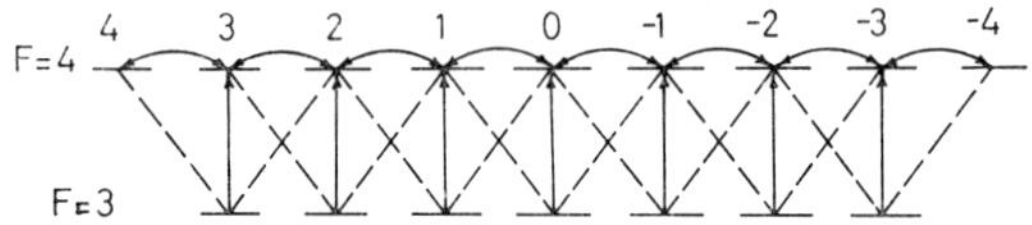

Fig. 1. Vertical arrows indicate π excitations in an $F=3\rightarrow F=4$ transition. Dashed lines represent σ modes of excitation and decay. Curved arrows above indicate radiofrequency transitions among the excited state Zeeman levels.

$(I=\frac{1}{2})$ level and of an excited $F=4$ level. Both $\pi(\Delta m=0)$ and $\sigma(\Delta m=\pm 1)$ transitions occur in the decay, and the reemitted light has both π and σ components. A second linear polarizer in front of the photomultiplier detector selects the π component. Radiofrequency transitions between excited state sublevels (indicated by circular arrows in the figure) alter the intensity of the reemitted π component. Sharp signals result, whose width is a measure of the natural lifetime of the excited state. In our experiments, the intensity of the π component is monitored as a function of an applied magnetic field while the atoms are subjected to an oscillating magnetic field of the appropriate frequency. The swept external field is modulated at 31 c/s so that lock-in detection can be used to improve the signal to noise ratio.

The dense atomic beam apparatus has been described elsewhere[6]). The radiofrequency magnetic field was produced by a single loop of copper wire whose impedance was matched to the output of a Rohde–Schwarz SLRD signal generator with the aid of tuning stubs. A single loop of wire was chosen rather than a more elaborate termination for two important reasons. First, the loop permits maximum encounter between light and atoms with a minimum of instrumental scatter. To further reduce unwanted reflected light, the copper wire was blackened by painting with chloroplatinic acid. Second, thulium is slightly magnetic and must not be permitted to condense on any surface in the proximity of the scattering region. The loop allows maximum transmission of the atomic beam.

The levels at 17343 cm^{-1}, 17614 cm^{-1} and 19754 cm^{-1} were studied in our experiments, as well as other levels belonging primarily to the $(4f)^{12}5d$ $(6s)^2$ configuration. These levels communicate with the ground state via photons of wavelength 5764 Å, 5675 Å, and 5060 Å, respectively as shown in fig. 2. Interference filters peaked at 5760 Å and 5050 Å were used to select the desired atomic transition. A study of our light source revealed that 5675 Å radiation emerged from the first mentioned filter in intensity equal to that of the 5764 Å radiation. The excited levels giving rise to these radiations have very different g-factors and hfs, and could be distinguished by these characteristics.

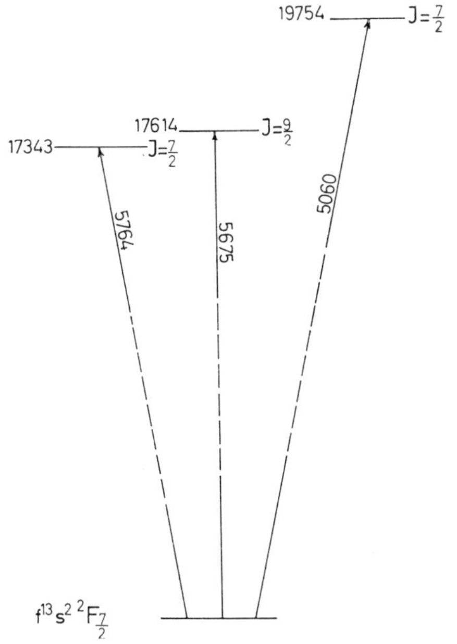

Fig. 2. Levels studied in the present work. The energy, angular momentum and resonance wavelength of each level are indicated in the figure.

3. Experimental results

We were guided in our work by recently published optical spectroscopy results for the g-factors and hfs splittings of the excited levels[7]). However, the transitions labelled α, β, γ and δ in fig. 3 were followed up from zero magnetic field to fields of 530 gauss in order to be absolutely certain of their identification. At low magnetic field, all the transitions in a given F state are degenerate and a superposition of signals is observed. As the field is increased, the degeneracy is removed and a number of transitions are observable.

We determined the lifetimes, τ, given in table 1 using the Hanle effect (zero field level crossings). The lifetime for the 19754 cm^{-1} level could be deduced directly from its Hanle effect. However, as mentioned above, both the 5675 Å and 5764 Å radiations were transmitted by our interference filter and the zero field curves are superpositions of signals from both excited levels. We analyzed the zero field curves using:

a) the measured intensity of each line after filtering;

b) a crude value for the ratio of the lifetimes of the two levels obtained from our radiofrequency work;

c) calculated values for the intensity of the Hanle effect for each of the four F states involved.

In this manner the values for the lifetimes τ of the levels at 17343 cm^{-1} and at 17614 cm^{-1} were obtained.

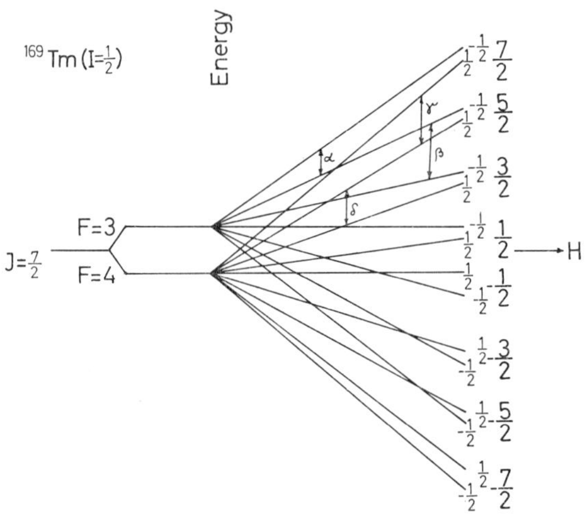

Fig. 3. Schematic Zeeman splitting of an excited $J=\frac{7}{2}$ state. The transitions whose field dependence was studied carefully are labelled.

The hfs constants and g-values listed in table 1 were derived from a least squares fit to $\Delta F=0$ transitions observed at three intermediate magnetic fields. All four transitions were observed at each field. The quoted uncertainty is twice that given by our computer fit. For comparison, we include calculated g-values[1]) and experimental values measured by optical spectroscopy. Observations at still higher magnetic fields, as well as observation of the direct $\Delta F=1$ transitions are expected to increase the precision of our work.

4. Conclusion

It is apparent from table 1 that the coupling scheme suggested by Racah does indeed lead very long-lived excited states. This phenomenon, in turn, permits

TABLE 1

Summary of observed and calculated parameters. Quantities measured in the present work have errors in parentheses. The parameters for each level are listed in the column headed by the appropriate energy. Row three gives the per cent ^3P (of the 6s 6p electrons) composition as calculated in ref. 1. g^{calc} and g^{opt} are also taken from this reference. The sign of the A-values is probably negative on the basis of optical work (ref. 7)

Level (cm^{-1})	17343	17614	19754
J (total)	$\frac{7}{2}$	$\frac{9}{2}$	$\frac{7}{2}$
λ (Å)	5764	5675	5060
$\%\,^3P_J$	75.7% $^3P_1$	86.8% $^3P_1$	94.3% $^3P_2$
τ (μsec)	1.4 (7)	0.7*	1.0 (2)
$\|A\|$ (Mc/s)	166.34 (31)	630.7 (18)	
g^{calc}	1.059	1.188	1.180
g^{opt}	1.022	1.188	1.18
g^{meas}	1.02153 (6)	1.18598 (10)	

* This value is a lower limit.

the determination of hfs constants and g-values to high precision. Work is in progress on lutetium where a precise measurement of the A-values for the two naturally occurring isotopes will yield a value for the hfs anomaly of these highly deformed nuclei. In addition, work is continuing on four other long lived states in thulium.

References

1) P. Camus, J. Phys. (Paris) **27**, 717 (1966).
2) G. Racah, J. Opt. Soc. Am. **50**, 408 (1960).
3) A. Bohr and V. F. Weisskopf, Phys. Rev. **77**, 94 (1950).
4) B. Budick and J. Snir, Phys. Letters **24B**, 277 (1967).
5) J. Brossel and F. Bitter, Phys. Rev. **86**, 308 (1952).
6) B. Budick and L. A. Levin, *La Structure Hyperfine Magnétique des Atomes et des Molécules* (CNRS, Paris, 1967).
7) Y. Bordarier, R. Vetter and J. Blaise, J. Phys. (Paris) **24**, 1107 (1963).

Spectroscopic and group theoretical methods in physics

THE OPTICAL AND ESR SPECTRUM OF Yb(IV) IN THE CUBIC CRYSTAL FIELD

W. LOW*

Department of Physics,
The Hebrew University,
Jerusalem, Israel

1. Introduction

Trivalent ytterbium has an f^{13} configuration, one hole in the 4f shell. The optical spectrum is, therefore, particularly simple to calculate and to compare with experiment. The paramagnetic resonance spectrum can be calculated using the wavefunctions as deduced from the optical spectrum and be compared with the measured g factor. One can compare the experimental and theoretical values of the hyperfine structure. Deviations between theory and experiment can then be correlated to "solid state" effects such as covalent bonding and possibly to interactions with localized or continuous vibration spectrum.

2. Theory

The f^{13} configuration of the Yb^{13} gives rise to two level ${}^2F_{\frac{7}{2}}$ and ${}^2F_{\frac{5}{2}}$ approximately split by $\frac{7}{2}\lambda$, where λ is the spin–orbit coupling. It is fairly sure that configuration mixing can be neglected. The crystal field Hamiltonian for cubic symmetry can be written as

$$\mathscr{H} = B_4^0(O_4^0 + 5\,O_4^4) + B_6^0(O_6^0 - 21\,O_6^4), \tag{1}$$

* In 1956 I gave a lecture on the effects of crystal field on the optical spectra of Ni(III) and Co(III) at the Hebrew University. Professor G. Racah became very interested in this field. We directed two graduate students, Miss G. Schoenfeld who calculated the matrices for the d^2 and d^3 configurations in a cubic field, and Mr. G. Rosengarten who obtained the matrices for the d^4 and d^5 configurations. Professor G. Racah and Mr. Flato calculated the matrices of the d^2 and d^3 configurations for tetragonal and trigonal fields. All these calculations were made in the weak field representation, so that the LS matrices of Racah and the computing techniques could be easily adopted.

where O_4^0 and O_6^0 are operators expressing the angular dependence and

$$B_n^m = A_n^m \langle r^n \rangle \theta_n,$$

where θ_n are the so-called operator equivalents, and A_n^m are geometrical factors. The matrices can easily be found using the well-known formula

$$(lm \,|Y_L^M|\, l'm') = (-1)^{l-m} \langle l \,\|Y_L\|\, l' \rangle \begin{pmatrix} l & L & l \\ -m & M & m' \end{pmatrix} \tag{2}$$

and give to first order the following eigenvalues and eigenfunctions

$J = \frac{7}{2}$:

$$E_1 = -\tfrac{54}{7} b_4 - 12\, b_6 - \delta E_1 + \tfrac{3}{2}\lambda,$$

$$\Gamma_7 = \tfrac{1}{2}\sqrt{3}\,|\pm\tfrac{5}{2}\rangle - \tfrac{1}{2}\,|\mp\tfrac{3}{2}\rangle,$$

$$E_2 = \tfrac{6}{7} b_4 + 16\, b_6 - \delta E_2 + \tfrac{3}{2}\lambda,$$

$$\Gamma_8^{(1)} = \frac{1}{2\sqrt{3}}\{\sqrt{7}\,|\pm\tfrac{7}{2}\rangle - \sqrt{5}\,|\mp\tfrac{1}{2}\rangle\},$$

$$\Gamma_8^{(2)} = \tfrac{1}{2}\,|\pm\tfrac{5}{2}\rangle + \frac{\sqrt{3}}{2}\,|\mp\tfrac{3}{2}\rangle,$$

$$E_3 = 6\, b_4 - 20\, b_6 + \tfrac{3}{2}\lambda,$$

$$\Gamma_6 = \frac{1}{2\sqrt{3}}\{\sqrt{5}\,|\pm\tfrac{7}{2}\rangle + \sqrt{7}\,|\mp\tfrac{1}{2}\rangle\}, \tag{3}$$

$J = \frac{5}{2}$:

$$E_4 = -\tfrac{44}{7} b_4 + \delta E_1 - 2\lambda,$$

$$\Gamma_7 = \sqrt{\tfrac{1}{6}}\,\{|\pm\tfrac{5}{2}\rangle - \sqrt{5}\,|\mp\tfrac{3}{2}\rangle\},$$

$$E_5 = \tfrac{22}{7} b_4 + \delta E_2 - 2\lambda,$$

$$\Gamma_8^{(1)} = \sqrt{\tfrac{1}{6}}\,\{\sqrt{5}\,|\pm\tfrac{5}{2}\rangle + |\mp\tfrac{3}{2}\rangle\},$$

$$\Gamma_8^{(2)} = |\pm\tfrac{1}{2}\rangle,$$

where $b_4 = 60\, B_6^0$ and $b_6 = 1260\, B_6^0$.

The first order energy levels are slightly shifted because of the interaction of the respective Γ_7 and Γ_8 levels of the ground and the excited states. These can be calculated from the matrices

$$\begin{array}{cc} {}^2F_{\frac{7}{2}}, \Gamma_7 & {}^2F_{\frac{5}{2}}, \Gamma_7 \\ \hline \frac{3}{2}\lambda - \frac{54}{7}b_4 - 12b_6 & \frac{4\sqrt{3}}{7}(5b_4 + 42b_6) \\ & -2\lambda - \frac{44}{7}b_4 \end{array}$$

$$\begin{array}{cc} {}^2F_{\frac{7}{2}}, \Gamma_8 & {}^2F_{\frac{5}{2}}, \Gamma_8 \\ \hline \frac{3}{2}\lambda + 16b_6 + \frac{6}{7}b_4 & \frac{12\sqrt{5}}{7}(b_4 - 7b_6) \\ & -2\lambda + \frac{22}{7}b_4 \end{array} \tag{4}$$

if we write

$$\alpha_1 = \frac{4\sqrt{3}}{7}(5b_4 + 43b_6),$$

$$\alpha_2 = \frac{12\sqrt{5}}{7}(b_4 - 7b_6).$$

The energy shifts are given by

$$\delta E_1 \approx \frac{\alpha_1^2}{\frac{7}{2}\lambda - \frac{10}{7}b_4 - 12b_6},$$

$$\delta E_2 \approx \frac{\alpha_2^2}{\frac{7}{2}\lambda - \frac{16}{7}b_4 + 16b_6}. \tag{5}$$

3. Experimental results

Experiments were performed on single crystals of CaF_2 containing 0.1 to 0.005% Yb^{3+}. Ytterbium substitutes for calcium, but is has been shown from paramagnetic resonance data that charge compensation is possible, and that this may give rise to different point symmetries corresponding to different charge compensation mechanism. The following point symmetries have definitely been identified: cubic, several trigonal, tetragonal and rhombic symmetries [1,2,3]). These give rise to very different Zeeman splittings and can, therefore, be easily identified using ESR techniques, although often the nature of the impurity acting as the compensator is not known. By different experimental techniques (which will be published elsewhere), we have been able to isolate in part the cubic spectrum and to sort out its transitions. Two weak absorption lines appear (all measurements reported here are at liquid air temperature and no vacuum corrections are made), at 10845 and 10384 cm^{-1}. This determines b_4 to first order since δE_1 and δE_2 are relatively small. Two strong fluorescence transitions are at 10384 and 9737 cm^{-1}. Since these transitions are magnetic dipole transitions (this accounts for the weakness of the absorption spectrum compared with the absorption spectrum of other lower symmetry sites despite the fact that the occupation of the cubic site is often as high as 80%) the $\Gamma_7 \rightarrow \Gamma_6$ transition is forbidden. Hence the fluorescent transitions are from the Γ_7 ($J=\frac{5}{2}$) to Γ_7, Γ_8 ($J=\frac{7}{2}$). We have, therefore, enough data to determine b_4, b_6 and λ and these are

$$b_4 = 51.6 \text{ cm}^{-1},$$
$$b_6 = 6.39 \text{ cm}^{-1},$$
$$\lambda = 2909.4 \text{ cm}^{-1},$$
$$\delta E_1 = 25.9 \text{ cm}^{-1}.$$

The Γ_6 level is predicted to be about 608 cm^{-1}, slightly below the Γ_8 level, and cannot be observed in the pure cubic field. This should be compared with the isoelectronic spectrum of Tm^{2+} in CaF_2 which yields

$$b_4 = 45.8 \text{ cm}^{-1} \quad \text{and} \quad b_6 = 5.05 \text{ cm}^{-1}.$$

Since b_4 and b_6 are proportional to $\langle r^4 \rangle$ and $\langle r^6 \rangle$ respectively, one would have expected these to be smaller for Yb^{3+} compared with Tm^{2+}. Freeman and Watson[6]) calculated $\langle r^4 \rangle$ to be 1.552 (Tm^{2+}) and 0.960 (Yb^{3+}), and $\langle r^6 \rangle$ to be 7.510 (Tm^{2+}) and 3.104 (Yb^{3+}) respectively. The large crystal field constants can be accounted for if we assume that the Yb^{3+} with its unbalance of charge attracts the surrounding fluorine ions and thus increases the effective crystal field. Some evidence for this is found for the increased dipole–dipole interaction between the fluorine ions and the ytterbium ions as evidenced from ENDOR measurements[7]).

4. *g* Factor and hyperfine structure

The new Γ_7 eigenstates can be written as

$$|\Gamma_7\rangle = a\,|^2F_{\frac{7}{2}}, \Gamma_7\rangle - b\,|^2F_{\frac{5}{2}}, \Gamma_7\rangle, \qquad (6)$$
$$a^2 + b^2 = 1;$$

$$\frac{a}{b} = \frac{\alpha_1}{\frac{7}{2}\lambda - \frac{\alpha_1}{4\sqrt{3}} + \frac{1}{2}\left[\left(\frac{7}{2}\lambda\right)^2 - \frac{7}{2\sqrt{3}}\lambda\alpha + \left(\frac{7}{2}\frac{\alpha_1}{3}\right)^2\right]^{\frac{1}{2}}}, \tag{7}$$

$$\alpha_1 = \frac{4\sqrt{7}}{7}(5b_4 + 42b_6).$$

The g factor then yields

$$g = -2\left(\tfrac{5}{7}b^2 - \tfrac{12}{7}a^2 - \frac{8\sqrt{3}}{21}ab\right). \tag{8}$$

If we take into account divalent bonding by reducing the orbital contribution by a factor of k, then

$$g = 2\langle + | \beta(kL_z + 3S_z) | + \rangle$$

and this gives

$$g = 3g_J - (1-k)\left(\frac{18}{8} + \frac{16\alpha}{7\sqrt{3}}\right) + \frac{16\alpha}{7\sqrt{3}} + \text{higher order terms},$$

$$\alpha = \frac{\alpha_1}{E_4 - E_1}. \tag{9}$$

The hyperfine interaction can be written as

$$A = A(\text{core}) + 2\beta\beta_N\gamma\langle r^{-3}\rangle\, 2\left[\tfrac{8}{7}b^2 - \tfrac{8}{7}a^2 - \frac{4\sqrt{3}}{21}ab\right]. \tag{10}$$

Since in our case $a^2 \gg b^2$ and assuming some covalent bonding, we obtain

$$A - A(\text{core}) = 2pk\left[\tfrac{8}{7} - \frac{4\sqrt{3}}{21}ab\right], \tag{11}$$

where $p = 2\beta\beta_N\gamma\langle r^{-3}\rangle$.

The experimental data can be best expressed with the effective spin Hamiltonian

$$\mathscr{H} = g\beta \boldsymbol{H}\cdot\boldsymbol{S} + A\boldsymbol{S}\cdot\boldsymbol{I} + \sum_{i=1}^{8} \boldsymbol{S}\cdot T_i\cdot I_i^F - \gamma^F \boldsymbol{H}\cdot\boldsymbol{I}_i^F, \tag{12}$$

where T_i gives the tensor of the interaction with the surrounding eight fluorines. The parameters in the Hamiltonian are given for our case[1,7,8])

$$g = 3.442 \pm 0.0002\,,$$
$$^{171}A = (2658 \pm 4.5)\ \mathrm{Mc/s}\,,$$
$$^{173}A = (-\ 729 \pm 12)\ \mathrm{Mc/s}\,,$$
$$T_{\parallel} = (36.8 \pm 0.1)\ \mathrm{Mc/s}\,,$$
$$T_{\perp} = (15.9 \pm 0.05)\ \mathrm{Mc/s}\,.$$

The g factor of the Γ_7 ground state is about $3g_J$, i.e., about $\frac{24}{7}$. The experimental g_J factor for Tm(I) is 1.4122 (ref. 9). This value is not expected to be very different for Yb (IV). Assuming this value we find

$$g = 3g_J + 0.0646 + 2.184(1-k)\,, \tag{13}$$

for which we obtain that $(1-k)=0.02\pm0.005$. This is similar to the values obtained by Low and Rubins[10]) for Yb^{3+} in CaO (Γ_6) and only slightly larger than that of Tm^{2+} in CaF_2. (In the paper by Bleaney[5]) there is a slight mistake; after correction one obtains $(1-k)=0.012$.)

The orbital reduction factor, however, is not the only source to explain the discrepancy between the calculated and experimental g factor.

Inoue[11]) has calculated the effect of the orbit lattice interaction for Tm^{2+} in CaF_2. Using our parameters in her calculation, we find a shift in the g factor of about -0.01, still too small to explain these results. Taking this into account, the orbital reduction factor is reduced to 0.015.

The fractional change in the hyperfine interaction caused by crystal field is given by

$$\frac{\Delta A}{A} = \left(\frac{\alpha}{2\sqrt{3}} - 2\alpha^2\right). \tag{14}$$

Comparison between the experimental value of A found in the solid, corrected for the admixture of the Γ_7 level, yields a value of about 2% higher than that found in atoms. An explicit comparison cannot be made without a detailed knowledge of the core polarization of Yb^{3+} in the solid.

Finally, it is interesting to compare the fine structure value with that obtained spectroscopically. Judd and Lindgren[12]) quote an experimental value of 2940 cm^{-1} and a calculated value of 2951 cm^{-1} which should be compared with 2909.4 cm^{-1} obtained in the crystal. Like the hyperfine value the fine structure is about 1–2% higher than the value found in free atoms.

Acknowledgements

The crystals of CaF_2 were grown by Mr. M. Foguel using the Stockbarger method. They were grown under different conditions: (a) without a charge compensation and without a scavenger, (b) with a PbF_2 as scavenger, and (c) with Na as charge compensation with or without a scavenger. The crystals were either heat-treated to 1000 °C in vacuum and suddenly quenched to room temperature to freeze in the cubic spectrum or slowly cooled to room temperature[13]).

The optical data were taken in part by Mr. Dan Polotzky.

References

1) W. Low, Phys. Rev. **118**, 1608 (1960).
2) U. Ranon, Thesis, Jerusalem (1963).
3) J. Kirton and S. D. McLaughlan, Phys. Rev. **155**, 279 (1967).
4) Z. Kiss, Phys. Rev. **127**, 718 (1962).
5) B. Bleaney, Proc. Roy. Soc. (London) **A 277**, 289 (1964).
6) A. J. Freeman and R. E. Watson, in: *Magnetism*, Vol. IIA, Eds. G. T. Rado and H. Suhl (Academic Press, New York, 1965).
7) U. Ranon and J. S. Hyde, Phys. Rev. **141**, 259 (1966).
8) W. Hayes and J. W. Twidell, J. Chem. Phys. **35**, 1521 (1961).
9) A. Y. Cabezas and I. P. K. Lindgren, Phys. Rev. **120**, 42 (1960).
10) W. Low and R. S. Rubins, Phys. Rev. **131**, 2527 (1963).
11) M. Inoue, Phys. Rev. Letters **11**, 196 (1963).
12) B. R. Judd and I. Lindgren, Phys. Rev. **122**, 1802 (1961).
13) E. Friedman and W. Low, J. Chem. Phys. **33**, 1275 (1960).

Spectroscopic and group theoretical methods in physics
© North-Holland Publ. Co., Amsterdam, 1968

THE ATOMIC PHOTOEFFECT FOR PHOTON ENERGIES 1–2000 keV

G. RAKAVY and A. RON
Department of Theoretical Physics, The Hebrew University, Jerusalem, Israel

1. Introduction

The photoelectric phenomenon is one of the basic quantum processes and the evaluation of photoelectric cross-sections is important for many and varied applications. Numerous attempts to calculate the cross-sections have been made during the last four decades. Usually it was attempted to find approximate closed expressions for the photoelectric cross-sections. Only in recent years with the aid of modern fast computers, it became feasible to attack the problem directly, making no approximations except those which are inherent in the atomic shell model. At this new stage of the art, the comparison of accurately measured photoelectric cross-sections with the calculated values can be considered as a means of probing the atomic shell model wave functions. In this sense the present work may be a contribution to the task to which the late Professor Giulio Racah has devoted so much of his life. It should also be said that it is very doubtful if even the modern computer would be adequate to perform all the summations on magnetic quantum numbers appearing in the expression of the photoelectric cross-section. These summations are performed very elegantly and easily by techniques developed by Professor Racah.

Although the evaluation of the photoelectric cross-sections seems at first to be quite straightforward, several complications arise. In the first place the atom is a bound many body system and actually no proper relativistic formalism exists for treating such a system. It is thus inevitable to separate the photoelectron and treat it as moving in an effective potential. Second, the computational difficulties are quite severe particularly in the high energy range.

At low energies and for low Z atoms non-relativistic formulas can be used. In the non-relativistic case closed expressions for the cross-section of K and L electrons, moving in a pure Coulomb potential, were given by Fischer and Sauter[1,2]). Somewhat simpler, though less accurate, expressions had been given earlier. The simple expressions are usually based on a dipole (or quadrupole) approximation for the interaction or a plane wave for the continuum state (i.e., first-order Born approximation) or both*. At the low energies at which the non-relativistic formulas are valid, high atomic shells contribute significantly to the photoelectric cross-sections and the deviations of the effective atomic potential from a pure Coulomb field are large. For high Z atoms even the bound electrons are effectively relativistic and thus the non-relativistic formulas are inaccurate even at low energies.

Several approximate expressions for the photoelectric cross-section, applicable to the relativistic domain, have been derived. All expressions are valid only for a pure Coulomb field and are accurate to the lowest orders in $Z/137$ or $Zmc^2/137E_\gamma$. At intermediate energies (i.e. of the order of mc^2) and for high Z atoms none of the approximate formulas is expected to be accurate and one has to resort to numerical methods. At high energies (or low Z atoms) at which the approximate formulas are applicable, the main contribution to the transition matrix elements comes from a region near the nucleus. In this region the deviations of the atomic potential from a $1/r$ law are insignificant; thus, the formulas derived for pure Coulomb fields should be satisfactory. The fact that important contributions to the matrix elements come from a region near the nucleus, where the distortion of the continuum wave function is important, complicates the derivation of the high energy relativistic formulas. The first Born approximation (i.e., the use of a plane wave for the continuum state) does not yield correct results even in the high energy limit. The second Born approximation, or some alternative approximation method, has to be applied to obtain the photoelectric cross-sections. For a short review of the various approaches to the problem and for composite formulas which have a quite wide range of applicability, we refer the reader to the work of Pratt[3]).

The first numerical evaluation of photoelectric cross-sections was performed by Hulme and collaborators[4]) in 1935. In this calculation relativistic wave functions in a pure Coulomb field have been used. The calculations were performed for three values of Z (=26, 50, 84) and for two energies (354 keV and 1130 keV). For many years these calculations remained the

* For a review of early works on the atomic photoeffect, cf. H. A. Bethe and E. E. Salpeter, *Quantum Mechanics of One and Two Electron Atoms* (Springer-Verlag, Berlin, 1957).

only reference points in the relativistic domain. During the last few years a number of numerical evaluations of photoelectric cross-sections have been published[5–8]. In all these calculations the screening of the Coulomb field has either been neglected completely, or treated in a rather primitive form. Moreover, only K and L shell cross-sections were calculated.

In the present paper we report on comparatively accurate calculations of photoelectric cross-sections for many atoms and energies. In these calculations contributions of high atomic shells have been evaluated and investigated rather carefully. The calculations have been performed with various atomic potentials, so as to obtain some estimate for the errors in the photoelectric cross-sections resulting from the uncertainties in the effective atomic fields. The potentials used in our calculations (Shalitin's FAM potential[9]) are taken to be almost as accurate as Hartree–Fock potentials and should yield results accurate within a few percent.

In section 2 the general expressions for the photoelectric cross-section are derived. The numerical procedures employed in evaluating these expressions and the checks on the accuracy of our calculations are described in section 3. The results are presented and discussed in section 4.

2. The photoelectric cross-section formula

2.1. General formulation of the problem

In order to obtain an expression for the photoelectric cross-section of an atom, we first replace the many electron problem by an approximate single electron shell model. Each electron is assumed to move in an effective spherical symmetric potential $V(r)$. The expression for the differential cross-section for a particular photoelectric transition is[10])

$$\frac{\mathrm{d}\sigma}{\mathrm{d}\Omega_{\mathrm{e}}} = \frac{2\pi p_{\mathrm{e}} E_{\mathrm{e}}}{(2\pi\hbar c)^3} V_{\mathrm{norm}}^2 |T_{\mathrm{fi}}|^2 . \tag{1}$$

Here E_{e} is the energy of the photoelectron (including the rest mass) as calculated from the expression

$$E_{\mathrm{e}} = E_{\gamma} + mc^2 - E_{\mathrm{b_i}} , \tag{2}$$

where E_{γ} is the energy of the photon and $E_{\mathrm{b_i}}$ is the binding energy of the electron in the initial state. Further,

$$p_{\mathrm{e}} = (E_{\mathrm{e}}^2 - m^2c^4)^{\frac{1}{2}}/\hbar c$$

is the wave number of the photoelectron. The arbitrary normalization volume V_{norm} appearing here will drop out from the final expressions. The transition matrix element is given by

$$T_{\text{fi}} = \langle \psi_{\text{f}}^{-} |\, e(\boldsymbol{\alpha A})\, | \phi_{\text{i}} \rangle . \tag{3}$$

In this exact form of the transition elements enter the wave functions ϕ_{i} and ψ_f^{-} which are eigenstates of the Hamiltonian

$$\mathscr{H}_0 = \mathscr{H}(\text{electromagnetic waves}) + [c(\boldsymbol{\alpha p}) + \beta mc^2 - eV(r)] \tag{4}$$

and

$$\mathscr{H} = \mathscr{H}_0 + e(\boldsymbol{\alpha A}) \tag{5}$$

respectively. The state ϕ_{i} contains one circularly polarized photon with momentum $\hbar k$ moving along the z axis, and an electron bound in an atom. The eigenstate ψ_f^{-} of the complete Hamiltonian $\mathscr{H}$ contains a plane electron wave of amplitude $1/V_{\text{norm}}^{\frac{1}{2}}$, moving in the direction Ω_{e} with momentum $\hbar p_{\text{e}}$ not accompanied by any photons; besides it contains only incoming waves in all other channels.

In order to evaluate the transition matrix T_{fi} we have to make one further approximation; the state ψ_f^{-} is replaced by the eigenstate ϕ_f^{-} of the Hamiltonian $\mathscr{H}_0$, with the same "boundary conditions" as ψ_f^{-}. The photon degree of freedom can be factored out from the states ϕ. The matrix element $e(\boldsymbol{\alpha A})$ between the photon states is easily calculated[11]) and the transition amplitude becomes

$$T_{\text{fi}} = \left(\frac{2\pi e^2 c^2 \hbar}{\omega V_{\text{norm}}}\right)^{\frac{1}{2}} \int \phi_{\text{f}}^{-*}(\boldsymbol{r})\, \mathrm{e}^{ikz}\, \sigma_q \gamma_5 \phi_{\text{i}}(\boldsymbol{r})\, \mathrm{d}^3 r . \tag{6}$$

For the Dirac matrices γ_5 and σ_q we choose the representation

$$\gamma_5 = \begin{pmatrix} & \mathrm{I} \\ \mathrm{I} & \end{pmatrix},$$

$$\sigma_q = -q/\sqrt{2}\{\sigma_x + \mathrm{i}q\sigma_y\}; \qquad q = \pm 1,$$

$$\sigma_x = \begin{pmatrix} & 1 & & \\ 1 & & & \\ & & & 1 \\ & & 1 & \end{pmatrix}, \qquad \sigma_y = \begin{pmatrix} & -\mathrm{i} & & \\ \mathrm{i} & & & \\ & & & -\mathrm{i} \\ & & \mathrm{i} & \end{pmatrix}.$$

2.2. The expressions for the interaction and the wave functions in spherical coordinates

In order to evaluate the expression (6) we write the wave functions $\phi^{\pm}$ and the interaction operators $\mathrm{e}^{ikz}\sigma_q\gamma_5$ in spherical coordinates. The integration over the angular and spin coordinates can be performed and expressed as recoupling coefficients. One-dimensional integrations on the radial coordinate remain to be performed numerically.

In spherical coordinates the interaction can be expanded as follows

$$e^{ikz}\sigma_q\gamma_5 = \sum_{L,\Lambda} 2i^{\Lambda}[4\pi(2\Lambda+1)]^{\frac{1}{2}}(\Lambda 0;\, 1q|Lq)\, j_{\Lambda}(kr)\, S_{\Lambda Lq}\gamma_5\,, \tag{7}$$

$$S_{\Lambda Lq} = \sum_{\lambda\mu} (\Lambda\lambda;\, 1\mu|Lq)\, Y_{\Lambda\lambda}\, s_{\mu}\,. \tag{8}$$

Here, $j_{\Lambda}(x)$ denotes a spherical Bessel function of order Λ, and $Y_{\Lambda\lambda}(\Omega)$ a spherical harmonic. The initial, bound state is written

$$\phi_i = \frac{a^{\frac{1}{2}}}{r}\begin{pmatrix} g_{l_i j_i} & \chi_{l_i j_i m_i} \\ i f_{\bar{l}_i j_i} & \chi_{\bar{l}_i j_i m_i}\end{pmatrix}, \tag{9}$$

and the final, continuum state is expanded in the form

$$\phi_f^- = \left(\frac{1}{V_{\text{norm}}^{\frac{1}{2}}}\right)\left(\frac{E_e + mc^2}{2E_e}\right)^{\frac{1}{2}} \cdot \left(\frac{4\pi}{p_e}\right)\sum_{ljm\mu} i^l e^{-i\delta_{lj}}(l\mu;\, \tfrac{1}{2}\nu|jm)\, Y_{l\mu}^*(\Omega_e)\, \psi_{ljm}\,, \tag{10}$$

with

$$\psi_{ljm} = \frac{1}{r}\begin{pmatrix} g_{lj}(r) & \chi_{ljm} \\ i f_{\bar{l}j}(r) & \chi_{\bar{l}jm}\end{pmatrix}. \tag{11}$$

Here we use the notation χ_{ljm} for

$$\chi_{ljm} = \sum_{\mu\nu}(l\mu;\, \tfrac{1}{2}\nu|jm)\, Y_{l\mu}(\Omega)\, \chi_{\nu}\,, \tag{12}$$

with

$$s_z\chi_\nu = \nu\chi_\nu; \qquad \nu = \pm\tfrac{1}{2}$$

and

$$\bar{l} = 2j - l\,.$$

The length a in eq. (9) is an arbitrary normalization constant. The radial functions g_{lj} and f_{lj} satisfy the radial Dirac equations

$$\begin{aligned} \frac{dg_{lj}}{dr} &= -\frac{kg_{lj}}{r} + \frac{E_e + mc^2 + eV(r)}{\hbar c} f_{lj}\,, \\ \frac{df_{lj}}{dr} &= -\frac{E_e - mc^2 + eV(r)}{\hbar c} g_{lj} + \frac{kf_{lj}}{r}\,, \\ k &= (l-j)(2j+1)\,. \end{aligned} \tag{13}$$

The normalization of the initial state is $\int \phi_i^\dagger \phi_i \,\mathrm{d}^3 r = 1$ or,

$$\int_0^\infty (g^2_{l_i j_i} + f^2_{l_i j_i})\, \mathrm{d}(r/a) = 1\,. \tag{14}$$

The normalization of the final state is determined so that at large distances the wave function has the asymptotic behaviour,

$$\phi_\mathrm{f}^- = \frac{1}{V^{\frac{1}{2}}_\mathrm{norm}} \left(\frac{E_\mathrm{e} + mc^2}{2E_\mathrm{e}}\right)^{\frac{1}{2}} \begin{pmatrix} \chi_\nu \\ \dfrac{\hbar c}{E_\mathrm{e} + mc^2} (p_\mathrm{e}\sigma)\, \chi_\nu \end{pmatrix} \mathrm{e}^{\mathrm{i}(p_\mathrm{e} r)} + F(\Omega) \frac{\mathrm{e}^{-\mathrm{i} p_\mathrm{e} r}}{r}\,, \tag{15}$$

where $F(\Omega)$ is a spinor function of the direction $\mathbf{\Omega}$. Expanding expression (15) in spherical harmonics and comparing the coefficients with those of the expansion (10) gives

$$\begin{aligned} g_{lj} &\to \sin(p_\mathrm{e} r - \tfrac{1}{2}\pi l + \delta_{lj})\,, \\ f_{lj} &\to [\hbar c p_\mathrm{e}/(E_\mathrm{e} + mc^2)] \cos(p_\mathrm{e} r - \tfrac{1}{2}\pi l + \delta_{lj})\,. \end{aligned} \tag{16}$$

Outside the range R_0 of the potential $V(r)$ the functions g_{lj} and f_{lj} thus become[3])

$$\begin{aligned} g_{lj} &= p_\mathrm{e} r \{\cos\delta_{lj}\, j_l(p_\mathrm{e} r) + \sin\delta_{lj}\, n_l(p_\mathrm{e} r)\}\,, \\ f_{lj} &= \frac{k}{|k|} \frac{\hbar c p_\mathrm{e}}{E_\mathrm{e} + mc^2}\, p_\mathrm{e} r \{\cos\delta_{lj}\, j_{\bar l}(p_\mathrm{e} r) + \sin\delta_{lj}\, n_{\bar l}(p_\mathrm{e} r)\}\,. \end{aligned} \tag{17}$$

Inside the range of the potential the functions g_{lj} and f_{lj} must be obtained numerically. Let us write

$$g_{lj} = C \cdot G\,, \qquad f_{lj} = C \cdot F\,, \tag{18}$$

C being a normalization constant, G and F satisfy the same equations as g_{lj} and f_{lj}. We start the numerical integration at some small value of the radius $r = R_1$ with an arbitrary value G_1 for $G(r)$. The initial value of F is obtained from the relation[12]):

$$\lim_{r\to 0} \frac{F}{G} = -\,\text{‘137’} \frac{k + \gamma}{Z}; \qquad \gamma = \left(\frac{k^2 - Z^2}{\text{‘137’}^2}\right)^{\frac{1}{2}}; \qquad \text{‘137’} = \frac{\hbar c}{e^2}\,. \tag{19}$$

Continuing the integration up to some value $r = R_n \geqslant R_0$ we obtain the values $G(R_n)$ and $F(R_n)$. The normalization C and the phase shift δ_{lj} can now be determined by equating expressions (17) and (18) at $r = R_n$. For the phase shift we obtain

$$-\operatorname{tg}\delta_{lj}=\frac{j_{\bar{l}}-\dfrac{F}{G}\dfrac{k}{|k|}\dfrac{\hbar c p_{\mathrm{e}}}{E_{\mathrm{e}}+mc^{2}}\,j_{l}}{n_{\bar{l}}-\dfrac{F}{G}\dfrac{k}{|k|}\dfrac{\hbar c p_{\mathrm{e}}}{E_{\mathrm{e}}+mc^{2}}\,n_{l}} \tag{20}$$

and the normalization

$$C=p_{\mathrm{e}}R_{n}\{\cos\delta_{lj}\,j_{l}+\sin\delta_{lj}\,n_{l}\}/G(R_{n}). \tag{21}$$

To obtain the bound states the eigenvalues $E_0=-E_{\mathrm{b_i}}+mc^2$ must be determined. This is done quite easily by an iterational procedure. A rough first guess $E=-E_{\mathrm{b}}^{(0)}+mc^2$ is chosen. With this value of E the Dirac equation is integrated from the origin to some radius $r=R_2$. The initial conditions near the origin are the same as for the continuum function (eq. (19)). With the same value of E the Dirac equation is also integrated inwards, starting at some radius $r=R_3>R_0$ up to the point $r=R_2$. The starting point $r=R_3$ is chosen far enough so that the asymptotic relation[12])

$$\lim_{r\to\infty}\frac{F}{G}=-\left(\frac{mc^{2}-E}{mc^{2}+E}\right)^{\frac{1}{2}} \tag{22}$$

can be used to start the integration. From the two ratios $F(R_2)/G(R_2)$ obtained from the outgoing integration and the ingoing integration a better guess for E_{b} is obtained. Let $E_{\mathrm{b}}^{(n)}$ be the nth iterate on E_{b}, then[13])

$$E_{\mathrm{b}}^{(n+1)}=E_{\mathrm{b}}^{(n)}+\frac{(F/G)_{\mathrm{out}}-(F/G)_{\mathrm{in}}}{\displaystyle\int_{0}^{R_2}(F^{2}+G^{2})\,\mathrm{d}r/G_{\mathrm{out}}^{2}+\int_{R_2}^{\infty}(F^{2}+G^{2})\,\mathrm{d}r/G_{\mathrm{in}}^{2}}. \tag{23}$$

Here F_{in}, G_{in}, F_{out}, G_{out} are the values (of the unnormalized) Dirac functions at the matching point $r=R_2$. After the iterations on $E_{\mathrm{b}}^{(n)}$ converge the functions are checked for the appropriate number of maxima and minima and normalized:

$$\left.\begin{matrix}g_{l_i j_i}\\ f_{l_i j_i}\end{matrix}\right\}=\begin{matrix}C/G_{\mathrm{out}}\begin{cases}G\\F\end{cases} & r\leqslant R_2\\[2ex] C/G_{\mathrm{in}}\begin{cases}G\\F\end{cases} & r\geqslant R_2\end{matrix} \tag{24}$$

with

$$C^{-2}=\int_{0}^{R_2}\frac{F^{2}+G^{2}}{G_{\mathrm{out}}^{2}}\,\mathrm{d}\left(\frac{r}{a}\right)+\int_{R_2}^{\infty}\frac{F^{2}+G^{2}}{G_{\mathrm{in}}^{2}}\,\mathrm{d}\left(\frac{r}{a}\right).$$

2.3. The transition amplitude

Inserting the expressions (7) and (10) into (6) the transition amplitude T_{fi} becomes

$$T_{\mathrm{fi}} = -\frac{1}{V_{\mathrm{norm}}}\left[\frac{256\pi^4 e^2 \hbar^3 c^4}{\omega E_{\mathrm{e}}(E_{\mathrm{e}} - mc^2)}\right]^{\frac{1}{2}} \sum_{ljm}\sum_{\mu}\sum_{L\Lambda}(2\Lambda + 1)^{\frac{1}{2}}\, \mathrm{i}^{\Lambda - l}\, \mathrm{e}^{\mathrm{i}\delta_{lj}} \times$$
$$\times (l\mu; \tfrac{1}{2}\nu|jm)(\Lambda 0; 1q|Lq)\langle\psi_{ljm}|\, j_\Lambda S_{\Lambda Lq}\gamma_5\, |\phi_{\mathrm{i}}\rangle\, Y^*_{l\mu}(\Omega_{\mathrm{e}}), \tag{25}$$

and by the Wigner–Eckart theorem[14]) the dependence of the matrix element $\langle\psi_{ljm}|\, j_\Lambda S_{\Lambda Lq}\gamma_5\, |\phi_{\mathrm{i}}\rangle$ on the magnetic quantum numbers can be separated

$$\langle\psi_{ljm}|\, j_\Lambda S_{\Lambda Lq}\gamma_5\, |\phi_{\mathrm{i}}\rangle = (2j+1)^{-\frac{1}{2}}(j_{\mathrm{i}}m_{\mathrm{i}}; Lq|jm)\,(\psi_{lj}|\,|j_\Lambda S_{\Lambda L}\gamma_5|\,|\phi_{\mathrm{i}}). \tag{26}$$

Introducing (9), (11) into this expression the reduced matrix element becomes

$$(\psi_{lj}|\,|j_\Lambda S_{\Lambda L}\gamma_5|\,|\phi_{\mathrm{i}}) =$$
$$= \mathrm{i}\frac{k}{|k|}(\bar{l}j|\,|S_{\Lambda L}|\,|l_{\mathrm{i}}j_{\mathrm{i}}) \int_0^\infty g_{l_{\mathrm{i}}j_{\mathrm{i}}}(r)\, j_\Lambda(kr) f_{lj}(r)\, \mathrm{d}\left(\frac{r}{a}\right) +$$
$$- \mathrm{i}(lj|\,|S_{\Lambda L}|\,|\bar{l}_{\mathrm{i}}j_{\mathrm{i}}) \int_0^\infty f_{l_{\mathrm{i}}j_{\mathrm{i}}}(r)\, j_\Lambda(kr)\, g_{lj}(r)\, \mathrm{d}\left(\frac{r}{a}\right). \tag{27}$$

The reduced matrix elements of the tensorial operator $S_{\Lambda Lq}$ can be expressed by recoupling coefficients by using standard techniques[15])

$$(l_1 j_1|\,|S_{\Lambda L}|\,|l_2 j_2) =$$
$$= [(2j_1+1)(2j_2+1)(2L+1)]^{\frac{1}{2}}(l_1|\,|Y_\Lambda|\,|(l_2)(\tfrac{1}{2}|\,|s|\,|\tfrac{1}{2})\, X\begin{pmatrix}\Lambda & 1 & L\\ l_1 & \frac{1}{2} & j_1\\ l_2 & \frac{1}{2} & j_2\end{pmatrix} =$$
$$= (-)^{l_2}[(2j_1+1)(2j_2+1)(2l_1+1)(2l_2+1)(2L+1)\cdot 3/8\pi]^{\frac{1}{2}} \times$$
$$\times (l_1 0; l_2 0|\Lambda 0)\, X\begin{pmatrix}\Lambda & 1 & L\\ l_1 & \frac{1}{2} & j_1\\ l_2 & \frac{1}{2} & j_2\end{pmatrix}. \tag{28}$$

2.4. Cross-sections

In order to obtain the photoelectric cross-section for *all the electrons in a particular (closed) subshell* $l_{\mathrm{i}}j_{\mathrm{i}}$ we have to insert the expression (25) into (1) and sum up the result over all values of m_{i}. For circularly polarized photons and for unpolarized photons the cross-sections are the same, thus we may delete the averaging over the polarization q. The products of the two spherical harmonics appearing in the square of the transition amplitude can be reduced by using the formula[16])

$$\begin{aligned} Y_{l_1\mu}(\Omega_e)\, Y^*_{l_2\mu}(\Omega_e) &= \sum_n (-)^{n-l_1} [(2l_2+1)/4\pi]^{\frac{1}{2}} (n0;\, l_2\mu|l_1\mu) \times \\ &\quad \times (l_10;\, l_20|n0)\, Y_{n0}(\Omega_e) = \\ &= \sum_n [(-1)^{n-l_1}/4\pi]\, [(2l_2+1)(2n+1)]^{\frac{1}{2}} \times \\ &\quad \times (n0;\, l_2\mu|l_1\mu)\,(l_10;\, l_20|n0)\, P_n(\cos\theta_e)\,. \end{aligned} \tag{29}$$

After this reduction the expression for the cross-section becomes a series of the form

$$\frac{d\sigma}{d\Omega_e} = \frac{8\pi E_e}{\text{`137'}\, p_e^2 E_\gamma} \left(\frac{E_e + mc^2}{2E_e}\right)^{\frac{1}{2}} \sum_{n=0} B_n P_n(\cos\theta_e)\,. \tag{30}$$

The summations over all magnetic quantum numbers in the expression of B_n can be performed and one obtains

$$\begin{aligned} B_n = 4p_e a \sum_{L_1L_2} \sum_{\Lambda_1\Lambda_2} \sum_{l_1l_2} \sum_{j_1j_2} & (-1)^{j_i - \frac{1}{2} + L_1 + L_2 + j_1 + j_2}\, i^{l_2 - l_1 + \Lambda_1 - \Lambda_2} \times \\ & \times \exp[i(\delta_{l_1j_1} - \delta_{l_2j_2})] \times \\ & \times [(2\Lambda_1+1)(2\Lambda_2+1)(2l_1+1)(2l_2+1)(2j_1+1)(2j_2+1)]^{\frac{1}{2}} \times \\ & \times (l_10; l_20|n0)\,(\Lambda_10; 1q|L_1q)\,(\Lambda_20; 1q|L_2q)\,(L_1q; L_2-q|n0) \times \\ & \times W(L_1L_2j_ij_2;\, nj)\, W(l_1l_2j_1j_2;\, n\tfrac{1}{2}) \times \\ & \times (\psi_{l_1j_1}|\, |j_{\Lambda_1} S_{\Lambda_1L_1}\gamma_5|\, |\phi_i)\,(\psi_{l_2j_2}|\, |j_{\Lambda_2} S_{\Lambda_2L_2}\gamma_5|\, |\phi_i)^*\,. \end{aligned} \tag{31}$$

The total photoelectric cross-section for an unpolarized photon is easily obtained by integrating (30) over angles

$$\sigma = \frac{32\pi^2}{\text{`137'}} \frac{1}{p_e^2} \frac{E_e}{E_\gamma} \left(\frac{E_e + mc^2}{2E_e}\right)^{\frac{1}{2}} B_0\,. \tag{32}$$

For $n=0$ the expression (31) simplifies to

$$\begin{aligned} B_0 = 4p_e a \sum_L \sum_l \sum_j & \{|(\psi_{lj}|\, |j_L S_{LL}\gamma_5|\, |\phi_i)|^2 + \\ & + \frac{L}{2L+1} |(\psi_{lj}|\, |j_{L+1} S_{(L+1)L}\gamma_5|\, |\phi_i)|^2 + \\ & + \frac{L+1}{2L+1} |(\psi_{lj}|\, |j_{L-1} S_{(L-1)L}\gamma_5|\, |\phi_i)|^2 - \frac{2[L(L+1)]^{\frac{1}{2}}}{2L+1} \times \\ & \times \mathrm{Re}\{(\psi_{lj}|\, |j_{L+1} S_{(L+1)L}\gamma_5|\, |\phi_i) \times \\ & \times (\psi_{lj}|\, |j_{L-1} S_{(L-1)L}\gamma_5|\, |\phi_i)^*\}\,. \end{aligned} \tag{33}$$

The reduced matrix elements $(\psi_{lj}||j_{\Lambda}\,S_{\Lambda L}\,\gamma_5|\,|\phi_i)$ are given by expressions (27) and (28).

For the sake of completeness we also write down the cross-section for linearly polarized photons. The transition amplitude for a photon linearly polarized along the y axis is obtained from expressions (6) or (25) by summing on $q=\pm 1$ and multiplying by $i/\sqrt{2}$. The cross-section can be written in the following form

$$\frac{d\sigma}{d\Omega_e} = \frac{8\pi}{\text{‘137’}} \frac{1}{p_e^2} \frac{E_e}{E_\gamma} \left(\frac{E_e + mc^2}{2E_e}\right)^{\frac{1}{2}} \times$$
$$\times \sum_n \{B_n P_n(\cos\theta_e) + B_n^{(2)}\, P_n^{(2)}(\cos\theta_e)\cos 2\phi_e\}\,. \tag{34}$$

Here $p_n^{(2)}$ $(\cos\theta_e)$ are the associated Legendre polynomials and ϕ_e is the azimuthal angle of the electron measured with respect to the polarization plane. The coefficients $B_n^{(2)}$ obtained, after the summation on magnetic quantum numbers, the following form,

$$B_n^{(2)} = 4p_e a \sum_{q_1 q_2} \sum_{L_1 L_2} \sum_{\Lambda_1 \Lambda_2} \sum_{l_1 l_2} \sum_{i_1 i_2} (-1)^{j_i - \frac{1}{2} + L_1 + L_2 + j_1 + j_2}\, i^{l_2 - l_1 + \Lambda_1 - \Lambda_2} \times$$
$$\times \exp[i(\delta_{l_1 j_1} - \delta_{l_2 j_2})]\,[(2\Lambda_1 + 1)(2\Lambda_2 + 2)(2j_1 + 1)(2j_2 + 2) \times$$
$$\times (2l_1 + 1)(2l_2 + 2)(n-2)!/(n+2)!]^{\frac{1}{2}} \times$$
$$\times (l_1 0; l_2 0|n0)(\Lambda_1 0; 1q_1|L_1 q_1)(\Lambda_2 0; 1q_2|L_2 q_2) \times$$
$$\times (L_1 q_1; L_2 - q_2|n-2) \times$$
$$\times W(L_1 L_2 j_1 j_2; n j_i)\, W(l_1 l_2 j_1 j_2; n\tfrac{1}{2})\,(\psi_{l_1 j_1}||j_{\Lambda_1} S_{\Lambda_1 L_1} \gamma_5|\,|\phi_i) \times$$
$$\times (\psi_{l_2 j_2}||j_{\Lambda_2} S_{\Lambda_2 L_2} \gamma_5|\,|\phi_i)^*\,. \tag{35}$$

3. Numerical procedures

3.1. General procedures

The radial Dirac equations, eq. (13), have been integrated by the Runge–Kutta–Gill[17]) method with automatic error control. The integration is started at

$$R_1 = \left[4 \times 10^{-4}\left(\frac{92 - Z}{91}\right) + 5 \times 10^{-5}\left(\frac{Z-1}{91}\right)\right]\text{Å},$$

with the ratio F/G given by eq. (19). The matching point R_2 for the bound state (cf. eq. (23)) is chosen at the last maximum of the bound wave function. The inward integration of the bound wave function is started at a radius R_3

which is 5–20 times larger than R_2 (depending on the values of the principal quantum number of the state: $R_3/R_2=20$ for $n=1$, $R_3/R_2=10$ for $n=2, 3, 4$ and $R_3/R_2=5$ for $n\geqslant 5$). The ratio F/G at R_3 is given by eq. (22). The normalization of the continuum states is performed at a radius R_n which is larger than the largest of the radii R_3 of all the levels treated in one specific atom. In order to check whether the normalization radius is large enough, R_n is increased by 20% and the normalization constant C (eq. (21)) is recalculated. If C changes by more than 0.1% the radius R_n is further increased.

The potentials and bound wave functions are calculated separately and supplied in tabular form to a computer program named FOTO. This program calculates simultaneously all partial waves of the continuum state and performs the radial integrations. In FOTO the values of the potential (more precisely, the values of $(Z_{\text{eff}}(r)/Z)=(rV(r)/Ze)$ and the values of the bound wave functions are obtained by a four point Lagrange interpolation formula from the tables. The spherical Bessel functions are obtained by a recursion procedure. The radial integrals appearing in eq. (27) are calculated using Simpson's formula. The program FOTO calculates all the recoupling coefficients and performs all the summations necessary to obtain the angular distribution, eq. (30), and the total cross-section, eq. (32)*.

3.2. The numerical accuracy

The automatic error control of the Runge–Kutta–Gill routine has been set so as to retain a relative accuracy better than 2×10^{-5} in the important range of the wave functions. Actually the accuracy is usually even better than 4×10^{-6}. Recoupling coefficients and Bessel functions are calculated accurately to at least six decimals. The largest errors enter into the radial integrals through the Simpson integration and the phase shift calculation. The overall relative errors in the radial integrals are kept below 0.03%.

The overall accuracy obtained in the calculation of the cross-sections has been checked by comparing the differential cross-sections as calculated by FOTO, i.e. by eq. (30), with the plane wave Born approximation**. In these calculations $Z_{\text{eff}}(r)$ is set to zero but the bound states are taken as the eigenstates in a pure Coulomb field. The check has been performed at several

* In the calculations the following values of physical constants have been used: $\hbar c/e^2 = $ '137' $= 137.0372$, $mc^2 = 510.976$ keV, $\lambda\!\!\!^{-}_c = 0.003\,861\,52$ Å.

** As explained in the introduction the plane wave Born approximation has not much physical significance but yields closed expressions without making any approximation beyond replacing the final electron state by a plane wave. The somewhat lengthy formulas are given in A. Ron's Ph. D. Thesis (unpublished).

energies in the hundred keV range. The relative difference between the two results, around the maximum of the angular distribution, is less than 0.5%. At larger angles the errors rise up to a few percents. An additional check on the calculation has been performed at 100 eV. The total cross-sections, as calculated by FOTO, are compared to those calculated by analytic expressions using the non-relativistic, dipole and Born approximations for hydrogen atoms. The deviations are of order of 0.2%. It can be stated quite safely that the *numerical* accuracy of the calculated cross-sections is better than 0.5%. This accuracy is believed to be quite sufficient in view of the approximate nature of the shell model wave functions used in the calculations.

4. Discussion of results

4.1. The effect of screening and comparison with previous calculations

The effect of using various potentials in the calculation of the photoeffect can be seen in tables 1–3 and figs. 1 and 2. In the tables the results of Pratt et al. (appearing under the heading CCP), of Alling and Johnson (CCA), of Hulme (CCH) and of Matese and Johnson (MJ) are cited for comparison with our results (cf. refs. 4, 6, 7, 8).

When a Coulomb potential is used, a considerable ambiguity arises, due to the large difference between the experimental binding energies and the binding energies as calculated with this potential. For a given photon

TABLE 1

Photoelectric cross-sections (in barns) for uranium

Subshell	E_γ (keV)	Type of calculation					
		CC	CCP	CCA	CE	TF	MJ
K	2000	2.377	2.33	–	–	2.325	–
K	1332	–	4.93	4.928	4.483	4.822	4.884
K	1173	–	–	–	5.706	6.136	–
K	662	–	20.4	20.21	–	19.74	20.04
K	412	–	59.9	59.47	53.11	58.02	58.99
K	208	–	319.0	–	279.6	316.2	–
L_I	279	19.8	–	19.86	17.84	17.75	18.44
L_{II}	279	9.708	–	9.710	7.895	8.118	8.675
L_{III}	279	6.214	–	6.213	5.102	5.012	5.357
L_I	81	382.5	–	382.4	313.0	339.4	367.3
L_{II}	81	323.2	–	322.6	220.7	269.1	300.3
L_{III}	81	297.5	–	297.6	198.4	239.3	263.2

TABLE 2

Photoelectric cross-section (in barns) for lead

Subshell	E_γ (keV)	Type of calculation			
		CC	CCA	TF	MJ
K	1130	4.094	–	3.99	–
K	354	54.98	–	53.36	54.40
L_I	279	–	12.75	11.18	11.46
L_{II}	279	–	4.367	3.538	3.737
L_{III}	279	–	3.294	2.595	2.774
L_I	103	–	153.9	134.5	142.1
L_{II}	103	–	81.23	65.8	72.25
L_{III}	103	–	78.29	61.52	66.89
L_I	81	–	275.2	239.8	256.7
L_{II}	81	–	166.2	134.4	149.3
L_{III}	81	–	170.0	133.4	146.4

TABLE 3

K shell cross-sections

Z	E_γ (keV)	Type of calculation			
		CCH	CC	CCP	TF
13	354	–	0.01545	0.01543	0.01357
26	354	0.39	0.3882	0.3885	0.361
50	354	7.1	7.054	7.06	6.75
84	354	60.2	60.42	60.6	58.73
13	1130	–	0.00091	0.00091	0.00080
26	1130	0.023	0.02368	0.0237	0.02212
50	1130	0.46	0.463	0.462	0.4446
84	1130	4.61	4.544	4.54	4.432

energy the energy of the photoelectron is calculated by Einstein's relation, eq. (2). In eq. (2) one can insert for E_b either the experimental binding energy or the calculated one. In all previously published calculations (CCA, CCH, CCP) the calculated energies were used in eq. (2). Calculations which employ Coulomb wave functions and calculated Coulomb binding energies we denoted CC. On the other hand, calculations employing Coulomb wave functions but experimental binding energies are denoted CE. In the CE calculations the continuum state is thus calculated with the correct experimental energy.

Considering the results in tables 1 and 3, we see that there is an excellent

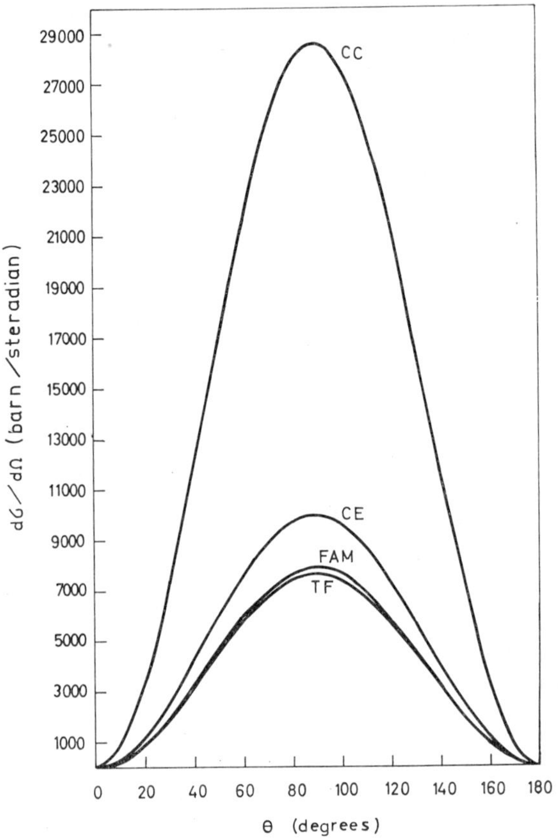

Fig. 1. The angular distribution of photoelectrons ejected from the L_I subshell of aluminum by photons of energy $E_\gamma = 0.6$ keV. The designations CC, CE, FAM, TF on the graphs are as explained in the text.

agreement between our results of type CC and the results of Hulme et al. (CCH), Pratt et al. (CCP) and of Alling and Johnson (CCA). From fig. 1 and table 1 we see that results of the type CE differ significantly from the results of type CC. Comparing these results to results obtained with Thomas–Fermi potentials (type TF in table 1 and fig. 1) the results of type CE are not found to be better than the results of type CC.

When using screened potentials of the Thomas–Fermi type there appears no ambiguity due to binding energies. The calculated binding energies rarely differ by more than 5% from the experimental ones. Two kinds of screened potentials have been employed in our calculations. The usual

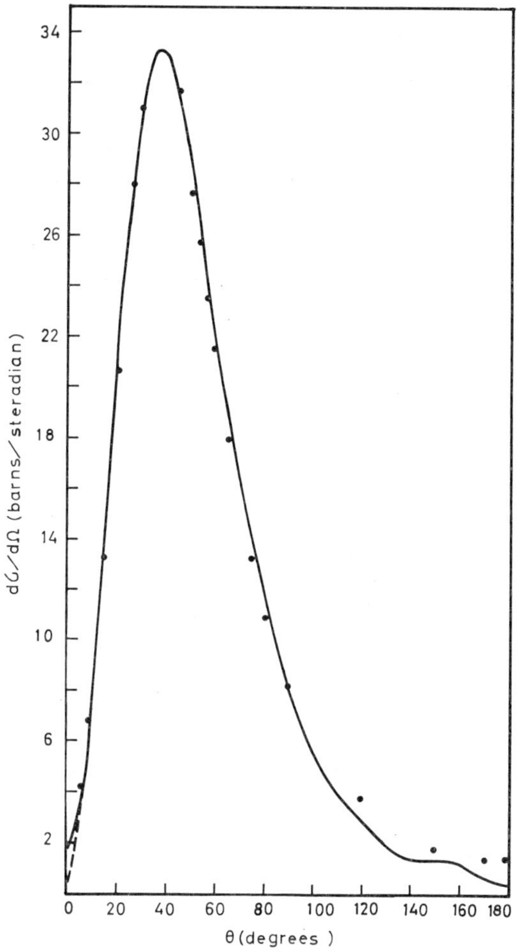

Fig. 2. The angular distribution of photoelectrons ejected from the K shell of uranium by photons of energy 279 keV. The full line is calculated with a TF potential. The broken line, which coincides with the full line over almost the whole range, is calculated with a Coulomb potential. The points designate experimental values obtained by Z. Sujkowski [21]).

Thomas–Fermi potential denoted TF and a modified Fermi–Amaldi potential [9]) denoted FAM. For comparison of binding energies as calculated with these potentials and experiment, we refer to Shalitin's work [9]). However, it was found that the difference between cross-sections evaluated for $Z=50$ and $Z=74$ with the two types of potentials (TF and FAM) is not more than 1.5%. From fig. 1 it is seen that even for Z as low as 13 the difference between the two types is small. Actually in none of the cases which we checked did the difference exceed 5%.

In tables 1 and 2 results of Matese and Johnson (denoted MJ) are listed along with TF results. The MJ cross-sections were calculated with a screened potential of the Yukawa type. It is seen that the MJ cross-sections are usually larger than our TF results. Recently Schmickley[18]) obtained results which are close to our TF values.

Considering table 3 and fig. 2 it may be concluded that the effect of screening is not significant in the K shell. From tables 1–3 and fig. 1 it is seen that for higher shells the screening of the Coulomb field is quite important.

4.2. Survey of the Numerical Results

Total photoelectric cross-sections for many subshells of the elements uranium ($Z=92$), tungsten ($Z=74$), tin ($Z=50$), iron ($Z=26$) and aluminum

Table 4

Total cross-sections in barns for the K and L subshells of uranium, $Z=92$ (calculated with a TF potential)

Photon energy (keV)	Subshell			
	K	L_I	L_{II}	L_{III}
2000	2.325	0.2854	0.0926	0.0415
1332	4.822	0.5856	0.1975	0.0908
1173	6.136	0.759	0.252	0.1187
662	19.74	2.438	0.8818	0.4496
412	58.02			
279	150.5	17.75	8.118	5.012
208	316.2	36.13	18.36	12.30
150	725.4			
130	1040			
120	1268			
116.5	1365			
103		194.9	135.8	112.2
81		339.4	269.1	239.3
60		661.2	626.8	610.5
42		1399	1672	1819
30		2692	4077	4941
22		4669	8895	12030
21.5			9401	
20				15720
17.5				22670

TABLE 5

Total cross-sections in barns for M subshells of uranium, $Z=92$ (calculated with a TF potential)

Photon energy (keV)	Subshell				
	M_I	M_{II}	M_{III}	M_{IV}	M_V
2000	0.0647				
662	0.554	0.2185	0.1188	0.00496	0.00461
279	4.030				
208	8.198				
103	44.48	30.17	26.76	2.88	2.843
81	77.94	58.08	55.47	7.043	7.162
50	230.9	208.8	230.7	42.14	45.50
25	981.7	1151	1570	513	597.5
10	5182	7643	14350	10930	13860
6	11010	16615			
5.5		18425			
5			56100	84920	114000
4				154600	211500

TABLE 6

Total cross-sections in barns for N subshells of uranium, $Z=92$ (calculated with a TF potential)

Photon energy (keV)	Subshell				
	N_I	N_{II}	N_{III}	N_{IV}	N_V
103	12.11	7.95	7.103	0.8394	0.8266
10	1616	2075	3683	2374	3013
5	5290	6863	15420	15300	20570
3	11430				
2	19310	19970	72170	101800	149100
1.75		21690			
1.5			106000		
1				212700	350000

($Z=13$) are presented in tables 4–17 and in figs. 3–7. According to Shalitin[9]) the TF potential yields the best binding energies for the very heavy elements ($Z>80$) and for the rest of the elements the FAM model is, on the average, the best. Thus, the uranium cross-sections listed in the tables were calculated using a TF potential and all other cross-sections are calculated with FAM potentials. The energy range of the calculations is limited to 1–2000 keV. At

TABLE 7
Total cross-sections in barns for N and O subshells of uranium $Z = 92$
(calculated with a TF potential)

Subshell	Photon energy (keV)				
	103	10	5	3	1
N_{VI}	0.01515	418.3	5933	125500	801800
N_{VII}	0.01564	501.1	7281	158500	1037000
O_{I}	3.096	427.8	1472	6472	17040
O_{II}	1.896	499.7	1735	6466	13390
O_{III}	1.636	842.9	3595	18540	52180
O_{IV}	0.1599	427.8	2703	18640	50880
O_{V}	0.1544	532.5	3558	26400	77110

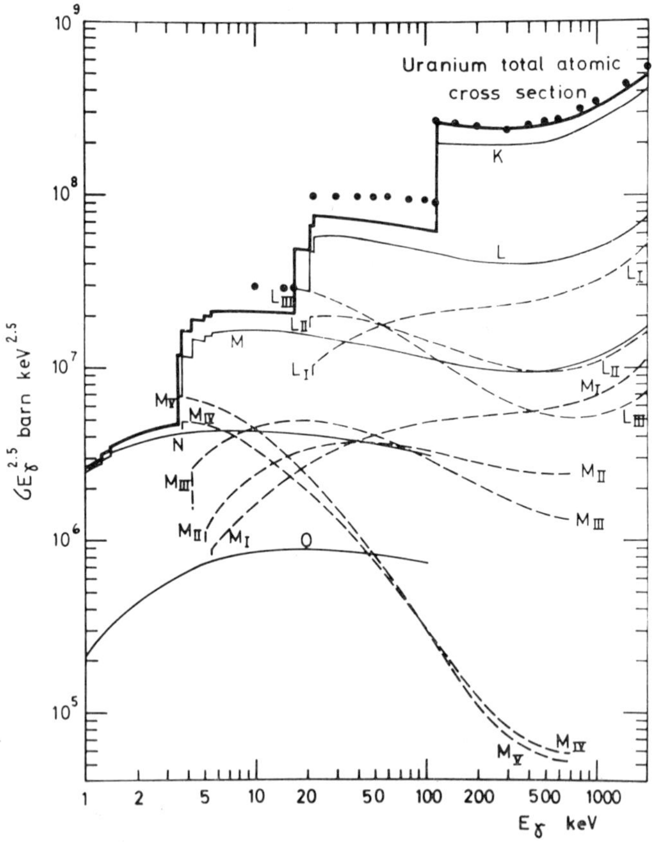

Fig. 3. Photoelectric cross-sections of various subshells and shells of uranium. The uppermost line gives the total atomic cross-section. The points indicate values taken from Davisson's tabulation[19]).

TABLE 8

Total cross-sections in barns for K and L subshells of tungsten, $Z = 74$ (calculated with FAM potentials)

Photon energy (keV)	Subshell			
	K	L_I	L_{II}	L_{III}
2000	0.9168	0.1054	0.01722	0.01216
1173	2.399	0.2771	0.04707	
662	7.911	0.9126	0.1703	0.1257
279	66.66	7.378	1.742	1.445
103	964.2	95.41	35.14	35.99
81	1803.5	173.6	73.51	79.28
71	2536			
50		549.8	319.4	380.5
30		1712	1450	1909
15		6732	10030	15110
12.75		8942		
12.2			17170	
11				35920

TABLE 9

Total cross-sections in barns for M subshells of tungsten, $Z = 74$ (calculated with FAM potentials)

Photon energy (keV)	Subshell				
	M_I	M_{II}	M_{III}	M_{IV}	M_V
103	20.48	7.719	8.215	0.4920	0.5287
81	37.27	15.81	17.73	1.256	1.381
50	119.0	65.04	80.60	8.260	9.558
30	380.3	273.0	373.8	58.86	71.18
10	3605	4266	7153	3123	4083
5	12200	17320	33800	29560	40140
3.5	20980	31020			
3			88060		
2.5				214200	302500

lower energies the contribution of very high atomic shells dominates and at higher energies very high partial waves of the continuum states must be considered. At both edges of the energy range calculations lose accuracy and require much computer time. In figs. 3–7 dots indicate values taken from Davisson's tabulation[19]). Davisson's values, which have been partially ob-

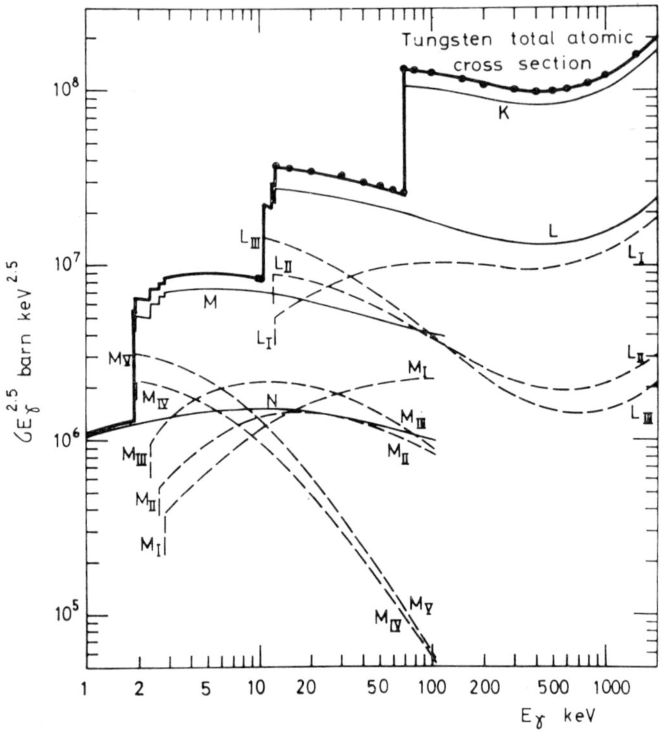

Fig. 4. Photoelectric cross-sections of various subshells and shells of tungsten. The uppermost line gives the total atomic cross-sections. The points indicate values taken from Davisson's tabulation[19]).

TABLE 10

Total cross-sections in barns for N subshells of tungsten, $Z=74$ (calculated with FAM potentials)

Photon energy (keV)	Subshell				
	N_I	N_{II}	N_{III}	N_{IV}	N_V
103	5.012	1.812	1.921	0.1177	0.1255
81	9.123	3.696	4.127	0.2977	0.3260
50	29.20	15.06	18.59	1.917	2.203
30	93.92	62.55	85.20	13.23	15.94
10	930.7	966.9	1596	618.0	805.8
5	3422	4123	7693	5075	6894
1	41550	42760	121200	170900	254400

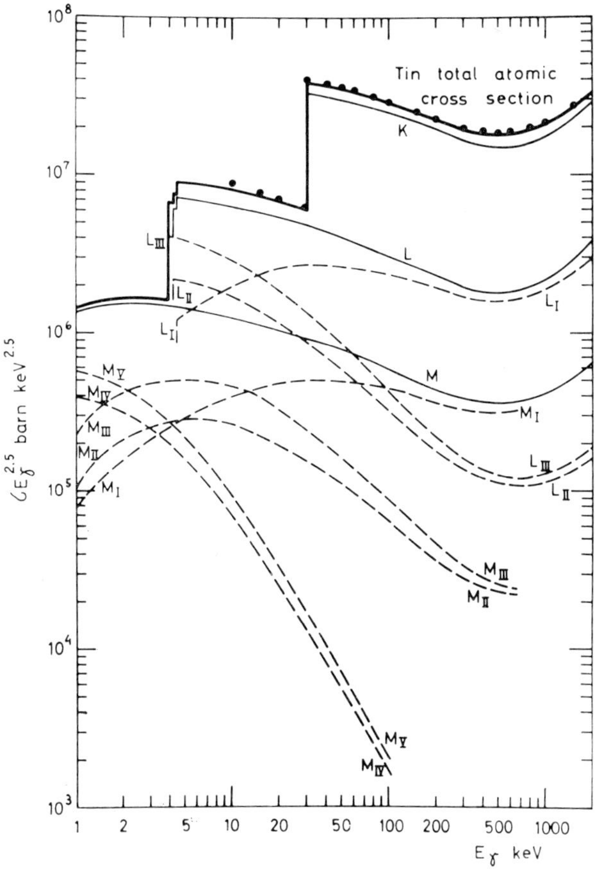

Fig. 5. Photoelectric cross-sections of various subshells and shells of tin. The uppermost line gives the total atomic cross-section. The points indicate values taken from Davisson's tabulation[19]).

TABLE 11

Total cross-sections in barns for N and O subshells of tungsten, $Z = 74$ (calculated with FAM potentials)

Photon energy (keV)	Subshell				
	N_{VI}	N_{VII}	O_I	O_{II}	O_{II}
5	701.8	873.1	707.7	718.0	1261
1	188100	242100	10580	9248	22660

TABLE 12

Total cross-sections in barns for K and L subshells of tin, $Z=50$ (calculated with FAM potentials)

Photon energy (keV)	Subshell			
	K	L_I	L_{II}	L_{III}
2000	0.1635	0.01718	0.0009111	0.001108
1173	0.4207	0.04432	0.002565	0.002934
662	1.416	0.1490	0.009764	0.01071
279	13.24	1.358	0.1140	0.1308
103	229.3	21.76	2.924	3.884
81	455.2	42.05	6.557	8.923
40	3168	269.6	69.62	102.9
30	6683	551.8	179.0	273.4
10		6533	5494	9292
5		23910	38640	69100
4.5			50890	
4.25				107900

TABLE 13

Total cross-sections in barns for M subshells of tin, $Z=50$ (calculated with FAM potentials)

Photon energy (keV)	Subshell				
	M_I	M_{II}	M_{III}	M_{IV}	M_V
662	0.02847	0.001987	0.002214		
279	0.2588	0.02302	0.02655		
103	4.113	0.5746	0.7634	0.01475	0.01752
81	7.929	1.275	1.752	0.03982	0.04901
40	50.63	12.94	19.42	0.7770	0.9952
30	103.8	32.45	50.22	2.587	3.365
10	1287	850.4	1455	210.9	288.7
5	5273	5143	9297	2702	3788
3	13660	16450	31090	15370	21880
1	75360	106600	230600	391300	571500

tained by interpolation between few experimental points, seem to fit quite well on our graphs except for uranium in the range $E_\gamma=10$–100 keV.

In fig. 8 total atomic cross-sections (σ_A) in the range $E_\gamma=100$–2000 keV are presented. It is seen that the combination $\sigma_A E_\gamma^{2.5}/Z^{4.5}$ is a rather slowly

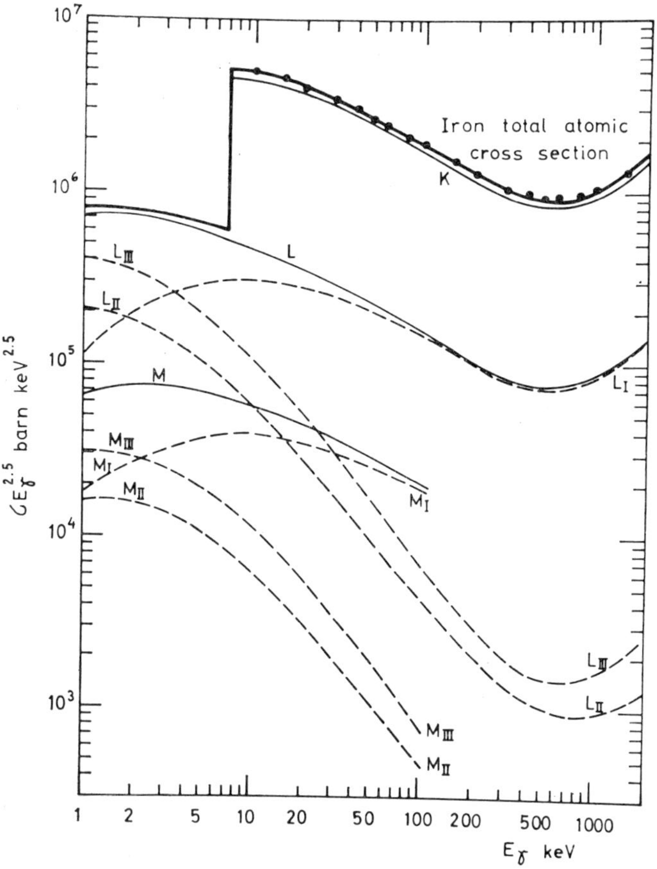

Fig. 6. Photoelectric cross-sections of various subshells and shells of iron. The uppermost line gives the total atomic cross-section. The points indicate values taken from Davisson's tabulation[19]).

varying function of E_γ and Z. Particularly for $E_\gamma > 600$ keV and $Z > 26$ the cross-section varies rather accurately as $Z^{4.5}$. This is in contradiction to the Z^5 variation predicted by various theories.

In table 18 the ratio (σ_A/σ_K) between the atomic and K shell photoelectric cross-sections is presented for various elements. It is found that only for the highest Z's the widely used "five fourth law" is justified.

Some angular distributions are presented in figs. 1 and 2. Some forward photoelectrons are predicted in agreement with the approximate relativistic expressions.

TABLE 14

Total cross-sections in barns for N subshells of tin, $Z=50$ (calculated with FAM potential)

Photon energy (keV)	Subshell		
	N_I	N_{II}	N_{III}
103	0.7552		
81	1.455		
40	9.287		
30	19.04		
10	238.3		
5	997.3	801.8	1424
3	2664	2581	4762
1	18200	20080	40480

TABLE 15

Total cross-sections in barns for K and L subshells of iron, $Z=26$ (calculated with FAM potential)

Photon energy (keV)	Subshell			
	K	L_I	L_{II}	L_{III}
2000	0.008414	0.0007505	0.000007201	0.00001441
1173	0.02116	0.001890	0.00002072	0.0000367
662	0.07196	0.006419	0.00008249	0.0001253
279	0.7388	0.06531	0.001109	0.001625
120	9.574			
103	15.34	1.315	0.03706	0.05924
81	32.12	2.721	0.08989	0.1466
30	639.3	50.26	3.577	6.297
10	13940	964.3	182.4	334.6
7.65	27600			
5		5113	1856	3483
3		15630	9272	17640
1		112450	203900	400400

4.3. Comparison with experiment

Early experimental determinations of photoelectric cross-sections have been performed either by following tracks in cloud chambers or by observing the total absorption coefficient. The cloud chamber experiments yield quite accurate results but demanded a considerable amount of work. This method was therefore abandoned. The determination of photoelectric cross-sections

TABLE 16
Total cross-sections in barns for M subshells of iron, $Z=26$
(calculated with FAM potentials)

Photon energy (keV)	Subshell		
	M_I	M_{II}	M_{III}
103	0.168	0.00416	0.006649
81	0.3472	0.01011	0.01643
30	6.375	0.3953	0.6927
10	121.6	19.28	35.42
5	648.4	185.6	347.5
3	2014	870.7	1650
1	17570	15770	30590

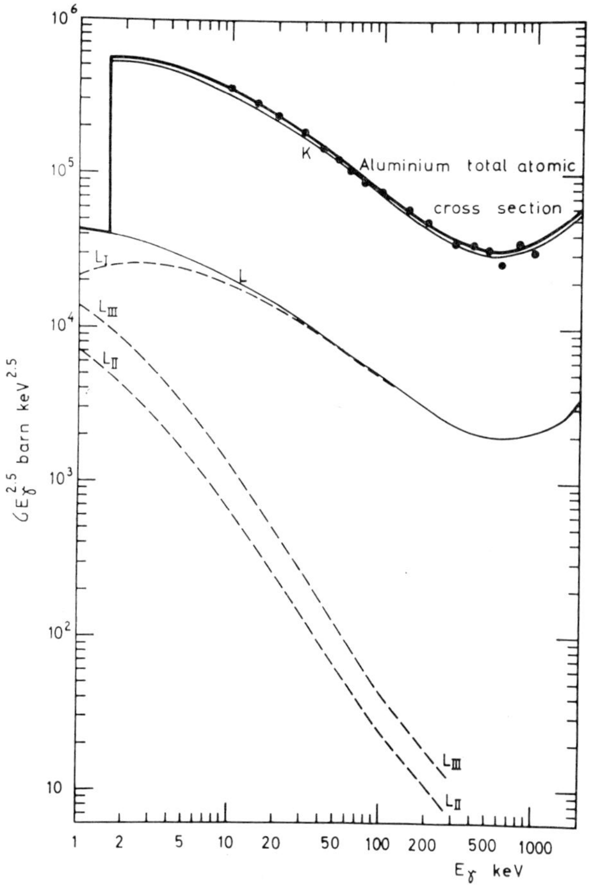

Fig. 7. Photoelectric cross-sections of various subshells and shells of aluminum. The uppermost line gives the total atomic cross-section. The points indicate values taken from Davisson's tabulation[19]).

TABLE 17

Total cross-sections in barns for K and L subshells of aluminum, $Z=13$ (calculated with FAM potentials)

Photon energy (keV)	Subshell			
	K	L_I	L_{II}	L_{III}
2000	0.0003185			
662	0.002692			
279	0.0291	0.001894	0.000005535	0.000009354
103	0.6765	0.04382	0.0002101	0.0003775
81	1.468	0.09491	0.00053	0.0009589
30	35.19	2.205	0.02736	0.0516
10	1036	60.80	2.051	3.928
5	7862	430.2	27.96	54.65
3		1664	178.0	346.4
2	93645			
1		22750	7152	14070

TABLE 18

Comparison of experimental with theoretical cross-section ratios

The cross-section ratio			Experiment		Theory
Z	E_γ (keV)	type	value	ref.	
13	K edge	σ_A/σ_K	1.09	22	1.06*
26			1.12		1.10*
50			1.18		1.18–1.14*
74			1.20		1.23–1.15*
92			1.235		1.28–1.25*
92	208	σ_K/σ_L		23	4.73
	279				4.87
	662				5.24
	1173		5.3 ± 0.2		5.43
	1332				5.52
	2000				5.45
92	103	$\sigma_{L_I+L_{II}}/\sigma_{L_{III}}$	3.03 ± 0.15	21	2.95
	103	σ_L/σ_M	3.7 ± 0.2		4.13
	81	$\sigma_{L_{II}}/\sigma_{L_{III}}$	0.92 ± 0.15		1.125

* The value varies smoothly from the K edge to 2000 keV.

from absorption coefficients is inaccurate owing to the necessity to subtract the contribution to the absorption of various processes which are not known much better than the photoeffect itself. Also the contribution of different

TABLE 19

Comparison of experimental with theoretical cross-sections

Z	E_γ (keV)	ref.	Experiment		Theory	
			σ_a	σ_k	σ_a	σ_k
92	1332	24	5.9 ± 0.1	4.7	5.97	4.822
92	662	24	24.9 ± 0.2	19.7	24.7	19.74
92	412	24	73.2 ± 0.2	58.1	73.0	58.02
92	1332	25		5.4 ± 0.3	5.97	4.822
92	1173	25		7.2 ± 0.5	7.626	6.136
82	511	26		23.4 ± 0.7		21.88
79	662	27		10.2 ± 0.3		10.34

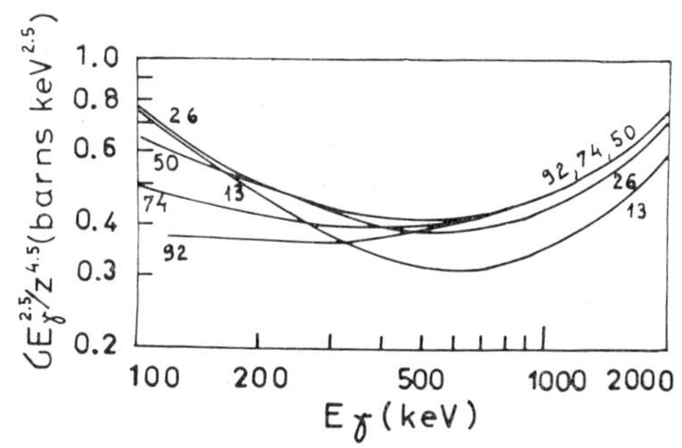

Fig. 8. Total atomic cross-sections of various elements at intermediate photon energies. The numbers on the curves designate the Z of the element. Notice that the cross-sections vary roughly as $Z^{4.5}/E_\gamma^{2.5}$.

shells to the photoelectric cross-sections cannot be separated by this method. Neither can angular distributions be determined.

In 1947 Latyshev[20]) suggested a method for direct measurement of the differential photoelectric cross-section by means of a beta spectrometer. The method has been further elaborated by Hultberg[21]) and is today the main source of experimental data.

The only experimental results on the photoeffect about which we are aware of and which can be compared with theory are the following:

1) A few angular distributions of photoelectrons. As a typical example we present the angular distribution of K shell photoelectrons from 279 keV gamma's on uranium[21]) (fig. 2).

2) Various ratios of atomic to K shell cross-sections and ratios between contributions of various subshells (table 18).

3) Some atomic and K shell cross-sections (table 19).

Acknowledgment

It is a pleasure to thank Mr. Dan Shalitin for generous help and advice through many phases of our work.

References

1) J. Fischer, Ann. Physik **8**, 821 (1931).
2) F. Sauter, Ann. Physik **9**, 217 (1931).
3) R. H. Pratt, Phys. Rev. **117**, 1017 (1960).
4) H. R. Hulme, J. McDougall, R. H. Buckingham and R. H. Fowler, Proc. Roy. Soc. (London) A **149**, 131 (1935).
5) S. Hultberg, B. Nagel and P. Olsson, Arkiv Fysik **20**, 555 (1960).
6) R. H. Pratt, R. D. Levee, R. L. Pexton and W. Aron, Phys. Rev. **134**, A898 (1964).
7) W. R. Alling and W. R. Johnson, Phys. Rev. **139**, A1050 (1965).
8) J. J. Matese and W. R. Johnson, Phys. Rev. **140**, A1 (1965).
9) D. Shalitin, Phys. Rev. **140**, A1857 (1965).
10) A. Messiah, *Quantum Mechanics* (North-Holland Publ. Co., Amsterdam, 1962) pp. 836 and 839; cf. also W. Heitler, *The Quantum Theory of Radiation*, 3rd ed. (Oxford Univ. Press, 1954) p. 205, eq. (4).
11) W. Heitler, ibid, p. 143, eq. (21).
12) M. E. Rose, *Relativistic Electron Theory* (John Wiley, New York, 1961).
13) D. R. Hartree, *The Calculation of Atomic Structures* (Chapman and Hall, London, 1957) p. 80ff.
14) U. Fano and G. Racah, *Irreducible Tensorial Sets* (Academic Press, New York, 1959) p. 79, eq. (14.4).
15) U. Fano and G. Racah, ibid, p. 84, eq. (15.4).
16) U. Fano and G. Racah, ibid, p. 81, eq. (14.12).
17) A. Ralston and H. S. Wilf, *Mathematical Methods for Digital Computers* (John Wiley, New York, 1962).
18) Ronald Schmickley, Thesis, Stanford University, 1966; R. H. Pratt and R. D. Schmickley, Phys. Rev., to be published.
19) C. M. Davisson, in: *Alpha-, Beta- and Gamma-Ray Spectroscopy*, Vol. I, Ed. K. Siegbahn (North-Holland Publ. Co., Amsterdam, 1965) ch. 2 and app. 1.
20) G. D. Latyshev, Rev. Mod. Phys. **19**, 132 (1947).
21) Z. Sujkowski, Arkiv Fysik **20**, 269 (1961).
22) F. Kirchner, in: *Handbuch der Experimentalphysik*, Eds. W. Wien and F. Harms, Vol. 24/1 (Akademische Verlagsgesellschaft, 1930) p. 256.
23) S. Hultberg, Arkiv Fysik **15**, 307 (1959).
24) S. A. Colgate, Phys. Rev. **87**, 592 (1952).
25) S. Hultberg and R. Stockendal, Arkiv Fysik **15**, 355 (1959).
26) K. W. Seeman, Bull. Am. Phys. Soc. **1**, 198 (1956).
27) G. Missoni, as cited in ref. 6.

Spectroscopic and group theoretical methods in physics

DYNAMICAL THEORY OF NUCLEAR RESONANCES

LÉON ROSENFELD

NORDITA, Copenhagen, Denmark

1. Introduction

The physical concept of resonance takes its name from the theory of sound, but it has found a wide range of application in all aperiodic quantal processes at the atomic, nuclear and subnuclear levels. The elucidation of the dynamical features responsible for an effect common to such different types of interaction is a problem that would have appealed to Racah's turn of mind, and it would no doubt have afforded him particular satisfaction to see that methods developed in atomic and molecular physics by one of his nearest collaborators, U. Fano, proved extremely well suited to the analysis of the corresponding nuclear phenomena. It is in this last domain that the mechanism of resonance may be most completely studied. Optical resonances are not particularly informative because of the smallness of the interaction of atomic systems with the radiation field. In collisions between atoms and electrons or in chemical reactions, in which the interactions have no such clear-cut characteristics as the short range of the nuclear forces, resonance effects only become prominent at high energy resolution, or in rather special circumstances, like predissociation; this may explain why the need for a precise definition of the resonant states of atomic and molecular systems was not acutely felt. As to the processes involving so-called elementary particles, on the other hand, where such resonant states play a dominant role, our present inability to treat the relevant interactions hampers their detailed analysis.

A full clarification of the nature and mechanism of nuclear resonances requires the solution of two distinct problems, which may be conveniently called the structural and the dynamical problem. The former consists in establishing the typical resonance structure of the energy dependence of the elements of the S-matrix as a consequence of a precise definition of the resonant states: it can be shown that an adequate definition for this purpose is obtained by associating the resonant states with certain complex poles of the S-matrix regarded as a function of the complex energy variable in a specified domain of analyticity. The task of the dynamical problem then is the derivation of the resonance poles of the S-matrix from the Hamiltonian which describes the compound system of interacting nucleons; it is this determination that affords an insight into the mechanism leading to the occurrence of resonant states in such a system. In principle, the dynamical problem, for a given Hamiltonian, is a straightforward one in quantum mechanics; it is in fact a simple generalization of the usual eigenvalue problems to a more extended type of boundary conditions; but it is only with the utmost schematization of the actual interactions by fixed potentials (allowing for no other processes than elastic and inelastic scattering) that such a direct approach can be successful. For a general analysis recourse to a more elaborate "model" of the nuclear system is unavoidable; this model is also characterized by some schematization of the Hamiltonian, but this is ultimately corrected by the explicit consideration of the "residual" interactions. The dynamical problem then naturally divides itself into two successive steps: the first is the derivation of an expression for the elements of the S-matrix in terms of the energy, the second is the determination of the resonance poles of these functions in the complex energy plane – a problem which reduces to the solution of a transcendental equation in the energy.

In order to clarify the logical situation, it should be realized that the first step alone does not involve any concept of resonance at all: it leads to a representation – complete in principle – of the energy dependence of the reaction cross-sections, which exhibits the various maxima or other features associated with resonance effects, but it says nothing about the precise relation of such features to resonant states of the system. The answer to this last question can of course first be given when the resonant states of the system have been given a precise characterization, which is the object of the structural problem. Some theories of nuclear reactions which have received wide currency are in fact limited to what we have called the first step of the dynamical problem and are therefore (apart from other defects) essentially incomplete with respect to the analysis of resonance effects; it is true that users of these theories indulge in loose talk about "resonances" and list under the name "resonance parameters" certain numbers to which no precise physical meaning can be attached, but such practices are no substitute for logical thinking. In this connexion it must be stressed that resonant states are conceived to be intrinsic properties of the nuclear systems, whose definition must be independent of any arbitrariness in the description of the latter, such as the arbitrary separation of the Hamiltonian into a model Hamiltonian and a residual interaction operator. This is achieved in the structural analysis by characterizing these states with the help of a mathematical idealization; thus, it is ensured that the final step of the dynamical problem, for a given Hamiltonian, will always yield the same values for the resonance parameters, irrespectively of the choice of the model Hamiltonian in the first step of the dynamical analysis. Of course, the values obtained for the resonance parameters will depend on the specification of the total Hamiltonian, involving a phenomenological description of the nuclear interactions which has no secure theoretical foundation and is by no means unique; however, since all other sources of arbitrariness have been eliminated, the parameters defining resonant states obtained by the rational procedure just outlined, provide – like those defining bound states – unambiguous information about the properties of the nuclear forces schematically represented by the phenomenological interaction operators; this cannot be said of the unreliable "resonance parameters" still in current use.

The present article, in which I shall describe the main features of the dynamical analysis of resonance effects in nuclear reactions, is a sequel to the outline I have recently given of the structural point of view[1]). I shall endeavour to make the exposition self-contained, but must refer the reader to the previous paper for a fuller explanation of the structural aspects. I adopt in all essentials, with some changes which – I hope – are improvements, the method developed by H. A. Weidenmüller and his collaborators[2]) in Heidelberg, which is directly inspired by Fano's work on cognate atomic problems, alluded to above, and the principle of which was in fact set out by Dirac in one of his early papers. I should like to point out, however, that an equally powerful method, based on a variational principle, is being applied to atomic and molecular problems by A. Herzenberg and his group[3]) in Manchester. It is noteworthy that in spite of all specific differences between atomic and nuclear systems, the treatment is qualitatively the same for both, owing to the analogous roles played by the field of the atomic nuclei in the former case and the model potential in the latter.

2. Model Hamiltonian and residual interactions

Whatever method is used, the basis of the argument is the separation of the total Hamiltonian into a "model" part and a "residual interaction": the model is supposed to describe some average behaviour of the system, while the residual interaction is responsible for fluctuations around this average, as well as for aperiodic processes such as the "reactions" in which the total system of nucleons passes from one "channel" configuration (in which it is separated into definite fragments in specified relative motion) to another such configuration. The choice of the model is not crucial; every model is in the last resort derived from the shell-model, based on the conception of individual nucleon states in some potential representing the average interaction of any nucleon with all the others (including, when necessary, the Coulomb interaction). The shell-model configurations characterized by the occupation of given individual states by the nucleons of the system, in accordance with the exclusion principle, form an adequate starting-point for a more accurate description of the compound system of nucleons, taking account of the residual interactions. The effect of the latter will be to couple together the shell-model stationary states. The complete spectrum of these states consists of a discrete and a continuous part, forming two complementary subspaces characterized by projection operators B and C, respectively, with $B+C=1$, $BC=CB=0$; the residual interaction operator V is accordingly decomposed into the terms $V_B \equiv BVB$, $V_C \equiv CVC$ and $V_{BC} \equiv BVC+CVB$, which bring about couplings within the discrete subspace, within the continuum, and between the discrete states and the continuum, respectively.

The first coupling does not change the discrete or continuous character of the two subspaces; all it does is to modify the orthonormal basis of the discrete subspace, as well as the shape of the discrete energy spectrum. In particular, it includes the "pairing" interaction between correlated nucleons, which may have considerable effect on the properties of the bound states of the system. Moreover, it is the handling of the coupling V_B that gives scope for the introduction of various nuclear models; since my aim in this article is only to present the main line of argument, I shall not insist on this point, although it is of great practical interest, but simply take as orthonormal basis of the discrete subspace the set of discrete eigenfunctions ψ_i of the operator $\hat{H} \equiv \hat{H}^{(0)} + V_B$ (where $\hat{H}^{(0)}$ is the shell-model Hamiltonian); the corresponding eigenvalues of the energy will be denoted by ${}^0E_i$.

Besides this discrete spectrum, the Hamiltonian $\hat{H}$ has a continuous spectrum, unaffected by the residual interaction V_B; an orthonormal basis is conveniently built up of states which asymptotically represent the various channel configurations; each basis function $\phi_c(E)$ will thus be an eigenfunction of the Hamiltonian $\hat{H}^{(0)}$, belonging to the eigenvalue E and further specified (we shall presently explain more fully how) by its asymptotic behaviour, defined in terms of a set of channel quantum numbers c. The effect of the residual coupling V_C upon the continuous spectrum – like that of the coupling V_B on the discrete spectrum – is to reshuffle the basis states $\phi_c(E)$ coupling together the different channels. One may then construct a new orthonormal basis out of eigenfunctions $\psi^{(c)}(E)$ of the Hamiltonian ${}^0H \equiv \hat{H} + V_C$, each of which is again associated with a definite channel c by the asymptotic condition of having an incoming component in channel c only. The bases of discrete eigenfunctions ψ_i and of continuum eigenfunctions $\psi^{(c)}(E)$ of the Hamiltonian ${}^0H$ form together a complete orthonormal set of functions by means of which we can represent all states of the compound system, and analyse the effect of the remaining residual interaction V_{BC}, coupling the bound states with the continuum.

This last coupling will give rise to resonance phenomena whenever the discrete spectrum of bound states of the model system described by the Hamiltonian ${}^0H$ overlaps with the continuous spectrum. This situation, not unfamiliar in atomic and molecular physics, is of general occurrence for nuclear systems. Indeed there will always be shell-model configurations in which one or more nucleons from the inner shells are excited to individual states unoccupied in the ground-state configuration, in such a way that the excitation energy, if it were concentrated on a single nucleon of the uppermost shell, would raise this nucleon to an unbound individual state, thus producing a shell-model state of the continuum. It is the coupling of such a bound state "embedded in a continuum" to the neighbouring continuum states that establishes a "resonance" between the former and the latter. As a result, transitions between the continuum states will be enhanced, producing the typical peaks in the cross-sections. The bound state itself – if we imagine for a moment that the residual coupling has been suddenly switched on and look at the time evolution of the process – loses its stationary character and decays essentially according to an exponential law. It thus gives rise to a "broad" state of the nuclear system, with a "width" inversely proportional to its life-time; this resonant state formally appears as a complex pole of the S-matrix. In the nuclear case, processes of the type just described are designated as "compound resonances", because they involve the intermediary of metastable configurations of the whole compound system.

Resonance effects, however, are even exhibited by the shell-model described by the Hamiltonian $\hat{H}^{(0)}$, ignoring all residual couplings. These processes are usually called "single-particle resonances", since they concern the behaviour of a single nucleon in a fixed potential field. The elastic scattering amplitude in any channel c is expressed as $\hat{S}^{(0)}_{cc} - 1$ in terms of the element $\hat{S}^{(0)}_{cc}$ of the S-matrix associated with the Hamiltonian $\hat{H}^{(0)}$; regarded as a complex function of the energy, it has in general complex poles corresponding to a typical resonance behaviour of the cross-section. These resonances can in fact be ascribed – albeit somewhat artificially – to a mechanism not essentially different from that outlined above. Imagine all the nucleons of the compound system confined within a finite region of space by an infinitely high potential barrier. The stationary states of this fictitious system have a purely discrete energy spectrum, whereas in the region exterior to the barrier, a nucleon has a continuous spectrum of stationary states at its disposal. Let us now reduce the fictitious potential barrier to its actual shape, given by the shell-model Hamiltonian; this effectively amounts to introducing a coupling between the discrete bound states of the fictitious system and the adjacent continuum states in the exterior region. Thereby the stationary character of the bound states is destroyed and they are transformed into resonant states of the shell-model Hamiltonian. The effect of adding to the shell-model Hamiltonian the residual interaction between the continuum states will be – as we shall see in detail in a later section – merely to displace the single-particle resonance poles on the complex energy surface, without changing their character.

We thus expect that both the bound states and the single-particle resonant states of the shell-model Hamiltonian will give rise to resonant states of the nuclear system, the former leading to compound resonances, the latter to single-particle resonances. From the structural point of view, there is no difference between these two types of resonance, and we have just seen that they have ultimately the same dynamical origin. The distinction between them refers only to the character of the shell-model states from which they originate, and accordingly depends very much on the choice of the parameters defining the model. Thus, a slight change in the strength of the shell-model potential may suffice to change a bound state into a single-particle resonance or vice-versa. Still, once the underlying model Hamiltonian is fixed, the distinction is a clear-cut one, and necessitates separate formal treatments of the two types of resonance.

In the following sections, we shall accordingly proceed by successive steps. In the first place, it will be necessary to set up explicitly the two bases which, as mentioned above, may be applied to the description of the continuum, and to establish the relation between them, which is the starting point for the discussion of the single-particle resonances. It will be more convenient, however, to postpone this last discussion, and to go over first to the analysis of the compound resonance mechanism, in which the essential features appear more clearly and completely. The treatment of the single-particle resonances and of the related non-resonant processes of direct interaction will then round-off this general survey of the dynamical theory of nuclear reactions.

3. Stationary states in the continuum and residual interactions between them

In deciding how to define channel configurations, in which the compound system is divided into two or more fragments, we are faced at the outset with a formal difficulty connected with the application of the exclusion principle. From the physical point of view, the most natural procedure would be to include in the description of the individual states of the fragments as much as possible of the effect of the residual interactions; however, this leads to complications in the antisymmetrization of the total wave-function. These complications are avoided if in the specification of the channel configuration one leaves all the nucleons in their individual shell-model states, and takes account of their binding explicitly in the course of the calculation of the elements of the S-matrix; but this procedure raises other practical problems, inherent in any treatment of systems of more than two particles in relative motion, with regard to the most judicious choice of coordinates. This is a technical point of serious concern, since it is after all the labour of the computations that will set a limit to the usefulness of the one or other approach. The matter being as yet undecided, we shall here dodge the issue by confining the discussion to the well-studied case of channels composed of a target or residual nucleus and a single nucleon in relative motion to it. This will cover both elastic and inelastic scattering of nucleons, as well as (p, n) and (n, p) reactions, – an extensive and varied class of reactions.

For a channel of this restricted type, it is convenient, in constructing the eigenfunction of the residual nucleus, to take into account the effect of the residual interaction between its constituent nucleons. The difficulties we want to avoid would again arise if this eigenfunction would include shell-model configurations containing nucleons in unbound individual states; we explicitly exclude such states of the residual nucleus from consideration. Then, the residual interactions operating in the residual nucleus are included in the Hamiltonian $\hat{H}$, and all the matrix elements of the remaining residual interaction between states of the continuous spectrum will be finite. The asymptotic form of the basis wave-function $\phi_c(E)$ may then be written as the antisymmetrized product of two factors $R_c(r_c, k_c)$ and $\varphi_c(\Omega_c)$. The first factor $R_c(r_c, k_c)$ represents a stationary spherical wave, depending on the radial variable r_c – the distance of the unbound nucleon from the barycentre of the residual nucleus – and the wave number k_c, related to the kinetic energy E_c

of the relative motion of the fragments by the expression $E_c = \hbar^2 k_c^2 / 2M_c$ (where M_c denotes the reduced mass of the fragments). The second factor $\varphi_c(\Omega_c)$ is a function of all the other variables (symbolized as Ω_c) which describe the internal configuration of the residual nucleus and the state of the unbound nucleon; it includes the eigenfunction of the residual nucleus, corresponding to an energy ε_c, and the wave-function of the angular variables of the relative motion and the spin and isospin variables of the nucleon.

The total energy E of the compound system determines the kinetic energy of the relative motion by the equation

$$E_c = E - \varepsilon_c , \tag{1}$$

and it will often be convenient to use E_c instead of E as the energy variable in channel c; the relation (1) will then always be understood to hold. The energy ε_c represents the threshold at which the channel opens, and the continuous spectrum of real energy values extends from ε_c upwards. We fix the zero of the energy E at the threshold of the channel of least internal energy; all other threshold energies ε_c are accordingly positive. The continuous spectrum of the compound system is thus conceived as a superposition of a number of continua, corresponding to the various channels, and starting from the respective thresholds ε_c.

Returning to the radial factor $R_c(r_c, k_c)$, we write it more explicitly (omitting an inessential numerical factor) as

$$R_c(r_c, k_c) \propto \frac{1}{v_c^{\frac{1}{2}} r_c} \left[\mathrm{e}^{-\mathrm{i}\delta_c(k_c)} I_c(r_c, k_c) - \mathrm{e}^{\mathrm{i}\delta_c(k_c)} O_c(r_c, k_c) \right]; \tag{2}$$

the functions I_c, O_c are those solutions of the free particle radial equation (including if necessary the Coulomb potential) that behave asymptotically (for real values of k_c) as an incoming and an outgoing wave, respectively. The phase-shift $\delta_c(k_c)$ is due to the distortion of the waves by the shell-model Hamiltonian. As to the factor $v_c^{-\frac{1}{2}}$, where v_c is the velocity of the unbound nucleon, it is required in order to ensure the normalization

$$\langle \phi_{c'}(E'_{c'}) | \phi_c(E_c) \rangle = \delta_{c'c} \, \delta(E'_{c'} - E_c) . \tag{3}$$

We may observe that the form (2) of the radial factor (involving only one wave-number k_c) and the orthonormality relation (3) would cease to hold rigorously if we admitted in the residual nucleus eigenfunction any admixture of unbound shell-model configurations.

Let us now introduce the residual interaction V_C and the corresponding orthonormal basis $\psi^{(c)}(E_c)$ of eigenfunctions of the Hamiltonian ${}^0H$. These functions may be expressed in terms of the basis $\phi_c(E_c)$, to which they are related by a unitary transformation of the form

$$\psi^{(c)}(E_c) = \sum_{c'} \int \mathrm{d}E'_{c'}\, \phi_{c'}(E'_{c'})\, \langle E'_{c'}|\, {}^0a\, |E_c\rangle\,. \tag{4}$$

The expansion coefficients $\langle E'_{c'}|\, {}^0a\, |E_c\rangle$ are solutions of the equations

$$(E' - E)\, \langle E'_{c'}|\, {}^0a\, |E_c\rangle + \\ + \sum_{c''} \int \mathrm{d}E''_{c''}\, \langle \phi_{c'}(E'_{c'})|\, V\, |\phi_{c''}(E''_{c''})\rangle\, \langle E''_{c''}|\, {}^0a\, |E_c\rangle = 0\,. \tag{5}$$

As one would expect, these equations do not determine the coefficients completely, but leave open the possibility of adding to any solution terms proportional to $\delta(E'-E)$; this is just the freedom needed to satisfy the asymptotic boundary conditions imposed upon the functions $\psi^{(c)}(E_c)$. We want the asymptotic radial factor

$$\sum_{c'} \int \mathrm{d}E'_{c'}\, R_{c'}(r_{c'}, k_{c'})\, \langle E'_{c'}|\, {}^0a\, |E_c\rangle \tag{6}$$

of $\psi^{(c)}(E_c)$ to contain only outgoing waves, except in channel c. This is achieved by taking $\langle E'_{c'}|\, {}^0a\, |E_c\rangle$ in the form

$$\langle E'_{c'}|\, {}^0a\, |E_c\rangle = \frac{\langle E'_{c'}|\, {}^0T\, |E_c\rangle}{E' - E^+} + \delta_{c'c}\, \delta(E' - E)\,, \tag{7}$$

where the notation E^+ indicates that the pole $E' = E$ on the real axis of the E'-plane is displaced by an infinitesimal amount into the upper half of the plane; such a displacement, as is well-known, has the effect of eliminating the incoming wave-components from all the terms in the expression (6) containing the factor $(E'-E^+)^{-1}$. The asymptotic form of the wave-function $\psi^{(c)}(E)$ thus becomes (if $\mathscr{A}$ denotes the antisymmetrization operator, and the summation extends over the open channels c')

$$\psi^{(c)}(E) \sim \mathscr{A}\, \{R_c(r_c, k_c)\, \varphi_c(\Omega_c) - \\ - \sum_{c'} \frac{2\pi \mathrm{i}}{v_{c'}^{\frac{1}{2}}\, r_{c'}}\, \mathrm{e}^{\mathrm{i}\delta_{c'}(k_{c'})}\, O_{c'}(r_{c'}, k_{c'})\, \varphi_{c'}(\Omega_{c'})\, \langle E_{c'}|\, {}^0T\, |E_c\rangle\}\,, \tag{8}$$

in conformity with our requirement.

This asymptotic expression exhibits a very simple relation between the elements of the matrix $\langle E_{c'}|\,{}^0T\,|E_c\rangle$ corresponding to continuum states "in the energy shell" (i.e. with $E'=E$) and the elements ${}^0S_{c'c}(E)$ of the S-matrix for the reaction leading from channel c to channel c' at the energy E when the interaction is described by the Hamiltonian ${}^0H$. Indeed, the latter matrix element appears in the asymptotic wave-function when it is written as

$$\psi^{(c)}(E_c) \sim \mathscr{A}\left\{\frac{1}{\sqrt{v_c}}\,\mathrm{e}^{-\mathrm{i}\delta_c(k_c)}\left[\frac{1}{r_c}\,I_c(r_c,k_c)\,\varphi_c(\Omega_c) - \right.\right.$$
$$\left.\left. - \sum_{c'}\sqrt{\frac{v_c}{v_{c'}}}\,{}^0S_{c'c}\,\frac{1}{r_{c'}}\,O_{c'}(r_{c'},k_{c'})\,\varphi_{c'}(\Omega_{c'})\right]\right\}, \tag{9}$$

and the comparison with the expression (8), together with eq. (2), shows that

$${}^0S_{c'c} = \mathrm{e}^{\mathrm{i}[\delta_{c'}(k_{c'})+\delta_c(k_c)]}\,\{\delta_{c'c} + 2\pi\mathrm{i}\,\langle E_{c'}|\,{}^0T\,|E_c\rangle\}\,. \tag{10}$$

The matrix $\langle E'_{c'}|\,{}^0T\,|E_c\rangle$, according to its definition (7), is determined as the solution of the inhomogeneous integral equation, replacing eq. (5),

$$\langle E'_{c'}|\,{}^0T\,|E_c\rangle + \sum_{c''}\int \mathrm{d}E''_{c''}\,\langle\phi_{c'}(E'_{c'})|\,V\,|\phi_{c''}(E''_{c''})\rangle\,\frac{1}{E''-E^+}\,\langle E''_{c''}|\,{}^0T\,|E_c\rangle +$$
$$+\langle\phi_{c'}(E'_{c'})|\,V\,|\phi_c(E_c)\rangle = 0\,. \tag{11}$$

We see that – just as we can obtain the bound shell-model states ψ_i by taking the residual interaction V_B separately into account – we can treat separately the effect of the residual interaction V_C within the continuum by solving the integral equation (11). We shall assume for the time being that this last operation is accomplished, and pass directly to the discussion of the residual coupling V_{BC} between the discrete and the continuous spectrum, respectively defined by the orthonormal bases ψ_i and $\psi^{(c)}(E_c)$.

4. Compound resonances

We are now interested in an eigenfunction $\psi(E)$ of the total Hamiltonian

$$H = {}^0H + BVC + CVB$$

belonging to an energy E in the continuum of the compound system, and specified by given amplitudes $y_c(E)$ of the incoming waves in the various channels open at the energy E. We expand this eigenfunction in terms of the complete orthonormal set ψ_i, $\psi^{(c)}(E_c)$:

$$\psi(E) = \sum_i \psi_i\, a_i(E) + \sum_{c'} \int \mathrm{d}E'_{c'}\, \psi^{(c')}(E'_{c'})\, \langle E'_{c'}|\, a\, |E\rangle\,, \tag{12}$$

and obtain for the expansion coefficients the following set of coupled equations:

$$({}^0E_i - E)\, a_i(E) + \sum_{c'} \int \mathrm{d}E'_{c'}\, \langle i|\, V\, |E'_{c'}\rangle\, \langle E'_{c'}|\, a\, |E\rangle = 0\,, \tag{13}$$

$$(E' - E)\, \langle E'_{c'}|\, a\, |E\rangle + \sum_k \langle E'_{c'}|\, V\, |k\rangle\, a_k(E) = 0; \tag{14}$$

the matrix elements of the residual interaction are expressed in the representation defined by the bases ψ_i, $\psi^{(c)}(E_c)$.

By the same argument as in the preceding section, we replace $\langle E'_{c'}|\, a\, |E\rangle$ by

$$\langle E'_{c'}|\, a\, |E\rangle = \frac{\langle E'_{c'}|\, \alpha\, |E\rangle}{E' - E^+} + y_{c'}(E)\, \delta(E' - E) \tag{15}$$

in order to satisfy the asymptotic conditions characterizing the eigenfunction $\psi(E)$. The ansatz (15) transforms eqs. (13) into a set of inhomogeneous linear equations, the terms not containing the unknown quantities being $\sum_{c'} y_{c'}(E)\, \langle i|\, V\, |E_{c'}\rangle$. This means that the unknown quantities themselves are linear combinations of the arbitrarily given amplitudes $y_c(E)$, of the form

$$\begin{aligned} a_i(E) &= \sum_c y_c(E)\, b_i(E, c)\,, \\ \langle E'_{c'}|\, \alpha\, |E\rangle &= \sum_c y_c(E)\, \langle E'_{c'}|\, T\, |E_c\rangle\,. \end{aligned} \tag{16}$$

The new coefficients are now determined by the equations

$$\begin{aligned} ({}^0E_i - E)\, b_i(E, c) + \sum_{c'} \int \mathrm{d}E'_{c'}\, \langle i|\, V\, |E'_{c'}\rangle\, \frac{1}{E' - E^+}\, \langle E'_{c'}|\, T\, |E_c\rangle\, + \\ + \langle i|\, V\, |E_c\rangle = 0\,, \end{aligned} \tag{17}$$

$$\langle E'_{c'}|\, T\, |E_c\rangle + \sum_k \langle E'_{c'}|\, V\, |k\rangle\, b_k(E, c) = 0\,. \tag{18}$$

Moreover, the asymptotic form of the eigenfunction becomes, on account of eqs. (12), (15), (16) and (9),

$$\psi(E) \sim \mathscr{A} \sum_c y_c(E) \left\{ \psi^{(c)}(E_c) + \sum_{c'} \int \mathrm{d}E'_{c'}\, \psi^{(c')}(E'_{c'}) \frac{\langle E'_{c'} | T | E_c \rangle}{E' - E^+} \right\}$$

$$\sim \mathscr{A} \sum_c y_c(E) \Big\{ \psi^{(c)}(E_c) -$$

$$- \sum_{c'} 2\pi\mathrm{i} \, \langle E_{c'} | T | E_c \rangle \, \mathrm{e}^{-\mathrm{i}\delta_{c'}(k_{c'})} \sum_{c''} \frac{1}{v_{c''}^{\frac{1}{2}} r_{c''}} \, {}^0S_{c''c'} \, O_{c''}(r_{c''}, k_{c''}) \, \varphi_{c''}(\Omega_{c''}) \Big\};$$

by comparing this form with its expression in terms of the S-matrix belonging to the total Hamiltonian H,

$$\psi(E) \sim \mathscr{A} \sum_c y_c(E) \frac{1}{\sqrt{v_c}} \mathrm{e}^{-\mathrm{i}\delta_c(k_c)} \Big[I_c(r_c, k_c) \, \varphi_c(\Omega_c) -$$

$$- \sum_{c'} \sqrt{\frac{v_c}{v_{c'}}} \, S_{c'c} \frac{1}{r_{c'}} \, O_{c'}(r_{c'}, k_{c'}) \, \varphi_{c'}(\Omega_{c'}) \Big],$$

we find for the matrix element $S_{c'c}$ the expression

$$S_{c'c} = {}^0S_{c'c} + 2\pi\mathrm{i} \, \mathrm{e}^{\mathrm{i}[\delta_{c'}(k_{c'}) + \delta_c(k_c)]} \times \\ \times \sum_{c''} \mathrm{e}^{-\mathrm{i}[\delta_{c'}(k_{c'}) + \delta_{c''}(k_{c''})]} \, {}^0S_{c'c''} \, \langle E_{c''} | T | E_c \rangle . \tag{19}$$

This formula shows that, besides ${}^0S_{c'c}$, we have to determine the elements in the energy shell of the matrix $\langle E'_{c'} | T | E_c \rangle$. The latter are immediately given by eq. (18) in terms of the $b_k(E, c)$, and we may therefore write for $S_{c'c}$, instead of eq. (19),

$$S_{c'c} = {}^0S_{c'c} - 2\pi\mathrm{i} \, \mathrm{e}^{\mathrm{i}[\delta_{c'}(k_{c'}) + \delta_c(k_c)]} \sum_k \langle \tilde{E}_{c'} | V | k \rangle \, b_k(E, c), \tag{20}$$

where we have introduced the dual of the state vector

$$|\tilde{E}_c\rangle = \sum_{c'} |E_{c'}\rangle \, {}^0S^*_{c'c} \, \mathrm{e}^{\mathrm{i}[\delta_{c'}(k_{c'}) + \delta_c(k_c)]}. \tag{21}$$

The physical meaning of this new state vector is readily derived from its asymptotic form. According to eq. (9), and in virtue of the unitarity of the matrix ${}^0S$ (in the subspace of open channels, to which the summations are confined), we have

$$|\tilde{E}_c\rangle \sim -\mathscr{A}\left\{\frac{1}{\sqrt{v_c}}\,\mathrm{e}^{\mathrm{i}\delta_c(k_c)}\left[\frac{1}{r_c}\,O_c(r_c,k_c)\,\varphi_c(\Omega_c) - \right.\right.$$

$$\left.\left. - \sum_{c'}\sqrt{\frac{v_c}{v_{c'}}}\,{}^0S^*_{c'c}\,\frac{1}{r_{c'}}\,I_{c'}(r_{c'},k_{c'})\,\varphi_{c'}(\Omega_{c'})\right\}\right.,$$

i.e. $|\tilde{E}_c\rangle$ is essentially the transform of $|E_c\rangle$ by time-reversal; it may differ from the time-reverse by its sign, according to the choice of the phases of the factors $\varphi_c(\Omega_c)$, but this sign is in any case the same for all channels which are coupled with each other, and is therefore without interest.

There only remains to determine the coefficients $b_k(E,c)$ from the set of linear equations

$$\sum_k d_{ik}(E)\,b_k(E,c) + \langle i|\,V\,|E_c\rangle = 0\,, \tag{22}$$

$$d_{ik}(E) \equiv ({}^0E_i - E)\,\delta_{ik} - \sum_{c'}\int \mathrm{d}E'_{c'}\,\frac{\langle i|\,V\,|E'_{c'}\rangle\,\langle E'_{c'}|\,V\,|k\rangle}{E' - E^+}\,, \tag{23}$$

derived from eqs. (17), (18) by elimination of the $\langle E'_{c'}|\,T\,|E_c\rangle$. The algebraic solution of these equations may be expressed as

$$b_k = -\frac{1}{D(E)}\sum_i D_{ki}(E)\,\langle i|\,V\,|E_c\rangle\,, \tag{24}$$

where $D(E)$ denotes the determinant of the matrix $\{d_{ik}(E)\}$ and $D_{ki}(E)$ the minor of the element $d_{ik}(E)$. We may now re-write eq. (20), combined with eq. (10), in the form

$$S_{c'c} = \mathrm{e}^{\mathrm{i}[\delta_{c'}(k_{c'})+\delta_c(k_c)]}\,\{\delta_{c'c} + 2\pi\mathrm{i}\,\langle E_{c'}|\,{}^0T\,|E_c\rangle + 2\pi\mathrm{i}\,\langle \tilde{E}_{c'}|\,{}^1T\,|E_c\rangle\}\,, \tag{25}$$

where, according to eq. (23), we have

$$\langle \tilde{E}_{c'}|\,{}^1T\,|E_c\rangle = \sum_{i,k}\langle \tilde{E}_{c'}|\,V\,|k\rangle\,\frac{D_{ki}(E)}{D(E)}\,\langle i|\,V\,|E_c\rangle\,. \tag{26}$$

Eqs. (25), (26) solve the first part of the dynamical problem, the determination of the S-matrix as a function of the energy. They will form our starting point for the second part of the problem, the elucidation of the relationship between the singularities of the S-matrix which govern the resonance phenomena and the residual couplings we are considering. In the previous paper[1]) dealing with the analytic structure of the S-matrix, it is shown that resonances are associated with a certain family of complex poles $\mathscr{E}_j = E_j - \frac{1}{2}\mathrm{i}\Gamma_j$ of the S-matrix, situated below the real E-axis. In view of the double determination of all channel wave-numbers k_c for each value of the energy, one must consider the distribution of the poles on the whole Riemann surface of the energy and specify by appropriate cuts, starting from the branch-points of energies $E=\mathscr{E}_c$ on the real axis, those portions of the various sheets of this surface that contain the poles of physical interest. We need not repeat here the details of this discussion, but may summarize its conclusion in a sufficiently definite way by saying that the resonance poles are those most easily accessible from the real axis on a "physical" energy-plane in which cuts are drawn from the branch-points parallel to the imaginary axis.

If we examine from this point of view the analytic properties of the matrix element (25), we may in the first place leave out of consideration the factor $\exp[i\delta_{c'}(k_{c'})+i\delta_c(k_c)]$, which represents the effect of the "potential scattering" by the average field of the shell-model Hamiltonian. It is true that the phase-shift $\delta_c(k_c)$, related to the matrix-element $\hat{S}^{(0)}_{cc}$ of the shell-model S-matrix by the equation $\hat{S}^{(0)}_{cc}=\exp[2i\delta_c(k_c)]$, has complex poles in the k_c-plane corresponding to the shell-model single-particle resonances; but in the expression (25), it only occurs for a real value of its argument, and has therefore no influence on the integrated cross-sections. The threshold values $k_c=0$, $k_{c'}=0$, which are also critical points, can be approached as closely as we wish, owing to the continuity of the functions $\delta_c(k_c)$. The resonance contributions are contained in the factor between brackets of the expression (25), and the two matrix-elements of ${}^0T$ and ${}^1T$, according to their origin, contain the respective contributions of the single-particle resonances and the compound resonances. We cannot yet discuss the former, but we may analyse the latter with the help of the explicit form (26) of the matrix-element $\langle \tilde{E}_{c'}|\,{}^1T\,|E_c\rangle$. Indeed, eq. (26) immediately shows that the poles of the S-matrix corresponding to compound resonances are found among the roots of the equation

$$D(E)=0; \tag{27}$$

it is not superfluous to stress that this is not an algebraic equation of the "secular" type, but a transcendental equation in the energy, since this variable also appears in each element $d_{ik}(E)$ in the indirect manner exhibited by eq. (23).

Let us examine more closely the form of this equation. The complex integrals occurring in the expression (23) for the matrix-element $d_{ik}(E)$ may be evaluated by re-placing the pole $E'=E$ on the real E'-axis and deforming the path of integration in its neighbourhood into an infinitesimal half-circle in the lower half-plane; each integral is then expressed as the sum of its principal part and the contribution from the pole, which is $i\pi G_{ik}^{(c')}(E)$, with

$$G_{ik}^{(c')}(E) \equiv \langle i| V |E_{c'}\rangle \langle E_{c'}| V |k\rangle . \tag{28}$$

Since the matrix $\{G_{ik}^{(c')}\}$ is hermitean, we thus obtain a separation of the hermitean and the anti-hermitean part of $\{d_{ik}\}$:

$$d_{ik} = ({}^0E_i - E)\,\delta_{ik} - R_{ik}(E) - i\pi G_{ik}(E), \tag{29}$$

where

$$R_{ik}(E) = \mathrm{P}\int \mathrm{d}E' \sum_{c'} \frac{G_{ik}^{(c')}(E')}{E' + \varepsilon_{c'} - E}, \qquad G_{ik}(E) = \sum_{c'} G_{ik}^{(c')}(E); \tag{30}$$

the symbol P indicates that the principal part of the following integral has to be taken. It may further be observed that the $G_{ik}(E)$ are real quantities, and accordingly symmetrical with respect to the indices i, k; this follows from the invariance of the operator V and the state-vectors $|k\rangle$ for time-reversal, which allows us to write, e.g.

$$\langle E_{c'}| V |k\rangle^* = \langle \tilde{E}_{c'}| V |k\rangle ,$$

and from the relation

$$\sum_{c'} |E_{c'}\rangle \langle E_{c'}| = \sum_{c'} |\tilde{E}_{c'}\rangle \langle \tilde{E}_{c'}| ,$$

which results from eq. (21) and the unitarity of the matrix ${}^0S$.

A considerable simplification occurs if the energy dependence of the $G_{ik}^{(c')}$ is weak enough to be neglected, for in this case the R_{ik} vanish, and eq. (27) takes the form of a secular equation

$$\det\{({}^0E_i - E)\,\delta_{ik} - i\pi G_{ik}\} = 0 .$$

There is then a one-to-one correspondence between the complex roots $\mathscr{E}_j$ and the bound-state energies ${}^0E_i$, and by imagining the residual coupling, absent at first, to increase gradually to its full strength, one can vizualize the formation of a resonant state from a shell-model bound state as a displacement on the energy-plane of the point of the real axis corresponding to the latter state towards a final position in the lower half of the physical plane, representing the resonant state. In the general case, a correspondence can still be established between the shell-model states and the complex roots of eq. (27) by following the movement of the latter on the energy surface as the strength of the residual coupling varies. There may then correspond more than one root $\mathscr{E}_j$ to each bound-state energy ${}^0E_i$; but starting from a given resonance pole situated in the physical region of the cut energy-plane and letting the residual coupling decrease, we can uniquely assign this resonant state to a definite bound state of the chosen shell-model.

One may approach the question from a somewhat different angle. The matrix $\{d_{ik}(E)\}$ is a representation, in the basis ψ_i of the discrete subspace, of the operator ${}^1H(E)-E$ acting in this subspace, where ${}^1H(E)$ is given by

$$ {}^1H(E) = {}^0H - VC \frac{1}{{}^0H - E^+} CV. \tag{31} $$

The solution of the set of equations (22) therefore amounts to the inversion of this non-hermitean operator. This is performed algebraically in the way expressed by eq. (24); alternatively, one may proceed by diagonalizing the operator ${}^1H(E)$ and its adjoint ${}^1H(E)^\dagger$, which is obtained from the expression (31) by replacing E^+ by E^-, i.e. by displacing the pole E into the lower half of the energy plane. The two sets of eigenvectors $|n\rangle$, $|\tilde{n}\rangle$ of ${}^1H$ and ${}^1H^\dagger$ are transforms of each other by time reversal, and form together a biorthogonal set of eigenfunctions to the complex eigenvalues ${}^1\mathscr{E}_n(E)=\varepsilon_n(E)-\frac{1}{2}i\gamma_n(E)$ and ${}^1\mathscr{E}_n(E)^*$ of the two operators; this means that

$$ \langle \tilde{n}|m\rangle = \delta_{nm}\langle \tilde{n}|n\rangle . $$

The determining factor $\langle \tilde{E}_{c'}|\,{}^1T\,|E_c\rangle$ in the term of the S-matrix we are discussing becomes, according to eq. (26) and the meaning just explained of the operator ${}^1H(E)$,

$$ \langle \tilde{E}_{c'}|\,{}^1T\,|E_c\rangle = \langle \tilde{E}_{c'}|\,VB \frac{1}{{}^1H(E) - E} BV\,|E_c\rangle . \tag{32} $$

If we go over to the basis $|n\rangle$, $\langle \tilde{n}|$ in the discrete subspace, it takes the form

$$ \langle \tilde{E}_{c'}|\,{}^1T\,|E_c\rangle = \sum_n \langle \tilde{E}_{c'}|\,V\,|n\rangle \frac{1}{[\varepsilon_n(E) - E - \frac{1}{2}i\gamma_n(E)]\,\langle \tilde{n}|n\rangle} \langle \tilde{n}|\,V\,|E_c\rangle . \tag{33} $$

Such a form may give the misleading impression that resonances could be accounted for by means of the complex eigenvalues ${}^1\mathscr{E}_n(E)$ of the operator ${}^1H(E)$, without further consideration of the analytical behaviour of the S-matrix. If we start from the representation $\{d_{ik}(E)\}$ of the operator ${}^1H(E)-E$, the eigenvalues ${}^1\mathscr{E}_n(E)$ are obtained from the equation $D(E)=0$, provided that one solves it as if it were a secular equation, keeping E fixed in the matrix elements of ${}^1H(E)$; it thus appears, by the same argument as above, that the eigenvalues ${}^1\mathscr{E}_n(E)$ quite generally stand in a one-to-one correspondence to the shell-model bound states ${}^0E_i$. Since the matrix elements $\langle i|\,V\,|E_c\rangle$ of the residual interaction are the same as those of the total

Hamiltonian H, the operator ${}^1H(E)$, restricted to the discrete subspace, may be written in the form $H-HG(E)\,H$, with

$$G(E)=\int \mathrm{d}E' \sum_{c'} \frac{|\psi^{(c')}(E')\rangle\,\langle\psi^{(c')}(E')|}{E'+\varepsilon_{c'}-E^+},$$

which shows that it only depends on the choice of the model Hamiltonian ${}^0H$ through the specification of the continuum basis $|\psi^{(c)}(E)\rangle$. This implies, however, that the eigenvalues ${}^1\mathscr{E}_n(E)$ may depend to that extent on the choice of the model; at any rate, their dependence on the energy deprives them of fundamental significance. The complex poles $\mathscr{E}_j$ of the S-matrix, on the other hand, do not, of course, exhibit any model or energy dependence; they are related to the eigenvalues ${}^1\mathscr{E}_n(E)$ by being roots of the equations ${}^1\mathscr{E}_n(E)-E=0$, equivalent to eq. (27); even if these equations look different for different choices of the shell-model Hamiltonian, their roots $\mathscr{E}_j$ will necessarily be the same. There will be cases when some eigenvalue ${}^1\mathscr{E}_n$ will turn out to be practically energy-independent, and thus accidentally coincide with some pole of the S-matrix, but one has obviously to use the latter for an unambiguous and universal characterization of resonant states as intrinsic properties of the compound system.

This is not to say that the states represented by the eigenfunctions and eigenvalues of the operator ${}^1H(E)$ are entirely deprived of physical meaning. Within the framework of the adopted model description of the various configurations of the compound system, these states represent the outcome of the residual coupling of such configurations to the continuum, – a coupling which changes configurations that would be bound without it into metastable states decaying into the various open channels of the continuum. From this point of view, the "width function" $\gamma_n(E)/\hbar$ represents the total probability per unit time of all these decay processes, whereas the difference $\varepsilon_n(E)-{}^0E_i$ (for corresponding states) can be interpreted as a mean "shift" in energy of the shell-model state ${}^0E_i$ owing to the residual coupling.

Our analysis, however, does not stop at this pattern of metastable states, changing with the energy of the compound system, but shows that its formation is governed by an invariable set of resonant states $\mathscr{E}_j$, to which they are related by the identities ${}^1\mathscr{E}_n(\mathscr{E}_j)=\mathscr{E}_j$. We rather regard the shell-model states "embedded in the continuum" as the limiting forms taken by the intrinsic resonant states when the residual coupling is fictitiously made to vanish; as the coupling gradually decreases, each complex pole $\mathscr{E}_j$ in the physical energy plane moves along a definite path towards some point of the real axis representing one of the shell-model states ${}^0E_i$. This gives a clear picture of the connection between the resonant states and the shell-model states, without any intervention of the metastable states. Nor is the determination of these states helpful as an intermediate step for the computation of the resonant state parameters $\mathscr{E}_j$: for this purpose, a direct solution of eq. (27) is more expeditious.

A somewhat more detailed insight into the mechanism of the resonance phenomena can be obtained if one makes more definite assumptions about the form of the nuclear interactions. In particular, it is interesting to pursue the consequences of the commonly adopted assumption that the couplings between pairs of nucleons play the dominant part, whereas direct interactions involving more than two nucleons are negligible. Let us then go back to the eigenstates of the shell-model Hamiltonian $\hat{H}^{(0)}$, i.e. the bound configurations of nucleons in uncoupled individual shell-model states. We can make a distinction among these states according as they are or are not directly coupled by pair interactions to the channel states of the continuum. Only those of the first class are immediately involved in the resonance mechanism; the others take part in the resonance indirectly, by being coupled to the states of the first class through the residual interactions of the type V_B; hence the picturesque name of "doorway states" given to the states of the first class by Feshbach[4]), who (albeit without regard to the intrinsic resonant states) was the first to call attention to their special role in the production of resonance phenomena. The coupling of the states of the second class to the doorway states may itself proceed by a chain of any number of pair interactions, and we thus arrive at a description of the resonance phenomena involving a whole network of coupled shell-model configurations which all concur more or less indirectly to the process through the intermediary of some doorway state directly coupled to the continuum. This is the counterpart in quantal terms of Bohr's classical analogy picturing the formation of the compound nucleus by multiple collisions among the nucleons. It is for this reason that the resonant states so far discussed, which result from the residual coupling between bound shell-model states and the continuum, are called "compound resonances".

For a formal treatment of the doorway state mechanism, all we need is a slight modification of the preceding formalism. We now understand our basis in the discrete subspace to consist of the eigenstates of the Hamiltonian $\hat{H}^{(0)}$; we distinguish the doorway states $|\alpha\rangle, |\beta\rangle, \ldots$ from those of the second class denoted by $|a\rangle, |b\rangle, \ldots$ and call the respective eigenvalues $\hat{E}_\alpha^{(0)}, \ldots; \hat{E}_a^{(0)}, \ldots$. We must then introduce in the definition (23) of the coefficient $d_{ik}(E)$ the additional term $\langle i|\, V\,|k\rangle$, and the equation giving the resonant states becomes, instead of eq. (27),

$$\begin{vmatrix} \delta_{\alpha\beta}(\hat{E}_\alpha^{(0)} - E) + \langle\alpha|\, V\,|\beta\rangle - \left\langle \alpha|\, VC\, \dfrac{1}{\hat{H}^{(0)} - E^+}\, CV\,|\beta \right\rangle & \langle\alpha|\, V\,|b\rangle \\ \langle a|\, V\,|\beta\rangle & \delta_{ab}(\hat{E}_a^{(0)} - E) + \langle a|\, V\,|b\rangle \end{vmatrix} = 0.$$

In this form, the equation clearly exhibits the special role of the doorway states and the indirect coupling of the other states to the continuum by the intermediary of the doorway states.

5. Single-particle resonances and direct interaction processes

We may now turn to the integral equation (11) for the matrix $\langle E'_{c'}|\, {}^0T\,|E_c\rangle$, which we have still to solve. This will give us the contribution of the continuum couplings to the S-matrix element given by eq. (25). Regarded as a mathematical problem, the solution of this equation is not straightforward, since the usual iteration procedure will not converge for every real value of E. This difficulty is not a deep one; it can be circumvented in various ways. However, our problem is not just the calculation of the S-matrix, but the analysis of the way in which resonances occur; to this particular end, it is not indifferent how one treats the couplings between states of the continuum. Thus, the method adopted by the French group headed by C. Bloch and V. Gillet[5]) cannot be commended from this point of view: they just replace the continuum by an arbitrary discrete sequence of states, and thus reduce the problem to purely algebraic operations, which are abandoned to a computer. Such a treatment "à la hussarde" (an approach which may relieve a pressing need, but does not afford deeper satisfaction) leaves in the dark interesting aspects which a more systematic investigation brings out. We shall therefore follow a slower course. Our first task will be to determine the domain of convergence, on the energy surface, of the iteration series for the inverse of the operator $1 + V_C(\hat{H} - E^+)^{-1}$ in the continuum subspace; it will turn out that this discussion will give us the means of carrying out the inversion in the exceptional regions as well.

Let us first consider the operator $V_C(\hat{H} - E^+)^{-1}$ in the upper-half of the physical energy plane, i.e. in the region characterized by positive imaginary parts of all channel wave-numbers k_c. In this region, we can define the eigenfunctions of the operator, which behave asymptotically in all channels as outgoing waves only; and regarding them, as well as the associated complex eigenvalues, as functions of the energy, it will prove possible to continue their definition to the lower half of the physical plane (including the real axis), which is the region of interest to us. It will be convenient to start with the "left" eigenfunctions $\langle\tilde{\psi}_n|$; the tilda serves to indicate that the dual state vectors $|\tilde{\psi}_n\rangle$ are the transforms by time-reversal of a set of state vectors $|\psi_n\rangle$ which likewise asymptotically consist of outgoing waves. Calling the corresponding eigenvalues $-\lambda_n$, we have, for each value of the energy in the region indicated,

$$\langle\tilde{\psi}_n(E)| \left\{\lambda_n(E) + V_C \frac{1}{\hat{H} - E^+}\right\} = 0. \tag{34}$$

Writing this equation in the form

$$\langle\tilde{\psi}_n(E)| \{\hat{H} - E + \eta_n(E)\, V_C\} = 0, \qquad \eta_n(E) \equiv \frac{1}{\lambda_n(E)}, \tag{35}$$

we see that we can interpret $\langle\tilde{\psi}_n(E)|$ as an eigenfunction, belonging to the eigenvalue E, of the Hamiltonian corresponding to the non-hermitean interaction operator $\eta_n(E)V_C$, and further specified by the asymptotic condition of comprising only outgoing waves. Taking the adjoint and the time-reverse of eq. (35), on the assumption that $\hat{H}$ and V_C are self-adjoint and invariant for time-reversal, we get

$$\{\hat{H} - E + \eta_n(E)\, V_C\}\, |\psi_n(E)\rangle = 0, \tag{36}$$

which may also be written

$$\left\{\lambda_n(E) + \frac{1}{\hat{H} - E^+}\, V_C\right\} |\psi_n(E)\rangle = 0. \tag{37}$$

Acting from the left with the operator V_C, and putting

$$|\phi_n(E)\rangle = V_C\, |\psi_n(E)\rangle, \tag{38}$$

we derive from eq. (37)

$$\left\{\lambda_n(E) + V_C \frac{1}{\hat{H} - E^+}\right\} |\phi_n(E)\rangle = 0. \tag{39}$$

On the assumption that the operator V_C is such that no state vector $|\phi_n(E)\rangle$, defined by eq. (38), identically vanishes, we conclude from eq. (39) that these vectors $|\phi_n(E)\rangle$ are the set of "right" eigenfunctions of our operator $V_C(\hat{H} - E^+)^{-1}$, belonging to the same eigenvalues $-\lambda_n(E)$. Assuming further that these eigenstates present no degeneracy, it is easy to prove the biorthogonality of the sets $|\phi_n\rangle$, $\langle\tilde{\psi}_n|$:

$$\langle\tilde{\psi}_m(E)|\phi_n(E)\rangle = \delta_{mn}\, V_n(E), \tag{40}$$

with the normalization factor

$$V_n(E) = \langle \tilde{\psi}_n(E)| \, V_C \, |\psi_n(E)\rangle \,. \tag{41}$$

Now, since in our case the operator V_C is of limited range, and may even be taken to vanish outside a finite region of space, its matrix elements $\langle \tilde{\psi}_m(E)| \, V \, |\psi_n(E)\rangle$ are finite for any value of the complex energy variable, and the biorthogonality relations (40), (41), whose validity was originally restricted to the upper half of the physical energy plane, may therefore be continued to the whole physical plane. The same continuation may be achieved for the eigenvalues $\lambda_n(E)$; indeed, by multiplication from the left with $\langle \tilde{\psi}_m(E)|$, we derive from eq. (39) the relation

$$\lambda_n(E) \, V_n(E) \, \delta_{nm} + \left\langle \tilde{\psi}_m(E)| \, V_C \frac{1}{\hat{H} - E^+} V_C \, |\psi_n(E)\right\rangle = 0 \,, \tag{42}$$

in which the matrix element of the operator $V_C(\hat{H}-E^+)^{-1} V_C$ is finite on the whole physical plane, excepting isolated points which are poles of the functions $\lambda_n(E)$.

We are now prepared to discuss the integral equation (11), which we write in operator form, in the continuum subspace,

$$\left(1 + V_C \frac{1}{\hat{H} - E^+}\right) {}^0T + V_C = 0 \,. \tag{43}$$

Let us single out some group of eigenstates $|\phi_n(E)\rangle$, $\langle \tilde{\psi}_n(E)|$ by means of its projection operator

$$R(E) = \sum_n R_n(E) \,, \qquad R_n(E) = \frac{1}{V_n(E)} \, |\phi_n(E)\rangle \, \langle \tilde{\psi}_n(E)| \,, \tag{44}$$

and decompose the operators ${}^0T$ and V_C into two parts:

$${}^0T = {}^0T_R + {}^0T_D \,, \qquad V_C = V_R + V_D \,, \tag{45}$$

with

$${}^0T_R = R \, {}^0T, \qquad V_R = RV. \tag{46}$$

Eq. (43) yields separate equations for each component of ${}^0T_R$ and for ${}^0T_D$:

$$(1 - \lambda_n(E)) \, R_n(E) \, {}^0T + R_n(E) \, V = 0 \,, \tag{47}$$

$$\left(1 + V_D \frac{1}{\hat{H} - E^+}\right) {}^0T_D + V_D = 0 \,. \tag{48}$$

Whatever the value of $\lambda_n(E)$, eq. (47) immediately solves the inversion problem for ${}^0T_R$. At the same time, it shows that the iteration procedure (which here amounts to expressing $(1-\lambda_n)^{-1}$ as a power expansion) will converge provided $|\lambda_n|<1$, i.e. $|\eta_n(E)|>1$. In other words, the exceptional regions on the energy plane are those mapping the interior of the circles $|\eta_n|=1$ in the η_n-planes; and among such regions, only those which include some interval of the real axis require attention. In any case, the exceptional regions will correspond to a finite number of eigenstates $|\phi_n\rangle$, $\langle\tilde{\psi}_n|$; it will suffice to project these out according to the above pattern and obtain their contributions to ${}^0T$ by means of eqs. of the form (47). The equation (48) for the remaining part ${}^0T_D$ will then be soluble by iteration. It may be advisable to project out more terms than strictly necessary, in order to improve the convergence of the iteration by reducing the remaining coupling V_D.

The distribution of the exceptional regions on the physical energy plane is easily discussed. The centres of the circles $|\eta_n|=1$ correspond to roots of the equations $\eta_n(E)=0$ situated on this part of the energy surface. As shown by eq. (36), these are the single-particle resonant states $\hat{\mathscr{E}}_i$ of the model system of nucleons described by the Hamiltonian $\hat{H}$, and appearing as poles of the scattering amplitudes $\hat{S}_{cc}-1$, in the manner explained in section 3. Together with the bound states ${}^0E_i$ they form the set of poles of physical interest of the S-matrix associated with the Hamiltonian $\hat{H}$, from which the resonant states of the Hamiltonian ${}^0H$ originate. Indeed, as the residual coupling V_C is introduced and increases to its full strength, the pole $\hat{\mathscr{E}}_i$ moves, according to eq. (36), towards a new position ${}^0\mathscr{E}_l$, which is a root of the equation $\eta_n(E)=1$ and a resonant state of the Hamiltonian ${}^0H$. The boundary of the exceptional region around $\hat{\mathscr{E}}_i$ passes through the point ${}^0\mathscr{E}_l$, and although no general statement can be made about the range of variation of the distances $|{}^0\mathscr{E}_l-\hat{\mathscr{E}}_i|$ or the shape of the boundaries, examples indicate that no considerable fluctuations in the size of the exceptional regions or irregularities in their shape should be expected. Accordingly, only those exceptional regions around poles near the real axis – which are those giving rise to marked resonance effects – are likely to include segments of the real axis. We thus see that the term ${}^0T_R$ separated from the operator ${}^0T$ by the procedure described above corresponds precisely to the most important resonant states of the single-particle type.

We are now in a position to write down the solution of the integral equation (11) in a form susceptible to direct physical interpretation. We select a set of eigenstates $|\phi_n(E)\rangle$, $\langle\tilde{\psi}_n(E)|$ embodying (in the sense just explained) the important single-particle resonances, and leaving over in the residual interaction V_C a remainder V_D small enough to ensure a rapid convergence of the iteration series solving eq. (48). According to eq. (47) – which has to be written in the representation of basis $\phi_c(E_c)$ in order to conform with eq. (11) – and eqs. (44), (45), we get immediately

$$\langle E'_{c'}|\,{}^0T_R\,|E_c\rangle = -\sum_n \langle\phi_{c'}(E'_{c'})|\,V\,|\psi_n(E)\rangle \frac{1}{[1-\lambda_n(E)]\,V_n(E)} \times \\ \times \langle\tilde{\psi}_n(E)|\,V\,|\phi_c(E_c)\rangle\,. \tag{49}$$

As to ${}^0T_D$, we shall here just retain the lowest approximation

$$\langle E'_{c'}|\,{}^0T_D\,|E_c\rangle \approx -\langle\phi_{c'}(E'_{c'})|\,V_D\,|\phi_c(E_c)\rangle\,. \tag{50}$$

A slight transformation of eq. (49) is desirable in order to isolate the contributions from single-particle resonances from a non-resonant background on which they are superposed. In fact, writing

$$-\frac{1}{1-\lambda_n} = -\frac{\lambda_n}{1-\lambda_n} - 1 = \frac{1}{1-\eta_n} - 1\,,$$

we get

$$\langle E'_{c'}|\,{}^0T_R\,|E_c\rangle = -\langle\phi_{c'}(E'_{c'})|\,V_R\,|\phi_c(E_c)\rangle + \\ + \sum_n \langle\phi_{c'}(E'_{c'})|\,V\,|\psi_n(E)\rangle \frac{1}{[1-\eta_n(E)]\,V_n(E)} \langle\tilde{\psi}_n(E)|\,V\,|\phi_c(E_c)\rangle\,. \tag{51}$$

Now, writing eq. (36) in the form

$$({}^0H - E)\,|\psi_n\rangle = (1-\eta_n(E))\,V_C\,|\psi_n\rangle, \tag{52}$$

and using eqs. (38) and (44), we derive from it

$$|\psi_n\rangle \frac{1}{(1-\eta_n)\,V_n} \langle\tilde{\psi}_n| = \frac{1}{{}^0H - E^+} R_n = \tilde{R}_n^\dagger \frac{1}{{}^0H - E^+} R_n\,. \tag{53}$$

This allows us to express the last term in eq. (51) as the matrix element of an operator:

$$\langle E'_{c'}|\,{}^0T_{R_1}\,|E_c\rangle = \langle\phi_{c'}(E'_{c'})|\,V\tilde{R}^\dagger \frac{1}{{}^0H - E^+} RV\,|\phi_c(E_c)\rangle\,. \tag{54}$$

In the operator form (54), the matrix element in the energy shell $\langle E_{c'}|\,{}^0T_{R_1}\,|E_c\rangle$, which enters into the expression (25) for the S-matrix of the total Hamiltonian, is entirely parallel to the compound resonance term (32). In its more explicit form given by eq. (51), it can be compared to the corresponding expression (33). The complex poles ${}^0\mathscr{E}_l$ defining the single-particle resonances are roots of the equations $\eta_n(E)=1$, corresponding to the equations ${}^1\mathscr{E}_n(E)-E=0$ which determine the compound-resonance poles. The background term $-\langle\phi_{c'}(E_{c'})|\, V_R\, |\phi_c(E_c)\rangle$ can be combined with the remaining term $\langle E_{c'}|{}^0T_D\,|E_c\rangle$, which has the same form, and arises both from non-resonant processes and from broad resonances corresponding to poles far away from the real axis, not included in the subspace R of the selected states. To the approximation (50), the general background effects are thus given by the simple expression

$$\langle E_{c'}|\ {}^0T_{D_1}\,|E_c\rangle = -\ \langle\phi_{c'}(E_{c'})|\ V\,|\phi_c(E_c)\rangle\,. \tag{55}$$

Thus, our analysis, which in this respect resembles an argument first put forward by Mac Donald, clarifies the relationship between resonance and direct interaction processes and indicates how the treatment of the latter, if necessary, can be carried out to higher approximations by means of the further terms of the iteration series solving eq. (48) for ${}^0T_D$. The symmetry of the S-matrix with respect to the entrance and exit channels is readily verified by transforming the expressions (32), (54) and (55) for its different terms according to the scheme

$$\langle\tilde{c}'|\ O\ |c\rangle = \langle c'|\ O^\dagger\ |\tilde{c}\rangle^* = \langle\tilde{c}|\ O\ |c'\rangle\,.$$

6. Applications

Actual calculations according to the method here outlined proceed in three stages: (1) the choice of the shell-model and the construction of the basis ψ_i, $\phi_c(E)$; (2) the construction of the basis $\psi^{(c)}(E)$; (3) the calculation of the S-matrix and the determination of its resonance poles. The first stage needs no comment. The second stage requires the calculation of the whole ${}^0T$ matrix (and not only of its elements in the energy shell); this cannot be carried out directly by following the ideal pattern of the preceding section, since finding the eigenstates $|\phi_n\rangle$, $\langle\tilde{\psi}_n|$ would be tantamount to solving an eigenvalue problem of the type (36), involving an interaction operator V_C of complicated structure, which is precisely what we want to avoid. Accordingly, one will replace in practice V_C by some simple potential $V_C^{(0)}$, for which the eigenstates $|\phi_n^{(0)}\rangle$, $\langle\tilde{\psi}_n^{(0)}|$ and their eigenvalues $\eta_n^{(0)}$ can be evaluated in terms of the total energy E. This gives an approximate determination of the single-particle resonances of interest by appropriate roots of the equations $\eta_n^{(0)}(E)=1$.

We still decompose ${}^0T$ and V_C into two parts:

$$ {}^0T = {}^0T^{(0)} + {}^0T^{(1)}, \qquad V_C = V_C^{(0)} + V_C^{(1)}, \tag{56}$$

and we directly identify $V_C^{(0)}$ with $R^{(0)}\,V_C^{(0)}$, where

$$R^{(0)} = \sum_n R_n^{(0)}, \qquad R_n^{(0)} = \frac{1}{V_n^{(0)}}\,|\phi_n^{(0)}\rangle\,\langle\tilde{\psi}_n^{(0)}|, \tag{57}$$

$$|\phi_n^{(0)}\rangle = V_C^{(0)}\,|\psi_n^{(0)}\rangle, \qquad V_n^{(0)} = \langle\tilde{\psi}_n^{(0)}|\,V_C^{(0)}\,|\psi_n^{(0)}\rangle. \tag{58}$$

Now, ${}^0T^{(0)}$ is defined as the solution of the equation

$$\left(1 + V_C^{(0)}\,\frac{1}{\hat{H} - E^+}\right){}^0T^{(0)} + V_C^{(0)} = 0; \tag{59}$$

it is of the form $R^{(0)}\,{}^0T^{(0)}$ (but this is no longer $R^{(0)}\,{}^0T$), and the components $R_n^{(0)}\,{}^0T^{(0)}$ are given by equations similar to eq. (17),

$$(1 - \lambda_n^{(0)})\,R_n^{(0)}\,{}^0T^{(0)} + R_n^{(0)}\,V_C^{(0)} = 0. \tag{60}$$

For the part ${}^0T^{(1)}$ we now obtain by some simple operator algebra, using eqs. (43), (45) and (59),

$$\left(1 + V_C^{(0)}\,\frac{1}{\hat{H} - E^+}\right){}^0T^{(1)} + V_C^{(1)}\left(\frac{1}{\hat{H} - E^+}\,{}^0T + 1\right) = 0; \tag{61}$$

moreover, by taking the adjoint and the time-reversed of eq. (59) we derive an equation for the transformed matrix ${}^0T^{(0)T}$:

$${}^0T^{(0)T}\left(1 + \frac{1}{\hat{H} - E^+}\,V_C^{(0)}\right) + V_C^{(0)} = 0,$$

from which it follows that

$$\left(1 + {}^0T^{(0)T}\,\frac{1}{\hat{H} - E^+}\right)\left(1 + V_C^{(0)}\,\frac{1}{\hat{H} - E^+}\right) = 1,$$

and that therefore eq. (61) yields

$${}^0T^{(1)} = -\left(1 + {}^0T^{(0)T}\,\frac{1}{\hat{H} - E^+}\right)V_C^{(1)}\left(\frac{1}{\hat{H} - E^+}\,{}^0T + 1\right). \tag{62}$$

The matrix-element $\langle E'_{c'}|\,{}^0T^{(1)}\,|E_c\rangle$ has to be calculated from eq. (62) in the representation of basis $\phi_c(E_c)$. According to eqs. (4) and (7), one has

$$\left(\frac{1}{\hat{H} - E^+}\,{}^0T + 1\right)|\phi_c(E_c)\rangle = |\psi^{(c)}(E_c)\rangle; \tag{63}$$

similarly, we define a new basis $\chi^{(c)}(E_c)$ in the continuum subspace by

$$\left(\frac{1}{\hat{H} - E^+}\,{}^0T^{(0)} + 1\right)|\phi_c(E_c)\rangle = |\chi^{(c)}(E_c)\rangle; \tag{64}$$

this gives

$$\langle \tilde{\chi}^{(c)}(E_c)| = \langle \phi_c(E_c)| \left(1 + {}^0T^{(0)T} \frac{1}{\hat{H} - E^+}\right), \tag{65}$$

and accordingly, from eq. (62),

$$\langle E'_{c'}| \, {}^0T^{(1)} \, |E_c\rangle = \langle \tilde{\chi}^{(c')}(E'_{c'})| \, V_C^{(1)} \, |\psi^{(c)}(E_c)\rangle . \tag{66}$$

This is an exact expression, generalizing eq. (50).

Eq. (66) cannot be used directly, since it involves the unknown basis $\psi^{(c)}(E_c)$; however, it may be made the framework of an iteration process leading to an approximate determination of increasing accuracy of both ${}^0T^{(1)}$ and the basis $\psi^{(c)}(E_c)$. With the help of the basis $\chi^{(c)}(E_c)$ calculated by eq. (64), we can indeed start from the approximate value

$$\langle E'_{c'}| \, {}^0T^{(1)} \, |E_c\rangle \approx \langle \tilde{\chi}^{(c')}(E'_{c'})| \, V_C^{(1)} \, |\chi^{(c)}(E_c)\rangle .$$

The corresponding approximation of the total matrix ${}^0T$, inserted in eq. (60), yields a first approximation to the required basis $\psi^{(c)}(E_c)$. If necessary, this first result may be used to obtain from eq. (66) an improved value of ${}^0T^{(1)}$, which again will lead, through eq. (63), to a more accurate determination of the basis $\psi^{(c)}(E_c)$.

I shall leave it at these general indications; only the study of the papers describing the application of the method to concrete problems can enable the reader to appreciate its power. A particularly impressive case is that of elastic and inelastic neutron scattering on ^{15}N, treated by the Heidelberg group[6]). An analysis of elastic neutron scattering on ^{12}C by I. Lovas[7]), carried out by a somewhat different method, but essentially on the same principles, affords an interesting example of the comparison between metastable, energy-dependent states and corresponding poles of the S-matrix; in Lovas' case, one of the metastable states results from a compound mechanism, the other is of the single-particle type. The most extensive application of the method at Heidelberg so far is the very thorough investigation[8]) of the analogous bound and resonant states in the spectra of isobaric nuclei, differing by substitution of neutrons for protons and vice-versa. Mention should also be made, of course, of the results obtained by the French group[5]), as well as of independent investigations along essentially the same lines carried out by Mac Donald, Balashov and many other physicists[9]); a discussion of this work will be found in papers of the Heidelberg group[2,8,10]). The theory has recently received two important extensions, which, when fully explored, will give the account of nuclear reaction processes a much-needed completion. The first aspect calling for renewed examination in the light of the analysis here outlined is the statistical distribution in energy of the large number of resonances revealed by high-resolution techniques; the search for the adequate formulation of the statistical properties underlying the observed features, extensively pursued from various points of view by P. A. Moldauer[11]), has been taken up again by C. Mahaux, H. A. Weidenmüller and A. Lejeune[12]), and some interesting conclusions have already been reached. A related problem is then the formulation of a simplified theory of the processes observed at moderate resolution, when the effects of many resonances are superposed to give a smoothed out variation of the cross-sections with energy; considered in their time evolution, such processes are those involving direct interaction of short duration between projectile and target. An extreme model representation of these direct interaction processes is suggested by the optical analogy of the complex refractive index, which includes the absorption by the scatterer: it is found that the addition of a small imaginary part to the shell-model potential is sufficient to reproduce the general features of the direct reactions. For a more accurate description, however, the optical model needs to be supplemented by contributions from compound nucleus formation, with the correct phase relationships between them. This can only be achieved by a theory starting from first principles, and in which a rational definition of the optical model potential is built in. The first to give a clear formulation and an elegant discussion of the problem was Mac Donald[9]), who, however, did not pursue the matter in detail. A renewed analysis by the Heidelberg group[12]) on the basis of the techniques here described shows that they lead to a complete solution, allowing of practical computations, and giving the precise justification and limitation of the *ad hoc* procedures widely used in the interpretation of experimental data, but hitherto lacking a firm foundation. The elucidation of the still outstanding questions concerning the extension of the method to many-fragment channels will reveal its full scope and possible limitations.

References

1) L. Rosenfeld, in: *Proc. Intern. Conference on Elementary Particles, Kyoto, 1965*, p. 182.
2) H. A. Weidenmüller, Nucl. Phys. **75**, 189 (1966);
H. A. Weidenmüller and K. Dietrich, Nucl. Phys. **83**, 332 (1966);
W. Glöckle, J. Hüfner and H. A. Weidenmüller, Nucl. Phys. **A 90**, 481 (1967).
3) A. Herzenberg and F. Mandl, Proc. Roy. Soc. (London) **A 270**, 48 (1962); **A 274**, 253 (1963);

A. Herzenberg, K. L. Kwok and F. Mandl, in: *Proc. Third Intern. Conference on the Physics of Electronic and Atomic Collisions, London, 1963* (North-Holland Publ. Co., Amsterdam, 1964) p. 98;
J. N. Bardsley, A. Herzenberg and F. Mandl, in: *Proc. Third Intern. Conference on the Physics of Electronic and Atomic Collisions, London, 1963* (North-Holland Publ. Co., Amsterdam, 1964) p. 415;
A. Herzenberg, K. L. Kwok and F. Mandl, Proc. Phys. Soc. (London) **84**, 345, 477 (1964);
A. Herzenberg, D. Sherrington and M. Süveges, Proc. Phys. Soc. (London) **84**, 465 (1964);
K. L. Kwok and F. Mandl, Proc. Phys. Soc. (London) **86**, 501 (1965);
F. Mandl, Proc. Phys. Soc. (London) **87**, 871 (1966);
R. Phythian, Proc. Phys. Soc. (London) **87**, 171 (1966);
J. N. Bardsley, A. Herzenberg and F. Mandl, Proc. Phys. Soc. (London) **89**, 305, 321 (1966);
F. Mandl, Proc. Phys. Soc. (London) **90**, 913 (1967);
J. N. Bardsley, Proc. Phys. Soc. (London) **91**, 300 (1967).

4) H. Feshbach, in: *Comptes-rendus du Congrès intern. de physique nucléaire, Paris, 1964,* Vol. 1, pp. 227–251, especially p. 248.
5) C. Bloch and V. Gillet, Phys. Letters **16**, 62 (1965); **18**, 58 (1965);
V. Gillet, M. A. Melkanoff and J. Raynal, Nucl. Phys. **A 97**, 631 (1967);
J. Raynal, M. A. Melkanoff and T. Sawada, Nucl. Phys. **A 101**, 369 (1967).
6) W. Ebenhöh, W. Glöckle, J. Hüfner and H. A. Weidenmüller, Z. Physik **202**, 302 (1967).
7) I. Lovas, Nucl. Phys. **81**, 353 (1966).
8) H. A. Weidenmüller, Nucl. Phys. **85**, 241 (1966);
C. Mahaux and H. A. Weidenmüller, Nucl. Phys. **89**, 33 (1966);
C. Mahaux and C. A. Wiedner, Nucl. Phys. **A 93**, 327 (1967);
C. Mahaux and H. A. Weidenmüller, Nucl. Phys. **A 94**, 1 (1967);
H. A. Weidenmüller, Nucl. Phys. **A 99**, 269, 289 (1967);
see also R. Lipperheide, Nucl. Phys. **A 105**, 545 (1967).
9) W. M. Mac Donald, Nucl. Phys. **54**, 393 (1964); **56**, 636 (1964);
W. W. Balashov et al., J. Nucl. Phys. (USSR) **2**, 643 (1965);
M. Bauer and F. Prats, Nucl. Phys. **89**, 230 (1966);
other references cited in refs. 2, 8, 10 and 13.
10) C. Mahaux and H. A. Weidenmüller, Nucl. Phys. **A 97**, 378 (1967).
11) P. A. Moldauer, Phys. Rev. **135**, B 642 (1964); Rev. Mod. Phys. **36**, 1079 (1964); Phys. Rev. **136**, B 947 (1964); Phys. Letters **8**, 70 (1964); in: *Proc. Intern. Conference Nucl. Physics, Gatlinburg, 1966;* in: *Annual Meeting American Physical Society, New York, Jan. 1967;* Phys. Rev. Letters **18**, 249 (1967); Phys. Rev. **157**, 907 (1967).
12) C. Mahaux and H. A. Weidenmüller, Nucl. Phys. **A 91**, 241 (1967);
A. Lejeune and C. Mahaux, Z. Physik **207**, 35 (1967).
13) J. Hüfner, C. Mahaux and H. A. Weidenmüller, Nucl. Phys. **A 105**, 489 (1967).

Note added in proof

The reader's attention is called to a forthcoming paper by K. Dietrich and K. Hara, in which the "random phase approximation" method is extended so as to allow the inclusion in the model Hamiltonian of the ground state correlations and the collective features of the excited configurations.

Spectroscopic and group theoretical methods in physics
© North-Holland Publ. Co., Amsterdam, 1968

EFFECT OF EXCHANGE AND THE PAULI PRINCIPLE ON NUCLEON–NUCLEUS SCATTERING I*

WILLIAM A. FRIEDMAN and HERMAN FESHBACH
Laboratory for Nuclear Science and Physics Department,
Massachusetts Institute of Technology, Cambridge, Massachusetts, U.S.A.

1. Introduction

This paper is concerned with the elastic and inelastic scattering of nucleons by nuclei and particularly with the effects which arise because the incident and emergent nucleon cannot be distinguished from the nucleons making up the target nucleus. It has been a common practice to describe this scattering process in terms of the interaction of a single nucleon with the A particle target system considered as a unit, the "target nucleus". The direct attempt to solve the $(A+1)$ particle problem has rarely been employed for the calculation of scattering states. It is perforce restricted to light nuclei. On the other hand, the description in terms of the target nucleus plus nucleon is limited according to the extent to which a detailed description of the target nucleus exists. If only the ground state of the target nucleus is included in the description, one is restricted to the optical model. For many nuclei information on the wave functions for the low lying levels of the target nucleus in terms of some model is often available. Under these circumstances, it becomes possible to employ the coupled channel approach, including in the calculation those reliably known states of the target nucleus which are important for the process under consideration. In most such treatments, the exclusion principle and the exchange scattering are not considered. Rather, it is hoped that the effective energy dependent potentials employed will in

* This work is supported in part through funds provided by the Atomic Energy Commission under Contract AT(30-1)-2098.

some way simulate their effects. If collective rather than "microscopic" coordinates are used to describe the target nuclear states, a discussion of the identical particle effects is automatically precluded.

In this paper, we shall discuss a method for the explicit consideration of identical particle effects in the case of the N coupled channel problem. We shall discuss in a qualitative way the problems which anti-symmetrization and exchange scattering raise and how the N coupled channel problem should be formulated so as to eliminate these difficulties. In a subsequent paper, one of us (W.F.) will develop this formulation further and apply it to neutron–nucleus scattering.

To introduce the subject in its least complex form, let us first consider "pure" elastic scattering in which the only open channel is the elastic one. Moreover, let us first examine the impact of the exclusion principle on the properties of the scattering amplitude. It will be a relatively simple matter to generalize to the case of N coupled channels, including inelastic open channels as well as the open elastic channel.

Perhaps the most straightforward way of dealing with the anti-symmetrization problem is that outlined by Mott and Massey [1]). In this procedure, one first obtains a solution, ϕ, of the Schroedinger equation disregarding the identity of the incident particle and the target nucleons. In the asymptotic region in which the nucleon and the target no longer interact, one finds in this solution a direct scattering amplitude in which the incident and emergent particles are the same and an exchange scattering amplitude in which the incident particle and target nucleon exchange so that the emergent particle is a target nucleon. Since the nuclear Hamiltonian is symmetric once ϕ is obtained, any permutation of particle coordinates in ϕ yields a wave function which is also a solution. The particular one that is of physical interest is the totally anti-symmetric one. Anti-symmetrizing ϕ produces a solution of the Schroedinger equation which satisfies the Pauli exclusion principle.

Let us describe this procedure more formally. Let $\phi_t(\boldsymbol{r}_1, \ldots, \boldsymbol{r}_A)$ describe the anti-symmetrized eigenfunctions of the target nucleus with Hamiltonian, $\mathscr{H}_t$:

$$\mathscr{H}_t \phi_t = \varepsilon_t \phi_t . \tag{1}$$

Let the solution, ϕ, of the full problem

$$\mathscr{H} \phi = \varepsilon \phi , \tag{2}$$

not satisfying the Pauli principle, be expanded in the asymptotic region in terms of ϕ_t as follows:

$$\phi(\mathbf{r}_0, \mathbf{r}_1, \ldots, \mathbf{r}_A) \to \sum_t u_t(\mathbf{r}_0)\, \phi_t(\mathbf{r}_1, \ldots, \mathbf{r}_A). \tag{3}$$

This sum includes an integration over the continuum eigenstates of $\mathscr{H}_t$ as well as the bound states. Eq. (3) is concerned with the *asymptotic region*, in which one of the coordinates, r_i, approaches infinity. If the limit r_0 to infinity is examined, ϕ is found to consist of an incident wave plus an outgoing spherical wave whose amplitude is then the direct scattering amplitude. On the other hand, if one of the target nucleon coordinates, say r_1, is allowed to go to infinity, the first terms in expansion (3) go to zero exponentially. However, the continuum part of the series will in general be singular in such a way as to yield an outgoing wave in variable r_1. If only elastic scattering is energetically possible, this outgoing wave must in the limit of large r_1 have the form

$$\phi \to v_1(\mathbf{r}_1)\, \phi_0(\mathbf{r}_0, \mathbf{r}_2, \ldots, \mathbf{r}_A) \qquad r_1 \to \infty .$$

The incident particle and particle r_1 of the target nucleus have exchanged roles, and for this reason the corresponding amplitude is referred to as the exchange scattering amplitude. A similar term exists for each coordinate r_1. It is clear that truncation of the series (3) at N terms is not permissible as the exchange scattering would be completely omitted.

The resolution of this difficulty is suggested by the form of the asymptotic amplitude which is obtained upon antisymmetrization. Suppose asymptotically the direct contribution to the scattering is given by $u_0(\mathbf{r}_0)\, \phi_0(\mathbf{r}_1, \mathbf{r}_2, \ldots, \mathbf{r}_A)$ and the exchange amplitudes by $v_i(\mathbf{r}_i)\, \phi_0(\mathbf{r}_1, \mathbf{r}_2, \ldots, \mathbf{r}_{i-1}, \mathbf{r}_0, \mathbf{r}_{i+1}, \ldots, \mathbf{r}_A)$. Then the anti-symmetrized asymptotic wave function is asymptotically proportional to

$$\psi \to \mathscr{A}\big[u_0(\mathbf{r}_0)\, \phi_0(\mathbf{r}_1, \ldots, \mathbf{r}_A) + \\ + \sum_i v_i(\mathbf{r}_i)\, \phi_0(\mathbf{r}_1, \mathbf{r}_2, \ldots, \mathbf{r}_{i-1}, \mathbf{r}_0, \mathbf{r}_{i+1}, \mathbf{r}_A)\big], \tag{4}$$

where $\mathscr{A}$ is the anti-symmetrization operator. This can be written

$$\psi \to \mathscr{A}\big[u_0(\mathbf{r}_0) - \sum v_i(\mathbf{r}_0)\big]\, \phi_0(\mathbf{r}_1, \ldots, \mathbf{r}_A). \tag{5}$$

The term in the anti-symmetrized ψ which contains $\phi_0(\mathbf{r}_1, \ldots, \mathbf{r}_A)$ in the limit r_0 approaching infinity contains both the direct and exchange scattering amplitudes. Moreover, those terms not included in the asymptotic ψ of eq. (5) will be free of singularities. They go to zero exponentially as r_i increases to infinity.

Eq. (5) suggests that the appropriate form to be used for the anti-symmetrized solution of eq. (2) is one with the asymptotic form

$$\psi \to \mathscr{A}\,\chi_0(\boldsymbol{r}_0)\,\phi_0(\boldsymbol{r}_1, \ldots, \boldsymbol{r}_A)\,. \tag{6}$$

By requiring ψ to have this asymptotic form, we have not yet guaranteed that χ_0 will contain completely both the direct and exchange scattering amplitudes as in eq. (5). We must exclude the possibility that the terms not explicitly shown in eq. (6) could contribute in the asymptotic region. For this purpose it is sufficient to require that asymptotically the difference $[\psi - \mathscr{A}(\chi_0\phi_0)]$ not contain any dependence upon ϕ_0, where the argument of ϕ_0 is *any* set of A coordinates taken from the $(A+1)$ coordinates, $(\boldsymbol{r}_0, \boldsymbol{r}_1, \ldots, \boldsymbol{r}_A)$. When this *supplementary* condition is met, the amplitude $\chi_0(\boldsymbol{r}_0)$ must contain all of the elastic scattering amplitude. Instead of the $(A+1)$ amplitudes, $u_0, v_1, \ldots, v_A$, only one amplitude, χ_0, is required in order to specify the elastic scattering. The problem of calculating the exchange amplitudes is now replaced by the problem of enforcing the supplementary condition.

It should be noted that the function, χ_0, is not unique. It is always possible to add to χ_0 a function, χ_0', which satisfies the condition

$$\mathscr{A}\,\chi_0'(\boldsymbol{r}_0)\,\phi_0(\boldsymbol{r}_1, \ldots, \boldsymbol{r}_A) \equiv 0\,. \tag{7}$$

For example if ϕ_0 were a Slater determinant of single particle wave functions, then a χ_0' equal to any of these single particle wave functions would satisfy eq. (7). It is important to know the functions χ_0' at least implicitly, for a number of reasons. For the present (other reasons will be given below) note that the most efficient description of χ_0 is obtained if it is taken to be orthogonal to all the χ_0'. For the simple case of ϕ, a Slater determinant, this amounts to the trivial remark that the $(A+1)$st particle should be put into an excited single particle state not included among the A single particle wave functions making up ϕ_0. For a more elaborate wave function involving dynamical correlations for ϕ_0, χ_0' satisfying eq. (7) will exist but will not be as readily ascertained.

To summarize, in the single channel case we look for a wave function ψ of the asymptotic form eq. (6) which satisfies the supplementary condition stated immediately below eq. (6). In addition, we need the solutions χ_0' of eq. (7).

These problems were solved in refs. 2 and 3. A projection operator P was found which when acting on an anti-symmetrized wave function Ψ yields:

$$P\,\Psi = \mathscr{A}[\chi_0\,\phi_0(\boldsymbol{r}_1, \ldots, \boldsymbol{r}_A)]\,, \tag{8}$$

as well as

$$\langle \phi_0(\boldsymbol{r}_1, \ldots, \boldsymbol{r}_A)(1-P)\Psi \rangle = 0 \qquad \text{for all } \boldsymbol{r}_0 . \tag{9}$$

We see that by virtue of eq. (9) that the supplementary condition is satisfied. The Schroedinger equation satisfied by $P\Psi$ involving an "effective Hamiltonian," $\mathscr{H}_{\text{eff}}$ can be easily obtained [2]). Its solution gives a complete solution of the original problem eq. (2) satisfying the Pauli exclusion principle. We shall not review the details of this method as it can be easily extracted from the N coupled channel discussion to be given below by putting $N=1$.

One more point before we leave the one channel case. It is generally more convenient as far as calculations are concerned to deal with the amplitude U_0 rather than χ_0, where U_0 is uniquely defined by

$$U_0(\boldsymbol{r}_0) \equiv \langle \phi_0(\boldsymbol{r}_1, \boldsymbol{r}_2, \ldots, \boldsymbol{r}_A), \Psi(\boldsymbol{r}_0, \boldsymbol{r}_1, \ldots, \boldsymbol{r}_A) \rangle . \tag{10}$$

From eq. (9) it follows that

$$U_0(\boldsymbol{r}_0) = \langle \phi_0(\boldsymbol{r}_1, \boldsymbol{r}_2, \ldots, \boldsymbol{r}_A), P\Psi(\boldsymbol{r}_0, \boldsymbol{r}_1, \ldots, \boldsymbol{r}_A) \rangle ,$$

or

$$U_0(\boldsymbol{r}_0) = \langle \phi_0(\boldsymbol{r}_1, \boldsymbol{r}_2, \ldots, \boldsymbol{r}_A), \mathscr{A}[\chi_0(\boldsymbol{r}_0)\, \phi_0(\boldsymbol{r}_1, \boldsymbol{r}_2, \ldots, \boldsymbol{r}_A)] \rangle . \tag{11}$$

For large values of r_0, U_0 and χ_0 approach each other so that the scattering amplitude can be obtained from the asymptotic behavior of either U_0 or χ_0. Because χ_0 is not unique in virtue of (7), the relation between U_0 and χ_0 given in eq. (11) is singular. We can, however, make χ_0 unique by insisting that it be orthogonal to all χ_0'. Then it becomes possible to invert eq. (11) and obtain the more interesting χ_0 in terms of the more convenient U_0.

In the N channel approximation, the expansion of the exact solution in terms of the states of the target nucleus defined by eq. (1):

$$\psi = \mathscr{A} \sum_{t=0}^{\infty} \chi_t(\boldsymbol{r}_0)\, \phi_t(\boldsymbol{r}_1, \ldots, \boldsymbol{r}_A) \tag{12}$$

is truncated at N terms. These N terms should include the elastic channel, the inelastic channels, and important bound states such as doorway states. Let P_N be a projection operator which exactly projects out these N states:

$$P_N \psi = A \sum_{t=0}^{N-1} \chi_t(\boldsymbol{r}_0)\, \phi_t(\boldsymbol{r}_1, \ldots, \boldsymbol{r}_A) . \tag{13}$$

The P of eq. (8) is just P_1. Indeed, we may consider the determination of P_N to be given below as the generalization of the procedure used in the one channel case [2]). Just as in the one channel case, supplementary conditions on

$P_N\psi$ are required or are implied by eq. (13). In particular, we require that the difference, $\psi - P_n\psi$, not contain any dependence on ϕ_t, $0 \leqslant t \leqslant N-1$, where the argument of each ϕ_t is allowed to be any selection of the A coordinates from the $(A+1)$ coordinates, $(\boldsymbol{r}_0, \boldsymbol{r}_1, \ldots, \boldsymbol{r}_A)$. As in the $N=1$ case this condition guarantees that the amplitudes χ_t contain all the information about the N channels of physical interest, elastic, inelastic and important bound state channels. Moreover, from the supplementary condition it is certain that the remainder of ψ, $(1-P_N)\psi$ decays exponentially with large values of any of the coordinates r_i and so does not contribute to the scattering amplitudes. Once this separation has been accomplished, a valid truncation becomes possible, i.e., one can now approximate ψ by $P_N\psi$. Or one can to some approximation take the effect of $(1-P_N)\psi$ into account by considering the exact equation satisfied by $P_N\psi$ and in that equation approximating the terms arising from the coupling of $P_N\psi$ to $(1-P_N)\psi$. This leads to the same form for the equation satisfied by $P_N\psi$ as that which obtains when truncation is applied, except that effective interactions (complex if we are dealing with energy averaged amplitudes) are used.

As in the one channel case, it should be realized that the set (χ_t) may not be unique. In other words, χ_t' may exist which satisfy the analogue of eq. (7):

$$\mathscr{A} \sum_{0}^{N-1} \chi_t'(\boldsymbol{r}_0)\, \phi_t(\boldsymbol{r}_1, \ldots, \boldsymbol{r}_A) = 0 . \tag{14}$$

As in the one channel case, knowledge of these χ_t' is important for two reasons. First it permits one the most succint description of χ_t by requiring, for example, that $P\psi_n$ be orthogonal to all wave functions satisfying eq. (14). Second, it is required in order to obtain a relationship between the amplitudes χ_t and the more convenient U_t defined by

$$\begin{aligned} U_t(\boldsymbol{r}_0) &\equiv \langle \phi_t(\boldsymbol{r}_1, \ldots, \boldsymbol{r}_A), \psi \rangle = \langle \phi_t(\boldsymbol{r}_1, \ldots, \boldsymbol{r}_A), P_N\psi \rangle = \\ &= \sum_{\tau=0}^{A-1} \langle \phi_t(\boldsymbol{r}_1, \ldots, \boldsymbol{r}_A), \mathscr{A}\chi_\tau(\boldsymbol{r}_0)\, \phi_\tau(\boldsymbol{r}_1, \ldots, \boldsymbol{r}_A) \rangle . \end{aligned} \tag{15}$$

In order to invert eq. (15) to obtain χ_τ from U_t, it is necessary to determine all the sets χ_τ'. Then by insisting that

$$\langle \sum \chi_\tau \phi_\tau, \mathscr{A} \sum \chi_t' \phi_t \rangle = 0 \tag{16}$$

for all sets χ_t', eq. (14) can be inverted to obtain a unique χ_τ in terms of U_t.

The determination of P_N, satisfying the supplementary condition, as well as the determination of χ_t' satisfying eq. (14) will be the subject of the next section. As in the one channel case, the determination of P_N automatically yields the solution of the second problem, the evaluation of the χ_t'. The effective Hamiltonian as well as the Schroedinger equation for $P_N\psi$, including the changes which are a consequence of the identity of the particles and of the Pauli principle will be explicitly derived. This is an exact Schroedinger equation. The terms which arise because of the coupling between $P_N\psi$ and $(1-P_N)\,\psi$ are completely visible and approximations can be readily inserted.

This problem has been considered by many authors. A recent review has been made by Mittelman[4]). Some researches like this one have been concerned with an explicit treatment of the Pauli principle for all channels. We mention here the paper of Coester and Kummel[5]) and Lipperheide[6]). These authors obtain an infinite set of coupled channels, but they do not solve the problem of truncation which, as we have pointed out here and as Villars[7]) emphasized earlier, require special attention. Bloch and Gillet and Weidenmuller[8]) use a new channel formalism employing a restricted class of channel wave functions: those which may be expressed as Slater determinants of single particle levels. They do not use, as in this paper, channels which are specifically associated with target states. Another approach is that of Hahn[9]) who treats each permutation in the anti-symmetrized wave function as an independent channel. Levin[10]), Lippmann, Mittelman and Watson[11]) use the Lippmann–Schwinger integral equation where the source term is the anti-symmetrized incident wave. A somewhat different method is used by MacDonald[21]). Finally, we mention the perturbation theory approach of Bell and Squire[12]) and Vagradov[13]) who derive an optical potential which includes the effect of the Pauli exclusion principle.

In the Wigner R matrix formalism[14]) the problem of anti-symmetrization is resolved by postulating that the right hand of eq. (6) holds exactly for r_i larger than or equal to a channel radius a. Joining this $r_i \geqslant a$ form to the inside $(r_i < a)$ wave function guarantees the satisfaction of the supplementary condition. It has been pointed out by A. K. Kerman[15]) that this procedure is approximate even if, as the R matrix theory requires, it is assumed that the nucleon–nucleus interaction vanishes outside $r_i = a$. Form (6) does not hold precisely for any finite r_i. The other components of the exact wave function ψ are not zero outside a but rather decrease exponentially. Upon anti-symmetrization, these will contribute in the elastic channel and affect the joining of the inside and outside wave functions. This in addition beclouds the question as to whether or not exchange scattering has been correctly accounted for. These effects become smaller as a is increased, but then the R matrix parameters become correspondingly less physical. For a of the order of the nuclear radius which it is claimed is the "best" value of a, the overlap is appreciable, and, therefore, the anti-symmetrization problem is serious. The R matrix theory has been reformulated in ref. 2 in 1962 where a projection operator, P, appropriate for R matrix theory is exhibited and the Bloch[16]) interaction term derived. If the analysis of the present paper is applied only to $P\psi$, valid anti-symmetrization and truncation can be obtained.

2. General theory

Let us first consider the problem of satisfying formally what we have referred to as the supplementary condition. This condition, which is required to hold only asymptotically, is certainly satisfied if we require it to be valid everywhere. Let Ψ be any anti-symmetrized wave function of the $A+1$ variables $(\boldsymbol{r}_0, \ldots, \boldsymbol{r}_A)$. It need not be the solution of Schroedinger equation (2). We require that

$$\langle \phi_t(\boldsymbol{r}_1, \ldots, \boldsymbol{r}_A)\,[\Psi - \mathscr{A} \sum_0^{N-1} \chi_{t'}(\boldsymbol{r}_0)\, \phi_{t'}(\boldsymbol{r}_1, \ldots, \boldsymbol{r}_A)]\rangle = 0 \tag{17}$$

for $t=0, 1, \ldots, N-1$. Eq. (17) must hold for all $\boldsymbol{r}_0$ and therefore it follows that

$$\langle \mathscr{A} \sum f_t(\boldsymbol{r}_0)\, \phi_t(\boldsymbol{r}_1, \ldots, \boldsymbol{r}_A), [\Psi - \mathscr{A} \sum \chi_{t'}(\boldsymbol{r}_0)\, \phi_{t'}(\boldsymbol{r}_1, \ldots, \boldsymbol{r}_A) = 0]\rangle \tag{18}$$

for arbitrary f_t. Eq. (17) is the statement in analytic form of the requirement that the part of Ψ not included in $\mathscr{A}\, \Sigma\, \chi_{t'}\phi_{t'}$, namely $\Psi - \mathscr{A}\, \Sigma\, \chi_{t'}\phi_{t'}$, be orthogonal to ϕ_t where the argument of ϕ_t can be any selection of A coordinates from the $A+1$ coordinates $(\boldsymbol{r}_0, \boldsymbol{r}_1, \ldots, \boldsymbol{r}_A)$. Eq. (17) can be solved for $\chi_{t'}$ in terms of Ψ. The functions $\chi_{t'}$ depend linearly on Ψ so that a projection operator P_N exists which when acting on an anti-symmetrized wave function projects out the dependence on ϕ_t, $t=0, \ldots, N-1$:

$$P_N \Psi = \mathscr{A} \sum_{t=0}^{N-1} \chi_t(\boldsymbol{r}_0)\, \phi_t(\boldsymbol{r}_1, \ldots, \boldsymbol{r}_A). \tag{19}$$

Eq. (17) may be written

$$U_t(\boldsymbol{r}) = \chi_t(\boldsymbol{r}) - \sum_{t'=0}^{N-1} \langle K_{tt'}(\boldsymbol{r}', \boldsymbol{r}), \chi_{t'}(\boldsymbol{r}')\rangle, \tag{20}$$

where U_t has been defined in eq. (15) and

$$K_{tt'}(\boldsymbol{r}', \boldsymbol{r}) \equiv A \langle \phi_t(\boldsymbol{r}', \boldsymbol{r}_2, \ldots, \boldsymbol{r}_A), \phi_{t'}(\boldsymbol{r}, \boldsymbol{r}_2, \ldots, \boldsymbol{r}_A)\rangle. \tag{21}$$

It is convenient to define columnar matrices of N elements,

$$\chi = \begin{pmatrix} \chi_0 \\ \vdots \\ \chi_{N-1} \end{pmatrix}, \qquad U = \begin{pmatrix} U_0 \\ \vdots \\ U_{N-1} \end{pmatrix},$$

and a square $N \times N$ matrix operator K whose matrix element is $\int K_{tt'}(\boldsymbol{r}', \boldsymbol{r})$. Eq. (20) becomes

$$U = (1 - K)\,\chi, \tag{22}$$

where

$$1 \equiv \int \delta(\boldsymbol{r} - \boldsymbol{r}')\,\delta_{tt'}\,.$$

The problem of satisfying the supplementary condition (or equivalently of determining P_N), and the problem of inverting $(1-K)$ to obtain χ in terms of U are seen to be identical. That is, once $(1-K)$ is inverted, it is a simple matter to extract P_N. Moreover, the problem of determining the inverse $(1-K)^{-1}$ requires the determination of its singularities. We shall now see that these singularities occur because there are the "supererogatory" χ' satisfying eq. (14). In solving eq. (22) for χ it will consequently be necessary to determine χ'.

The inversion of $(1-K)$ may be expressed in terms of the eigenfunctions $\omega^{(\alpha)}$ of the K with eigenvalue λ_α namely

$$\lambda_\alpha K \omega^{(\alpha)} = \omega^{(\alpha)}\,. \tag{23}$$

K is hermitean so that λ_α is real. The corresponding eigenfunctions $\omega^{(\alpha)}$ form an orthogonal (but not complete) set which we shall also normalize. K may be expressed in terms of $\omega^{(\alpha)}$:

$$K = \sum_\alpha \frac{\omega^{(\alpha)}\,\omega^{(\alpha)\dagger}}{\lambda_\alpha}, \tag{24}$$

where $\omega^{(\alpha)}$ is a single column matrix while $\omega^{(\alpha)\dagger}$ is a single row matrix with elements $\omega_t^{(\alpha)*}$. Hence,

$$K_{tt'}(\boldsymbol{r}', \boldsymbol{r}') = \sum_\alpha \frac{\omega_t^{(\alpha)}(\boldsymbol{r}')\,\omega_{t'}^{(\alpha)*}(\boldsymbol{r})}{\lambda_\alpha}\,.$$

The eigenfunctions with $\lambda_\alpha = 1$ are of special importance. They will be denoted by $\chi^{(\alpha)'}$.

Turning now to eq. (22), we must investigate the meaning of

$$\frac{1}{1-K} U,$$

before we can solve (22) for χ. We note that $1/(1-K)$ is singular in the sense that if the overlap $\langle \chi^{(\alpha)'}, U \rangle$ were not zero, $(1-K)^{-1}U$ would be infinite. As we shall show (see eq. (30)) $\langle \chi^{(\alpha)'}, U \rangle$ is in fact zero so that $(1-K)^{-1}U$ is finite. However, then the amplitude $\chi^{(\alpha)'}$ in the final result for $(1-K)^{-1}U$ is arbitrary although it is not infinite. Suppose that we define a new K operator, K' which omits the terms $\lambda_\alpha = 1$:

$$K' \equiv \sum_{\alpha, \lambda_\alpha \neq 1} \frac{\omega^{(\alpha)} \omega^{(\alpha)\dagger}}{\lambda_\alpha}. \tag{25}$$

Then $(1-K')^{-1}$ is singular free and is given by:

$$\left(\frac{1}{1-K'}\right)_{tt'} = \delta_{tt'} \delta(\boldsymbol{r} - \boldsymbol{r}_,) + \sum_{\alpha, \lambda_\alpha \neq 1} \frac{\omega_t^{(\alpha)}(\boldsymbol{r}') \omega_{t'}^{(\alpha)*}(\boldsymbol{r})}{\lambda_\alpha - 1}. \tag{26}$$

The solution of eq. (22) is then

$$\chi = \frac{1}{1-K'} U + \sum_\alpha C_\alpha \chi^{(\alpha)'}, \tag{27}$$

where C_α are arbitrary.

This degree of arbitrariness is a consequence of the existence of the supererogatory solutions. As we shall now show the $\chi^{(\alpha)'}$ are just the χ' alluded to in eq. (14), i.e.

$$\mathscr{A} \sum (\chi^{(\alpha)'}(\boldsymbol{r}_0))_t \phi_t(\boldsymbol{r}_1, \ldots, \boldsymbol{r}_A) = 0. \tag{28}$$

To prove this, we note that $\chi^{(\alpha)'}$ is a solution of eq. (23), $\lambda_\alpha = 1$

$$K \chi^{(\alpha)'} = \chi^{(\alpha)'}, \tag{29}$$

or, retracing our steps back to eq. (17):

$$\langle \phi_t(\boldsymbol{r}_1, \ldots, \boldsymbol{r}_A), \mathscr{A} \sum \chi_{t'}^{(\alpha)'}(\boldsymbol{r}_0) \phi_{t'}(\boldsymbol{r}_1, \ldots, \boldsymbol{r}_A) \rangle = 0$$

for all $\boldsymbol{r}_0$ and for $0 \leqslant t \leqslant N-1$. It immediately follows that

$$\langle \mathscr{A} \sum \chi_t^{(\alpha)'}(\boldsymbol{r}_0) \phi_t(\boldsymbol{r}_1, \ldots, \boldsymbol{r}_A), \mathscr{A} \sum \chi_{t'}^{(\alpha)'}(\boldsymbol{r}_0) \phi_{t'}(\boldsymbol{r}_1, \ldots, \boldsymbol{r}_A) \rangle = 0.$$

Eq. (28) follows from this result.

In a similar way we can show that

$$\langle \chi^{(\alpha)'}(\boldsymbol{r}_0), U(\boldsymbol{r}_0)\rangle = 0\,. \tag{30}$$

Inserting the definition of U, eq. (30) becomes

$$\langle \chi_t^{(\alpha)'}\phi_t, \Psi\rangle$$

which vanishes because of eq. (28).

To summarize, the functions χ' satisfying eq. (28) are given by the eigenvectors of K with eigenvalue 1. The vector χ which satisfies eq. (17) and eq. (22), which is orthogonal to $\chi^{(\alpha)'}$, is given by eq. (27) with $C_\alpha = 0$

$$\chi = \frac{1}{1-K'}U; \qquad \langle \chi^{(\alpha)'}, \chi\rangle = 0\,. \tag{31}$$

Finally we note that

$$P_N\Psi = \mathscr{A}\sum_t \chi_t\phi_t = \mathscr{A}\left[\sum_{t't}\left(\frac{1}{1-K'}\right)_{tt'} U_{t'}\right]\phi_t\,, \tag{32}$$

where we have used eq. (31). Note that eq. (32) holds for arbitrary values of C_α in eq. (27) as a consequence of eq. (28). Substituting for $U_{t'}$ from its defining eq. (15) we obtain

$$P_N = \mathscr{A}\left[\sum_{tt'}\phi_t\rangle\left(\frac{1}{1-K'}\right)_{tt'}\langle\phi_{t'}\right]. \tag{33}$$

$(1/(1-K'))_{tt'}$ is given explicitly in eq. (26). P_N projects out of an anti-symmetric Ψ all the dependence on ϕ_t, for all t between 0 and $N-1$. We can obtain the operator derived in ref. 2 for the one channel case by limiting the sum in eq. (33) to $t=t'=0$. Note that P_N, $\omega^{(\alpha)}$, $\chi^{(\alpha)'}$ are determined by the properties of the target nucleus and particularly by the properties of the N states of the target nucleus.

To complete the discussion we need to present the coupled equations satisfied by χ_t or U_t. Toward this end premultiply the Schroedinger equation

$$\mathscr{H}\Psi = E\Psi$$

by ϕ_t and integrate. We obtain

$$\langle \phi_t, \mathscr{H}\Psi\rangle = EU_t\,. \tag{34}$$

Let

$$\mathscr{H} = \mathscr{H}_t + T + V, \tag{35}$$

where $\mathscr{H}_t$ is the target Hamiltonian, T is the kinetic energy operator for the incident nucleon and V is the potential between the nucleon and those of the target nucleus. Eq. (34) becomes

$$[E - E_t]\, U_t = [TU_t + \langle \phi_t, V\Psi \rangle]. \tag{36}$$

If we now approximate Ψ by $P_N\Psi$, eq. (36) may be rewritten in several forms:

$$\text{when} \quad \Psi \to P_N\Psi$$

$$[E - E_t]\, U_t = TU_t + \left\langle \phi_t, V\mathscr{A} \sum_{t't''} \phi_{t'} \left(\frac{1}{1-K'}\right)_{t't''} U_{t''} \right\rangle \tag{37a}$$

or

$$[E - E_t][1 - K']\, \chi_t = T[1 - K']\, \chi_t + \langle \phi_t, V\mathscr{A} \sum_{t'} \chi_{t'} \phi_{t'} \rangle, \tag{37b}$$

or

$$E\Omega_t = \left\langle \phi_t \left(\frac{1}{\sqrt{1-K'}}\right), \mathscr{H}\mathscr{A} \sum \phi_{t'} \frac{1}{\sqrt{1-K'}}\, \Omega_{t'} \right\rangle, \tag{37c}$$

where

$$\Omega_t \equiv \left(\frac{1}{\sqrt{1-K'}}\right)_{tt'}, \qquad U_{t'} = (\sqrt{1-K'})_{tt'}\, \chi_{t'}. \tag{38}$$

We note that since the eigenvalues $(1/\lambda_\alpha)$ of K' are smaller than unity (for proof see ref. 17) the operator $(1-K')^{\frac{1}{2}}$ is hermitean. As a consequence, the effective Hamiltonian in eq. (37c) is hermitean, so that the solution of the coupled Schroedinger equations for Ω_t will not involve any false absorption or production. This must also be the case for the equation for U_t in which the effective Hamiltonian is not directly hermitean. The equation for U_t is, however, probably the most convenient of the three forms given in eq. (37) since it concentrates the effects of the identity of the particles in the effective coupling potential which is energy independent but non-local.

Eq. (37) is approximate only because we have replaced Ψ by $P_N\Psi$, i.e. we have truncated the coupled equations describing the scattering. The exact equation for $P_N\Psi$ is (see ref. 2)

$$\left[E - P_N\mathscr{H}P_N - P_N\mathscr{H}Q_N \frac{1}{E - Q_N\mathscr{H}Q_N}\right] Q_N\mathscr{H}P_N(P_N\Psi) = 0, \tag{39}$$

where

$$Q_N \equiv 1 - P_N \quad \text{and} \quad Q_N\Psi = \frac{1}{E - Q_N\mathscr{H}Q_N}\, Q_N\mathscr{H}P_N(P_N\Psi). \tag{40}$$

Eq. (37) is obtained by omitting the third term in the square bracket in eq. (39) which as eq. (40) demonstrates involves the coupling of $P_N\Psi$ with the rest of Ψ given by $Q_N\Psi$. By our particular choice of P_N, we have guaranteed that $Q_N\Psi$ will not make any contributions asymptotically ($r_t \to \infty$). By choosing the set $\{\phi_t\}$ properly so as to include important states such as the doorway states (18) which couple importantly with the entrance channel or with the exit channels, we reduce the contribution $Q_N\Psi$ can make within the interaction region. However, important effects may still remain. Much of the compound nucleus contribution, except for light nuclei, remains in $Q_N\Psi$. Possible improvements include replacing $Q_N\Psi$ by some appropriate average[18–20]). This introduces complex terms in the interaction, so that the coupled equations are those of a generalization of the single channel optical model. For further details see refs. 18 and 20.

3. Summary

Eq. (37) provides a formulation of the N coupled channel approximation to elastic and inelastic scattering which takes correctly into account effects which are a consequence of the identity of the incident and emergent nucleon with those forming the target nucleus. To include these effects within the coupled channel equations, it is necessary to invert operator $(1-K')$ which can be accomplished by determining the eigenvectors of K and their corresponding eigenvalues. The solution of this problem requires the solving of a set of N coupled equations, the operator K (see eq. (21)) depending only upon the properties of the target nuclear states involved in the description of the N channels. The solution of these equations as well as the properties of the K matrix for the case where the target nucleus states are expressed in terms of a general number of particle and hole levels in a self consistent Hartree–Fock potential are given in ref. 17. In this reference, cases in which the states consist of single Slater determinants or linear combinations of such determinants where the number of mixing configurations is N are discussed.

References

1) N. H. Mott and H. S. W. Massey, *The Theory of Atomic Collisions* (Oxford, 1949).
2) H. Feshbach, Ann. Phys. (N.Y.) **5**, 357 (1958); **19**, 287 (1962).
3) A. K. Kerman, in: *Lectures in Theoretical Physics* (University of Colorado Press, Boulder, Colorado, 1965).
4) M. H. Mittelman, in: *Advances in Theoretical Physics*, Vol. 1, Ed. K. A. Brueckner (Academic Press, New York, 1965).
5) F. Coester and H. Kummel, Nucl. Phys. **9**, 225 (1958).
6) R. Lipperhiede, Ann. Phys. (N.Y.) **17**, 114 (1962).

7) F. M. H. Villars, *On Nuclear Reactions*, unpublished (1964).
8) C. Bloch and V. Gillet, Phys. Letters **16**, 62 (1965); **18**, 58 (1965); H. A. Weidenmuller, Nucl. Phys. **75**, 189 (1966).
9) Y. Hahn, Phys. Rev. **142**, B 603 (1966).
10) F. S. Levin, Phys. Rev. **140**, B1099 (1965).
11) B. A. Lippmann, M. H. Mittelman and K. M. Watson, Phys. Rev. **116**, 920 (1959).
12) J. S. Bell and E. J. Squire, Phys. Rev. Letters **3**, 96 (1959).
13) G. M. Vagradov, Nucl. Phys. **49**, 44 (1963).
14) T. Teichman and E. P. Wigner, Phys. Rev. **87**, 123 (1952); A. N. Lane and R. G. Thomas, Rev. Mod. Phys. **30**, 257 (1958).
15) A. K. Kerman, private communication.
16) C. Bloch, Nucl. Phys. **4**, 503 (1957).
17) W. A. Friedman, to be published in Ann. Phys. (N.Y.).
18) H. Feshbach, A. K. Kerman, R. H. Lemmer, Ann. Phys. (N.Y.) **41**, 230 (1967).
19) A. de Toledo-Piza and A. K. Kerman, to be published in Ann. Phys. (N.Y.).
20) F. Iachello, to be published in Ann. Phys. (N.Y.).
21) W. M. MacDonald, Nucl. Phys. **56**, 636 (1964).

Spectroscopic and group theoretical methods in physics

ON THE APPLICATION OF THE GROUP Sp(4) OR R(5) TO NUCLEAR STRUCTURE

S. GOSHEN

Nuclear Research Center, Negev, P.O.B. 9001, Beer-Sheva, Israel

and

H. J. LIPKIN*

Palmer Physical Laboratory, Princeton University, Princeton, New Jersey, U.S.A.

1. Introduction

In the last years of his life, Professor Racah devoted much thought to the problem of finding the "missing quantum number" in several group theoretical classifications of physical interest. The work presented in this paper was stimulated by a series of seminars given by Professor Racah in Rehovoth, and combines his general approach with the use of Lie algebras constructed from bilinear products of second-quantized operators. Professor Racah followed this work closely and we learned much from discussions with him. We therefore think that it is particularly appropriate to include this paper in the present volume dedicated to his memory.

Symplectic groups arise naturally in the treatment of many particle systems when operators are used which change the number of particles in the system[1]). The simplest example is the usc of quasispin to describe pairing correlations in nuclei[2]) and in superconductors[3]), and of a non-compact "quasispin" to describe monopole excitations in the harmonic oscillator shell model[4]). That these quasispins are better described by the group Sp(2) rather than the rotation group R(3) is discussed in detail in ref. 1. In general the group Sp($2n$) can be used to describe pairing correlations in systems containing n different kinds of particles. A non-compact version of this group can be used to describe collective vibrational excitations of a system of particles moving in an n-dimensional harmonic oscillator potential.

* On leave of absence from the Weizmann Institute of Science, Rehovoth, Israel.

In this paper we consider the case $n=2$ and the group Sp(4). This is a 10 parameter group of rank 2 whose Lie algebra is isomorphic to that of the five-dimensional rotation group R(5). The non-compact version of Sp(4) relevant to the two-dimensional harmonic oscillator has a Lie algebra which is isomorphic to that of the non-compact version R(3, 2) of R(5). The compact group is suitable for classifying states of systems containing both neutrons and protons in a single shell in the *jj* coupling nuclear shell model[1,5,6]). The non-compact group is suitable for describing collective rotational and vibrational states of a system of particles moving in a two-dimensional harmonic oscillator potential. In both of the cases considered a particular SU(2) × U(1) subgroup of Sp(4) is of physical interest. For the compact case the SU(2) is the isospin group and the U(1) is the number of particles. For the non-compact case the SU(2) is the invariance group of the harmonic oscillator Hamiltonian. This SU(2) group is the two-dimensional version of the SU(3) group used by Elliott[7]) for the classification of states exhibiting collective rotations. We shall call this the Elliott quasispin. The U(1) is the number of oscillator quanta.

If the Lie algebra of Sp(4) is interpreted as being that of R(5), the relevant SU(2) subgroup corresponds to a subgroup R(3) of R(5) describing rotations in a three-dimensional subspace of the five-dimensional space, and the U(1) is the R(2) in the remaining two dimensions. In the non-compact version R(3, 2) the subgroup is the maximal compact subgroup R(3) × R(2). A desirable classification of states for these problems would be one in which the Casimir operator of this SU(2) subgroup and the U(1) generator should be diagonal. The states should be eigenfunctions of the total isospin and number of particles for the compact case and of the total Elliott quasispin and the oscillator Hamiltonian for the non-compact case.

The classification of the representations of the group R(5) according to the chain R(5) ⊃ R(3) × R(2) encounters a serious difficulty. There is one quantum number needed for a complete specification of the states within a given representation which cannot be defined in any simple way. It has been pointed out by Racah[8]) that one cannot define this quantum number by means of a simple operator having rational eigenvalues. Any operator constructed from products of generators of the group which can fulfill the role of defining the desired additional quantum number will have eigenvalues determined by diagonalization of a matrix whose size is determined by the number of relevant states.

The same problem exists in the conventional classification of seniority in *jj* coupling using symplectic groups of transformations which do not change the number of particles [9]). For this case, Goldberg and Racah [10]) have proposed the use of an additional quantum number describing the number of four particle clusters having both zero angular momentum and zero isospin, by analogy with the seniority quantum number which is related to the classification of particles into pairs of zero angular momentum. However, the number of four particle clusters in a state is not determined in a simple way by the use of a single operator. There is no operator analogous to the Casimir operator of the symplectic group used in defining seniority [9]). Rather one must define a whole hierarchy of operators $(A_1, A_2, \ldots, A_n)$ having the property that any state containing less than n four particle clusters is an eigenfunction of A_n with the eigenvalue zero. The states having n or more four particle clusters are not simply described using this particular operator and the non-zero eigenvalues of the operator are probably not rational.

The eigenstates of the new quantum number are defined by using those eigenfunctions corresponding to zero eigenvalues of certain members of the set of operators. The state which is a simultaneous eigenfunction with zero eigenvalue of all the operators $(A_1, \ldots, A_n)$ contains no four particle clusters of this type and is defined to have the eigenvalue zero for this new quantum number. The states having zero eigenvalues for all the operators except A_1 are generally mixtures of states having two eigenvalues of the new quantum number, namely zero and one. The states corresponding to the eigenvalue 1 are obtained by orthogonalization with respect to the states already defined for the eigenvalue zero. In general the states containing n four particle clusters and classified with the eigenvalue n of the new quantum number are obtained by finding those states which are simultaneous eigenfunctions with zero eigenvalue of all the operators A_m for which $m > n$ and which are orthogonal to all states having lower values of the new quantum number. Using this definition of states it is possible to construct a representation and obtain matrix elements of the operators of the group. In this work we follow the Racah procedure in defining a hierarchy of operators related to the number of four particle clusters in the system to define the additional quantum number.

After the completion of this work, the authors received a paper [13]) by Professor Hecht where ways of defining the additional quantum number are discussed and criticized. That paper [13]) is dealing with the compact case and it contains some of our results for that case.

2. The compact case: the seniority scheme

Consider a single shell in the jj coupling shell model which is being filled by both protons and neutrons. Let $a^{\dagger}_{\mathrm{p},m}$ and $a^{\dagger}_{\mathrm{n},m}$ be the creation operators for a proton and a neutron respectively in a state of total angular momentum j with projection m on the z-axis, while $a_{\mathrm{p},m}$ and $a_{\mathrm{n},m}$ are the corresponding annihilation operators. The index j is suppressed as it is the same for all states in a single shell. The operators satisfy the following anti-commutation relations:

$$a_{\tau m}a_{\tau' m'} + a_{\tau' m'}a_{\tau m} = 0\,, \tag{1a}$$

$$a^{\dagger}_{\tau m}a^{\dagger}_{\tau' m'} + a^{\dagger}_{\tau' m'}a^{\dagger}_{\tau m} = 0\,, \tag{1b}$$

$$a_{\tau m}a^{\dagger}_{\tau' m'} + a^{\dagger}_{\tau' m'}a_{\tau m} = \delta(\tau, \tau')\,\delta(m, m')\,, \tag{1c}$$

where τ may be p or n.

It is sometimes convenient to define the tensor operators

$$(b_{\tau})_m = a^{\dagger}_{\tau m}\,, \tag{2a}$$

$$(b^{\dagger}_{\tau})_m = (-)^{j-m}a_{\tau -m}\,. \tag{2b}$$

The operators (b_{p}), $(b^{\dagger}_{\mathrm{p}})$, (b_{n}) and $(b^{\dagger}_{\mathrm{n}})$ can be regarded as four irreducible tensors of degree j with respect to the total angular momentum operator $\boldsymbol{J}$. By forming all possible scalar products between these tensors, ten operators are obtained which commute with the total angular momentum $\boldsymbol{J}$, and which satisfy the commutation relations of the R(5) algebra among themselves. These operators can be used in order to construct quantum numbers for the classification of different shell model states having the same total angular momentum J.

The generators of R(5) can be defined as follows[1]):

$$\tau_{+} = \frac{-1}{\sqrt{2}}\sum_{m} a^{\dagger}_{\mathrm{p}m}a_{\mathrm{n}m}\,, \tag{3a}$$

$$\tau_{0} = \frac{1}{2}\sum_{m} (a^{\dagger}_{\mathrm{p}m}a_{\mathrm{p}m} - a^{\dagger}_{\mathrm{n}m}a_{\mathrm{n}m})\,, \tag{3b}$$

$$\tau_{-} = \frac{1}{\sqrt{2}}\sum_{m} a^{\dagger}_{\mathrm{n}m}a_{\mathrm{p}m}\,, \tag{3c}$$

$$N_{0} = \frac{1}{2}\sum_{m} (a^{\dagger}_{\mathrm{p}m}a_{\mathrm{p}m} - a_{\mathrm{n}m}a^{\dagger}_{\mathrm{n}m}) = \frac{1}{2}\sum_{m} (a^{\dagger}_{\mathrm{p}m}a_{\mathrm{p}m} + a^{\dagger}_{\mathrm{n}m}a_{\mathrm{n}m}) - \frac{2j+1}{2}\,, \tag{3d}$$

$$A_{\mathrm{c}+} = \sum_{m>0} (-)^{j-m}a^{\dagger}_{\mathrm{p}m}a^{\dagger}_{\mathrm{p}-m}\,, \tag{3e}$$

$$A_{c0} = \frac{1}{\sqrt{2}} \sum_m (-)^{j-m} a^\dagger_{pm} a^\dagger_{n-m}, \tag{3f}$$

$$A_{c-} = \sum_{m>0} (-)^{j-m} a^\dagger_{nm} a^\dagger_{n-m}, \tag{3g}$$

$$A_{d+} = - \sum_{m>0} (-)^{j-m} a_{n-m} a_{nm}, \tag{3h}$$

$$A_{d0} = \frac{1}{\sqrt{2}} \sum_m (-)^{j-m} a_{n-m} a_{pm}, \tag{3i}$$

$$A_{d-} = - \sum_{m>0} (-)^{j-m} a_{p-m} a_{pm}. \tag{3j}$$

They satisfy the following commutation relations:

$$\begin{aligned}
&[N_0, \tau_i] = 0, \qquad [N_0, A_{ci}] = A_{ci}, \qquad [N_0, A_{di}] = -A_{di}, \\
&[\tau_i, \tau_k] = -\sqrt{2}(11\, ik|111\,(i+k))\, \tau_{(i+k)}, \\
&[\tau_i, A_{ck}] = -\sqrt{2}(11\, ik|111\,(i+k))\, A_{c(i+k)}, \\
&[\tau_i, A_{dk}] = -\sqrt{2}(11\, ik|111\,(i+k))\, A_{d(i+k)}, \\
&[A_{ci}, A_{dk}] = -\sqrt{3}(11\, ik|11\,00)\, N_0 - \sqrt{2}(11\, ik|111\,(i+k))\, \tau_{(i+k)}, \\
&[A_{ci}, A_{ck}] = 0, \qquad [A_{di}, A_{dk}] = 0,
\end{aligned} \tag{4}$$

where $(11\, ik|11\,00)$ and $(11\, ik|111\,(i+k))$ are Clebsch–Gordan coefficients, $i=+1$ when referring to an operator with index $+$ and $i=-1$ when referring to an operator with index $-$. Eqs. (4) are the commutation relations of the generators of the five-dimensional rotation group R(5). The operator N_0 represents half the number of particles counted from the center of the shell; i.e. the total number of particles in the shell is $2j+1+2N$. The τ_i are isospin components and satisfy commutation relations of angular momentum operators. N_0 is a scalar, while $\boldsymbol{A}_c$ and $\boldsymbol{A}_d$ satisfy commutation relations of vectors with respect to $\boldsymbol{\tau}$.

We choose a scheme in which $\boldsymbol{\tau}^2$, τ_0 and N_0 are diagonal, and $T(T+1)$, M_T and N are the corresponding eigenvalues. Using the Wigner–Eckart theorem we obtain the following expression for the matrix elements:

$$\langle \alpha\, T M_T | A_i | \alpha'\, T'\, M'_T \rangle = (-)^{T-M_T} \begin{pmatrix} T & 1 & T' \\ -M_T & i & M'_T \end{pmatrix} (\alpha\, T \| A \| \alpha'\, T'), \tag{5}$$

where A is either A_c or A_d, α represents the additional quantum numbers needed for a complete classification of the eigenstates,

$$\begin{pmatrix} T & 1 & T' \\ -M_T & i & M'_T \end{pmatrix}$$

is the symmetric Wigner coefficient and $(\alpha\, T\|A\|\alpha'\, T')$ is the reduced matrix element.

From the commutation relations (4) of N_0 with A it is seen that A_{ci} and A_{di} are operators which raise and lower respectively the eigenvalue of N_0 by unity. Thus the only non-vanishing matrix elements of A are $\langle\alpha\, N+1|A_{ci}|\alpha'\, N\rangle$ and $\langle\alpha\, N-1|A_{di}|\alpha'\, N\rangle$. Since A_d is the hermitean conjugate of A_c,

$$(\alpha\, N+1\, T\|A_c\|\alpha'\, N\, T') = (-)^{T-T'}\,\overline{(\alpha'\, N\, T'\|A_d\|\alpha\, N+1\, T)}. \tag{6}$$

The five-dimensional rotation group is B_2 (fig. 1) according to Cartan's classification. Therefore, each representation is specified by two numbers, and there exist two operators which commute with every operator of the group. The first is the operator of Casimir:

$$2A_d\cdot A_c + \tau^2 + N_0^2 + 3N_0, \tag{7a}$$

while the second is,

$$\begin{aligned}2(\tau\cdot A_d)(\tau\cdot A_c) + 2iN_0(\tau\cdot A_d\times A_c) + (A_d\cdot A_c)^2 - A_d^2A_c^2 + N_0^2\tau^2 + \\ + 3i(\tau\cdot A_d\times A_c) + N_0A_d\cdot A_c + 3N_0\tau^2 - \tfrac{1}{2}N_0^2 + \tfrac{3}{2}\tau^2 - \tfrac{3}{2}N_0.\end{aligned} \tag{7b}$$

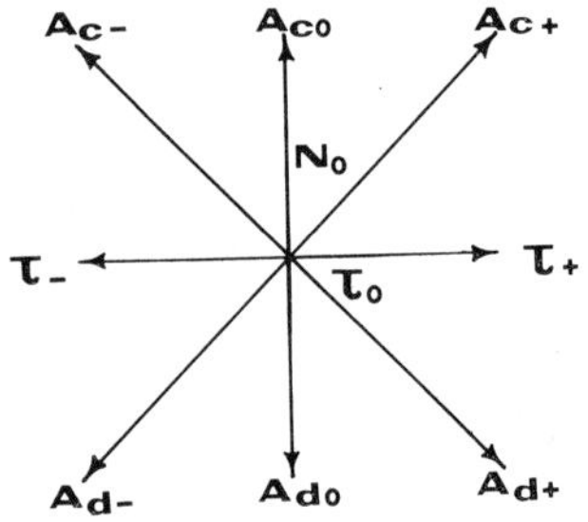

Fig. 1. Vector diagram of B_2.

Let w be the largest eigenvalue of N_0 present in the representation, and t the isospin of a state corresponding to this eigenvalue. The operators (7a) and (7b) can be expressed in terms of w and t as follows:

$$w(w+3) + t(t+1), \tag{8a}$$

$$(w^2 + 3w + \tfrac{3}{2})\, t(t+1) - \tfrac{1}{2}w(w+3). \tag{8b}$$

It is convenient to specify the representations by the numbers w and t. The number w is related to the seniority v by the formula:

$$v = 2j + 1 - 2w. \tag{9}$$

The number t is Flowers' reduced isospin. Since B_2 is a group of rank 2 with 10 parameters, two quantum numbers are needed[11]), in addition to N and M_t, for a complete classification of the states in a given representation. Hecht[6]) has defined them in a way very appropriate for numerical calculations. It is seen from the vector diagram of B_2 (fig. 1) that the lines $A_{d+} \leftrightarrow A_{c-}$ and $A_{c+} \leftrightarrow A_{d-}$ commute. Therefore every representation can be described as a sum of direct products of the "spins" defined by these lines. Let us define:

$$K_+ = \frac{1}{\sqrt{2}} A_{c+}, \tag{10a}$$

$$K_0 = \tfrac{1}{2}(N_0 + \tau_0), \tag{10b}$$

$$K_- = \frac{1}{\sqrt{2}} A_{d-}, \tag{10c}$$

$$\Lambda_+ = \frac{1}{\sqrt{2}} A_{c-}, \tag{10d}$$

$$\Lambda_0 = \tfrac{1}{2}(N_0 - \tau_0), \tag{10e}$$

$$\Lambda_- = \frac{1}{\sqrt{2}} A_{d+}. \tag{10f}$$

The two spins $\boldsymbol{K}$ and $\boldsymbol{\Lambda}$ commute with one another. The components of $\boldsymbol{K}$ and $\boldsymbol{\Lambda}$ each satisfy the angular momentum commutation relations among themselves. Hecht[6]) used $\boldsymbol{K}^2$, $\boldsymbol{\Lambda}^2$, K_0 and Λ_0 with the eigenvalues $K(K+1)$, $\Lambda(\Lambda+1)$, M_k and M_Λ in order to classify the states in a given representation. K and Λ were the two additional quantum numbers needed for a complete classification, while the representations themselves were specified by two quantum numbers, K_m and Λ_m. These are related to w and t by:

$$K_m = \tfrac{1}{2}(w + t), \tag{11a}$$

$$\Lambda_m = \tfrac{1}{2}(w - t). \tag{11b}$$

According to Hecht the quantum numbers take the following values:

$$K = K_m - \tfrac{1}{2}n - \tfrac{1}{2}m, \qquad 0 \leqslant n \leqslant 2(K_m - \Lambda_m), \tag{12a}$$

$$\Lambda = \Lambda_m + \tfrac{1}{2}n - \tfrac{1}{2}m, \qquad 0 \leqslant m \leqslant 2\Lambda_m, \tag{12b}$$

$$M_K = K - x, \qquad 0 \leqslant x \leqslant 2K, \tag{12c}$$

$$M_\Lambda = \Lambda - y, \qquad 0 \leqslant y \leqslant 2\Lambda. \tag{12d}$$

Using (11) we can derive a more symmetrical form of (12):

$$K = \tfrac{1}{2}w - \tfrac{1}{2}n - \tfrac{1}{2}m\,, \qquad -t \leqslant n \leqslant +t\,, \tag{13a}$$

$$\Lambda = \tfrac{1}{2}w + \tfrac{1}{2}n - \tfrac{1}{2}m\,, \qquad 0 \leqslant m \leqslant w - t\,, \tag{13b}$$

$$M_K = -K, -K+1, \ldots, +K\,, \tag{13c}$$

$$M_\Lambda = -\Lambda, -\Lambda+1, \ldots, +\Lambda\,. \tag{13d}$$

In Hecht's scheme protons and neutrons were treated separately with $\boldsymbol{K}$ operating on protons and $\boldsymbol{\Lambda}$ on neutrons. Thus the isospin was not a good quantum number in this scheme. The scheme suggested at the beginning of the present section, where N_0, $\boldsymbol{\tau}^2$, τ_0 are diagonal, is more appropriate for nuclear spectroscopic calculations because both the isospin and the number of particles emerge as good quantum numbers. Unfortunately, we have in this scheme only one quantum number, T, instead of the two needed for a complete classification of the states. In section 6 a possible additional quantum number is defined.

As an example of passage from one scheme to the other, let us examine the representation $w=3$, $t=1$; i.e. $K_m=2$, $\Lambda_m=1$. The states in Hecht's scheme can be plotted in a diagram of K vs. Λ, fig. 2. Every dot represents

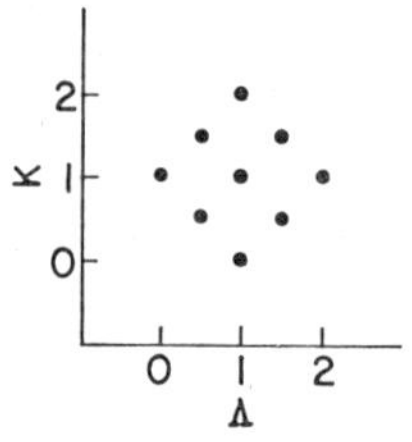

Fig. 2. (Λ, K) diagram; $w=3$, $t=1$.

the $(2K+1)(2\Lambda+1)$ states defined by $M_k=-K, -K+1, \ldots, +K$, and $M_\Lambda=-\Lambda, -\Lambda+1, \ldots, +\Lambda$. From this an (M_K, M_Λ) diagram can be obtained (fig. 3) where every line represents a single state. Using the relations:

$$N = M_K + M_\Lambda\,, \qquad M_T = M_K - M_\Lambda\,,$$

an (N, M_T) diagram is obtained (fig. 4), from which an (N, T) diagram (fig. 5) can be further derived. In this diagram every dot represents $(2T+1)$ states: $M=-T, -T+1, \ldots, +T$. The states with $(N, T)=(-1, 0)$, $(0, 2)$ and $(1, 0)$ are seen to be doubly degenerate and not completely classified by the quantum numbers N, T and M_T.

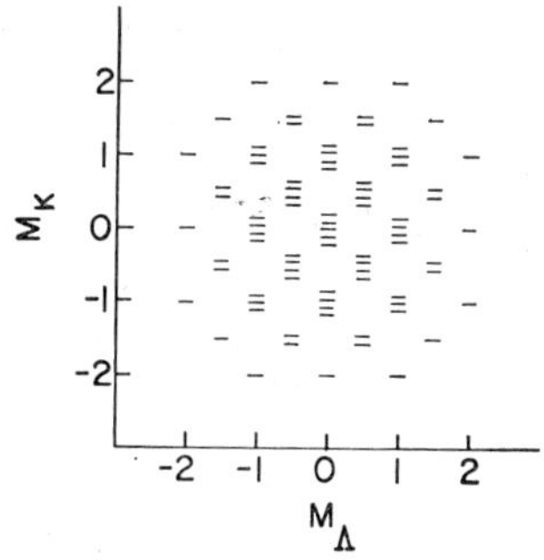

Fig. 3. (M_K, M_Λ) diagram; $w=3$, $t=1$.

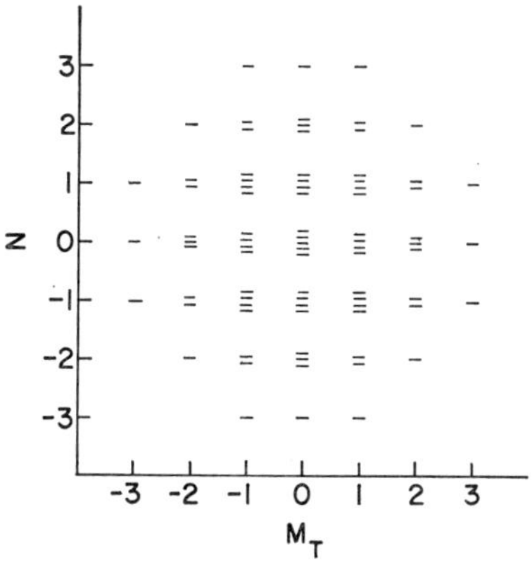

Fig. 4. (N, M_T) diagram; $w=3$, $t=1$.

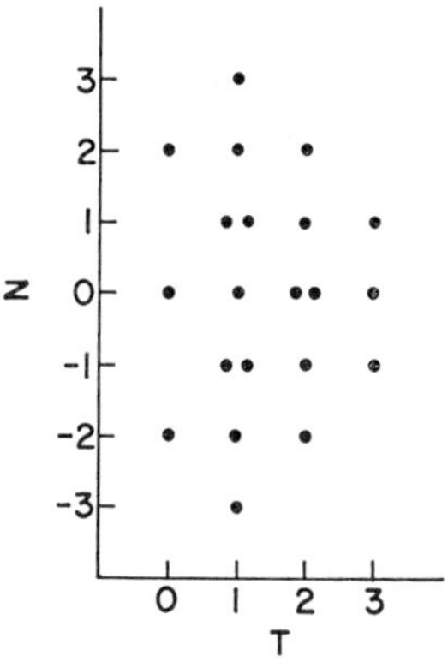

Fig. 5. (N, T) diagram; $w=3$, $t=1$.

3. The non-compact case: the two-dimensional isotropic harmonic oscillator

Consider A particles moving in a two-dimensional isotropic harmonic oscillator potential. Let $x_\mu, y_\mu, p_{x\mu}$ and $p_{y\mu}$ be the Cartesian coordinates and momenta of the μth particle. The Hamiltonian is:

$$H = \frac{1}{2m}\sum_\mu (p_{x\mu}^2 + p_{y\mu}^2) + \frac{m\omega^2}{2}\sum_\mu (x_\mu^2 + y_\mu^2), \tag{15}$$

where m is the mass of a particle and ω the angular frequency. At this stage we do not assume any particular statistics for the particles. The implications of our classification on statistics are discussed below. Let us define the Cartesian creation and annihilation operators of the oscillator system:

$$a_{x\mu}^\dagger = \sqrt{\frac{m\omega}{2\hbar}}\, x_\mu - \frac{\mathrm{i}}{\sqrt{2m\omega\hbar}}\, p_{x\mu}, \tag{16a}$$

$$a_{y\mu}^\dagger = \sqrt{\frac{m\omega}{2\hbar}}\, y_\mu - \frac{\mathrm{i}}{\sqrt{2m\omega\hbar}}\, p_{y\mu}, \tag{16b}$$

$$a_{x\mu} = \sqrt{\frac{m\omega}{2\hbar}}\, x_\mu + \frac{\mathrm{i}}{\sqrt{2m\omega\hbar}}\, p_{x\mu}, \tag{16c}$$

$$a_{y\mu} = \sqrt{\frac{m\omega}{2\hbar}}\, y_\mu + \frac{\mathrm{i}}{\sqrt{2m\omega\hbar}}\, p_{y\mu}. \tag{16d}$$

The polar creation and annihilation operators are

$$a_{\pm\mu}^\dagger = \frac{a_{x\mu}^\dagger \pm \mathrm{i} a_{y\mu}^\dagger}{\sqrt{2}}, \tag{17a}$$

$$a_{\pm\mu} = \frac{a_{x\mu} \mp \mathrm{i} a_{y\mu}}{\sqrt{2}}. \tag{17b}$$

These operators satisfy the commutation relations:

$$[a_{\tau\mu}^\dagger, a_{\tau'\mu'}^\dagger] = 0, \tag{18a}$$

$$[a_{\tau\mu}, a_{\tau'\mu'}] = 0, \tag{18b}$$

$$[a_{\tau\mu}, a_{\tau'\mu'}^\dagger] = \delta(\tau, \tau')\,\delta(\mu, \mu'), \tag{18c}$$

where τ is $+$ or $-$.

We define the following ten operators analogous to those of the seniority scheme[1]):

$$\lambda_+ = \frac{-1}{\sqrt{2}} \sum_\mu a^\dagger_{+\mu} a_{-\mu}, \tag{19a}$$

$$\lambda_0 = \frac{1}{2} \sum_\mu (a^\dagger_{+\mu} a_{+\mu} - a^\dagger_{-\mu} a_{-\mu}), \tag{19b}$$

$$\lambda_- = \frac{1}{\sqrt{2}} \sum_\mu a_{+\mu} a^\dagger_{-\mu}, \tag{19c}$$

$$N_0 = -\frac{1}{2} \sum_\mu (a^\dagger_{+\mu} a_{+\mu} + a_{-\mu} a^\dagger_{-\mu}), \tag{19d}$$

$$A_{c+} = \frac{1}{2} \sum_\mu a^{\dagger 2}_{+\mu}, \tag{19e}$$

$$A_{c0} = \frac{1}{\sqrt{2}} \sum_\mu a^\dagger_{+\mu} a^\dagger_{-\mu}, \tag{19f}$$

$$A_{c-} = \frac{1}{2} \sum_\mu a^{\dagger 2}_{-\mu}, \tag{19g}$$

$$A_{d+} = -\frac{1}{2} \sum_\mu a^2_{-\mu}, \tag{19h}$$

$$A_{d0} = \frac{1}{\sqrt{2}} \sum_\mu a_{+\mu} a_{-\mu}, \tag{19i}$$

$$A_{d-} = -\frac{1}{2} \sum_\mu a^2_{+\mu}. \tag{19j}$$

The operators of the harmonic oscillator are symmetric with respect to permutations of particles. Therefore, all states of the same representation obey the same statistics. If a state belonging to some particular representation is allowed for a dynamical system, then all states of this representation are also allowed.

The operators (19) satisfy the commutation relations:

$$
\begin{aligned}
&[N_0, \lambda_i] = 0, \qquad [N_0, A_{ci}] = A_{ci}, \qquad [N_0, A_{di}] = -A_{di}, \\
&[\lambda_i, \lambda_k] = -\sqrt{2}(11\, ik|111\,(i+k))\, \lambda_{(i+k)}, \\
&[\lambda_i, A_{ck}] = -\sqrt{2}(11\, ik|111\,(i+k))\, A_{c(i+k)}, \\
&[\lambda_i, A_{dk}] = -\sqrt{2}(11\, ik|111\,(i+k))\, A_{d(i+k)}, \\
&[A_{ci}, A_{dk}] = \sqrt{3}(11\, ik|11\,00)\, N_0 + \sqrt{2}(11\, ik|111\,(i+k))\, \lambda_{(i+k)}, \\
&[A_{ci}, A_{ck}] = 0, \qquad [A_{di}, A_{dk}] = 0,
\end{aligned} \tag{20}
$$

where $(11\,ik|111(i+k))$ and $(11\,ik|11\,00)$ are Clebsch–Gordan coefficients. Here, as before, $i = \pm 1$ refers to an operator with index $\pm$. The physical meaning of the set of operators is evident. N_0 is proportional to the Hamiltonian,

$$N_0 = \frac{1}{2\hbar\omega} H. \tag{21}$$

The λ_i are the three constants of motion. They generate the SU(2) quasispin group. The ten operators generate the group R(3, 2). This is a non-compact group and its unitary representations are infinite, but the formulae and the problems of classification are very similar to those of the compact R(5). The two operators which commute with every operator of the group are:

$$2\boldsymbol{A}_c \cdot \boldsymbol{A}_d + 3N_0 - N_0^2 - \boldsymbol{\lambda}^2, \tag{22a}$$

$$
\begin{aligned}
&2(\boldsymbol{\lambda}\cdot\boldsymbol{A}_c)(\boldsymbol{\lambda}\cdot\boldsymbol{A}_d) - 2\mathrm{i}N_0(\boldsymbol{\lambda}\cdot\boldsymbol{A}_c \times \boldsymbol{A}_d) + \boldsymbol{A}_c^2\boldsymbol{A}_d^2 + (\boldsymbol{A}_c\cdot\boldsymbol{A}_d)^2 - N_0^2\boldsymbol{\lambda}^2 + \\
&\quad - N_0\boldsymbol{A}_c\cdot\boldsymbol{A}_d + 3\mathrm{i}(\boldsymbol{\lambda}\cdot\boldsymbol{A}_c \times \boldsymbol{A}_d) + 3N_0\boldsymbol{\lambda}^2 - \tfrac{3}{2}\boldsymbol{\lambda}^2 + \tfrac{1}{2}N_0^2 - \tfrac{3}{2}N_0.
\end{aligned} \tag{22b}
$$

These formulae are analogous to formulae (7) for the compact case. In a scheme where $\boldsymbol{\lambda}^2$, λ_0 and N_0 are diagonal with eigenvalues $L(L+1)$, M_L and N respectively; the formulae (5) and (6) remain valid if L is substituted for T. In every representation there exists a minimum value of N which we denote by w. We also denote by l the corresponding L. The representation contains an infinite spectrum of N-values, with several values of L corresponding to each N of the spectrum. The operators (22) can be written as a function of w and l in the form:

$$3w - w^2 - l(l+1) \tag{23a}$$

and

$$(-w^2 + 3w - \tfrac{3}{2})\, l(l+1) + \tfrac{1}{2}w(w-3). \tag{23b}$$

Thus w and l completely specify the representation. Again, a scheme most appropriate for calculations is obtained by defining:

$$K_+ = \frac{1}{\sqrt{2}} A_{c+}, \tag{24a}$$

$$K_0 = \tfrac{1}{2}(N_0 + \lambda_0), \tag{24b}$$

$$K_- = \frac{1}{\sqrt{2}} A_{d-}, \tag{24c}$$

$$\Lambda_+ = \frac{1}{\sqrt{2}} A_{c-}, \tag{24d}$$

$$\Lambda_0 = \tfrac{1}{2}(N_0 - \lambda_0), \tag{24e}$$

$$\Lambda_- = \frac{1}{\sqrt{2}} A_{d+}. \tag{24f}$$

$\boldsymbol{K}$ and $\boldsymbol{\Lambda}$ commute. The components of $\boldsymbol{K}$ and $\boldsymbol{\Lambda}$ each satisfy the commutation relations of the non-compact group $R(2, 1)$

$$\begin{aligned} [K_0, K_+] &= K_+, & [\Lambda_0, \Lambda_+] &= \Lambda_+, \\ [K_0, K_-] &= -K_-, & [\Lambda_0, \Lambda_-] &= -\Lambda_-, \\ [K_+, K_-] &= K_0, & [\Lambda_+, \Lambda_-] &= \Lambda_0. \end{aligned} \tag{25}$$

The Casimir operators for the two R(2, 1) groups are:

$$K_+ K_- + K_0^2 + K_- K_+, \tag{26a}$$

and

$$\Lambda_+ \Lambda_- + \Lambda_0^2 + \Lambda \Lambda_+. \tag{26b}$$

The eigenvalues of these operators are denoted by $K(K-1)$ and $\Lambda(\Lambda-1)$ respectively. Let us define M_K and M_Λ as the eigenvalues of K_0 and Λ_0. Then [4])

$$M_K = K, K+1, K+2, \ldots, \qquad M_\Lambda = \Lambda, \Lambda+1, \Lambda+2, \ldots. \tag{27}$$

Thus we obtain in the non-compact case thc following equivalent of Hecht's classification:

$$K = \tfrac{1}{2}w - \tfrac{1}{2}n + \tfrac{1}{2}m, \qquad -l \leqslant n \leqslant +l, \tag{28a}$$

$$\Lambda = \tfrac{1}{2}w + \tfrac{1}{2}n + \tfrac{1}{2}m, \qquad 0 \leqslant m \leqslant +\infty, \tag{28b}$$

$$M_K = K, K+1, K+2, \ldots, \tag{28c}$$

$$M_\Lambda = \Lambda, \Lambda+1, \Lambda+2, \ldots. \tag{28d}$$

As an example, let us examine Hecht's classification for $w=3$, $l=1$ (fig. 6). Each dot stands for an infinite number of states given by (27). The arrows symbolize that the representation continues to infinity in the specified direction. From this an (M_K, M_Λ) diagram can be obtained. Using the relations

$$N = M_K + N_\Lambda \tag{29a}$$

$$M_L = M_K - M_\Lambda \tag{29b}$$

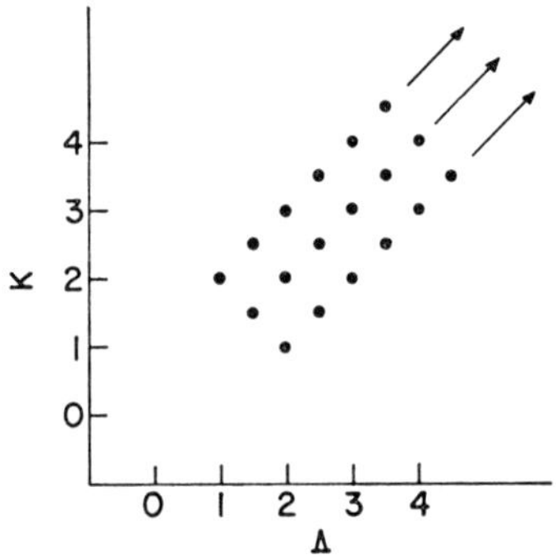

Fig. 6. (K, Λ) diagram; $w=3$, $l=1$.

one can pass to an (N, M_L) diagram, and further obtain the (N, L) diagram (fig. 7). It can be seen that degeneracies exist for some states of this representation, e.g. $(N, L)=(5, 1), (6, 2), (7, 1), \ldots$, and an additional quantum number is needed for a complete classification.

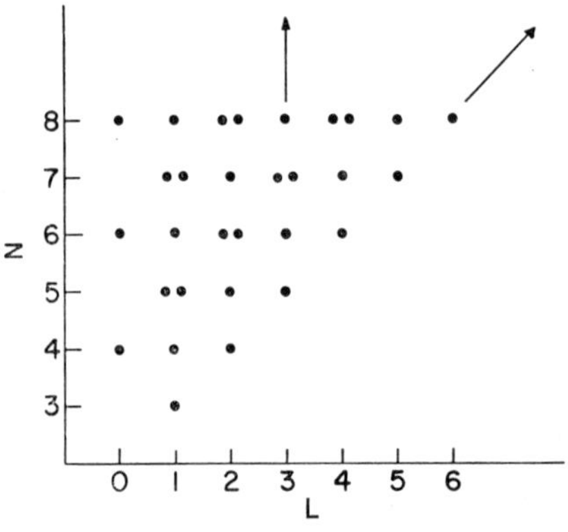

Fig. 7. (N, L) diagram; $w=3$, $l=1$.

4. The simplest representations of the non-compact case and their physical meaning

The physical meaning of the scheme discussed above is illustrated by examination of the simplest representations. We begin with the non-compact case in which the simplest representations are most easily defined by describing the motion of a single particle, i.e. a single two-dimensional harmonic oscillator. In this case the summations over μ appearing in formula (19) reduce to single terms, and the following relations hold:

$$\boldsymbol{\lambda}^2 = N_0^2 - \tfrac{1}{4}, \tag{30a}$$

$$\boldsymbol{A}_c^2 = \boldsymbol{A}_d^2 = 0, \tag{30b}$$

$$\boldsymbol{\lambda} \cdot \boldsymbol{A}_c = \boldsymbol{\lambda} \cdot \boldsymbol{A}_d = 0, \tag{30c}$$

$$\boldsymbol{A}_c \cdot \boldsymbol{A}_d = N_0^2 - \tfrac{3}{2}N_0 + \tfrac{1}{2} = (N_0 - 1)(N_0 - \tfrac{1}{2}), \tag{30d}$$

$$\boldsymbol{A}_d \cdot \boldsymbol{A}_c = N_0^2 + \tfrac{3}{2}N_0 + \tfrac{1}{2} = (N_0 + 1)(N_0 + \tfrac{1}{2}), \tag{30e}$$

$$\boldsymbol{A}_c \times \boldsymbol{A}_d = \mathrm{i}N_0\boldsymbol{\lambda} - \mathrm{i}\boldsymbol{\lambda}, \tag{30f}$$

$$\boldsymbol{\lambda} \cdot \boldsymbol{A}_c \times \boldsymbol{A}_d = \mathrm{i}N_0\boldsymbol{\lambda}^2 - \mathrm{i}\boldsymbol{\lambda}^2 = \mathrm{i}(N_0 - 1)(N_0^2 - \tfrac{1}{4}). \tag{30g}$$

Using the first of the relations (30) we obtain:

$$L(L+1) = N^2 - \tfrac{1}{4}, \tag{31}$$

or

$$L = N - \tfrac{1}{2}. \tag{32}$$

Formulae (22) define operators which commute with every operator of the group. Substituting (30) in the formulae (22) we obtain for the first operator: $\frac{5}{4}$, and for the second: $-\frac{5}{8}$. Substituting these values for the functions (23) we obtain the following two solutions for the w and l:

$$w = \tfrac{1}{2}, \qquad l = 0; \tag{33a}$$

$$w = 1, \qquad l = \tfrac{1}{2}. \tag{33b}$$

The states of the representation $w = \frac{1}{2}$, $l = 0$ are classified in figs. 8 and 9. Fig. 8 is an (N, L) diagram while fig. 9 gives (N, M_L). Figs. 10 and 11 show the same diagrams for the representation $w = 1$, $l = \frac{1}{2}$.

The validity of formula (32) is demonstrated in figs. 8 and 10. Since M_L is half the angular momentum and N is proportional to the energy, examination of figs. 9 and 11 shows that degenerate states have either odd or even angular momentum. This is well known from calculations of oscillator wavefunctions in polar coordinates.

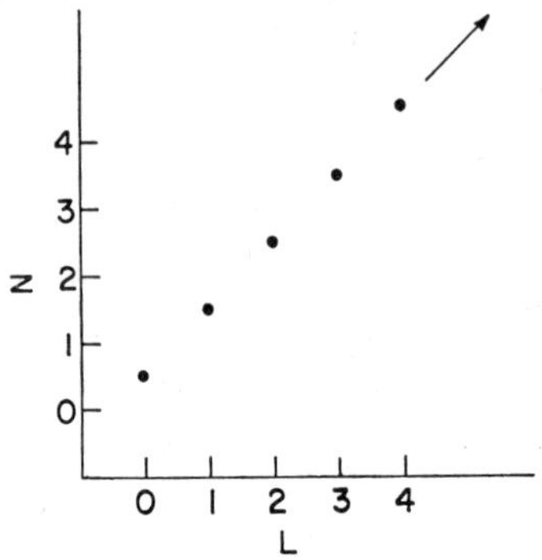

Fig. 8. (N, L) diagram; $w=\frac{1}{2}$, $l=0$.

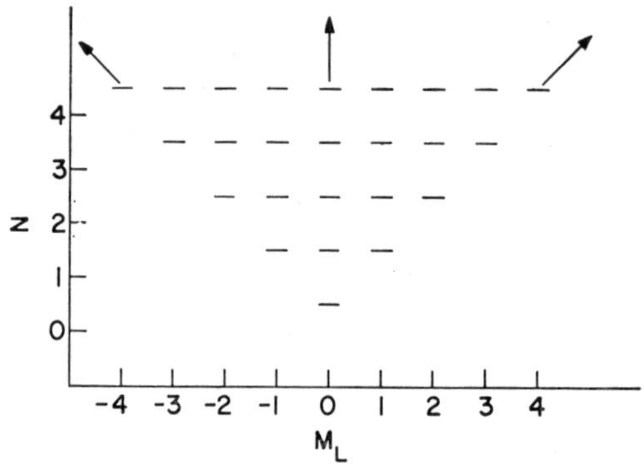

Fig. 9. (N, M_L) diagram; $w=\frac{1}{2}$, $l=0$.

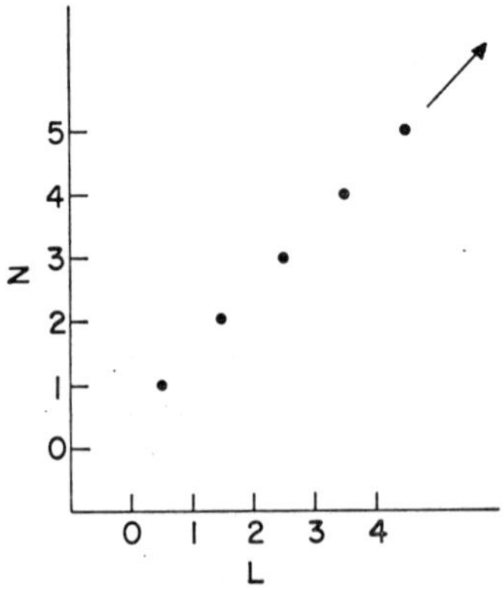

Fig. 10. (N, L) diagram; $w=1$, $l=\frac{1}{2}$.

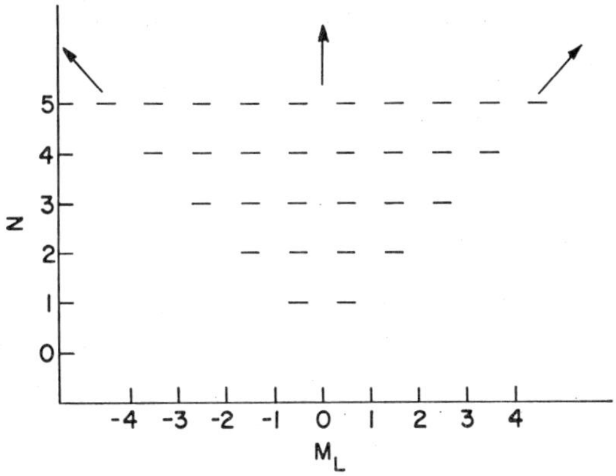

Fig. 11. (N, M_L) diagram; $w=1, l=\frac{1}{2}$.

5. The simplest representations of the compact case and their physical meaning

Consider the operators $\boldsymbol{\tau}$ and N_0 with the summations in (3) reduced to single terms. This case does not lead to any representation appearing in the nuclear shell model, where $j=\frac{1}{2}$ in the lowest shell and the summations defining N_0 and $\boldsymbol{\tau}$ contain two terms corresponding to $m=\frac{1}{2}$ and $m=-\frac{1}{2}$. This over-simplified case of a single m describes a system of protons and neutrons all having the same specified azimuthal quantum number. From the definitions (3) with the summations reduced to single terms we obtain:

$$\boldsymbol{\tau}^2 = 3\tau_0\,, \tag{34a}$$

$$\tau_0^2 + N_0^2 = \tfrac{1}{4}\,, \tag{34b}$$

and subsequently the equations:

$$T(T+1) = 3M_T\,, \tag{35a}$$

$$\tfrac{1}{3}T(T+1) + N^2 = \tfrac{1}{4}\,. \tag{35b}$$

These are satisfied only by:

$$T=0\,, \qquad N=\pm\tfrac{1}{2}\,, \tag{36a}$$

$$T=\tfrac{1}{2}\,, \qquad N=0\,. \tag{36b}$$

The solution $N=-\frac{1}{2}$, $T=0$ represents the vacuum state. When one particle is present, $N=0$, and the particle is either a proton, $M_T=\frac{1}{2}$, or a neutron, $M_T=-\frac{1}{2}$. The maximum possible number of particles is two, $N=+\frac{1}{2}$. The eigenfunction is antisymmetric in the isospin coordinates, $T=0$, because it must be symmetric in the remaining coordinates.

We now consider the shell $j=\frac{1}{2}$ which is the simplest system to which our formalism can be applied rigorously. According to the definitions (3) this system is a direct sum of two systems,

$$\tau = \tau_{m=+\frac{1}{2}} + \tau_{m=-\frac{1}{2}}, \tag{37a}$$

$$N_0 = N_{0\,m=+\frac{1}{2}} + N_{0\,m=-\frac{1}{2}}. \tag{37b}$$

The allowed quantum numbers of each system are given in (36). The allowed quantum numbers of the shell $j=\frac{1}{2}$ are obtained by summing the τ_m vectorially as angular momenta while the N_{0m} are summed up algebraically (see table 1). This means that the representation $(w, t)=(1, 0)$ (fig. 12) appears

TABLE 1

N	T	multiplicity
1	0	1
$\frac{1}{2}$	$\frac{1}{2}$	2
0	1	1
0	0	3
$-\frac{1}{2}$	$\frac{1}{2}$	2
-1	0	1

once, $(\frac{1}{2}, \frac{1}{2})$ (fig. 13) – twice, while $(0, 0)$ (fig. 14) – three times. The representation $(1, 0)$ describes states with $J=0$ which exist for the vacuum $(N=-1)$ for two particles $(N=0)$ and for a closed shell $(N=+1)$. The representation $(\frac{1}{2}, \frac{1}{2})$ describes the states with $J=\frac{1}{2}$ and therefore has multiplicity 2, while $(0, 0)$ has multiplicity 3 because it represents states with $J=1$.

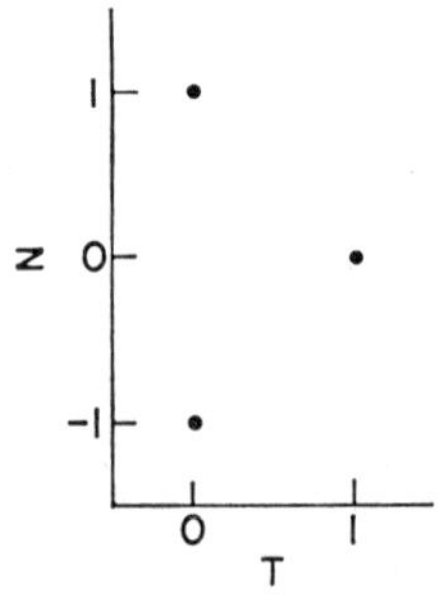

Fig. 12. (N, T) diagram; $w=1, t=0$.

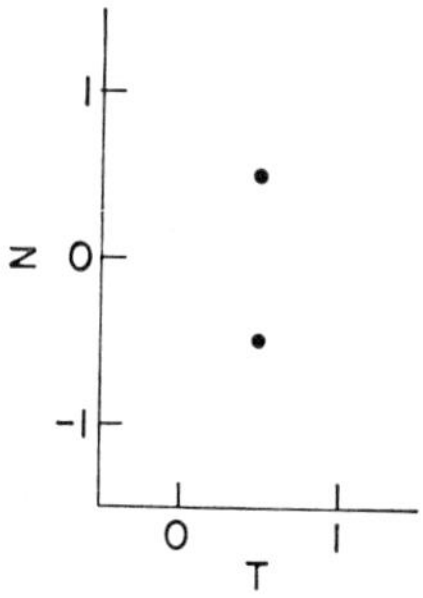

Fig. 13. (N, T) diagram; $w = \frac{1}{2}$, $t = \frac{1}{2}$.

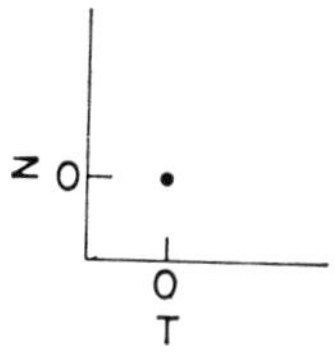

Fig. 14. (N, T) diagram; $w = 0$, $t = 0$.

6. The additional quantum number

The seniority concept was introduced by Racah for atomic spectroscopy [12]) and applied by Flowers [9]) for nuclear *jj* shell model calculations. In order to treat systems of neutrons and protons together the reduced isospin t was introduced in addition to the isospin T and the seniority v already used in atomic spectroscopy. These "natural" quantum numbers, however, were not sufficient for a complete classification of the eigenstates. An additional more complicated quantum number was needed. Such a quantum number was first defined by Goldberg [10]). Besides the inherent complications related to the definition of this new quantum number, he used the old formalism for the construction of the seniority scheme. This double difficulty lead to cumbersome calculations.

In section 2, the simple and more coherent description of seniority was presented by using creation and annihilation operators. It has been shown, however, that in this description an additional quantum number is still needed for a complete classification in the "physical scheme", i.e. when the isospin is diagonal. Moreover, the same difficulties encountered by Goldberg in defining this quantum number are still present. Yet the description of the additional quantum number, the derivation of its properties and the calculation of matrix-elements are facilitated in this formalism.

This additional quantum number is more complicated than the "natural" ones v, T and t, because it is impossible to find a single operator whose eigenvalues can be used for the additional classification of the states. We use, instead, a set of operators. Following Goldberg, the new quantum number is defined as the number of "alpha particles" in the state. This "alpha particle" is a cluster of four nucleons coupled together to $J=0$, $T=0$, and $v=0$. Although these "alpha particles" behave to some extent as bosons, they are really complex nuclei. When one of them is added to a given system the Pauli principle prevents a proton of the "alpha particle" from occupying a quantum state already occupied by some other proton of the system. The same is true for the neutrons. If the creation operator of an "alpha particle" is defined by

$$\Gamma_c = \boldsymbol{A}_c \cdot \boldsymbol{A}_c , \tag{38a}$$

and the annihilation operator by

$$\Gamma_d = \boldsymbol{A}_d \cdot \boldsymbol{A}_d , \tag{38b}$$

the following commutation relations hold*

$$[\Gamma_c, \Gamma_c] = 0 , \tag{39a}$$

$$[\Gamma_d, \Gamma_d] = 0 , \tag{39b}$$

$$[\Gamma_c, \Gamma_d] = -4i(\boldsymbol{\tau} \cdot \boldsymbol{A}_d \times \boldsymbol{A}_c) + 4N_0 \boldsymbol{A}_d \cdot \boldsymbol{A}_c - 4\tau^2 + 6N_0^2 + 3N_0 . \tag{39c}$$

The first two are the commutation relations of bosons, but the result of the third is neither a number nor an operator which commutes with the operators of the group. This relation reveals the complicated nature of the quantum number describing the "alpha particle content". When operating with Γ_c or Γ_d on a set of orthogonal states the resulting states are usually not orthogonal, due to the commutation relation (39c). Different classifications are therefore obtained if the "alpha particles" are counted by Γ_d (as the number of "particles" which can be annihilated), or by Γ_c (as the number of particles created for obtaining the state). We shall use the first classification Γ_d.

To understand the definition of the new quantum number, let us examine

* A second additional quantum number with different properties is obtained by the definition

$$\Gamma_c = \boldsymbol{\tau} \cdot \boldsymbol{A}_c , \qquad \Gamma_d = \boldsymbol{\tau} \cdot \boldsymbol{A}_d .$$

In the following definitions (38) are used because they lead to a treatment which is parallel to Goldberg's.

how new states are generated when N increases. In a representation (w, t) the lowest N is $N=-w$ with $T=t$. The states with $N=-w+1$ are obtained by applying A_c to the states with $N=-w$, $T=t$. As A_c is an isospin vector, we obtain $T=t+1, t, t-1$, each appearing once at most (when speaking about a state with a specified T, we mean the set of $(2T+1)$ states with $M_T=-T, -T+1, \ldots, +T$). Obviously, some of these states may vanish. The states with $N=-w+2$ are obtained by applying A_c a second time. A clearer picture of the non-vanishing states is obtained by examining all tensor products $A_c \times A_c$, of which there are three: these are the zero degree or scalar product

$$[A_c \times A_c]^{(0)}, \tag{40a}$$

the first degree product

$$[A_c \times A_c]^{(1)}, \tag{40b}$$

and the second degree product

$$[A_c \times A_c]^{(2)}. \tag{40c}$$

The components of A_c commute, as seen in (4). Therefore, the "symmetric products" of even degree (40a) and (40c) are the non-vanishing tensor products. The first degree product (40b) vanishes. All states with $N=-w+2$ are obtained by applying the tensors (40) to the state $N=-w$, $T=t$. States with $N=-w+2$, and $T=t\pm 2$ and $t\pm 1$, can appear only by application of (40c) and appear once at the most. States with $N=-w+2$ and $T=t$ can appear twice, by application of (40a) and (40c).

Let $|1\rangle$ and $|2\rangle$ be two orthonormal states with $N=-w+2$ and $T=t$,

$$\langle 1|2\rangle = 0, \tag{41a}$$

$$\langle 1|1\rangle = 1, \tag{41b}$$

$$\langle 2|2\rangle = 1. \tag{41c}$$

Operating with Γ_d on thesc states we obtain:

$$\Gamma_d |1\rangle = a_1 |N=-w\ T=t\rangle, \tag{42a}$$

$$\Gamma_d |2\rangle = a_2 |N=-w\ T=t\rangle. \tag{42b}$$

We define the states $|1'\rangle$ and $|2'\rangle$ as the following orthonormal linear combinations of $|1\rangle$ and $|2\rangle$:

$$|1'\rangle = \frac{a_2}{\sqrt{a_1^2+a_2^2}}|1\rangle - \frac{a_1}{\sqrt{a_1^2+a_2^2}}|2\rangle, \tag{43a}$$

$$|2'\rangle = \frac{a_1}{\sqrt{a_1^2+a_2^2}}|1\rangle + \frac{a_2}{\sqrt{a_1^2+a_2^2}}|2\rangle; \tag{43b}$$

$$\langle 1' | 2' \rangle = 0 , \tag{44a}$$

$$\langle 1' | 1' \rangle = 1 , \tag{44b}$$

$$\langle 2' | 2' \rangle = 1 . \tag{44c}$$

Applying Γ_{d} we obtain:

$$\Gamma_{\mathrm{d}} | 1' \rangle = 0 , \tag{45a}$$

$$\Gamma_{\mathrm{d}} | 2' \rangle = \sqrt{a_1^2 + a_2^2}\, | N = -w, T = t \rangle . \tag{45b}$$

Therefore the state $|2'\rangle$ is said to contain an "alpha particle" and to have been generated already at $N = -w$. It is specified by the additional quantum number $\gamma = -w$. The state $|1'\rangle$ does not contain "alpha particles", and is generated only at $N = -w+2$. It is specified by $\gamma = -w+2$.

In general, the additional quantum number γ is defined as follows. It assumes the values: $N, N-2, N-4, \ldots$. A state $|\gamma\rangle$ having this quantum number satisfies the following conditions:

$$(\Gamma_{\mathrm{d}})^s | \gamma \rangle = 0 \quad \text{for} \quad s = \tfrac{1}{2}(N - \gamma + 2) , \tag{46a}$$

$$(\Gamma_{\mathrm{d}})^s | \gamma \rangle \neq 0 \quad \text{for} \quad s = \tfrac{1}{2}(N - \gamma) , \tag{46b}$$

$$\langle \gamma' | \gamma \rangle = 0 \quad \text{if} \quad \gamma' > \gamma . \tag{46c}$$

An inconvenient property of the quantum number γ is the "asymmetry between particles and holes". If in a given representation there are r_N states with the same eigenvalues of N, T, M_T, there also exist in the same representation r_N states with the eigenvalues $-N, T, M_T$. Let the N, T, M_T states be classified by $\gamma_{+N}^{(1)}, \gamma_{+N}^{(2)}, \ldots, \gamma_{+N}^{(r_N)}$ and the $-N, T, M_T$ states by $\gamma_{-N}^{(1)}, \gamma_{-N}^{(2)}, \ldots, \gamma_{-N}^{(r_N)}$. The matrix-elements satisfy the following equation:

$$\sum_{\gamma\gamma'} |(N+1\; T\gamma \| A_{\mathrm{c}} \| N\; T'\gamma')|^2 = \sum_{\gamma\gamma'} |(-N-1\; T\gamma \| A_{\mathrm{d}} \| -N\; T'\gamma')|^2 , \tag{47}$$

but it is *impossible* to arrange the γ quantum numbers in such a way to exhibit particle–hole symmetry.

$$|(N+1\; T\gamma_{N+1}^{(i)} \| A_{\mathrm{c}} \| N\; T'\gamma_N^{(j)})| \neq |(-N-1\; T\gamma_{-N-1}^{(i)} \| A_{\mathrm{d}} \| -N\; T'\gamma_{-N}^{(j)})| . \tag{48}$$

The following properties of the quantum number γ are proved in the appendix:

Theorem 1: The states are completely classified by the additional quantum number γ; i.e. no two states in a representation have the same N, T, M_T, γ.

Theorem 2: The matrix elements of A_{c} and A_{d} satisfy the selection rule $\Delta\gamma = 1$

and
$$\left.\begin{aligned}(N\,T\gamma\|A_{\mathrm{c}}\|N-1\,T'\gamma')=0\\(N\,T\gamma\|A_{\mathrm{d}}\|N+1\,T'\gamma')=0\end{aligned}\right\}\quad\text{if}\quad|\gamma'-\gamma|\neq1\,. \tag{49}$$

Theorem 3a: Application of Γ_{c} on $|N\,T M_T\,\gamma\rangle$, results in a linear combination of $|N+2\,T M_T\,\gamma\rangle$ and $|N+2\,T M_T\,\gamma-2\rangle$:

$$\Gamma_{\mathrm{c}}\,|N\,T M_T\,\gamma\rangle = a\,|N+2\,T M_T\,\gamma\rangle + b\,|N+2\,T M_T\,\gamma-2\rangle\,. \tag{50}$$

Theorem 3b: Application of Γ_{d} on $|N\,T M_T\,\gamma\rangle$, results in a linear combination $|N-2\,T M_T\,\gamma\rangle$ and $|N-2\,T M_T\,\gamma+2\rangle$:

$$\Gamma_{\mathrm{d}}\,|N\,T M_T\,\gamma\rangle = a'\,|N-2\,T M_T\,\gamma\rangle + b'\,|N-2\,T M_T\,\gamma+2\rangle\,. \tag{51}$$

The additional quantum number for the non-compact case can be defined in a similar way. Theorems 1, 2, 3a, and 3b are also valid.

Appendix. Proof of the properties of γ

Lemma 1. The matrix-elements

$$\langle N-2\,\gamma|\,\Gamma_{\mathrm{d}}\,|N\,\gamma'\rangle = 0\,, \qquad \text{if } \gamma<\gamma';$$
$$\langle N+2\,\gamma|\,\Gamma_{\mathrm{c}}\,|N\,\gamma'\rangle = 0\,, \qquad \text{if } \gamma>\gamma'\,.$$

Proof. For $\gamma'=N$,

$$\Gamma_{\mathrm{d}}\,|N\,\gamma'=N\rangle = 0;$$

therefore,

$$\langle N-2\,\gamma|\,\Gamma_{\mathrm{d}}\,|N\,\gamma'=N\rangle = 0\,.$$

For $\gamma'=N-2$,

$$\Gamma_{\mathrm{d}}\,|N\,\gamma'=N-2\rangle = \sum_{\gamma''} a_{\gamma''}\,|N-2\,\gamma''\rangle\,. \tag{A1}$$

Let $\gamma_{\min}$ be the smallest γ belonging to $N-2$, and let $s=\frac{1}{2}(N-\gamma_{\min}-2)$. Then by operating with $(\Gamma_{\mathrm{d}})^s$ on both sides of eq. (A1), we obtain:

$$(\Gamma_{\mathrm{d}})^{s+1}\,|N\,\gamma'=N-2\rangle = \sum_{\gamma''} a_{\gamma''}\,(\Gamma_{\mathrm{d}})^s\,|N-2\,\gamma''\rangle\,. \tag{A2}$$

The left-hand side vanishes, while on the right hand side

$$(\Gamma_{\mathrm{d}})^s\,|N-2\,\gamma''\rangle = 0$$

for all γ'' except for $\gamma''=\gamma_{\min}$, whence:

$$a_{\gamma_{\min}} = 0\,. \tag{A3}$$

Let now $s=\frac{1}{2}(N-\gamma_{\min}-4)$. Then operating with $(\Gamma_{\mathrm{d}})^s$ on both sides of (A1), we obtain again the expression (A2) but with the new value of s. The left-hand side vanishes, and on the right-hand side:

$$(\Gamma_d)^s \, |N - 2\gamma''\rangle = 0$$

for all γ'' except for $\gamma''=\gamma_{\min}$ and $\gamma''=\gamma_{\min}+2$. Now, using (A3), we obtain:

$$a_{\gamma_{\min}+2} = 0 . \tag{A4}$$

Proceeding in the same way, by decreasing the value of s by a unit at each step, we obtain:

$$a_{\gamma''} = 0$$

for all γ'' except $\gamma''=N-2$. This proves the first part of the lemma for $\gamma'=N-2$. The lemma can be proved in the same way for any γ'. The second part of the lemma is obtained from the first part by taking its hermitean conjugate.

Lemma 2. In a given representation w, t there is at most one state having some specified N, T, M_T, γ; for all γ except for $\gamma=N$.

Lemma 3. If there exists the state $|N\,\gamma\rangle$, $\gamma<N$ (according to lemma 2, the state is unique), then

$$\langle N - 2\gamma| \, \Gamma_d \, |N\,\gamma\rangle \neq 0 .$$

Lemma 4. In a given representation there exists at most one state having some specified $N, T, M_T, \gamma=N$.

Proof. The lemmas 2, 3, 4, will be proved by induction, i.e., they will be proved for N, assuming that they are true for $N-2$.

Proof of lemma 2. Suppose that there are two states with identical sets $N, T, M_T, \gamma\neq N$. Let us denote them by $|1\rangle$ and $|2\rangle$. Defining $s=\frac{1}{2}(N-\gamma)$ we obtain by lemma 1:

$$(\Gamma_d)^s \, |1\rangle = a_1 \, |N = \gamma\,\gamma\rangle , \qquad (\Gamma_d)^s \, |2\rangle = a_2 \, |N = \gamma\,\gamma\rangle , \tag{A5}$$

where repeated use is made of the induction assumptions in order to attain a unique $|N=\gamma\,\gamma\rangle$. But instead of the states $|1\rangle$ and $|2\rangle$ let us consider the linear combinations $|1'\rangle$ and $|2'\rangle$:

$$\begin{aligned} |1'\rangle &= \frac{a_2}{\sqrt{a_1^2 + a_2^2}} \, |1\rangle - \frac{a_1}{\sqrt{a_1^2 + a_2^2}} \, |2\rangle , \\ |2'\rangle &= \frac{a_1}{\sqrt{a_1^2 + a_2^2}} \, |1\rangle + \frac{a_2}{\sqrt{a_1^2 + a_2^2}} \, |2\rangle , \end{aligned} \tag{A6}$$

and according to (A5):

$$(\Gamma_d)^s \, |1\rangle = 0 ,$$

which means that $|1'\rangle$ belongs to some larger γ than assumed.

Proof of lemma 3. According to lemma 1,

$$\Gamma_{\mathrm{d}}\,|N\,\gamma\rangle = \sum_{\gamma' \geqslant \gamma} a_{\gamma'}\,|N-2\,\gamma'\rangle\,. \tag{A7}$$

But the fact that the matrix-element

$$\langle N-2\,\gamma|\,\Gamma_{\mathrm{d}}\,|N\,\gamma\rangle = 0$$

means that

$$a_{\gamma} = 0$$

and instead of (A7) we obtain:

$$\Gamma_{\mathrm{d}}\,|N\,\gamma\rangle = \sum_{\gamma' > \gamma} a_{\gamma''}\,|N-2\,\gamma'\rangle\,. \tag{A8}$$

Let $s=\frac{1}{2}(N-\gamma-2)$. Then by operating with $(\Gamma_{\mathrm{d}})^{s}$ on both sides of (A8) the right-hand side vanishes and therefore:

$$(\Gamma_{\mathrm{d}})^{s+1}\,|N\,\gamma\rangle = 0 \tag{A9}$$

in contradiction with the definition of γ.

Proof of lemma 4. By forming the products of n operators of type A_{c}

$$A_{\mathrm{c}i_1}A_{\mathrm{c}i_2}\cdots A_{\mathrm{c}i_n} \tag{A10}$$

and applying this product to the "extremal states" with $N=-w$, $T=t$ and any $M_T=-T, -T+1, \ldots, +T$,

$$A_{\mathrm{c}i_1}A_{\mathrm{c}i_2}\cdots A_{\mathrm{c}i_n}\,|N=-\,w\;T=t\;M_T\rangle\,, \tag{A11}$$

we obtain states with $N=-w+n$. As will be explained later, any state with $N=-w+n$ can be obtained in such a way by using appropriate linear combinations of (A11); therefore we examine all possible linear combinations of (A10). Since all $A_{\mathrm{c}i}$ commute among themselves and satisfy commutation relations of vectors with respect to τ, we can treat the products (A10) as an assembly of vector bosons.

This space of all possible products (A10) can be reduced to irreducible tensors of degree $n, n-2, n-4, \ldots$. There is one and only one tensor of each degree. The tensor of highest degree will be denoted by $[A_{\mathrm{c}}]^n$, and generated by successively coupling the operators A_{c} in such a way as to obtain always the highest possible degree. The tensor of degree $n-2$ can be written as:

$$\Gamma_{\mathrm{c}}\,[A_{\mathrm{c}}]^{n-2}$$

and in general, the tensor of degree $n-2$ is:

$$\Gamma_{\mathrm{c}}^{p}\,[A_{\mathrm{c}}]^{n-2p}\,. \tag{A12}$$

There are $\frac{1}{2}(n+2)$ or $\frac{1}{2}(n+1)$ such tensors, when n is even or odd respectively. Therefore by applying these tensors to the set $|N=-w\,T=t\,M_T\rangle$ where $M_T=-T, -T+1, \ldots, +T$ and performing the coupling of angular momenta, we obtain at most $\frac{1}{2}(n+2)$ or $\frac{1}{2}(n+1)$ sets of states with $n=-w+n$, $T=t, M_T=-T, -T+1, \ldots, +T$. Obviously some results may vanish, thus reducing the number of states. For $T=t+1$, the number of sets of states is at most $\frac{1}{2}n$ if n is even, and $\frac{1}{2}(n+1)$ if n is odd. The largest T which can be obtained is $T=t+n$ and there is at most one set of states with this T.

We shall now show that all states with $N=-w+n$ can be obtained in this way. No additional states can be obtained by using the operator N_0. The operators τ can change only M_T. By the procedure described above the complete set of M_T states is readily obtained for some T. Let us now verify that A_d cannot introduce additional states. Formally,

$$A_{\mathrm{d}k}A_{\mathrm{c}l}(A_{\mathrm{c}i_1}A_{\mathrm{c}i_2}\cdots A_{\mathrm{c}i_n})\,|N=-w\;T=t\;M_T\rangle \tag{A13}$$

is a state with $N=w+n$. We shall now show that it is merely a linear combination of (A11). Using the commutation relations (4) we can shift the $A_{\mathrm{d}k}$ in (A13) to the extreme right. The result is a linear combination of the term

$$(A_{\mathrm{c}i_1}A_{\mathrm{c}i_2}\cdots A_{\mathrm{c}i_n})\,A_{\mathrm{c}l}A_{\mathrm{d}k}\,|N=-w\;T=t\;M_T\rangle \tag{A14}$$

with terms of the form (A11). But as

$$A_{\mathrm{d}k}\,|N=-w\;T=t\;M_T\rangle=0,$$

(A14) vanishes, and the states can be obtained by "pure A_c" products. By lemma 1, when Γ_c is applied to any state with some specified γ only states with $\gamma'\leqslant\gamma$ are obtained. Applying $[A_\mathrm{c}]^{n-2p}$ to $|N=-w\,T=t\rangle$ we obtain states with $N=-w+n-2p$ and therefore with $\gamma\leqslant -w+n-2p$. Hence application of $\Gamma_\mathrm{c}^p[A_\mathrm{c}]^{n-2p}$ produces states only with $\gamma\leqslant -w+n-2p$. The only tensor which creates a $\gamma=-w+n=N$ state is $[A_\mathrm{c}]^n$ and therefore there is only one state having specified w, t, N, T, M_T, $\gamma=N$. The lemmas 2 and 4 are combined to give the first theorem of section 5.

Lemma 5. $(N-1\;T\gamma\|A_\mathrm{d}\|N\;T'\;\gamma')=0$ when $\gamma'-\gamma>1$.

Proof. The proof is by induction. We assume that

$$(N-3\;T\gamma\|A_\mathrm{d}\|N-2\;T'\;\gamma')=0 \tag{A15}$$

when $\gamma'-\gamma>1$. According to the commutation relations (4) we obtain:

$$A_{\mathrm{d}i}\Gamma_\mathrm{d}-\Gamma_\mathrm{d}A_{\mathrm{d}i}=0, \tag{A16}$$

whence:

$$\langle N-3\; T M_T\; \gamma_{\min}|\; A_{\mathrm{d}i}\Gamma_{\mathrm{d}} - \Gamma_{\mathrm{d}}A_{\mathrm{d}i}\; |N\; T'\; M_T'\; \gamma'\rangle = 0\,, \tag{A17}$$

or,

$$\begin{aligned}\sum_{\gamma''} \langle N-3\; T M_T\; \gamma_{\min}|\; A_{\mathrm{d}i}\; |N-2\; T'\; M_T'\; \gamma''\rangle \times \\ \times \langle N-2\; T'\; M_T'\; \gamma''|\; \Gamma_{\mathrm{d}}\; |N\; T'\; M_T'\; \gamma'\rangle + \\ -\sum_{\gamma''} \langle N-3\; T M_T\; \gamma_{\min}|\; \Gamma_{\mathrm{d}}\; |N-1\; T M_T\; \gamma''\rangle \times \\ \times \langle N-1\; T M_T\; \gamma''|\; A_{\mathrm{d}i}\; |N\; T'\; M_T'\; \gamma'\rangle = 0\,.\end{aligned} \tag{A18}$$

The first sum of (A18) vanishes because of the induction assumption (A15) and lemma 1. From the second sum, the only non-vanishing term according to lemma 1 is

$$\langle N-3\; T M_T\; \gamma_{\min}|\; \Gamma_{\mathrm{d}}\; |N-1\; T M_T\; \gamma_{\min}\rangle \times \times \langle N-1\; T M_T\; \gamma_{\min}|\; A_{\mathrm{d}i}\; |N\; T'\; M_T'\; \gamma'\rangle\,,$$

which is equal to zero by (A18). As

$$\langle N-3\; T M_T\; \gamma_{\min}|\; \Gamma_{\mathrm{d}}\; |N-1\; T M_T\; \gamma_{\min}\rangle$$

cannot vanish according to lemma 3, we must have

$$\langle N-1\; T M_T\; \gamma_{\min}|\; A_{\mathrm{d}i}\; |N\; T'\; M_T'\; \gamma'\rangle = 0 \tag{A19}$$

again from (A16):

$$\langle N-3\; T M_T\; \gamma_{\min}+2|\; A_{\mathrm{d}i}\Gamma_{\mathrm{d}} - \Gamma_{\mathrm{d}}A_{\mathrm{d}i}\; |N\; T'\; M_T'\; \gamma'\rangle = 0 \tag{A20}$$

or,

$$\begin{aligned}\sum_{\gamma''} \langle N-3\; T M_T\; \gamma_{\min}+2|\; A_{\mathrm{d}i}\; |N-2\; T'\; M_T'\; \gamma''\rangle \times \\ \times \langle N-2\; T'\; M_T'\; \gamma''|\; \Gamma_{\mathrm{d}}\; |N\; T'\; M_T'\; \gamma'\rangle + \\ -\sum_{\gamma''} \langle N-3\; T M_T\; \gamma_{\min}+2|\; \Gamma_{\mathrm{d}}\; |N-1\; T M_T\; \gamma''\rangle \times \\ \times \langle N-1\; T M_T\; \gamma''|\; A_{\mathrm{d}i}\; |N\; T'\; M_T'\; \gamma'\rangle = 0\,.\end{aligned} \tag{A21}$$

Furthermore, the first sum of (A21) vanishes because of the induction assumption (A15) and lemma 1. The only non-vanishing terms from the second sum are, according to lemma 1:

$$\begin{aligned}\langle N-3\; T M_T\; \gamma_{\min}+2|\; \Gamma_{\mathrm{d}}\; |N-1\; T M_T\; \gamma_{\min}\rangle \times \\ \times \langle N-1\; T M_T\; \gamma_{\min}|\; A_{\mathrm{d}i}\; |N\; T'\; M_T'\; \gamma'\rangle + \\ + \langle N-3\; T M_T\; \gamma_{\min}+2|\; \Gamma_{\mathrm{d}}\; |N-1\; T M_T\; \gamma_{\min}+2\rangle \times \\ \times \langle N-1\; T M_T\; \gamma_{\min}+2|\; A_{\mathrm{d}i}\; |N\; T'\; M_T'\; \gamma'\rangle = 0\,.\end{aligned} \tag{A22}$$

The first term of (A22) vanishes because of (A19), and according to lemma 3 we must have:

$$\langle N-1\, T M_T\, \gamma_{\min}+2|\, A_{\mathrm{d}i}\, |N\, T'\, M_T'\, \gamma'\rangle = 0\,. \tag{A23}$$

The process can be continued by taking $\gamma = \gamma_{\min}+4,\ \gamma_{\min}+6, \ldots$, till $\gamma=\gamma'-3$.

Lemma 6. $(N-1\; T\,\gamma \| A_{\mathrm{d}} \| N\, T'\,\gamma') = 0$ when $\gamma - \gamma' > 1$.

Proof. The proof is by induction. We assume that

$$\left.\begin{array}{l}\langle N-4\,\gamma'|\, A_{\mathrm{c}i}\,|N-5\,\gamma\rangle = 0\\ \langle N-2\,\gamma'|\, A_{\mathrm{c}i}\,|N-3\,\gamma\rangle = 0\end{array}\right\}\ \text{when } \gamma-\gamma' > 1\,, \tag{A24}$$

and (the second line above), and proceed to prove that

$$\langle N\,\gamma'|\, A_{\mathrm{c}i}\,|N-1\,\gamma\rangle = 0 \quad \text{when } \gamma-\gamma' > 1\,. \tag{A25}$$

Using the commutation relations (4) we obtain:

$$[\Gamma_{\mathrm{d}}, [\Gamma_{\mathrm{d}}, A_{\mathrm{c}i}]] = -\,8A_{\mathrm{d}i}\Gamma_{\mathrm{d}}\,, \tag{A26}$$

or:

$$\Gamma_{\mathrm{d}}\Gamma_{\mathrm{d}}A_{\mathrm{c}i} - 2\Gamma_{\mathrm{d}}A_{\mathrm{c}i}\Gamma_{\mathrm{d}} + A_{\mathrm{c}i}\Gamma_{\mathrm{d}}\Gamma_{\mathrm{d}} + 8A_{\mathrm{d}i}\Gamma_{\mathrm{d}} = 0\,. \tag{A27}$$

Hence,

$$\begin{aligned}
&\sum_{\gamma''\gamma'''} \langle N-4\,\gamma'|\,\Gamma_{\mathrm{d}}\,|N-2\,\gamma''\rangle\,\langle N-2\,\gamma''|\,\Gamma_{\mathrm{d}}\,|N\,\gamma'''\rangle\,\times\\
&\qquad\qquad\times\langle N\,\gamma'''|\,A_{\mathrm{c}i}\,|N-1\,\gamma\rangle\,+\\
&\quad -2\sum_{\gamma''\gamma'''} \langle N-4\,\gamma'|\,\Gamma_{\mathrm{d}}\,|N-2\,\gamma''\rangle\,\langle N-2\,\gamma''|\,A_{\mathrm{c}i}\,|N-3\,\gamma'''\rangle\,\times\\
&\qquad\qquad\langle N-3\,\gamma'''|\,\Gamma_{\mathrm{d}}\,|N-1\,\gamma\rangle\,+\\
&\quad +\sum_{\gamma''\gamma'''} \langle N-4\,\gamma'|\,A_{\mathrm{c}i}\,|N-5\,\gamma''\rangle\,\langle N-5\,\gamma''|\,\Gamma_{\mathrm{d}}\,|N-3\,\gamma'''\rangle\,\times\\
&\qquad\qquad\langle N-3\,\gamma'''|\,\Gamma_{\mathrm{d}}\,|N-1\,\gamma\rangle\,+\\
&\quad +8\sum_{\gamma''} \langle N-4\,\gamma'|\,A_{\mathrm{d}i}\,|N-3\,\gamma''\rangle\,\langle N-3\,\gamma''|\,\Gamma_{\mathrm{d}}\,|N-1\,\gamma\rangle = 0\,.
\end{aligned} \tag{A28}$$

If $\gamma \geqslant \gamma'+3$, the fourth sum of (A28) vanishes according to lemma 5 and 1, while the second and the third sums vanish because of the induction assumptions (A24) and lemma 1. Substituting $\gamma' = \gamma_{\min}, \gamma_{\min}+2, \ldots$ in the first sum of (A28), and using lemma 3, we prove successively the relation (A25).

Combining lemmas 5 and 6, we obtain theorem 2 of section 3. The third theorem is easily proved using theorem 2 and lemma 1.

References

1) H. J. Lipkin, *Lie Groups for Pedestrians* (North-Holland Publ. Co., Amsterdam, 1965).
2) A. K. Kerman, Ann. Phys. (N.Y.) **12**, 300 (1961).
3) P. W. Anderson, Phys. Rev. **112**, 164 (1958).
4) S. Goshen and H. J. Lipkin, Ann. Phys. (N.Y.) **6**, 301 (1959).

5) K. Helmers, Nucl. Phys. **23**, 594 (1961).
6) K. T. Hecht, Nucl. Phys. **63**, 177 (1965).
7) J. P. Elliott, Proc. Roy. Soc. (London) **A 245**, 128 (1958).
8) G. Racah, in: *Group Theoretical Concepts and Methods in Elementary Particle Physics, Lectures*, Ed. F. Gürsey (Gordon and Breach, New York, 1964) p. 1, see in particular pp. 31–36.
9) B. H. Flowers, Proc. Roy. Soc. (London) **A 212**, 248 (1952).
10) H. Goldberg, Ph.D. Thesis, Hebrew University, Jerusalem, 1961, unpublished.
11) G. Racah, *Group Theory and Spectroscopy*, Vol. 37 of Springer Tracts in Modern Physics (Springer-Verlag, Berlin, 1965).
12) G. Racah, in: *Proc. Rehovoth Conference on Nuclear Structure, 1957*, Ed. H. J. Lipkin (North-Holland Publ. Co., Amsterdam, 1958) p. 155.
13) K. T. Hecht, Five Dimensional Quasispin. The *n, t* Dependence of Shell Model Matrix Elements in the Seniority Scheme. Technical Report, University of Michigan, Ann Arbor, Michigan, 1967.

Spectroscopic and group theoretical methods in physics
© North-Holland Publ. Co., Amsterdam, 1968

RESIDUAL INTERACTION IN ATOMIC NUCLEI

L. A. SLIV and YU. I. KHARITONOV
A. F. Ioffe Physico-Technical Institute,
Academy of Sciences of the USSR,
Leningrad, U.S.S.R.

1. Introduction

Investigation of nuclear structure brings forth the problem of taking into account the residual two-body interaction of nucleons. It concerns not only the n–n and p–p interactions, but also the n–p ones in both cases where neutrons and protons occupy either identical or different shells. The role of residual interaction comes to be especially transparent when we treat a nucleus as a system of closed shells plus several extra nucleons (quasiparticles) moving in a self-consistent shell-model field. The best and most elegant technique of handling such a problem was brilliantly developed by G. Racah. This technique will be used in the paper henceforward.

The two-body interaction potential $V(12)$ can be expressed in general as a scalar invariant in space $(\boldsymbol{r}_1, \boldsymbol{r}_2)$, spin $(\boldsymbol{\sigma}_1, \boldsymbol{\sigma}_2)$ and isospin $(\boldsymbol{\tau}_1, \boldsymbol{\tau}_2)$ variables of the two particles:

$$V(12) = vf_1(r) + v_\sigma f_2(r)(\boldsymbol{\sigma}_1 \cdot \boldsymbol{\sigma}_2) + v_T f_3(r) S_{12} + \\ + (\boldsymbol{\tau}_1 \cdot \boldsymbol{\tau}_2)[v' f_4(r) + v'_\sigma f_5(r)(\boldsymbol{\sigma}_1 \cdot \boldsymbol{\sigma}_2) + v'_T f_6(r) S_{12}], \quad (1)$$

where

$$r = r_{12} = |\boldsymbol{r}_1 - \boldsymbol{r}_2|, \qquad S_{12} = 3(\boldsymbol{\sigma}_1 \cdot \boldsymbol{r})(\boldsymbol{\sigma}_2 \cdot \boldsymbol{r}) r^{-2} - (\boldsymbol{\sigma}_1 \cdot \boldsymbol{\sigma}_2), \quad (2)$$

$f_i(r)$ are arbitrary functions of r, and v, v' are the interaction parameters.

Hence the particle–particle interaction in nuclei is a renormalized one, it differs considerably from the free particles interaction. A possible way to derive the parameters and functions in the $V(12)$ operator is to make a direct comparison of theoretical and experimental data on nuclear spectra, i.e. the energy levels, the magnetic and quadrupole moment, electromagnetic transition probabilities $B(\lambda)$ etc. We have the purest conditions for defining the $V(12)$ characteristics in nuclei with 2 particles (holes) above the closed shells in different region of the periodic table. The results gained in this way may then be checked and improved with the aid of calculations for nuclei with larger numbers of nucleons above the core. This procedure also shows that one need not consider the many-body forces.

The $V(12)$ operator affects the results of computation indirectly, via its matrix elements. Thus the nuclear level structure is really sensitive to the integral properties of the potential, i.e. to its effective range and to its depth, and not to its shape. So we may assume henceforth that $f_1(r),\ldots,f_6(r)$ obey the only major demand of being shortranged. In general different properties of nuclear levels have different sensitivity to various parameters of the two-body interaction (1). That is why it seems to be really of importance to investigate those general properties of the $V(12)$ matrix element which are independent of the choice of $f(r)$. Moreover in all the realistic cases we do not have sufficient information to define all the parameters of the $V(12)$ operator. So it is necessary to limit our consideration with the minimal number of parameters possible in order to make the results less arbitrary. Thus we should rather ommit the last three terms with $(\boldsymbol{\tau}_1 \cdot \boldsymbol{\tau}_2)$ in (1) in case of heavy nuclei for there are no independent data to define it. We assume that the dependence of $V(12)$ on $\boldsymbol{\tau}_1$, $\boldsymbol{\tau}_2$ will cause a certain renormalization of the first three terms in (1). Then we get an operator of an effective interaction

$$V(12) = [v + v_\sigma(\boldsymbol{\sigma}_1 \cdot \boldsymbol{\sigma}_2) + v_T\, S_{12}]\, f(r) . \qquad (3)$$

In order to compute the matrix elements of the residual interaction operator and to investigate its dependence on the total spin J it is convenient to express $V(12)$ as a linear combination of Wigner, singlet and tensor forces as follows:

$$V(12) = (v_0 + v_1\, \pi_s + v_T\, S_{12})\, \pi_0 , \qquad (4)$$

where $\pi_s = \frac{1}{2}[1 - (\boldsymbol{\sigma}_1 \cdot \boldsymbol{\sigma}_2)]$ is a singlet state projection operator, $\pi_0 = f(r)$, $v_0 = v + v_\sigma$ and $v_1 = -4v_\sigma$.

2. *J* dependence of the two-body matrix elements

We start with the investigation of splitting caused by the residual interaction. Let us consider the simplest configuration of one proton and one neutron, i.e. the configuration $\{j_1, j_2\}$ and find the dependence of the diagonal matrix elements on the total momentum J. As we shall show below, the case of two identical particles $\{j^2\}$ appears to be a particular example of the general configuration $\{j_1, j_2\}$.

2.1. Wigner forces

Expanding $\pi_0 = f(r)$ in terms of the irreducible tensor operator

$$\pi_0 = f(r) = \sum_k (2k+1) f_k(r_1, r_2) \left(\boldsymbol{T}^k(1) \cdot \boldsymbol{T}^k(2)\right) \tag{5}$$

and using the Racah formula for the matrix element of the scalar product of irreducible tensor operators[1]) we get:

$$\langle j_1 j_2 J | \pi_0 | j_1 j_2 J \rangle = \sum_k (2k+1) F^k (-1)^{j_1+j_2-J} \langle j_1 || \boldsymbol{T}^k || j_1 \rangle \times \\ \times \langle j_2 || \boldsymbol{T}^k || j_2 \rangle W[j_1 j_2 j_1 j_2; Jk]. \tag{6}$$

Here F^k are the radial integrals ($F^k > 0$), $\langle j || \boldsymbol{T}^k || j \rangle$ are the reduced matrix elements of irreducible tensor operators of rank k and $W[j_1 j_2 j_1 j_2; Jk]$ are the Racah coefficients. The sum goes over $k = 0, 2, \ldots, 2j' - 1$, where j' is the least of the j_1 and j_2 numbers. It is convenient to write (6) separating the term with $k = 0$:

$$\langle j_1 j_2 J | \pi_0 | j_1 j_2 J \rangle = F^0 + \sum_{k \geqslant 2} \Phi^k (-1)^{j_1+j_2-J} W[j_1 j_2 j_1 j_2; Jk], \tag{7}$$

where $\Phi^k = (2k+1) F^k \langle j_1 || \boldsymbol{T}^k || j_1 \rangle \langle j_2 || \boldsymbol{T}^k || j_2 \rangle$ are positive for all k and do not depend on J. The dependence of the matrix elements on the spin J is defined only by a factor $(-1)^{j_1+j_2-J} W[j_1 j_2 j_1 j_2; Jk]$, which can in general be both positive and negative, so it is impossible to tell in advance whether the sum in (7) will be added to F^0 or subtracted from it. Nevertheless using the explicit expression for the Racah coefficients, one can make a definite statement on the sign and magnitude of this sum in three special cases. Indeed, it is possible to show that for $J = J_{\min}$, $J = J_{\max}$ and $J = J_{\max} - 1$ the matrix elements (7) are respectively

$$\langle j_1 j_2 J_{\min} | \pi_0 | j_1 j_2 J_{\min} \rangle = F^0 + \sum_{k \geqslant 2} \Phi^k A(k), \tag{8}$$

$$\langle j_1 j_2 J_{\max} | \pi_0 | j_1 j_2 J_{\max} \rangle = F^0 + \sum_{k \geqslant 2} \Phi^k B(k), \tag{9}$$

$$\langle j_1 j_2 J_{\max} - 1 | \pi_0 | j_1 j_2 J_{\max} - 1 \rangle = F^0 - \sum_{k \geqslant 2} \Phi^k C(k), \tag{10}$$

where $A(k)$, $B(k)$ and $C(k)$ are positive and $A(k)/B(k) > 1$.

Thus for an arbitrary function $f(r)$ the largest of those three matrix elements will be the one $J = J_{\min}$, that with $J = J_{\max}$ is a bit smaller, while the one

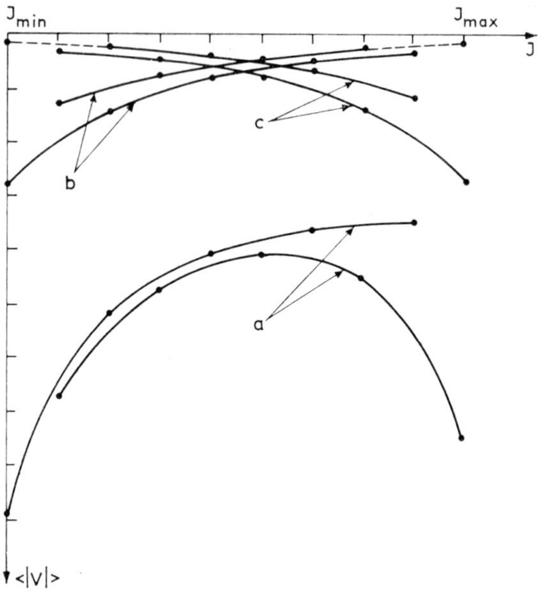

Fig. 1. The $\{j_1, j_2\}$ configuration splitting caused by central residual n–p interaction. Curves a correspond to the π_0 operator, curves b and c correspond to the $\pi_0\pi_s$ operator for N odd and even respectively.

with $J = J_{max} - 1$ is the smallest. The sum in (7) for intermediate values of J will be changing sign, thus causing the corresponding matrix elements to fall into the interval between the elements with $J = J_{min}$ and $J = J_{max} - 1$. The curves in fig. 1, demonstrating the dependence of the Wigner forces matrix element on J do support this result. These are the results of direct computations done for a number of $\{j_1, j_2\}$ configurations in the case of the Gaussian potentials. It is worth mentioning that connecting the alternate points one sets two smooth curves.

2.2. Singlet forces

Now we shall consider the diagonal matrix elements for singlet forces (the $\pi_0\pi_s$ operator). In this case with the aid of the Racah technique we get:

$$\langle j_1 j_2 J | \pi_0 \pi_s | j_1 j_2 J \rangle = \mathscr{A}^2 \begin{Bmatrix} l_1 & \frac{1}{2} & j_1 \\ l_2 & \frac{1}{2} & j_2 \\ J & 0 & J \end{Bmatrix} \times$$
$$\times \{F^0 + \sum_{k \geq 2} \theta^k (-1)^{l_1 + l_2 - J} W[l_1 l_2 l_1 l_2; Jk] . \qquad (11)$$

Here again the $\theta=(2k+1)\, F^k \langle l_1|\,|\boldsymbol{T}^k|\,|l_1\rangle \langle l_2|\,|\boldsymbol{T}^k|\,|l_2\rangle$ are positive for all k and do not depend on J, $\mathscr{A}\{...\}$ is the four-momentum decoupling coefficient. The expression in braces is analogous to (7). The $\mathscr{A}^2\{...\}$ variation with J depends on the Nordheim number N for a given configuration, which is defined as $N=l_1+j_1+l_2+j_2$. For even N the factor $\mathscr{A}^2\{...\}$ is increasing with J, for odd N it is decreasing. A number of direct computation results shows this J dependence of $\mathscr{A}^2\{...\}$ to be of major importance for the matrix element (11). The dependence of the matrix elements on J in cases of N even and N odd is shown in fig. 1 (curves c and b respectively). Again the alternate points fall in two smooth curves. The scale for these curves is the same as for curve a.

It is worth mentioning that the same considerations apply to identical particles $\{j^2\}$ as well. In this case the exclusion principle allows only the states with $J=0, 2, ..., 2j-1=J_{\max}-1$ and the Nordheim number is odd. Therefore, the $\{j^2\}$ configuration splitting caused by Wigner and singlet forces should follow the curves a and b connecting the points $J=J_{\max}$ and $J=J_{\max}-1$ respectively. Fig. 1 shows that the $\{j^2\}$ configuration splitting for Wigner and singlet forces exhibits the same J dependence decreasing with increased J.

2.3. Tensor forces

For the case of j–j coupling the tensor force operator $\pi_0 S_{12}$ can be expanded in terms of irreducible tensor operators as follows[2]):

$$\pi_0 S_{12} = \sqrt{6} \sum_{k_1,k_2,k} \mathrm{i}^{k_1+k_2}(2k_1+1)(2k_2+1)\, C^{20}_{k_1 0\, k_2 0}\, W[k_1 1\, k_2 1; k2] \times$$
$$\times\, v^{(k_1,k_2,2)}(r_1, r_2)([\boldsymbol{\sigma}_1 \times \boldsymbol{T}^{k_1}(1)]^k \cdot [\boldsymbol{\sigma}_2 \times \boldsymbol{T}^{k_2}(2)]^k). \qquad (12)$$

Here $C^{20}_{k_1 0\, k_2 0}$ is the Clebsch–Gordan coefficient, $W[k_1 1\, k_2 1; k2]$ is the Racah coefficient,

$$v^{(k_1,k_2,2)}(r_1, r_2) = \frac{2}{\pi} \int_0^\infty \int_0^\infty j_{k_1}(pr_1)\, j_{k_2}(pr_2) f(r)\, j_2(pr)\, r^2\, \mathrm{d}r\, p^2\, \mathrm{d}p,$$

$j_k(pr)$ is a spherical Bessel function, $[\boldsymbol{\sigma}_i \times \boldsymbol{T}^{k_i}(i)]^k$ is an irreducible tensor operator of rank k, formed by the tensor product of irreducible tensor operators $\boldsymbol{\sigma}_i$ and $\boldsymbol{T}^k$ of rank 1 and k, respectively.

Using (12) one can express the diagonal matrix element of tensor forces as follows:

$$\langle j_1 j_2 J|\, \pi_0 S_{12}\, | j_1 j_2 J\rangle = \sum_k \Omega^k(j_1 j_2)(-1)^J\, W[j_1 j_2 j_1 j_2; Jk]. \qquad (13)$$

We shall not put down the function $\Omega^k_{(j_1, j_2)}$ explicitly, but only point out that it is independent of J and that the sum in (13) goes over only odd k. Hence for $k \neq 0$ there is an expression for Racah coefficients[3]):

$$\sum_J (-1)^J (2J+1)\, W[j_1 j_2 j_1 j_2; Jk] = 0\,; \tag{14}$$

the shift of the centre of gravity ρ of the levels of configuration $\{j_1, j_2\}$ split by tensor forces is zero, i.e.

$$\rho = \frac{\sum_J (2J+1) \langle j_1 j_2 J |\, \pi_0 S_{12} \,| j_1 j_2 J \rangle}{\sum_J (2J+1)} = 0\,. \tag{15}$$

Thus the signs of the diagonal matrix elements of the tensor force change

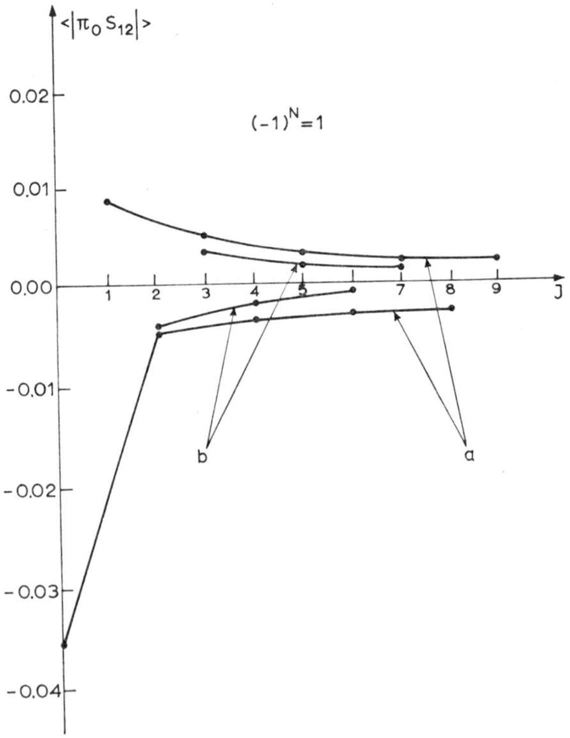

Fig. 2. The dependence of the diagonal matrix elements of the tensor forces on the total spin J for $\{j_1, j_2\}$ configurations with even N ($r_0 = 2$ fm). Curves a for the $\{2g_{9/2}, 1h_{9/2}\}$ configuration, curves b for the $\{3d_{5/2}, 1h_{9/2}\}$ configuration.

with changing J. One should stress that in the cases of Wigner and singlet forces all the matrix elements have the same sign.

We have carried out a number of computations of tensor force matrix elements for the configurations $\{j_1, j_2\}$ in order to find their dependence on J in details. For simplicity we used the oscillator wave functions choosing the parameter $\nu = m\omega/\hbar$, so that the functions resemble the Woods–Saxon ones[4]) as much as possible. The radial part of tensor interaction was taken in a Gaussian form, the interaction radius being 1.5–2.5 fm.

The calculation shows that the sign of the matrix element depends on the parity of J and N (see fig. 2). The matrix element for $J = J_{\min}$ is negative when N is even and positive when N is odd. Elements with $J = J_{\min}$ and $J = J_{\min} + 1$ turn out to have the largest magnitude. They differ considerably from the rest of the matrix elements only when $J_{\min} = 0$ or 1. Figs. 2 and 3 show a characteristic dependence of matrix elements on J in the case of $r_0 = 2$ fm for configurations with even and odd N. When r_0 is changed from 1.5 to

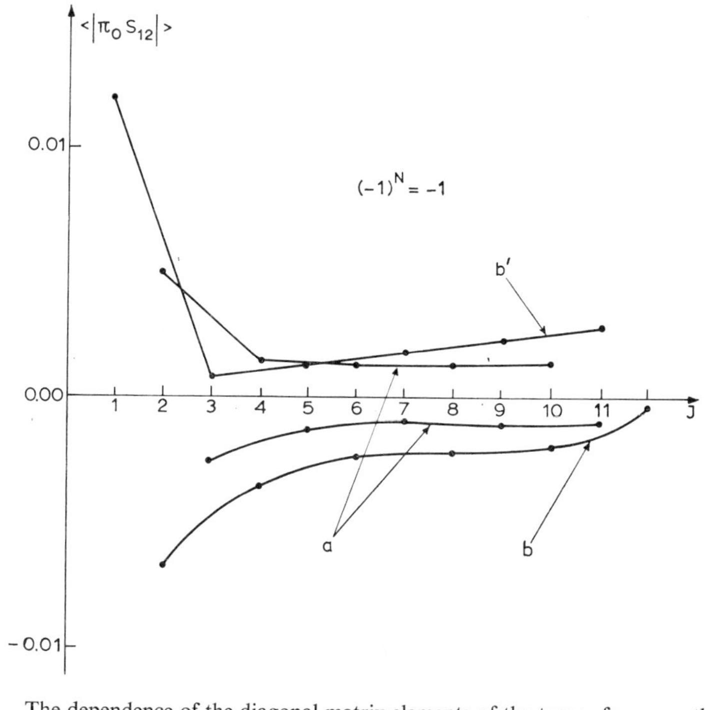

Fig. 3. The dependence of the diagonal matrix elements of the tensor forces on the total spin J for $\{j_1, j_2\}$ configurations with odd N ($r_0 = 2$ fm). Curves a for the $\{2g_{9/2}, 1i_{13/2}\}$ configuration, curves b and b′ for the $\{1i_{13/2}, 1h_{11/2}\}$ configuration.

2.5 fm the general character of the n–p configuration splitting remains unaltered, while the magnitude of matrix elements increases with increasing r_0.

Thus tensor forces seem to be essential in splitting the n–p configurations of the type $\{nlj, n'l'j\}$, e.g. the configuration $\{np_{\frac{1}{2}}, n's_{\frac{1}{2}}\}$ in ^{16}N and ^{206}Tl or configuration $\{2g_{\frac{9}{2}}, 1h_{\frac{9}{2}}\}$ in ^{210}Bi. The important point about tensor forces is that they shift the levels with $J=0$ and $J=1$ in different directions, while the central forces produce a shift in the same direction.

The curve a in fig. 2 for even J shows the identical particles configuration $\{j^2\}$ splitting caused by tensor forces. It is characteristic of this splitting that the matrix element for $J=0$ turns out to be the largest, while the one with $J=2$ is by an order smaller and turns out to be minimal. Further increasing of J causes a small linear growth of the matrix elements, the element with $J=J_{max}$ being only twice as large as the one with $J=2$. So in practical calculations for configurations $\{j^2\}$ the tensor forces should be taken into account only for states $J=0$.

3. *J* dependence in case of more neutrons and protons

Now we shall consider the effect of increasing the number of neutrons and protons on the configuration splitting. The seniority quantum numbers s_1 and s_2 now come to be of importance. The point is that residual interaction of identical particles causes the lowering of configurations with minimal s_1 and s_2. Thus for even–even and even–odd nuclei the most simple and the lowest configuration turns out to be that with one of the seniority numbers, say s_1, equal to zero. Then the total momentum of neutrons $J=0$ and the total momentum of all the nucleons is equal to the total momentum of protons, i.e. $J=J_2$. Using the fractional parentage technique one can calculate the diagonal matrix element of the n–p interaction V_{np}:

$$\begin{aligned}
&\langle j_1^{n_1} s_1 = 0\, J_1 = 0, j_2^{n_2} s_2 \alpha_2 J_2;\, J_2 |\, V_{np} | j_1^{n_1} s_1 = 0\, J_1 = 0, j_2^{n_2} s_2 \alpha_2 J_2;\, J_2 \rangle = \\
&= n_1 n_2 \sum \langle j_1^{n_1} s_1 = 0 0 |\} j_1^{n_1 - 1} s_1' = 1\, J_1' \rangle^2 \times \\
&\times \langle j_2^{n_2} s_2 \alpha_2 J_2 |\} j_2^{n_2 - 1} s_2' \alpha_2' J_2' \rangle^2 \mathscr{A}^2 \begin{Bmatrix} J_1' & j_1 & 0 \\ J_2' & j_2 & J_2 \\ J_\alpha & J_0 & J_2 \end{Bmatrix} \langle j_1 j_2 J_0 |\, V(12)\, | j_1 j_2 J_0 \rangle = \\
&= \frac{n_1 n_2}{(2j_1+1)(2j_2+1)} \sum_{J_0} (2J_0+1) \langle j_1 j_2 J_0 |\, V(12) | j_1 j_2 J_0 \rangle .
\end{aligned} \tag{16}$$

Here $\langle j^n s\alpha J |\} j^{n-1} s'\alpha' J' \rangle$ is the coefficient of fractional parentage for one particle[3,5]) which obeys

$$\langle j_1^{n_1} s_1 = 0\,0 | \} j_1^{n_1 - 1} s_1' = 1\, J_1' \rangle = \delta_{J_1' j_1} \tag{17}$$

and

$$\sum_{s_2' \alpha_2' J_2'} \langle j_2^{n_2} s_2 \alpha_2 J_2 | \} j_2^{n_2 - 1} s_2' \alpha_2' J_2' \rangle^2 = 1\,. \tag{18}$$

Using these relations and

$$\sum_{J_\alpha} \mathscr{A}^2 \begin{Bmatrix} j_1 & j_1 & 0 \\ J_2' & j_2 & J_2 \\ J_\alpha & J_0 & J_2 \end{Bmatrix} = \frac{2J_0 + 1}{(2j_1 + 1)(2j_2 + 1)} \tag{19}$$

one can easily get (16).

So the matrix element (16) depends neither on J nor on the proton state quantum numbers $(s_2 \alpha_2 J_2)$. It equals to an average diagonal matrix element for the $\{j_1, j_2\}$ configuration multiplied by a product of numbers of neutrons and protons in a given configuration.

Thus when the lowest states of even–even and even–odd nuclei are essentially described with functions of the type $|j_1^{n_1} s_1 = 0\,0, j_2^{n_2} s_2 \alpha_2 J_2;\, J_2\rangle$ and $|j_1^{n_1} s_1 \alpha_1 J_1, j_2^{n_2} s_2 = 0\,0;\, J_1\rangle$ the residual n–p interaction does not affect the position of the levels, i.e. the central forces shift all the levels by the same amount irrespective of their spins, while the contribution of the tensor forces is just zero.

Now we shall turn to more general configurations $\{j_1^{n_1} s_1 \alpha_1 J_1, j_2^{n_2} s_2 \alpha_2 J_2\}$ which have non-zero values of s_1 and s_2. Using the properties of irreducible tensor operators[3]), one can show that the diagonal matrix element is in this case:

$$\begin{aligned} &\langle j_1^{n_1} s_1 \alpha_1 J_1, j_2^{n_2} s_2 \alpha_2 J_2;\, J |\, V_{\mathrm{np}} \,| j_1^{n_1} s_1 \alpha_1 J_1, j_2^{n_2} s_2 \alpha_2 J_2;\, J \rangle = \\ &= \langle j_1^{s_1} s_1 \alpha_1 J_1, j_2^{s_2} s_2 \alpha_2 J_2;\, J | (v_0' \sum_{i,k} \pi_0(i,k) + v_1 \sum_{i,k} \pi_0(i,k)\, \pi_s(i,k) + \\ &+ v_T \sum_{i,k} \pi_0(i,k)\, S_{ik}) | \, | j_1^{s_1} s_1 \alpha_1 J_1, j_2^{s_2} s_2 \alpha_2 J_2; J \rangle + \\ &+ (v_0 + \tfrac{1}{4} v_1)(n_1 n_2 - \lambda_1 \lambda_2 s_1 s_2) F^0\,. \end{aligned} \tag{20}$$

Here

$$\lambda_i = \frac{2j_i + 1 - 2n_i}{2j_i + 1 - 2s_i} \leqslant 1 \quad \text{and} \quad v_0' = v_0 \left[\lambda_1 \lambda_2 + \frac{v_1}{4v_0} (\lambda_1 \lambda_2 - 1)\right]. \tag{21}$$

Thus we come to the idea of a parent configuration, i.e. the one which has $n_i = s_i$. If the dependence on J of states belonging to the parent configuration is known one may use (20) to find the splitting in the case of an increasing number of neutrons and protons. It is evident from (20) that increasing the number of particles leads to a new term, independent of J, as well as to a renormalization of the Wigner force parameter. The matrix elements of singlet and tensor forces depend only on the number of nucleons in the parent configuration. The above treated configuration $\{j_1, j_2\}$ is an example of the simplest parent configuration. In this case:

$$\langle j_1^{n_1} s_1 = 1 j_1, j_2^{n_2} s_2 = 1 j_2; J | V_{\rm np} | j_1^{n_1} s_1 = 1 j_1, j_2^{n_2} s_2 = 1 j_2; J \rangle =$$
$$= v_0' \langle j_1 j_2 J | \pi_0 | j_1 j_2 J \rangle + v_1 \langle j_1 j_2 J | \pi_0 \pi_s | j_1 j_2 J \rangle +$$
$$+ v_T \langle j_1 j_2 J | \pi_0 S_{12} | j_1 j_2 J \rangle + (v_0 + \tfrac{1}{4} v_1)(n_1 n_2 - \lambda_1 \lambda_2) F^0 . \qquad (22)$$

For a ratio $v_1/v_0 = 1$ the Wigner force effective parameter v comes to be:

$$v_0' = v_0 \Lambda = v_0 \left[\frac{5\lambda_1 \lambda_2 - 1}{4} \right]. \qquad (23)$$

The Λ factor has the same form for the particle–particle and the hole–hole configurations, that is, this factor is equal to unity when $n_1 = n_2 = \bar{n}_1 = \bar{n}_2 = 1$ (n is the number of particles, $\bar{n}$ is the number of holes). It falls down with the growth of the number of particles or holes and passes zero near the half-filled level. So the effect of Wigner forces becomes less important with the growth of the number of particles (holes) and the configuration splitting is essentially defined by singlet forces. One should remember that tensor forces are to be taken into consideration only for the states with $J = 0$ and 1. For the particle–hole configurations the Λ factor is negative. It reaches its maximum (in absolute magnitude) of $v_0' = -1.5\, v_0$ for the $\{j_1, j_2^{-1}\}$ configuration. Thus one should expect in the majority of the cases for particle–hole configurations that the level with $J = j_1 + j_2 - 1$ will be the lowest. This statement is independent of the N parity of a given configuration because the major role is played by Wigner forces (see fig. 1). Although the magnitude of the matrix element increases with the increasing number of particles, the contribution of Wigner forces into the configuration splitting falls down. This leads to the fact that the multiplet levels come closer to each other. This causes in turn the major role of pairing correlations in defining the sequence of nuclear levels.

4. The ground state spins for odd–odd nuclei

The investigated dependence of diagonal matrix elements on spin J for the configuration $\{j_1^{n_1} s_1 = 1 j_1, j_2^{n_2} s_2 = 1 j_2\}$ helps in understanding the so-called "revised" Brennan–Bernstein rules[6]) defining the ground state spins for odd–odd nuclei. This is an improved version of the original Nordheim rules[7]).

The curves in fig. 1 show that there are two cases with respect to N parity and v_0/v_1 ratio: either the ground state spin J is equal to $|j_1-j_2|$ (rule R1 of Brennan–Bernstein), or there is an alternative: $J=|j_1-j_2|$ and $J=j_1+j_2$ (rule R2). In this last case the arbitrariness in J disappears if either j_1 or j_2 is equal to $\frac{1}{2}$. Then Wigner forces do not split the configuration, the splitting being defined only by singlet forces. This leads to $J=j_1+j_2$. For the particle–hole configuration, irrespective of the N parity, the ground state spin will be $J=j_1+j_2-1$, i.e. we have rule R3 of Brennan–Bernstein. One should point out that the Brennan–Bernstein rules are explained under the condition that v_0/v_1 is negative.

Summarizing one may say that these rules reflect the dependence of the ground state configuration splitting in the diagonal approximation on the type of configuration. In cases when pairing correlations and interactions of extra particles with the core do not affect the ground state configuration essentially, these rules predict the ground state spins of odd–odd nuclei in consistence with experiment. The exclusions from these rules show that in some cases pairing correlations, core interactions and tensor forces are essential and do change the sequence of levels arising from the configuration splitting in diagonal approximation. This shows clearly that there is no use looking for new rules or trying to revise the Brennan–Bernstein rules if one starts with the Nordheim number parity for the ground state configuration of odd–odd nuclei. It is more important that the investigated dependence of the ground state configuration splitting on the structure of the states allows the prediction of the spin sequence for lower states. It also gives the probability of finding isomeric levels with a given spin in nuclei.

5. High isomeric states

The analytical approach to the investigation of the spin dependence of diagonal matrix elements for a complicated configuration $\{j_2^{s_1}\, s_1\alpha_1\, J_1,\; j_2^{s_2}\, s_2\alpha_2\, J_2\}$ is, in general, a very difficult task. Therefore we have studied in detail the splitting of parent configurations (1n+2p), (2n+1p), (2n+2p) and more complicated ones using the computational methods. This study shows that for given J_1 and J_2 the magnitude of the matrix elements exhibits complicated oscillations with J. But the case of a configuration with J_1 and J_2 equal to their respective maximum values stands apart. Its splitting turns out to be analogous to one for the most simple parent configuration $\{j_1, j_2\}$. It is of importance that in this case the amplitude of the variation of the matrix elements turns out to be maximal. This makes the n–p matrix element for the maximal J possible, sufficiently large to lower the level with

$J = J_{max}$, so that only levels with spins much smaller than J_{max} remain below it. It means that the state $J = J_{max}$ comes to be an isomeric one. Large spin values ($J = 10-20$) are characteristic of these states. Such a state arises when at least one pair of identical particles breaks down, the characteristic energy being quite large (1–3 MeV). These features of the isomeric levels under consideration make it possible to call them high isomeric states.

TABLE 1

Diagonal matrix elements of the n–p interaction (26) of the configurations $\{2g_{9/2}{}^2, 1h_{9/2}{}^2\}$ and $\{1i_{11/2}{}^2, 1h_{9/2}{}^2\}$, for different intermediate and total angular momenta

$\{2g_{9/2}{}^2, 1h_{9/2}{}^2\}$				$\{1i_{11/2}{}^2, 1h_{9/2}{}^2\}$			
J_1	J_2	J	$\langle\|V_{np}\|\rangle$	J_1	J_2	J	$\langle\|V_{np}\|\rangle$
0	0	0	−1.048	0	0	0	−1.336
8	8	0	−1.519	10	8	2	−1.666
6	6	12	−1.033	8	8	14	−1.390
6	8	14	−1.037	8	8	15	−1.473
8	8	13	−0.885	8	8	16	−1.632
8	8	14	−0.980	10	8	16	−1.421
8	8	15	−1.012	10	8	17	−1.564
8	8	16	−1.214	10	8	18	−1.912

In table 1 the calculated V_{np} matrix elements for two configurations $\{2g^2_{\frac{9}{2}}, 1h^2_{\frac{9}{2}}\}$ and $\{1i^2_{\frac{11}{2}}, 1h^2_{\frac{9}{2}}\}$ illustrate the preference of high spin states.

As an example of high isomeric states with large spins are the experimentally discovered levels $J = \frac{25}{2}^+$ (^{211}Po) and $J = 16^+$ (^{212}Po).

6. The residual interaction parameters in heavy nuclei

We shall define now the parameters of the effective two-body interaction operator $V(12)$ in heavy nuclei. The self-consistent shell-model potential parameters as well as the corresponding single particle wave functions are defined in the computation of the levels for nuclei with double closed shell $\pm$ extra nucleon[3]). In order to get the residual interaction parameters, one should use nuclei with two extra particles or holes. The technique in this case is as follows. We write the Hamiltonian $\mathscr{H}$ of the system:

$$\mathscr{H} = \mathscr{H}_0(1) + \mathscr{H}_0(2) + V(12), \tag{24}$$

where $\mathscr{H}_0(i)$ is a single particle Hamiltonian for an ith nucleon in the Woods–Saxon potential. We expand the eigenfunctions of $\mathscr{H}$ in terms of the eigenfunctions of $\mathscr{H}_0=\mathscr{H}_0(1)+\mathscr{H}_0(2)$, i.e.

$$|J\rangle = \sum_{\alpha} c^J(\alpha)\, |\alpha, J\rangle\,. \tag{25}$$

Diagonalizing the energy matrix we find the eigenvalues and coefficients $c^J(\alpha)$ as functions of the two-body interaction parameters. Comparing the calculated results with experimental data one finds the optimal values for these parameters.

Data on ^{206}Pb, ^{210}Pb and ^{210}Po were used to check the parameters of $V(12)$ in the case of identical particles. For the radial part of the two-body interaction, we used the function $\exp\{-r^2/r_0^2\}$ depending on one parameter r_0. The matrix elements for the $J=0$ levels turned out to be especially sensitive to variation of r_0. But the existence of tensor forces which can also change the $J=0$, $J=2$ level spacing makes the r_0 choice more complicated. Thus it appears necessary to make use of the r_0 binding energy dependence for nuclei with $n>2$ investigated in our work[8]). This dependence together with the spacing between ground and first excited states allows for the possibility of unambiguous determination of r_0 and v_T parameters. The resulting value of $r_0=2$ fm is a bit larger than that for free particle interaction which coincides with the nuclear matter calculations. We used data on binding energy and spectra of $J=4, 6, \ldots$ levels to check the other two parameters v_0 and v_1. This gave us $v_0=-20$ MeV and $v_1=-20$ MeV.

The parameters thus obtained were used to calculate excitation spectra and other properties of nuclei with 4 and 10 nucleons above the closed shell, i.e. for ^{212}Po and ^{218}Rn, respectively[8]). This made it possible to explain all the already known properties of these nuclei and to predict a number of new data on them. Thus we are led to the assertion that our choice of parameters is quite adequate for the problem.

In the case of odd–odd nuclei it was impossible to explain the ^{210}Bi and ^{206}Tl spectra without taking tensor forces into consideration.

It follows from the (d,p) reaction[9]) and β-decay[10]) data that the first ten levels of ^{210}Bi with spins $J=0$–9 have wave functions composed essentially of the $\{2g_{\frac{9}{2}}, 1h_{\frac{9}{2}}\}$ configuration, with small admixture of the $\{1i_{\frac{11}{2}}, 1h_{\frac{9}{2}}\}$ configuration. As it was shown in ref. 11, one cannot get such a function for the ground state $J=1^-$ of ^{210}Bi using only central forces and without violations of the positions of other levels. The use of tensor forces in the $V(12)$ operator permits us to circumvent the difficulty. Fig. 4 shows the level positions obtained by diagonalization of the energy matrix as a function of the residual interaction parameters. To simplify the choice of parameters one may use the following arguments:

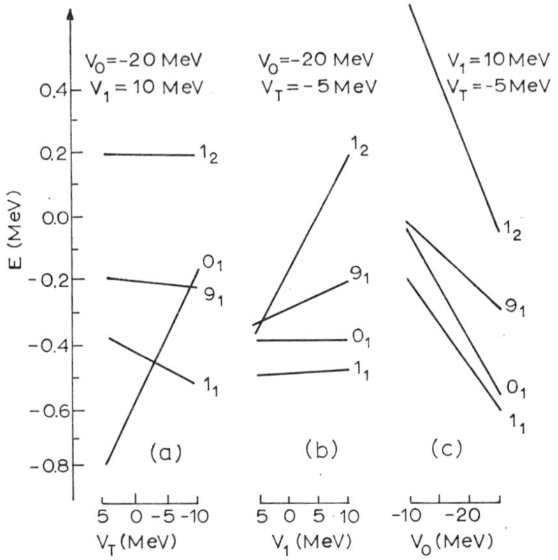

Fig. 4. Level shift in ^{210}Bi as a function of the parameters of tensor (a), singlet (b) and Wigner (c) forces when the parameters of the other two forces are fixed.

1. The position of the centre of gravity for a multiplet (binding energy) is essentially defined by Wigner forces.
2. The position of spin $J=9^-$ and $J=1^-$ levels is affected mostly by singlet forces.
3. The main contribution to the splitting of spin $J=0^-$ and $J=1^-$ levels arises from tensor forces.

One can use an analogous argumentation for the ^{206}Tl spectrum, the only difference being that in this case lower states consist of a mixture of three configurations: $\{3p_{\frac{1}{2}}, 3s_{\frac{1}{2}}\}$, $\{3p_{\frac{1}{2}}, 2d_{\frac{3}{2}}\}$ and $\{2f_{\frac{5}{2}}, 3s_{\frac{1}{2}}\}$.

Fitting the parameters for ^{210}Bi and ^{206}Tl nuclei separately gained approximately the same result:

$$V(12) = -(24 - 9\pi_s + 4S_{12}) \exp\{-\tfrac{1}{4}r^2\}. \tag{26}$$

The effects of short range repulsion and core excitation cannot change the residual interaction parameters by more than 10%. Hence the matrix elements of the singlet forces are small in the cases under consideration, and the value of v_1 is less precise than the rest.

We used the interaction (26) to calculate not only the ^{210}Bi and ^{206}Tl spectra, but also the α- and γ-transition probabilities[11]). The computation of the reduced widths γ^2 of α-decay from the 1^- and 9^- levels in ^{210}Bi into the levels of ^{206}Tl, provided an independent check of our wave functions. The structural factor depending on the overlap of the wave functions may change γ^2 by several orders. One cannot obtain a change of γ^2 which is that strong without making use of the residual interaction.

In conclusion we would like to stress that the many-particle approach with the Racah technique has a clear advantage in the study of many aspects of nuclear structure.

References

1) G. Racah, Phys. Rev. **62**, 438 (1942).
2) H. Horie and K. Sasaki, Progr. Theoret. Phys. (Kyoto) **25**, 475 (1961).
3) A. de-Shalit and I. Talmi, *Nuclear Shell Theory* (Academic Press, New York, 1963).
4) L. A. Sliv and B. A. Volchok, Zh. Eksperim. i Teor. Fiz. **36**, 539 (1959).
5) G. Racah, Phys. Rev. **63**, 367 (1943).
6) M. H. Brennan and A. M. Bernstein, Phys. Rev. **120**, 927 (1960).
7) L. W. Nordheim, Rev. Mod. Phys. **23**, 322 (1951).
8) I. M. Band, Yu. I. Kharitonov and L. A. Sliv, Nucl. Phys. **35**, 136 (1962); Nucl. Phys. **54**, 364 (1964).
9) I. R. Erskine, Phys. Rev. **138**, B 851 (1965).
10) A. Winter and J. Sodeman, Nucl. Phys. **69**, 369 (1965).
11) K. B. Baktybaev, I. M. Band, L. A. Sliv and Yu. I. Kharitonov, Yadernaja Fizika **6**, 270 (1967).

Spectroscopic and group theoretical methods in physics
© North-Holland Publ. Co., Amsterdam, 1968

ON THE RELATIVE SIZE AND BOUNDARY DIFFUSENESS OF THE NUCLEI ^{16}O, ^{17}O AND ^{18}O*

G. GOLDRING, H. M. LOEBENSTEIN, I. PLESSER
and M. W. SACHS**

Department of Nuclear Physics, Weizmann Institute, Rehovoth, Israel

The spatial distribution of the stable oxygen isotopes (more precisely of the $O+{}^{12}C$ systems) was examined in elastic scattering experiments. The information obtained in these measurements relates to both the relative extension and relative diffuseness of the nuclear boundary in the three isotopes ^{16}O, ^{17}O and ^{18}O.

Elastic scattering of heavy ions has become increasingly important in recent years as a tool in nuclear structure. The gross features of the angular distribution and the energy dependence can in general be reproduced quite well by a simple model for the reaction, namely the scattering by a uniformly charged opaque sphere. The detailed analysis of such experiments is generally carried out either by a phase shift analysis or by optical model methods. The parameters obtained from best fit procedures are not always unique and their significance is not always clear. The attitude adopted in the present work is that real physical significance can be ascribed to *relative* values of the parameters extracted from a series of experiments similar in their nature, performed on nuclei in one close neighbourhood.

In the experiments presented here the elastic scattering of the oxygen isotopes ^{16}O, ^{17}O and ^{18}O from ^{12}C was studied and analysed by phase shift methods. The angular distributions of the three isotopes exhibit significant differences which are interpreted as differences in the diffuseness of the boundaries of the various isotopes. The mean radial extension is found to be very nearly the same in all three cases.

The angular distribution of the elastic scattering of ^{16}O, ^{17}O and ^{18}O on

* Presented as a tribute to a great man and homage to a great teacher.

** NATO Fellow during 1965. Present address: Yale University, New Haven, Connecticut, U.S.A.

^{12}C was measured at a bombarding energy of 35.0 MeV corresponding to 15.0, 14.48 and 14.0 MeV respectively in the C.M. system. Carbon targets of 40–100 μg/cm^2 were bombarded by 5^+ oxygen beams from the tandem accelerator at the Heinemann accelerator laboratory in Rehovoth. The oxygen ions were produced in an RF ion source fed by oxygen gas. The ^{17}O and ^{18}O beams were produced from heavy oxygen gas generated from enriched water of 10% and 98% enrichment respectively which was electrolytically decomposed *in situ*. Typical beam intensities on a spot of about 1 mm in diameter were 200 nA for ^{16}O and ^{18}O and 70 nA for ^{17}O. The scattered particles were detected by a silicon surface barrier detector of an angular opening of 0.7° × 3.5°. The reaction products were identified by means of a

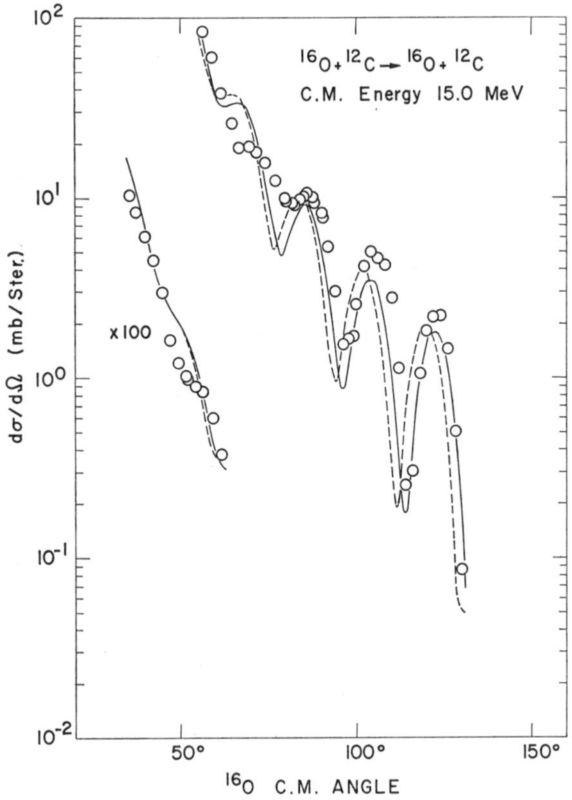

Fig. 1a. Angular distribution of ^{16}O + ^{12}C at 15.0 MeV C.M. energy. The solid line is the best fit curve calculated with $L = 9.40$, $\Delta L = 0.257$ and $\mu = 1.75$. The sensitivity of the parameter L is demonstrated by the broken line which is calculated with $L = 9.60$ and ΔL and μ unchanged.

second counter registering (in coincidence) the conjugate reaction product. As there is a slow build up of carbon on the target, the target was continuously monitored by a fixed counter and all measurements were normalized by means of this counter. The fixed counter and with it the entire measurement were calibrated in absolute cross section terms by carrying out a low energy measurement where the scattering is purely Rutherford scattering. The comparison of measurements at different bombarding energies was based on current measurements and the relative mean charge state of the oxygen beam at the two energies was determined by elastic scattering (Rutherford scattering) measurements from a nickel foil.

The angular distributions of ^{16}O, ^{17}O and ^{18}O on ^{12}C are shown in figs.

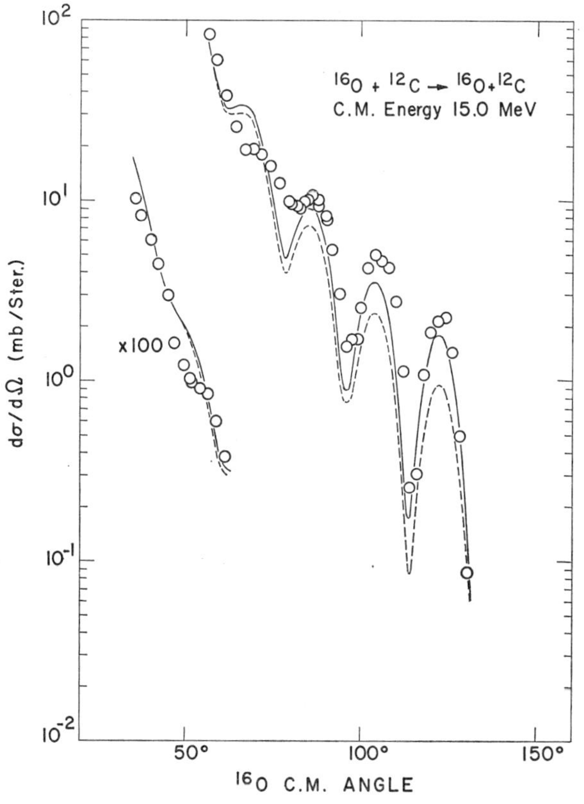

Fig. 1b. Angular distribution of $^{16}O+^{12}C$ at 15.0 MeV C.M. energy. The solid line is the best fit curve calculated with $L=9.40$, $\Delta L=0.257$ and $\mu=1.75$. The sensitivity of the parameter ΔL is demonstrated by the broken line which is calculated with $\Delta L=0.307$ and L and μ unchanged.

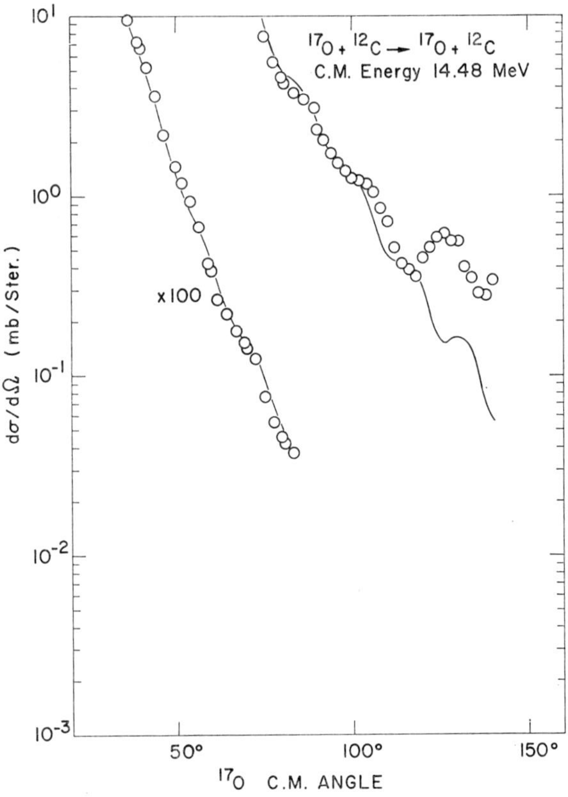

Fig. 2. Angular distribution of $^{17}O + ^{12}C$ at 14.48 MeV C.M. energy. Only the smooth part of the angular distribution up to $\theta_{C.M.} = 118°$ was used to minimize the error function, The calculated angular distribution shown by the solid line was calculated with $L = 11.36$. $\Delta L = 0.603$ and $\mu = 0.379$.

1a, 1b, 2 and 3. The error in the absolute scale is $\pm 6\%$. The curves shown in the figures were calculated with the scattering amplitude $f(\theta)$:

$$f(\theta) = f_c(\theta) - \frac{i}{2k} \sum_{l=0}^{L_{max}} (2l+1)(\eta_l e^{-2i\sigma_l} - 1) e^{2i\sigma_l} P_l(\cos\theta),$$

with η_l given by:

$$\mathrm{Re}(\eta_l e^{-2i\sigma_l}) = \left[1 + \exp\left(\frac{L-l}{\Delta L}\right)\right]^{-1},$$

$$\mathrm{Im}(\eta_l e^{-2i\sigma_l}) = \mu \Delta L \frac{d}{dl} \left\{\left[1 + \exp\left(\frac{L-l}{\Delta L}\right)\right]^{-1}\right\},$$

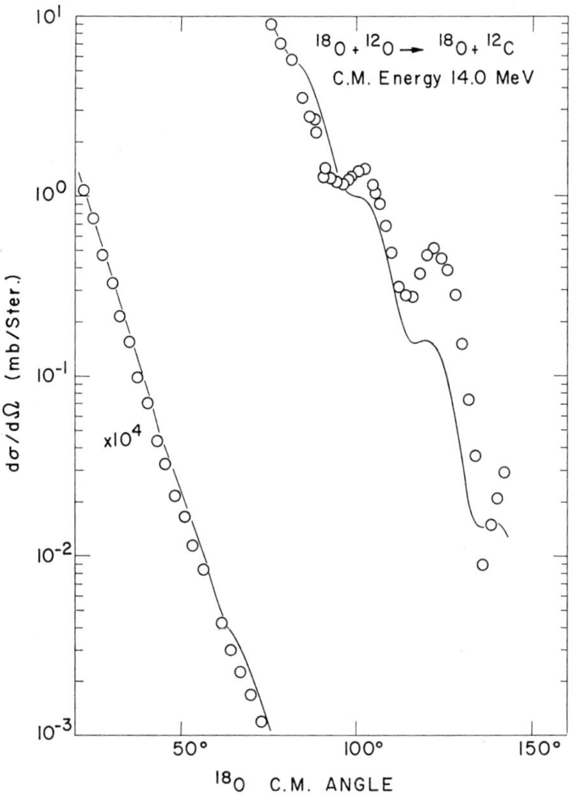

Fig. 3. Angular distribution of $^{18}O + ^{12}C$ at 14.0 MeV C.M. energy. The solid line is the best fit curve calculated with $L = 9.39$, $\Delta L = 0.55$ and $\mu = 1.068$.

where $f_c(\theta)$ is the Coulomb scattering amplitude and σ_l are the Coulomb phase shifts.

This is a simplified version of the procedure of Frahn and Venter[1]). In order to determine the parameters L, ΔL and μ which would best fit the experimental results an error function ε defined as:

$$\varepsilon = \sum_i \left[\frac{\sigma_{\text{exp.}}(\theta_i) - \sigma_{\text{cal.}}(\theta_i)}{\sigma_{\text{exp.}}(\theta_i)} \right]^2$$

was minimized by an iterative search program. All experimental points were equally weighted in this program, as the deviations are considered to be due to the oversimplification inherent in this treatment rather than the experimental errors. The choice of the error function and the density of points

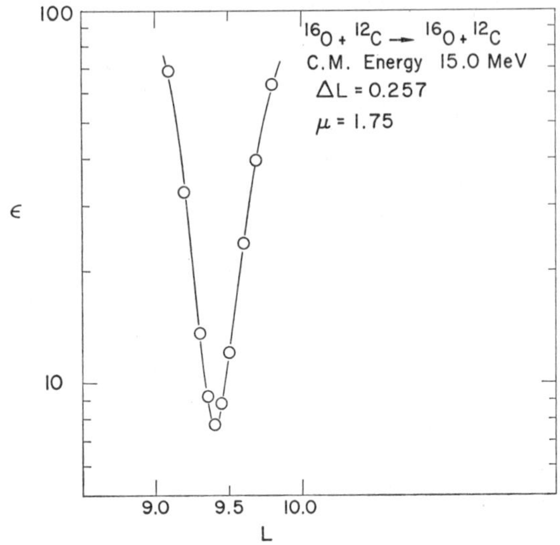

Fig. 4. The dependence of the error function ε on the parameter L for the case of $^{16}O+^{12}C$. ΔL and μ are kept constant and equal to $\Delta L=0.257$ and $\mu=1.75$.

contain a certain arbitrariness which will influence to some extent the derived parameters but only in a rather limited range.

The angular distributions of ^{16}O and ^{18}O are shown in fig. 1a, (1b) and fig. 3. The calculated cross sections giving best fit to the experimental points are drawn as solid lines and the parameters used for their calculation are summarized in table 1. The marked differences in the angular distributions are reflected in the differences of the parameters obtained. The error in the parameters is determined by the change in the error function ε they produce and also by examining the deterioration of the fit obtained with the changed parameters. Fig. 1a shows as an example the calculated angular distribution best fit, with $L=9.40$ (solid line) and with $L=9.60$ (broken line). Here ΔL and μ remained unchanged. Similarly, in fig. 1b, L and μ were kept constant and the two curves are drawn for $\Delta L=0.257$ (best fit, solid line), and $\Delta L=0.307$ (broken line). Fig. 4 shows for the case of $^{16}O+^{12}C$ the dependence of the error function ε on L while ΔL and μ remain unchanged. As one sees from the displacement of the broken line in fig. 1a, it is possible by varying L to shift the broken line so that it would be in phase again with the experimental points, but then the distance between adjacent peaks will be changed. Of course with a multiparameter fit there exists a certain freedom of changing one parameter and compensating the change with the others but this freedom is rather limited. For example, keeping L constant one can compensate to

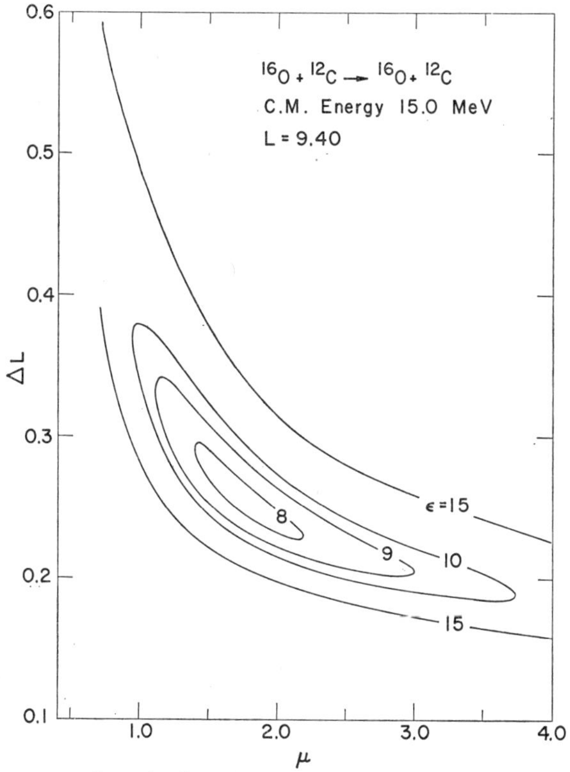

Fig. 5. The contours of equal values of the error function ε are shown as function of ΔL and μ for the case of $^{16}O+^{12}C$. L is kept constant ($L=9.40$).

some extent the change in the error function ε due to a change in μ by changing ΔL. For the case of $^{16}O+^{12}C$ this is demonstrated in fig. 5, which shows the contours of equal values of the error function ε. As in other works of this type, it was found that the parameters on which the angular distribution depends most sensitively are L and ΔL. These are also the parameters which are related most directly to specific physical properties: L to the nuclear radius and ΔL to its diffuseness.

In fig. 2 the angular distribution of ^{17}O in ^{12}C is shown. The analysis of the angular distribution by the same formulae which were used for ^{16}O and ^{18}O is questionable because of the nuclear spin of ^{17}O being different from zero. It was indeed found impossible to obtain a reasonable fit for the total experimental range. As the spin effects are expected to be most significant at backward angles, an attempt was made to fit only the smooth part of the angular distribution up to 118° with the same formulae used for ^{16}O and

TABLE 1

Parameters computed from the total angular range

Projectile	C.M. energy (MeV)	L	ΔL	μ	r_0 (fm)	d (fm)
^{16}O	15.0	9.40 ± 0.20	0.257 ± 0.050	1.75 ± 0.60	1.52 ± 0.02	0.10 ± 0.02
^{18}O	14.0	9.39 ± 0.20	0.55 ± 0.05	1.068 ± 0.200	1.55 ± 0.02	0.22 ± 0.02

TABLE 2

Parameters computed from the smooth part of the angular range

Projectile	C.M. energy (MeV)	L	ΔL	μ	r_0 (fm)	d (fm)
^{16}O	15.0	11.27 ± 0.70	0.39 ± 0.13	0.04 ± 0.25	1.68 ± 0.05	0.16 ± 0.05
^{17}O	14.48	11.36 ± 0.70	0.603 ± 0.100	0.379 ± 0.200	1.70 ± 0.06	0.25 ± 0.04
^{18}O	14.0	10.80 ± 0.60	0.845 ± 0.170	0.22 ± 0.18	1.66 ± 0.05	0.34 ± 0.07

^{18}O. The resulting fit is shown as the solid line in fig. 2 and the parameters that were used are given in table 2. In order to compare the parameters obtained for ^{17}O with those of ^{16}O and ^{18}O, the parameters for these two nuclei were also determined from the smooth part of their angular distribution. These parameters are summarized in table 2. Comparison with table 1 shows that the values of L obtained from analysis of the forward region are about 20% larger than those obtained from the complete range. The values of ΔL are likewise increased by some 50%. This dependence on the angular range emphasizes the shortcomings of the phase shift analysis. However, as was pointed out above, we believe the *relative* values of the parameters for the three isotopes to have a definite meaning and to reflect trends in the geometrical parameters of these nuclei.

The nuclear "radius" $R=r_0(A_1^{\frac{1}{3}}+A_2^{\frac{1}{3}})$ corresponding to the partial wave L and the diffuseness d are obtained from L and ΔL through the relation:

$$E = \frac{Z_1 Z_2 e^2}{(R+d)} + \frac{\hbar^2 (L+\Delta L)(L+\Delta L+1)}{2m(R+d)^2}.$$

From tables 1 and 2 one sees that r_0 remains essentially the same for the three isotopes but the diffuseness d shows a systematic increase with the neutron number. This is the trend to be expected if one views the ^{16}O nucleus as a closely bound structure and the heavier oxygen isotopes as made up of an ^{16}O core and one or two relatively loosely bound neutrons.

Reference

1) W. E. Frahn and R. H. Venter, Ann. Phys. (N.Y.) **24**, 243 (1963).

Spectroscopic and group theoretical methods in physics
© North-Holland Publ. Co., Amsterdam, 1968

HADRON MASSES IN THE QUARK MODEL

H. R. RUBINSTEIN

Department of Physics, The Weizmann Institute of Science, Rehovoth, Israel

and

I. TALMI*

Palmer Physical Laboratory, Princeton University, Princeton, New Jersey

Except for a few components of matter (leptons), all other particles seem to be composite. Atoms and nuclei are typical examples where compelling experimental evidence exists that they are made of particles that conserve their individuality rather well within the bound state.

In the last ten years the idea that the so-called elementary particles are also composite has been gaining momentum. Experimentally, the fact that instead of being point-like they have electromagnetic form factors is a rather convincing argument. Theoretically, the ever increasing number of particles and resonances discovered in the laboratories calls for some simplification. One idea is that all of them are composite. This approach, called bootstrap [1,2]), has very appealing features but has not been able to give agreement with the experiment. The other approach, which is the one discussed in this paper, is to consider the strongly interacting elementary particles as being built up of some fundamental objects called quarks [3,4]), yet unobserved. The possibility of having this physical situation is rather baffling. The point is that quarks must be heavy to remain unobserved with present accelerators. If they are as heavy as 5 GeV, since two are needed for mesons and three for baryons, the binding energy has to be of the order of the rest mass of the constituent quarks [5]).

Without calling for unconventional explanations, as hitherto unknown

* National Science Foundation Senior Foreign Scientist Fellow. On leave of absence from the Weizmann Institute of Science, Rehovoth, Israel.

conservation laws, it is rather hard to believe that these objects could perform non-relativistic motion and conserve their identity under these extreme physical conditions. Nevertheless, soon after Gell-Mann[3]) and Zweig[4]) proposed the quarks in order to explain the absence of the fundamental representation of SU(3), Morpurgo[6]) suggested that a non-relativistic model could give a possible explanation of the experimental data without running into the contradictions that a fully covariant SU(6) theory would imply[7]). This model[6,8]) presented an explanation for the neutron proton magnetic moment ratio in terms of additive contributions of one-body operators as in nuclear physics. Most remarkably, the radiative lifetime of the ω meson can be expressed under the same assumptions in terms of the nuclear magnetic moment, in agreement with experiment[8,9]).

Using standard techniques of additivity of the scattering amplitude, Lipkin and collaborators presented in a series of papers a large set of relations for high energy scattering[5]). Zero energy processes, including proton antiproton annihilation[5]), scattering lenghts[10]) and decays of resonances[5]) have been treated by several groups with success.

Though these indirect pieces of evidence cannot be considered a proof of the existence of quarks it is clear that whether mathematical or physical quarks exist these techniques are easy, neat and successful to deal with many problems, as in nuclear physics. In many cases, as the one presented below, the results are *not* equivalent to the symmetry approach. For example, assuming the perturbation which gives mass splittings to be a two-body operator and *not* to be an operator which transforms as some generator of a group the results may be different. However, in many cases the differences though significant cannot be tested experimentally. In this paper we present a detailed analysis of the masses of the best known particles using techniques familiar to nuclear physicists. The problem of masses in the quark model was first studied by Zweig in his unpublished CERN preprint of 1964[4]). He obtained some of the results developed in the present paper but he did not pursue them and in his published work he abandoned this approach and considered mass relations based on the symmetry approach.

In the quark model the baryons and mesons are considered as composed of quarks in the same way that nuclei are considered composed of nucleons and atoms are composed of nuclei and electrons. These methods were developed and perfected by the late G. Racah who showed great interest also in the applications of group theory to the study of elementary particles. Some of us remember how happy he was when he saw that the $-\frac{2}{3}$ value predicted by SU(6) for the ratio between neutron and proton magnetic moments, followed very simply from the quark model. In the following we shall use only such elementary considerations. We shall not use the language of group theory since we would like to emphasize the similarity of the present considerations with those of nuclear and atomic spectroscopy.

The quark model used here is a theory in which non-relativistic quantum mechanics is applied to a system of real or mathematical quarks for the study of effects which can be considered as perturbations. As has been often emphasized, most of the present considerations do not depend on the existence of real quarks. There are three spin $S=\frac{1}{2}$ quarks with the following quantum numbers (in order to form the fundamental representation of SU (6))

$$\begin{aligned} &\text{N-quark, } I=\tfrac{1}{2} \text{ (p-quark } I_3=\tfrac{1}{2}, \text{ n-quark } I_3=-\tfrac{1}{2}) \; Y=\tfrac{1}{3}, \\ &\lambda\text{-quark } I=0 \quad Y=-\tfrac{2}{3}. \end{aligned} \tag{1}$$

The baryons are composed of three quarks. The baryons in the SU(3) octet (with spin $S=\frac{1}{2}$) and SU(3) decuplet (with spin $S=\frac{3}{2}$) will be considered in this paper. Their wave functions in the spin and internal coordinates of the quarks belong to the $(56, \underline{1})$ representation of $U(6)\times U(6)$ where one U(6) operates on the spin and unitary coordinates of the quarks and the other U(6) on those of the antiquarks. These wave functions are fully symmetric in the three quarks. If the quark masses and interactions were completely symmetric, the masses of all these baryons would have been degenerate. We shall investigate in the following the effects of symmetry breaking interactions between the quarks. We shall assume that the effects of these on the wave functions are small and therefore the mass splittings can be calculated as a first-order perturbation. We shall first construct the wave functions of the various baryons and then calculate the mass splittings. We shall assume that the symmetry breaking interactions are isospin conserving (as well as rotationally invariant) and that the masses of the p-quark and n-quark are equal. Therefore, we can find the eigenstates of the system by constructing states with definite spin and isospin[12]). If we remove the restriction to isospin invariance, it is possible to calculate electromagnetic mass splittings of the baryons[13]). We shall discuss here only the isospin conserving, medium strong interaction[14, 15]), that gives rise to rather large mass splittings between states with different isospins.

The wave functions of the baryons are thus assumed to be fully symmetric with respect to the internal degrees of freedom of the three quarks, i.e. the spin, the isospin and hypercharge. Every such function is multiplied by the *same* wave function of the space coordinates of the quarks. In order to describe the properties of baryons it should have a total orbital angular momentum $L=0$. If the quarks are to be considered as fermions the spatial wave function should be fully antisymmetric under exchange of the quark coordinates. No simple function with these properties was found (as contrasted with a fully symmetric $L=0$, spatial wave function). We shall not further discuss this problem since for the calculations to be described in the following there is no need to make *any* assumption about the form of this function. The following considerations will hold, for instance, if the spatial wave function is fully symmetric.

In order to exhibit the similarity with nuclear spectroscopy [12]), let us use definite numbers to indicate the given quark coordinates and symmetrize the wave functions with respect to these numbers. As an example, let us consider the spin-unitary wave function of the Y^{*0} ($S=\frac{3}{2}$, $I=1$, $I_3=0$, $Y=0$). It must contain one proton-quark, one neutron-quark and one λ-quark. We start accordingly from the wave function

$$[(\mathrm{p}(1)\,\mathrm{n}(2))^{S_0=1}\,\lambda(3)]^{S=\frac{3}{2}}, \tag{2}$$

where p, n and λ refer to the three possible states of a quark and 1, 2 and 3 stand for the (internal) quark coordinates. In (2) the spins of quarks 1 and 2 are coupled with Clebsch–Gordan coefficients to $S_0=1$ and this spin is coupled to the spin of quark 3 to form a state with $S=\frac{3}{2}$. To symmetrize this wave function we have to apply to it the operator

$$\mathscr{S}=\sum_P P, \tag{3}$$

where P runs over all possible permutations of the particle coordinates 1, 2 and 3.

Fortunately we shall not have to deal with a large number of terms. We recall that for calculating matrix elements it is not necessary to symmetrize explicitly the wave functions with respect to particles in different states. Matrix elements of single particle operators are not affected at all by such symmetrization. When calculating matrix elements of two particle operators the symmetrization can be introduced in the last step of the computation i.e. only the two particle wave functions should be symmetrized. With this understanding we shall suppress quark coordinates and write in the following for (2) the expression

$$[(\mathrm{pn})^{S_0=1}\,\lambda]^{S=\frac{3}{2}}. \tag{4}$$

Let us now discuss the cases in which two identical quarks appear. If we couple their spins to a definite total S_0, the wave function will be symmetric if $S_0=1$ and antisymmetric if $S_0=0$. Thus, the only symmetric state of two

λ-quarks is the $(\lambda\lambda)^{S_0=1\, I_0=0}$ state. When dealing with p-quarks and n-quarks we can make use of their isospins and write down the symmetric wave functions of two nucleon-quarks (N-quarks). The isospin functions of two N-quarks are symmetric for $I_0=1$ (which includes the cases of two p-quarks or two n-quarks) and antisymmetric for $I_0=0$. The only two possible symmetric combinations of spin–isospin wave functions are thus

$$(\mathrm{NN})^{S_0=1\, I_0=1} \quad (\text{including } (\mathrm{pp})^{S_0=1} \text{ and } (\mathrm{nn})^{S_0=1}) \quad \text{and} \quad (\mathrm{NN})^{S_0=0\, I_0=0}.$$

The wave functions of a λ-quark and N-quark can be symmetrized, no matter what their total spin is. We have, therefore, two possible symmetric states

$$(\mathrm{N}\lambda)^{S_0=1\, I_0=\frac{1}{2}} \quad \text{and} \quad (\mathrm{N}\lambda)^{S_0=0\, I_0=\frac{1}{2}}.$$

We can now write down the spin-unitary wave functions of the baryons. Those of the SU(3) decuplet with $S=\frac{3}{2}$ are

$$\mathrm{N}^*(I=\tfrac{3}{2}, Y=1) \qquad [(\mathrm{NN})^{S_0=1\, I_0=1}\mathrm{N}]^{S=\frac{3}{2}\, I=\frac{3}{2}}, \tag{5}$$
$$Y^*(I=1, Y=0) \qquad [(\mathrm{NN})^{S_0=1\, I_0=1}\lambda]^{S=\frac{3}{2}\, I=1}, \tag{6}$$
$$\Xi^*(I=\tfrac{1}{2}, Y=-1) \qquad [(\lambda\lambda)^{S_0=1\, I_0=0}\mathrm{N}]^{S=\frac{3}{2}\, I=\frac{1}{2}}, \tag{7}$$
$$\Omega\ (I=0, Y=-2) \qquad [(\lambda\lambda)^{S_0=1\, I_0=0}\lambda]^{S=\frac{3}{2}\, I=0}. \tag{8}$$

These are the only possibilities to obtain symmetric wave functions of 3 quarks with $S_0=\frac{3}{2}$. It is worthwhile to mention that the wave functions of N* (eq. (5)) and Ω (eq. (8)) are fully symmetric. In spite of the apparent asymmetry in the writing of, say, $([\lambda(1)\,\lambda(2)]^{S_0=1}\,\lambda(3))^{S=\frac{3}{2}}$ no further symmetrization is necessary. This can be most easily seen for the states with $S_z=\frac{3}{2}$ (and also $I_3=\frac{3}{2}$ for N*) which are manifestly symmetric (all spins and isospins are parallel). All other states are obtained from these by acting with the symmetric lowering operator S_- (and the corresponding symmetric I_-).

The wave functions of the $S=\frac{1}{2}$ baryons in the SU(3) octet are

$$\mathrm{N}(I=\tfrac{1}{2}, Y=1) \quad \begin{array}{ll} \mathrm{p}(I_3=\frac{1}{2}) & [(\mathrm{pp})^{S_0=1}\,\mathrm{n}]^{S=\frac{1}{2}}, \\ \mathrm{n}(I_3=-\frac{1}{2}) & [(\mathrm{nn})^{S_0=1}\,\mathrm{p}]^{S=\frac{1}{2}}, \end{array} \tag{9}$$
$$\Lambda(I=0, Y=0) \qquad [(\mathrm{NN})^{S_0=0\, I_0=0}\,\lambda]^{S=\frac{1}{2}\, I=0}, \tag{10}$$
$$\Sigma(I=1, Y=0) \qquad [(\mathrm{NN})^{S_0=1\, I_0=1}\,\lambda]^{S=\frac{1}{2}\, I=1}, \tag{11}$$
$$\Xi(I=\tfrac{1}{2}, Y=-1) \qquad [(\lambda\lambda)^{S_0=1\, I_0=0}\,\mathrm{N}]^{S=\frac{1}{2}\, I=\frac{1}{2}}. \tag{12}$$

These are the only possibilities to obtain symmetric wave functions of 3 quarks with $S=\frac{1}{2}$. The wave functions of the nucleons were written above in terms of the p- and n-states of the quark rather than using the combined state of the N-quark. This is due to the fact that unlike the case of the N*, we have here the coupling of two N-quarks to the state with $S_0=0$, $I_0=0$ as well as the $S_0=1$, $I_0=1$ state. Thus, the fully symmetric wave function for the nucleon should have two terms, one like (5) and the other with $S_0=0$, $I_0=0$. The coefficients of these terms are the spectroscopic *coefficients of fractional parentage* introduced by Racah[16]).

If we want to carry out explicitly the symmetrization, we can start from the function $[(N_1N_2)^{S_0=1\,I_0=1}\,N_3]^{S=\frac{1}{2}\,I=\frac{1}{2}}$, where the quark numbers appear as subindices. Recalling that $(N_1N_2)^{S_0=1\,I_0=1}$ is symmetric, we obtain

$$\mathscr{S}[(N_1N_2)^{11}N_3]^{\frac{1}{2}\frac{1}{2}} = 2[(N_1N_2)^{11}N_3]^{\frac{1}{2}\frac{1}{2}} + \\ + 2[(N_1N_3)^{11}N_2]^{\frac{1}{2}\frac{1}{2}} + 2[(N_2N_3)^{11}N_1]^{\frac{1}{2}\frac{1}{2}}. \qquad (13)$$

We can now restore this expression to the form where N_3 is coupled last by using the product of two change of coupling transformations

$$\langle j_1j_2(J_{12})j_3J|j_1j_3(J_{13})j_2\rangle = \\ = (-1)^{j_2+j_3+J_{12}+J_{13}}\sqrt{(2J_{12}+1)(2J_{13}+1)}\begin{Bmatrix} j_1 & j_2 & J_{12} \\ J & j_3 & J_{13} \end{Bmatrix} \qquad (14)$$

one for the spins and the other for the isospins of the N-quarks. We obtain for (13) the expression

$$2[(N_1N_2)^{11}N_3]^{\frac{1}{2}\frac{1}{2}} + 2\sum_{S'I'}(-1)^{\frac{1}{2}+\frac{1}{2}+1+S'}\sqrt{3(2S'+1)}\,(-1)^{\frac{1}{2}+\frac{1}{2}+1+I'}\times \\ \times\sqrt{3(2I'+1)}\begin{Bmatrix} \frac{1}{2} & \frac{1}{2} & 1 \\ \frac{1}{2} & \frac{1}{2} & S' \end{Bmatrix}\begin{Bmatrix} \frac{1}{2} & \frac{1}{2} & 1 \\ \frac{1}{2} & \frac{1}{2} & I' \end{Bmatrix}[(N_1N_2)^{S'I'}N_3]^{\frac{1}{2}\frac{1}{2}} + \\ + 2\sum_{S'I'}(-1)^{\frac{1}{2}+\frac{1}{2}+1+S'}\sqrt{3(2S'+1)}(-1)^{\frac{1}{2}+\frac{1}{2}+1+I'}\times \\ \times\sqrt{3(2I'+1)}\begin{Bmatrix} \frac{1}{2} & \frac{1}{2} & 1 \\ \frac{1}{2} & \frac{1}{2} & S' \end{Bmatrix}\begin{Bmatrix} \frac{1}{2} & \frac{1}{2} & 1 \\ \frac{1}{2} & \frac{1}{2} & I' \end{Bmatrix}[(N_2N_1)^{S'I'}N_3]^{\frac{1}{2}\frac{1}{2}}. \qquad (15)$$

When we add the last two summations the terms corresponding to antisymmetric functions, $S'=1$, $I'=0$ and $S'=0$, $I'=1$ cancel each other. Inserting the actual values of the Racah coefficients

$$\begin{Bmatrix} \frac{1}{2} & \frac{1}{2} & 1 \\ \frac{1}{2} & \frac{1}{2} & 0 \end{Bmatrix} = \tfrac{1}{2}, \quad \begin{Bmatrix} \frac{1}{2} & \frac{1}{2} & 1 \\ \frac{1}{2} & \frac{1}{2} & 1 \end{Bmatrix} = \tfrac{1}{6}$$

we obtain

$$3[(N_1N_2)^{11}N_3]^{\frac{1}{2}\frac{1}{2}} + 3[(N_1N_2)^{00}N_3]^{\frac{1}{2}\frac{1}{2}}.$$

Thus, the normalized fully symmetric wave function for the nucleon can be written as

$$N(I=\tfrac{1}{2},\ Y=1)=\frac{1}{\sqrt{2}}[(N_1N_2)^{S_0=1\ I_0=1}N_3]^{S=\frac{1}{2}\ I=\frac{1}{2}}+$$

$$+\frac{1}{\sqrt{2}}[(N_1N_2)^{S_0=0\ I_0=0}N_3]^{S=\frac{1}{2}\ I=\frac{1}{2}}. \qquad (9')$$

We shall now calculate the baryon masses assuming that the breaking of the symmetry can be treated as a first-order perturbation. We assume that this symmetry breaking is due to two possible causes. One is some mass difference between the N-quarks and the λ-quark (ignoring the possible mass difference between p-quarks and n-quarks which contributes to the small electromagnetic mass difference between baryons). The other symmetry breaking is due to relatively small differences in the two body interactions between the quarks in various states. We shall calculate the mass splittings from these differences by evaluating their expectation values for the wave functions of the (56, $\underline{1}$) representation. These wave functions are presumably obtained by solving the three quark problem with equal masses and fully symmetric interactions (independent of spins, isospins and hypercharge). Let us denote by M_0 the mass of the three quark system with equal quark masses m and symmetric interaction. We now introduce the actual quark masses

$$m_N = m + \delta m_N, \qquad m_\lambda = m + \delta m_\lambda,$$

and denote by V_{ij} the (rotationally invariant) symmetry breaking part of the quark–quark interaction. We then obtain the various masses by diagonalizing the operator

$$M_0 + \sum_{i=1}^{3} \delta m_i + \sum_{i<j}^{3} V_{ij} \qquad (16)$$

within the submatrix defined by the wave functions which belong to the (56, $\underline{1}$) representation of U(6) × U(6).

As mentioned above, we also assume that the symmetry breaking V_{ij} do not connect two body states with different values of the isospin. As a result, the operator (16) has no non-diagonal elements between the baryon states (5) to (12). The expectation values of (16) in these states are linear combinations of δm_N, δm_λ and quark–quark diagonal matrix elements of V_{ij}. The integration over the space coordinates gives to a given matrix element the same contribution in all baryon states. Thus, the baryon masses are given as linear combinations of the following constants

$$M_0, \delta m_N, \delta m_\lambda, D_{NN}^{S=1\ I=1}, D_{NN}^{S=0\ I=0}, D_{\lambda\lambda}^{S=1\ I=0}, D_{N\lambda}^{S=1\ I=\frac{1}{2}}, D_{N\lambda}^{S=0\ I=\frac{1}{2}}. \qquad (17)$$

In (17) the $D^{SI}_{qq'}$ are the diagonal matrix elements of V_{ij} between the symmetric states of qq′ with given S and I. In the case of the N-quark–λ-quark system the symmetric states are given by $(1/\sqrt{2})\{[N(1)\,\lambda(2)]^S+[N(2)\,\lambda(1)]^S\}$.

The evaluation of the various masses can now be carried out. In the case of the fully symmetric states (5), (8) and (9′), it is easier to evaluate V_{12}, say, and multiply the result by 3 (each of the V_{ij} gives the *same* contribution between fully symmetric wave functions). The other cases have the form $[(q_1q_2)^{S_0I_0}q'_3]^{SI}$. The expectation value of V_{12} is $D^{S_0I_0}_{qq}$. The contributions of V_{13} and V_{23} are equal. In order to calculate the expectation value of V_{23}, say, we perform a change of coupling transformation

$$\langle j_1j_2(J_{12})j_3J|j_1,j_2j_3(J_{23})J\rangle = \\ = (-1)^{j_1+j_2+j_3+J}\sqrt{(2J_{12}+1)(2J_{23}+1)}\begin{Bmatrix} j_1 & j_2 & J_{12} \\ j_3 & J & J_{23}\end{Bmatrix} \tag{18}$$

on the spins of the quarks. In this case there is no need to recouple the isospins (either q′ has $I=0$ or $I_0=0$). Using it we obtain

$$\langle q_1q_2(S_0I_0)\,q'_3SI|\sum_{i<j}^{3}V_{ij}|q_1q_2(S_0I_0)\,q'_3SI\rangle = \\ = D^{S_0I_0}_{qq} + 2\sum(2S_0+1)(2S'+1)\begin{Bmatrix} \frac{1}{2} & \frac{1}{2} & S_0 \\ \frac{1}{2} & S & S'\end{Bmatrix}^2 D^{S'I'=\frac{1}{2}}_{qq'}. \tag{19}$$

For $S_0=0$ (and $I_0=0$) we must have $S=\frac{1}{2}$ and this expression (relevant for the Λ baryon) is simplified to

$$D^{S_0=0\,I_0=0}_{qq} + \tfrac{3}{2}D^{S'=1\,I'=\frac{1}{2}}_{qq'} + \tfrac{1}{2}D^{S'=0\,I'=\frac{1}{2}}_{qq'}, \tag{20}$$

which means that the terms with $S'=1$ and $S'=0$ have their statistical weights. For $S_0=1$ and $S=\frac{3}{2}$ only terms with $S'=1$ can appear yielding (for Y* and Ξ*)

$$D^{S_0=1\,I_0}_{qq} + 2D^{S'=1\,I'=\frac{1}{2}}_{qq'}. \tag{21}$$

For $S_0=1$ and $S=\frac{1}{2}$ (as is the case for Σ and Ξ) we obtain, using the actual values of the Racah coefficients,

$$D^{S_0=1\,I_0}_{qq} + \tfrac{1}{2}D^{S'=1\,I'=\frac{1}{2}}_{qq'} + \tfrac{3}{2}D^{S'=0\,I'=\frac{1}{2}}_{qq'}. \tag{22}$$

The various masses obtained from (16) are as follows

$$
\begin{aligned}
M(\mathrm{N}^*) &= M_0 + 3\delta m_{\mathrm{N}} + 3D^{11}_{\mathrm{NN}}, \\
M(Y^*) &= M_0 + 2\delta m_{\mathrm{N}} + \delta m_\lambda + D^{11}_{\mathrm{NN}} + 2D^{1\frac{1}{2}}_{\mathrm{N}\lambda}, \\
M(\Xi^*) &= M_0 + \delta m_{\mathrm{N}} + 2\delta m_\lambda + 2D^{1\frac{1}{2}}_{\mathrm{N}\lambda} + D^{10}_{\lambda\lambda}, \\
M(\Omega) &= M_0 + 3\delta m_\lambda + 3D^{10}_{\lambda\lambda}, \\
M(\mathrm{N}) &= M_0 + 3\delta m_{\mathrm{N}} + \tfrac{3}{2}D^{11}_{\mathrm{NN}} + \tfrac{3}{2}D^{00}_{\mathrm{NN}}, \\
M(\Lambda) &= M_0 + 2\delta m_{\mathrm{N}} + \delta m_\lambda + \tfrac{3}{2}D^{1\frac{1}{2}}_{\mathrm{N}\lambda} + D^{00}_{\mathrm{NN}} + \tfrac{1}{2}D^{0\frac{1}{2}}_{\mathrm{N}\lambda}, \\
M(\Sigma) &= M_0 + 2\delta m_{\mathrm{N}} + \delta m_\lambda + D^{11}_{\mathrm{NN}} + \tfrac{1}{2}D^{1\frac{1}{2}}_{\mathrm{N}\lambda} + \tfrac{3}{2}D^{0\frac{1}{2}}_{\mathrm{N}\lambda}, \\
M(\Xi) &= M_0 + \delta m_{\mathrm{N}} + 2\delta m_\lambda + \tfrac{1}{2}D^{1\frac{1}{2}}_{\mathrm{N}\lambda} + D^{10}_{\lambda\lambda} + \tfrac{3}{2}D^{0\frac{1}{2}}_{\mathrm{N}\lambda}.
\end{aligned} \tag{23}
$$

The central mass M_0 appearing in (23) can be presumably obtained from the solution of the (relativistic) three quark problem. Therefore, its calculation is beyond present day theory. The values of δm_{N} and δm_λ are not known. We do not have any idea about the symmetry breaking quark–quark interactions V_{ij}, nor do we know what are the spatial wave functions with which the matrix elements $D^{SI}_{\mathrm{qq}'}$ should be calculated. The sensible way to proceed in the quark model is to try and determine the various matrix elements and mass differences from experiment. This procedure is not arbitrary. As we shall see, the restriction to two body interactions between the quarks imposes certain consistency conditions on the baryon masses. These conditions are predictions of the model and if they are obeyed by the experimental masses this can be taken as evidence for the validity of the model. The situation is quite analogous to atomic and nuclear spectroscopy. In those cases we know much more about the interactions and the wave functions. Nevertheless the successful calculations of atomic and nuclear energies were made by using effective interactions determined from experiment.

There are altogether 8 different masses expressed in terms of 8 parameters. Each mass contains M_0, three quark mass differences δm and $\binom{3}{2}=3$ quark–quark matrix elements. Therefore these parameters are not independent. We can redefine M_0 by adding to it $3\delta m_{\mathrm{N}}$ as well as 3 times one of the D terms. This will leave, apart from the constant term, one mass difference $\delta m_\lambda - \delta m_{\mathrm{N}} = m_\lambda - m_{\mathrm{N}}$ and only 4 differences of quark–quark matrix elements. However, the number of independent parameters in (23) is actually only 5. It is possible to choose a linear combination of $D^{10}_{\lambda\lambda}$, $D^{1\frac{1}{2}}_{\mathrm{N}\lambda}$, and $D^{0\frac{1}{2}}_{\mathrm{N}\lambda}$ whose coefficients in (23) will be equal to the coefficients of δm_λ. If there are n λ-quarks in a baryon, the coefficient of $D^{10}_{\lambda\lambda}$ is $\binom{n}{2}=\frac{1}{2}n(n-1)$, whereas the sum of the coefficients of $D^{1\frac{1}{2}}_{\mathrm{N}\lambda}$ and $D^{0\frac{1}{2}}_{\mathrm{N}\lambda}$ is $(3-n)\,n$. Hence, the sum

$\binom{n}{2}+\frac{1}{2}(3-n)n=n$ is equal to the coefficient of δm_λ. We can thus choose as independent interactions $\frac{1}{2}D^{10}_{\lambda\lambda}+D^{1\frac{1}{2}}_{N\lambda}$ which can be added to δm_λ and only *two* other independent linear combinations of $D^{10}_{\lambda\lambda}$, $D^{1\frac{1}{2}}_{N\lambda}$ and $D^{0\frac{1}{2}}_{N\lambda}$ (like $2D^{1\frac{1}{2}}_{N\lambda}-D^{10}_{\lambda\lambda}$ and $D^{0\frac{1}{2}}_{N\lambda}-D^{1\frac{1}{2}}_{N\lambda}$).

We see that due to the assumption of additive two body interactions between the quarks there must exist *three* independent linear relations between the masses (23). Such relations could be written as [14])

$$M(\Omega)-M(\mathrm{N}^*)=3\left[M(\Xi^*)-M(Y^*)\right], \tag{24}$$

$$M(\Xi^*)-M(Y^*)=M(\Xi)-M(\Sigma), \tag{25}$$

$$\tfrac{2}{3}\left[M(\mathrm{N}^*)-M(\Xi^*)\right]=\tfrac{2}{3}\left[M(\mathrm{N})-M(\Xi)\right]+M(\Sigma)-M(\Lambda). \tag{26}$$

These relations should hold for *any* value of the mass difference between the λ-quark and N-quarks and for *any* form of the two body (spin and isospin conserving) interaction between quarks. Relation (24) links masses within the SU(3) decuplet and is a weaker form of the Gell-Mann–Okubo relation there. The other two relations go beyond SU(3) predictions since they link mass differences of different SU(3) multiplets. They can be obtained in some SU(6) mass relations which are rather involved. All three relations are, as is well known, in very good agreement with the experimental masses. It is worthwhile to mention that the first relation is satisfied better than the others. The equality of the two body matrix elements for all baryons is certainly a more drastic assumption than their equality in spin $S=\frac{3}{2}$ states only.

The assumption of the most general two body interactions between quarks does not lead yet to the Gell-Mann–Okubo relations. In order to obtain that relation for the decuplet which implies equal spacings between the masses of $S=\frac{3}{2}$ baryons, we have to make some specific assumption on the two quark interactions. Since one relation consistent with equal spacings was obtained above (24), we need one more relation to be satisfied. This leads to the following relations between $S=1$ quark–quark interactions

$$D^{1\frac{1}{2}}_{N\lambda}=\tfrac{1}{2}\left(D^{11}_{NN}+D^{10}_{\lambda\lambda}\right). \tag{27}$$

This assumption eliminates completely the $S=1$ two quark interactions as independent parameters (one of them, say D^{11}_{NN}, could have been absorbed into the constant term and now the parameter $2D^{1\frac{1}{2}}_{N\lambda}-D^{10}_{\lambda\lambda}$ vanishes). Therefore, this leads to a relation between the octet masses, obtained by eliminating the $S=0$ quark–quark interactions. In fact, the equal spacings in the decuplet with (25) and (26) lead to the following relation

$$M(\Xi) + M(\mathrm{N}) = \tfrac{1}{2}[3M(\Lambda) + M(\Sigma)]. \tag{28}$$

This relation is the only prediction of the Gell-Mann–Okubo formula in the octet. Thus, the assumption (27) about $S=1$ quark–quark interactions leads to the Gell-Mann–Okubo results *both* in the decuplet and in the octet. The condition (27) can be simply satisfied by putting all quark–quark interactions with $S=1$ to be equal. This, however, is a more drastic assumption and certainly is not required for the baryon masses. If this is really the case the mass splittings within the decuplet are determined by $m_\lambda - m_\mathrm{N}$ only.

We shall now briefly discuss the connection between these results and the group theoretical mass formulae. The mass operator must transform according to one (or more) representations that are contained in the product of the given representation and its conjugate. The Gell-Mann–Okubo formula which is so successful for baryon masses makes use of the octet operator of SU(3). The generalization to SU(6) is plagued with difficulties as pointed out by Harari and Lipkin[17]. As we shall see later, our approach does not simplify the case of the mesons. However, for the baryons there are immediate implications of the assumption of quark–quark interactions. In this case we have

$$56 \times \underline{56} = 1 + 35 + 405 + 2695\,,$$

and the mass operator has to be taken from this expansion. However, this operator must transform according to a representation included in the product of the *symmetric* two quark system 21 and its conjugate which yields

$$21 \times \underline{21} = 1 + 35 + 405\,.$$

Thus, the dynamical restriction to quark–quark operators is enough to eliminate the contribution of the 2695 representation of U(6). The absence of this representation is equivalent to the relations (24), (25) and (26). However, the Gell-Mann–Okubo relations are not yet obtained since the 405 representation of U(6) contains in addition to the 1 and 8 representations also the 27 representation of SU(3) (only operators with $S=I=Y=0$ components are considered in order to conserve spin, isospin and hypercharge). The additional dynamical assumption (27) is in fact equivalent to octet dominance. A general group theoretical analysis of the quark model results (including electromagnetic effects) was carried out by Lipkin[18].

A relation similar to (27) leads to the Gell-Mann–Okubo formula for three quark states which are fully antisymmetric in the spin and internal coordinates of the quarks. Such states belong to the $(20, \underline{1})$ representation of $\mathrm{U}(6) \times \mathrm{U}(6)$. Without more specific assumptions this is not the case for states with mixed symmetry which belong to the $(70, \underline{1})$ representation. However the main deviations from the Gell-Mann–Okubo formula occur for the mesons. From our point of view there is no reason whatsoever why this formula should hold for mesons.

Let us first consider the possible states of the quark–antiquark system. If we consider states with orbital angular momentum $L=0$, we can have triplet states with $S=1$ and singlet states with $S=0$. There are three quarks and three antiquarks and therefore 9 possible states for each value of S. If the quark–antiquark interactions are fully independent of spin, isospin and hypercharge combinations all these states which belong to the $(6, \underline{6})$ representation of $U(6) \times U(6)$ should have the same energy. As in the case of the baryons, we obtain mass splittings between the mesons by introducing a mass difference between the λ-quark and N-quarks and symmetry breaking (spin and isospin conserving) interactions between the various quarks and antiquarks. These latter interactions will be considered also here as first-order perturbations. We see that in our approach the various shifts are added to the (linear) meson masses and not to the masses squared.

The eigenstates of the interaction Hamiltonian within the space considered will have definite spins and isospins. For each value of spin S there will be a state with isospin $I=1$ composed of nucleon quark and antiquark, a state with $I=\frac{1}{2}$ composed of one nucleon and one lambda quark and antiquark and *two* states with $I=0$. The natural choice of wave functions in this case is to consider the lambda quark–antiquark system and the nucleon quark–antiquark system. The energies of these two states differ due to the $m_\lambda - m_N$ mass difference as well as by the expectation value of the two body interaction in the $(\lambda\bar{\lambda})$ and $(N\bar{N})$ states. However, our approach does not rule out a non-diagonal matrix element ("configuration interaction") between these two states. Only the experiment can determine the amount of mixing actually existing.

Considering the actual masses of the pseudoscalar and vector mesons we see that without making explicit assumptions on the quark–antiquark interaction we cannot find any mass relations between them. There are altogether four diagonal (and one non-diagonal) matrix elements of the quark–antiquark interaction for each value of S. There are only four different masses of pseudoscalar mesons and four of vector mesons. It is not possible to deduce any relations from the assumption of two body interactions. This should be contrasted with the situation in the case of the baryons where the three relations (24), (25) and (26) were obtained from the symmetry properties of the quark wave functions.

The masses of the pseudoscalar and vector mesons (in MeV) are listed below with their tentative wave functions

φ	1019	$(\lambda\bar{\lambda})^{S=1\,I=0}$	η'	958	$(N\bar{N})^{S=0\,I=0}$
K^*	892	$(N\bar{\lambda})^{S=1\,I=\frac{1}{2}}$	K	496	$(N\bar{\lambda})^{S=0\,I=\frac{1}{2}}$
ω	783	$(N\bar{N})^{S=1\,I=0}$	η	549	$(\lambda\bar{\lambda})^{S=0\,I=0}$
ρ	757	$(N\bar{N})^{S=1\,I=1}$	π	138	$(N\bar{N})^{S=0\,I=1}$

The $(\lambda\bar{\lambda})$ assignment of the φ is now well accepted. The $(\lambda\bar{\lambda})$ assignment for the η is non-conventional. There is some evidence in favor of this assignment, for example, the decays of spin 2^+ mesons. The question can be decided in principle by studying electromagnetic decays as pointed out by Dalitz and Sutherland [19]), but these experiments are rather difficult. In any case, the assignment or rather the exact amount of admixtures of the $\lambda\bar{\lambda}$ and $N\bar{N}$ states in the η and η' has no effect on the following considerations.

The masses of the vector mesons increase regularly with the number of λ-quarks in their wave functions as in the baryon decuplet. It is tempting to associate this regular behavior with the properties of $S=1$ interactions also in the case of quark–antiquark systems. We can postulate the following relation between such interactions in analogy with (27)

$$D^{1\frac{1}{2}}_{N\bar{\lambda}} = \tfrac{1}{2}\left(D^{11}_{N\bar{N}} + D^{10}_{\lambda\bar{\lambda}}\right). \tag{29}$$

This relation leads to equal spacings between the φ, K^* and ρ masses which is very well obeyed. The regularity observed in the baryon decuplet and the vector meson nonet is thus directly related to the regular properties of the quark–quark and quark–antiquark interactions in the triplet states. The more drastic assumption of putting all interaction matrix elements in (29) to be equal leads to the equal spacings in the vector meson nonet being also equal to the $m_\lambda - m_N$ mass difference. This value is ~ 130 MeV whereas in the case of the baryon decuplet it is ~ 145 MeV. Although the differencc is not large it may well be due to the small difference between $D^{10}_{\lambda\lambda} - D^{1\frac{1}{2}}_{N\lambda}$ and $D^{10}_{\lambda\bar{\lambda}} - D^{1\frac{1}{2}}_{N\bar{\lambda}}$. If, in addition, the $D^{10}_{N\bar{N}}$ is put equal to the other quark–antiquark triplet interactions the masses of ρ and ω should be equal. In any case, these assumptions cannot lead to any predictions on the masses of the pseudoscalar mesons. In the case of the baryons the interactions in singlet states have rather different values. In the case of the quark–antiquark interactions the differences are even larger and should account for the large mass splittings of the pseudoscalar mesons (in particular the very low pion mass).

The only other complete group of mesons for which quark model wave functions could be considered is that of $S=2^+$ mesons. These are f′ (with

$I=0$, mass 1500 MeV), K**($I=\frac{1}{2}$, 1415), $A_2(I=1$, 1300) and f($I=0$, 1254). Two possible descriptions of these mesons were given. One way is to consider them as excited states, with orbital angular momentum $L=1$, of the vector meson nonet[20]). The mesons listed above correspond to φ, K*, ρ and ω respectively. The mass differences, however, need not be equal in the two nonets even if all wave functions of the 2^+ mesons are the same. The reason is that there are additional possible two body interactions in the $L=1$ case, namely the (two body) spin orbit interaction. This latter interaction does not contribute in $L=0$ states. Differences between the matrix elements of this interaction (for $L=1$) in the various quark–antiquark states could account for the different mass splittings in the two nonets.

The other way of considering the 2^+ mesons is to put them into the $(21, \underline{21})$ representation of $U(6)\times U(6)$[20]), This means that they consist of two quarks and two antiquarks and their wave functions are symmetrized with respect to the quarks and with respect to the antiquarks (the orbital angular momentum is $L=0$). The masses can be calculated in a straightforward way in terms of matrix elements of the two body interaction in the various quark–quark and quark–antiquark states (these need not be the same as in the vector meson nonet). All these matrix elements are in triplet ($S=1$) states since all quark and antiquark spins must be parallel to yield total spin $S=2$. If we make the assumption that also in the present case relation (29) holds, we obtain equal mass splittings of $f'-K^{**}$ and $K^{**}-A_2$. Although the general behavior of the masses increasing with the number of λ-quarks (or λ-antiquarks) holds, the spacings are far from equal (85 and 115 MeV respectively). Further experimental work could shed more light on the nature of the 2^+ mesons. In particular, the question of the possible existence of the other mesons which should belong to the $(21, \underline{21})$ representation still awaits the experimental answer.

References and footnotes

1) See for example G. F. Chew, *S-Matrix Theory of Strong Interactions* (Benjamin, New York, 1961).
2) The ρ meson has been treated this way in many papers with good qualitative results but poor numerical agreement, see for example F. Zachariasen and C. Zemach, Phys. Rev. **131**, 2305 (1963).
3) M. Gell-Mann, Phys. Letters **8**, 214 (1964).
4) G. Zweig, CERN Report, 1964, unpublished.
5) For a thorough discussion of the quark model and a substantial number of references, see R. Dalitz, Rapporteur talk at the 1966 Berkeley Conference (University of California Press, 1967) p. 215.

6) G. Morpurgo, Physics **2**, 95 (1965).
7) For a discussion of the difficulties of relativistic SU(6), see ref. 5.
8) W. Thirring, Phys. Letters **16**, 335 (1965).
9) C. Becchi and G. Morpurgo, Phys. Rev. **140**, B687 (1965).
10) M. Elitzur and H. R. Rubinstein, Phys. Rev. Letters **18**, 417 (1967).
11) R. Dashen and M. Gell-Mann, Phys. Letters **17**, 275 (1965).
12) These methods are described, for example, by A. de Shalit and I. Talmi, *Nuclear Shell Theory* (Academic Press, New York, 1963).
13) H. R. Rubinstein, Phys. Rev. Letters **17**, 41 (1966); H. R. Rubinstein, R. Socolow and F. Scheck, Phys. Rev. **154**, 1608 (1967); and also Y. Anisovitch et al., Phys. Letters **16**, 194 (1966).
14) P. Federman, H. R. Rubinstein and I. Talmi, Phys. Letters **22**, 208 (1966).
15) H. R. Rubinstein, Phys. Letters **22**, 210 (1966).
16) G. Racah, Phys. Rev. **63**, 367 (1942).
17) H. Harari and H. J. Lipkin, Phys. Rev. Letters **14**, 570 (1965).
18) H. J. Lipkin, Nucl. Phys. **B1**, 597 (1967).
19) R. Dalitz and D. Sutherland, Nuovo Cimento **38**, 1945 (1965).
20) See for instance ref. 5.

Spectroscopic and group theoretical methods in physics
© North-Holland Publ. Co., Amsterdam, 1968

INVARIANCE PRINCIPLES

A. PAIS

The Rockefeller University, New York, New York 10021, U.S.A.

About four years ago, this author was asked to give a sketch of the development in physics during the last 50 years, of the role of invariance principles*. In that review, the author had occasion to refer to the development and application of group theoretical methods due to Racah which has led to considerable further clarifications of the physics of the atom and the nucleus. The present updated version of this outline is dedicated to Giulio Racah's memory.

In preparation for this survey, I talked to many of my senior colleagues about the earlier days. For example, I asked Dirac why he had not introduced parity in his famous book on quantum mechanics. With characteristic simplicity Dirac answered: "Because I did not believe in it" and he showed me a paper in the Reviews of Modern Physics in which he said so[1]). In that same paper, Dirac expressed doubts about time reversal invariance as well, but, four years ago, I did not pay much attention to that. Unjustifiedly, as we shall see.

However, I am running ahead of the subject by starting right away with such quantum mechanical concepts like parity, which have no classical counterparts. What will be attempted in this paper is first to discuss two major chapters concerning invariance principles which are already quite important in classical theory. These are: 1) the question of invariance of physical laws versus the generally non-invariant nature of boundary conditions and 2) the connection between invariance under continuous groups and the existence of conservation laws. Thereafter, the much larger and more significant role of invariance concepts in the quantum theory will be reviewed.

* Lecture presented at the Niels Bohr Commemoration Meeting in Kopenhagen, July 1963, unpublished.

In the search for physical laws it is always a very important thing to find out to what extent the initial conditions of a given experiment may be considered as inessential. In every major advance in physics in fact we witness a reconsideration precisely of what is immaterial in the initial conditions. The most beautiful example of that is the very tenet of natural science, because if we say that in natural science we are dealing with reproducible phenomena, we are really using invariance language. For it takes time to reproduce an experiment, and it takes space as well, and therefore when we talk about reproducibility, we really express our belief in the invariance of the physical phenomena under the displacements in time and the displacements in space. For that reason we may, as Wigner particularly emphasized[2]), consider these space and time displacement invariances as the first invariance laws in physics. In relativity theory we get a new view on the importance of the relative initial conditions of two observers. The great lesson of the quantum theory has been that the observer has to ask himself very carefully what questions he can meaningfully put, given the initial conditions of his own experiment.

It is not only so that one has to find out what is material in the initial conditions in order to get to the physical laws, but the converse is also true. For example, when we compare the cobalt-60 experiment, the parity experiment, with the fact that people have their hearts on their left side, then there is a fundamental difference in the sense that the fact that we bear our hearts to the left can be relegated to initial conditions, which may possibly be "local" in nature. When we compare the cobalt-60 experiment with the fact that all the nuclei on earth are positively charged then the difference in as far as charge conjugation is concerned is that the charge preference, which is expressed here in the case of the nuclei, may be again relegated to an initial condition, which again may be possibly "local" in nature. The pursuit of such questions leads us in the direction of cosmology, where "the" initial condition becomes of the essence and that is why so far cosmology is part an art, part a science.

On this large scale, such questions as the role of time reversal invariance are in fact open. Apart from this reminder to caution, I shall not go into cosmological aspects, except for one remark. The last time I saw Einstein, he expressed to me the view that possibly there are no fundamental constants in nature. That is to say, he considered it possible that the present values for c, h and e (for example) belong to the present only. Such remarks have been made by others as well, notably Dirac and Jordan. Quantum theory is based on the existence of h, but, as far as we know, its actual value (certainly within considerable latitude) is irrelevant for the structure of the theory. Related remarks can be made about c and e and perhaps even about the fine structure constant. Is hall have to leave all such questions aside, as the times do not seem ripe for them.

In a broad sense, the whole of classical mechanics can be stated in terms of invariance principles. Many contributions, of Lagrange, Maupertuis, Hamilton, Jacobi and others find their most concise expression in the invariance of the action integral for small continuous deformations but with fixed orbital end points. However, the restriction to fixed end points makes it impossible to see the connection between invariance and conservation laws.

In order to make these statements more explicit, let us consider the simplest case of a single particle which moves in some external field of force which may even be time dependent. Let $L(q, \dot{q}, t)$ be the Lagrangian. Consider the variation

$$\delta \int_1^2 L\,\mathrm{d}t = \int_1^2 [L(q + \delta q, \dot{q} + \delta \dot{q}, t + \delta t) - L(q, \dot{q}, t)]\,\mathrm{d}t,$$

where 1 and 2 denote two points on the orbit. We can write

$$\begin{aligned}\delta \int_1^2 L\,\mathrm{d}t = &\int_1^2 \left[\frac{\partial L}{\partial q} - \frac{\mathrm{d}}{\mathrm{d}t}\left(\frac{\partial L}{\partial \dot{q}}\right)\right] \delta q\,\mathrm{d}t + \\ &+ \int_1^2 \left[\frac{\partial L}{\partial t} - \frac{\mathrm{d}}{\mathrm{d}t}\left(L - \dot{q}\frac{\partial L}{\partial \dot{q}}\right)\right] \delta t\,\mathrm{d}t + \\ &+ \frac{\partial L}{\partial \dot{q}}\,\delta q\Big|_1^2 + \\ &+ \left(L - \dot{q}\frac{\partial L}{\partial \dot{q}}\right)\delta t\Big|_1^2 .\end{aligned} \tag{1}$$

Consider first the condition: $\delta \int_1^2 L\,\mathrm{d}t = 0$, assuming in addition that the end points are fixed, that is $\delta q(1) = \delta q(2) = \delta t(1) = \delta t(2) = 0$. Under these conditions the last two lines of (1) are to be dropped. The first line gives the Euler equations which, when substituted in the second line give identically zero.

Let us now *in addition* require that $\delta \int_1^2 L\,\mathrm{d}t = 0$ is *also* true if we let δq vary at the end points. In particular we take

$$\delta q(1) = \delta q(2) \tag{2}$$

which is a special case of a constant infinitesimal space displacement. The third line says then that momentum is conserved. Likewise if we take a constant time displacement δt, then the fourth line gives the conservation of energy H. Finally the integrand of the second line reads $\mathrm{d}H/\mathrm{d}t = 0$ if L does not explicitly depend on t.

I have dwelt at some length on this elementary example because it embodies the essence of the relation between invariance under continuous groups and conservation laws for systems of arbitrary complexity. What has been done for one particle can be done for an arbitrary mechanical system of particles. What has been done for small displacements can be done for small rotations and we get angular momentum conservation. All this is a 20th century contribution. Hamel was the first to state, for classical mechanical systems, the relation between invariance under any continuous group in the sense of Lie and the existence of conservation laws[3]). Herglotz did it for the 10-parameter inhomogeneous Lorentz group[4]). Fokker, I believe, started a similar program within the framework of general relativity[5]). All this work culminates in the general theorem of Miss Emmy Noether[6]). How novel this type of argument was at the time is expressed by one no less than Felix Klein who writes[7]) in 1918 (in discussing the conservation laws in general relativity):

> "Ich habe, wie man sehen wird...eigentlich überhaupt nicht mehr zu rechnen, sondern nur von den elementarsten Formeln der klassischen Variationsrechnung sinngemäszen Gebrauch zu machen."

This sense of surprise has often recurred in later generations, when we realized that certain selection rules and other relations can often be understood essentially without calculation (which is no excuse not to calculate).

Let us return once more to eq. (1). We see from it not only that invariance leads to conservation laws, but also that invariance arguments actually give the form of the quantity which is conserved, in terms of L and its derivatives. The same is true not only for discrete mechanical systems but also for systems with continuously many degrees of freedom, for fields. Euler equations become field equations. If we require invariance with respect to the Lorentz group, the "end point" terms (of the third and fourth line) become surface terms on a three-dimensional slice of the four-dimensional space time continuum. They yield the explicit form of the energy momentum tensor in terms of the Lagrangian density and its derivatives. The identity (second line of eq. (1)) now becomes the vanishing of the divergence of this tensor[8]).

All the foregoing remarks have their counterparts in quantum theory.

Here of course one has to watch one's language in stating conservation laws. To say that an observable satisfies a conservation law now must be taken to mean that the probability for finding that this observable takes on a certain value does not change with time. But otherwise the methods used for the invariance with respect to continuous groups can be taken over in the quantum case. The essential tool for the general derivation of the conservation of energy, momentum, angular momentum and center of mass motion remains the study of the behavior under infinitesimal space time displacements and rotations[9]).

We leave the subject of non-quantum theory with a brief remark on the evolution of the invariance argument from classical to relativistic theory. No attempt is made at this place to do full justice to this heroic development. In the classical domain, invariance emerged largely from the contemplation of the dynamical laws. In special relativity the transition takes place to a position where the invariance requirements become the point of departure. Finally, in the search for general relativity theory, invariance became a main guide. This last role of invariance principles has continued to persist. It is especially strong in today's particle physics, where it has been of great help, though no one sees as yet the grand design there.

In classical theory, it is a necessary condition for a symmetry to lead to conservation laws that the symmetry shall be expressible as the invariance under a group of canonical transformations. Whether the existence of a formal symmetry actually implies the existence of such transformations is something that remains to be examined from case to case. To this extent there exists a similarity between classical theory and quantum mechanics, where canonical transformation groups are represented by groups of unitary transformations.

However, in quantum mechanics the use of group properties and symmetry arguments have become far more significant and effective[10]). There are two main reasons for this. First, quantum mechanical states form linear manifolds to which one can apply the apparatus of representation theory. There exists no classical analog to this statement which in more physical language means that the existence of many quantum numbers and all selection rules can be understood from underlying group properties. Secondly, in quantum mechanics, unlike in classical theory, discrete groups appear on a par with continuous groups. Selection rules are associated with the invariance under such discrete group as space reflexions, charge conjugation and coordinate permutations (multiplet theory).

Wigner was the first one to realize this. In preparation of this report I read his 1926 and 1927 papers[11]) and made myself a fine theory as to how his thoughts developed. After Heisenberg's treatment of the 2-electron problem in a central field, Wigner went from 2 to 3 and then came to the disheartening conclusion that to go from 3 to 4 and higher by the same pedestrian methods would become pretty awful. Then, stimulated by discussions with J. von Neumann, the apparatus of the symmetric group was brought to bear. I reasoned (not without the satisfaction of meeting a familiar situation[12])) that the transition "3 to 4" marked the turning point. So I went to ask Wigner if this was true. He said that of course this had been important, but that his involvement with symmetry arguments had an earlier origin. Already before 1925 Wigner did not believe that the ground state of the H-atom was a plane, but rather a sphere, "something like a shell on which you had to introduce spherical harmonics". Now, after the facts, there is no better illustration of how different the role is of symmetries in classical and in quantum theory than by comparing the theoretical pictures of the ground state of the H-atom before 1925, when it was like a circle, and after 1925, when it became a sphere. (For me, the discussion with Wigner was also a good lesson in the pitfalls of the history of science.)

In one of his 1927 papers Wigner says, "These [group] methods have the advantage that with their help one can obtain results which...are rigorously valid for arbitrarily complicated systems. The disadvantage of the method is that it does not permit to derive approximation formulae." It was certainly not this disadvantage alone which (to put it mildly) caused reluctance to accept group theoretical methods in the early days of quantum mechanics. Especially in the non-relativistic domain one could of course calculate all kinds of new things without compounding further novelty by the use of group methods. At any rate, it seemed a particular source of gratification if one could do without them[13]).

For several reasons the situation has drastically changed since then. First of all, in atomic and molecular spectroscopy the problems are well set but, with few exceptions, extremely complicated. One has learned that the qualitative understanding by means of group theory often compares favorably with the insight gained from crude approximations. It is a tribute to Weyl that the monumental (but not exactly easy) book[14]) which he wrote as early as 1928 contains essentially all the necessary tools for the analysis of complex systems.

As Racah once told me, the quiet study of Weyl's books during his early years in Jerusalem (a period of relative isolation) had a great influence on him. It led him to devise theoretical methods which simplified considerably (and at least in one case made possible) his analysis of complex atomic spectra. His major contributions are found in a series of four papers[15]) written during the 1940's. They contain his contributions to the computation of fractional parentage coefficients; the recoupling coefficients now known as Racah coefficients; his introduction of the seniority quantum number. In the last paper of this series, his group theoretical methods come really to the fore, above all in the elegant treatment of f^n configurations. Later, Racah's methods were to play an important role in nuclear spectroscopy as well. Some of Racah's students made leading contributions in this domain[16]).

In the spring of 1951, Racah lectured on his work at the Institute for Advanced Study in Princeton. From the start it was evident that here we physicists were being taught the real craft. I found Eugen Merzbacher and David Park willing to take notes, out of which grew the widely known Racah lectures on group theory and spectroscopy, which have been of such great use ever since.

It is especially in quantum field theory and particle physics that the group theoretical method has reached its present prominence. The reasons are not far to seek. It is dubious, to say the least, that today we possess anything resembling a well-set dynamical scheme in this domain. Therefore the choice of bypassing the symmetry reasoning by a detailed calculation often does not exist. Indeed, there is currently a general consensus that the present features of particle physics which are most likely to survive further developments are precisely those which follow from symmetry arguments only. I think that it may be so that when I give a bird's-eye view of what physicists think about in 1967, the group theoretical arguments may have a certain over-emphasis. This may change. At the same time it should also be said that some of the most beautiful results which we have can really be understood only by group theory. For example, why are spins only integer or half-integer, why are there no particles with spin $\frac{1}{3}h$, say? Here group theory once and for all settles the issue.

There is one area of field theory, however, where we do have a dynamical scheme which is so good that presently we do not know of any fundamental limitations. That is quantum electrodynamics. I believe that Kramers was the first one to have the idea of mass renormalization[17]). In my years in hiding during the war I had the privilege of unforgettable hours with Kramers, in which we often talked about these questions. It was realized later that the various renormalizations can successfully be performed only if one recognizes in a covariant way how the infinities of the theory have to be handled. Here invariance arguments are an inextricable part of the dynamical rules for extracting finite information from the theory.

Beyond quantum electrodynamics, the theory is relatively in a far more phenomenological state. This is perhaps well illustrated by the fact that today the best definition we can give of an elementary particle is not so much a dynamical as a group theoretical one, namely that it is a member of an irreducible representation of a group. This group contains the inhomogeneous Lorentz group, in terms of which we specify the attributes mass and spin[18]). Where further degeneracy still exists, we may need an enlargement of this group, such as for isotopic spin.

In the foregoing discussion of the classical aspects of invariance principles, the existence of an action principle played a prominent role in establishing the relation invariance $\rightarrow$ conservation law. It is not only so in particle physics that we do not know *what* the Lagrangian is. We are not even sure that there should be one at all. This is not the place to enlarge on this present point of debate. For the present purposes it is sufficient to emphasize that in these current problems one rather uses the connection conservation $\rightarrow$ invariance, that is, one goes in the opposite direction. For example, a Lagrangian theory leads to an *S*-matrix. But an *S*-matrix may exist even though a Lagrangian does not. The conservation laws are now used in the sense that they restrict the possible form of *S*-matrix elements. Such considerations linked with very general features of a dynamical character may lead to experimental predictions. To give one example[19]), consider the decay of a K-particle into π-meson + electron + neutrino. From the covariance of the *S*-matrix element combined with the one dynamical assumption that the $e\nu$-pair acts locally one can predict a characteristic angular decay distribution if the interaction is vectorial. Along these lines one could interpret subsequent measurements as showing that the strangeness changing currents are four-vector currents.

After having given this brief sketch of the evolution of the invariance argument from the inception of quantum mechanics to the present day, I would like to devote the remaining part of this paper to a brief review of those symmetry principles which, with one notable exception, belong exclusively in the quantum domain. The discrete operations *P*, *C*, *T* will be considered first.

Parity. In a pre-1925 study of the iron-spectrum, Laporte discovered his famous intercombination rule[20]). In 1927 Wigner realized[21]) that this selection rule was a consequence of space reflexion invariance, a principle which hithertofore had been more of philosophical than of practical interest. A new quantum concept had arrived, parity (P). To the extent that parity is conserved (see below) we note the following general features.

The parity selection rule is the first instance of a multiplicative rule. Example: the parity of a two particle system (AB) in a state of definite relative orbital angular momentum is the product of the intrinsic parities of A and B respectively and the orbital parity. Nevertheless we say that the parity of a state of the H-atom is identical with the orbital parity. The intrinsic parity of the proton and the electron do not come into question, because for all of physics one may introduce the *convention* that these two parities are plus. Had we chosen any other convention, we might have had to change our language somewhat without changing any observable conclusion. The question whether the relative parities of two states are measurable or just conventional is related to the possibility of observing, in any experiment whatsoever, the relative phase of these two states. Where there exists no such possibility we have what is called a super selection rule. There are quite general considerations about this question [22]. In practice, the problem often arises in particle physics and it is always easily settled by considering what conservation laws allow or forbid transitions between pairs of states.

Charge conjugation (C-) invariance. This subject may be said to originate with the objections by Oppenheimer [23] and by Tamm [24] to the suggestion that the proton could be the anti-particle of the electron and with the observation by Weyl [25] that particle and anti-particle should have the same mass on symmetry grounds. The charge conjugation operation which interchanges particles and anti-particles was first performed (and so named) by Kramers [26]. The C-operation can consistently be defined only in the frame-work of a quantized field theory. Eigenstates of C are evidently neutral (γ, π^0) but the converse is not true (n, Λ). To the extent that C-invariance is valid one can assign a C-quantum number to the eigenstates which is two-valued, like P. For the photon, $C = -1$. This quantum number obviously plays no role in atomic physics, but is very useful in particle physics. Example: from C-invariance and the existence of $\pi^0 \rightarrow 2\gamma$ it follows that a π^0 cannot decay into any odd number of photons.

Time reversal (T-) invariance. This plays an important role in classical theory, for example when one discusses the reconciliation of the second law of thermodynamics with the T-invariance of the mechanical laws.

In quantum mechanics, time reversal has new facets. The first discussion of T-invariance in quantum theory is due to Wigner [27]. The stimulus came from Kramers' degeneracy theorem [28] which says (in its most general form) that the eigenstates of a system consisting of an odd number of spin $\frac{1}{2}$ particles are at least doubly degenerate in the absence of an external magnetic field. Kramers used specific dynamical considerations, Wigner reduced the theorem to its essence, a consequence of T-invariance. The theorem exemplifies a general feature of T-invariance consequences: these involve always relations between different states, never an intrinsic property of one state. There is never a quantum number related to T-invariance (as the T-operation is not unitary). Consider as a further example the elastic scattering $A + B \rightarrow A + B$ of two spin $\frac{1}{2}$ particles. Let $\langle l', s' | l, s \rangle$ be the partial amplitude, (l, s denote the initial orbital and spin angular momentum respectively, l', s' refer to the final state). T-invariance yields

$$\langle j+1, 1 | j-1, 1 \rangle = \langle j-1, 1 | j+1, 1 \rangle;$$

$$\langle j, 1 | j, 0 \rangle = \langle j, 0 | j, 1 \rangle, (= 0 \text{ if } A = B).$$

This demonstrates how in applying T we must not only reverse momenta but spins as well (unlike the situation in detailed balance arguments[29])).

Stimulated by Lee and Yang's analysis[30]) of existing evidence, experimental developments have drastically changed our views on the discrete symmetries. We now know that weak interactions do not obey P-conservation and C-invariance. Since 1956 a new trend in the use of invariance arguments has developed. Shaken as one was in previously held beliefs, one had now to look for the minimal sufficient ground for understanding the phenomena. For example, the absence of an electric dipole moment of the neutron was held as evidence for P-conservation[30]). However, "combined inversion", CP-invariance[31]) is a sufficient reason for this absence. Likewise, the idea of particle mixtures[32]), which is essentially a pure invariance argument, was proposed at a time that C-invariance was not in doubt. The whole idea remains unchanged in essence if CP-invariance only is used. And so, from 1956 on, the view became generally accepted that CP-invariance as a rigorous principle of nature restored to some degree a simplicity in our description of the phenomena – until the year 1964. Let us first review briefly, however, the developments in the intervening period.

More specific than CP-invariance is the γ_5-invariance for neutrinos. Their wave function ψ_ν enters in the dynamics in such a way that the transformation $\psi_\nu \rightarrow \gamma_5 \psi_\nu$ shall leave everything unchanged[33]). Implications: strictly zero mass and induced magnetic moment for neutrinos, strict suppression of one helicity state for neutrino and for anti-neutrino, for the former (latter) only the negative (positive) helicity survives. This violates P as P flips the helicity while (anti-) particle stays (anti-) particle. It violates C as C changes particle into anti-particle but does not change the helicity; and it satisfies *CP*.

If the *CPT*-theorem holds true, *CP*- and *T*-invariance imply each other (but are hardly the same, even so). One remarkable thing about this fundamental theorem is that it was discovered so late[34]), all the ingredients had been there for a considerable time. The theorem states sufficient conditions for the validity of the invariance of a quantized field theory under the product operation *CPT*, namely: invariance under the proper orthochronous Lorentz-group, hermitian local interactions, the validity of the canonical commutation rules for bare boson fields, of the anti-commutation rules for bare fermion fields. The most general proof of the theorem is due to Jost[35]) who relates it to the fact that *PT* can be generated continuously from the identity element of the complex extension of the Lorentz group. The following example[36]) shows how the theorem "works". Consider the interaction

$$\sum_{i=1} (C_i \bar{\psi}_1 \Gamma_i \psi_2 \cdot \bar{\psi}_3 \Gamma_i \psi_4 + C_i' \bar{\psi}_1 \Gamma_i \psi_2 \cdot \bar{\psi}_3 \Gamma_i \gamma_5 \psi_4) + \text{h.c.},$$

where the Γ_i are the usual five covariants. *P*-conservation implies that all C_i' (or all C_i) vanish. Then *C*-invariance requires all C_i (or all C_i') to be real, and so does *T*-invariance: "*P* and *C* imply *T*". In the general case, *P* is not conserved, C requires the C_i to be imaginary relative to C_i', *T* requires them to be relatively real: "*P* no and *C* yes imply *T* no", etc. *CPT*-invariance is believed to hold. It is the minimal sufficient ground for the existence of anti-particles to particles, and for the equality of masses and life times for particle and anti-particle[37]). How delicate the argument is, can perhaps be exemplified by the fact that if a particle can branch in two different decay modes, then *CPT* does *not* imply the same branching ratio for these reactions as compared to the corresponding anti-reactions.

Developments have taken a decidedly new turn with the discovery in 1964 of *CP*-violation in the decay into $\pi^+ + \pi^-$ of long lived neutral K-particles[38]). Precisely because strict *CP*-invariance seemed so attractive, there have been several theoretical attempts to save it. The general idea was that the assumption that the decays take place in vacuum might not be correct. Rather, it was supposed, there might be some long range field with properties such that the decay in question would be induced in its omnipresence, and in such a way that *CP* could be maintained. All these attempts have run into some trouble or other and the current consensus is that *CP* violation is genuinely there in this reaction. Retaining the *CPT*-theorem, violation of *T*-invariance is thereby implied.

A host of new questions are now to be faced. Is the effect due to a *C*-

violation in part of the strong interactions, or in electromagnetic interactions[39]), both of which play a virtual role in this weak process? Is the effect due to a *CP*-violation in some of the more conventional weak interactions? Is it due to a separate kind of "superweak" interaction? Have we been careful enough in our definitions[40]) of *C*, *P* and *T*? At this time there are no certain answers to these questions. It seems quite clear that here we are only at the beginning of a new chapter in physics.

It is somewhat curious that violations of *P* and *C* and of *CP* have remained such isolated facts. It has added to the book of rules but to not much else. By what "accidental degeneracies" are some interactions more invariant than others?

Till now we have considered only those symmetries which are related to space time operations (this includes *C* through the *CPT*-theorem). Let us next review the symmetries that thus far are not so related.

Isotopic spin and related quantities. The formalism of isotopic spin was introduced soon after the discovery of the neutron[41]). At the time, the motivation came from the charge independence of the two-nucleon system. In regard to the dynamics of nucleons and π-mesons the importance of isotopic spin became apparent first through the work of Kemmer[42]). It was at once clear to him that conservation of isotopic spin leads to physical statements which are independent of the then so popular second Born approximation, (popular still under another name). For the isotopic spin analysis of states containing only a few particles, the explicit use of only a few finite elements of the SU(2) group suffices. The question was therefore raised whether one can possibly dispense with SU(2) and use some discrete group instead[43]). This has not led to notable success.

Isotopic spin plays an important role in the multiplet theory of nuclear levels. However, the use of isotopic spin as an important practical tool in high energy physics was not fully appreciated till the time of the 1952 Rochester Conference[44]). It was then that the first π-nucleon resonance became a center of interest. The realization that isotopic spin alone gave an immediate qualitative insight in he relative magnitude of the π-nucleon cross sections at the resonance was quite liberating in view of the fact that accurate dynamical calculations were largely non-existent. These days, particle physicists carry in their wallet a list not only of fundamental constants but also of Clebsch–Gordan coefficients.

It is of considerable practical use to consider the product symmetry: *C* times charge symmetry, the latter being a finite element of the isotopic spin group. This was first shown when selection rules for boson decays were obtained by means of this operation[45]. Michel[46] realized that the operation is isomorphic to a parity in isotopic spin space which is now called *G*-parity[47]. For a neutral state to which *G*-parity applies, it is related to the charge conjugation quantum number C and the isotopic spin T by $G = C(-1)^T$.

The strange particles have added a new dimension to the isotopic spin description. The rule[48] $Q = T_3 + \frac{1}{2}Y$ for strongly interacting particles connects the electric charge Q and the 3-component of isotopic spin with a new additive quantum number, the hypercharge Y which is conserved in strong and electromagnetic but not in weak interactions. The approximate Y-conservation embodies in particular the principle of associated production[49] which had been proposed earlier as a rigorous property for strong and electromagnetic interactions.

It was conjectured soon[50] that the advent of the strange particles necessitates an enlargement of the isotopic spin group. Much work was done in this direction and conjectures about further approximate symmetries began to abound. In the process of this, theoretical physicists energetically made compact Lie groups their own[51]. As we now know, in the early years of this development there was not enough experimental material available to indicate a definite choice. Just as isotopic spin really came into its own when the 33-resonance was found, so the chapter of higher symmetries really started to flourish only after the recent veritable outpour began of baryon and meson resonances, starting with the $Y_1^*(1385 \text{ MeV})$ baryon resonance[52]. It is now clear that the approximate higher symmetry SU(3) constitutes a next phase in the description of particle physics phenomena[53].

Historically, isotopic spin conservation was the first approximate conservation law in particle physics. Of course, approximate invariance plays a great role in atomic and nuclear physics as well. Atomic Russell–Saunders coupling and nuclear supermultiplet theory[54] are cases in point. However, in these two instances the invariance appears whenever the neglect of spin orbit couplings is a good dynamical approximation. That is, atomic multiplets and nuclear supermultiplets appear as a result of a non-relativistic limiting process of the type $v/c \to 0$. In contrast, isotopic spin invariance is defined (to the best of present knowledge) as a relativistic limiting process: $e \to 0$. The former limiting type has been referred to as a dynamical symmetry, the latter as a kinematical symmetry[55].

More recently, dynamical symmetries have made their appearance also in particle physics, notably SU(6) which is a union of the dynamical spin group

SU(2) and the kinematical internal symmetry group SU(3)[55]. Many attempts are currently in progress to find the structure of dynamical equations such that SU(6) appears as a symmetry of some of their approximate solutions. These studies, notable amongst which is the work on current algebras, are still too much in flux to lend themselves to a general review of the present kind.

From the weak interactions we seem to be learning something else again, namely the possible existence of violation laws. Apart from a few exceptions to be mentioned shortly, the following laws are on the whole well obeyed: hypercharge changes by ± 1 unit, $|\Delta Y| = 1$, while for isotopic spin[56] $|\Delta \boldsymbol{T}| = \frac{1}{2}$. It should be emphasized that such rules are "first order" rules. In dynamical terms, this means that one treats weak interactions to lowest non-vanishing order. As has recently been remarked[57], it is not obvious that such a procedure is always justified. Though we are in the regime of very small couplings, it could be that we deal at the same time with highly singular theories which would require us to show cause why "higher order effects" are indeed negligible. At any rate, when a first order rule "works", this may have a dynamical significance beyond a manifestation of the smallness of a dimensionless coupling constant. Also, it remains to be understood how sharp the distinction is between weak and strong interactions at extremely high energies ($>$ 300 BeV in the center of mass system).

An example of an observed $|\Delta Y| = 2$ effect is the $K^0 - \bar{K}^0$ mass difference which is due to virtual transitions $K^0 \leftrightarrow \bar{K}^0$. Its magnitude makes it quite plausible that this is a second order effect of $|\Delta Y| = 1$ interactions. $|\Delta \boldsymbol{T}| > \frac{1}{2}$ effects are also known, such as the decay $K^+ \to \pi^+ + \pi^0$. It is often thought that this is due to the interference of a $|\Delta \boldsymbol{T}| = \frac{1}{2}$ weak effect and a $|\Delta \boldsymbol{T}| = 1$ electromagnetic effect, but so far this point has not yet been settled satisfactorily. In this connection the very recent observation should also be mentioned[58] that for the 2π-decay modes of the long lived neutral K-particles there is a strong violation of $|\Delta \boldsymbol{T}| = \frac{1}{2}$. Can this important effect be understood as an interference of the kind mentioned above? Or do these effectively extra weak effects have their own intrinsic violation laws?

Before leaving this class of invariance principles, the remarkable connection should be emphasized between the strength of interactions and their symmetries. This was already noted in connection with the *C*- and *P*-situation in weak as compared to other interactions, and it is also quite manifest for isotopic spin and related symmetries. This connection between dynamics and symmetries is part of the book of rules, to date there exists no deeper understanding of this fact.

Gauges and currents. I come now to the last and perhaps most difficult topic of invariances, those of the gauge type. Even though electromagnetic gauge invariance exists of course already classically, I have on purpose left this topic aside so far, in order to confront it with possible other gauge principles.

From the outset I should confess that I do not understand electromagnetic gauge invariance. To be sure, it is not so difficult to write down gauge transformations of the first kind (phase transformations) and to "derive" from this the differential conservation of current. But is this really a derivation or are we just running after the facts? If we say: invariance under an infinitesimal rotation around an axis $\rightarrow$ angular momentum conservation around that axis, we relate the physical idea of spatial isotropy to a dynamical law. I want to ask: what is so physical about an infinitesimal phase transformation? Is there any other justification for it than current conservation itself?

Also, coming back to the angular momentum picture, what *non-infinitesimal* feature[59]) of gauge or other transformations leads to quantization of electricity? Suppose a world in which the charge of the electron differs by an extremely small amount from that of (minus) the proton. In such a world one can still perform phase transformations. One gets of course not only the differential conservation law of electricity but another law as well[60]). I find this an ugly idea. But the ugly thing really is that there is nothing in the present theoretical structure which makes the idea wrong from the outset. On the level of particle physics we just do not understand electricity, the universality of the electric charge quantization which ties the diverse families of baryons, leptons and mesons to a whole.

In spite of such reservations, it is clear that the further study of gauge transformations is very necessary, if it were only because so many ununderstood current conservation laws are staring us in the face. The most important ones are:

(1) The conservation of baryons, first stated (for nucleons) by Stückelberg[61]).

(2) The conservation of hypercharge in strong interactions.

(3) Isotopic vector current of $\Delta Y = 0$ type, conserved in strong interactions. This approximately conserved current also plays an important role in weak interactions[62]).

(4) The conservation of leptons[30]), which has the physical consequence of correlating helicities in distinct leptonic reactions.

(5) (Possibly) the conservation of μ-number. The discovery[63]) that there

exist two distinct neutrinos, ν_μ and ν_e implies the existence of a further quantum number in the leptonic sector. It is presently not proven that this is an additive quantum number, though simple dynamical pictures make the idea attractive. If so, we can assign a μ-number $= 1\,(0)$ to μ, ν_μ(e, ν_e) which is additively conserved, just like electric charge, baryon number, etc.

Let us now consider gauge transformations of the second kind, local gauges. From electromagnetism we know that local gauge invariance implies the existence of a field which carries the current. If we consider the gauge transformation of the first kind only, this requirement does not appear. One related early the existence of a current like the baryon current with phase transformations. This amounts to a tautology. However, in recent years the question has come up if such currents have a relation to local gauges. Whatever may be still dark about gauge invariance, a local gauge seems much more attractive than a global one, a phase transformation. If there are such local gauges then there must be fields that carry them [64]). Are there such fields? It is believed by some that there are, for example that the ρ-mesons are the fields corresponding to the currents (3). It may be too early to take a firm position on this identification. There is however a very general question which is of the utmost importance in this context. This is the problem of gauge invariance and mass.

A simple application of local gauge (whether for Abelian gauges such as the one for electromagnetism, or non-Abelian ones such as possibly for isotopic spin) seems to indicate that the corresponding carrying field must have infinite range, the quanta must have zero mass. But such fields do not exist for the cases (1)–(5), (unless they are assumed to be infinitesimally weakly coupled, which seems escapism physics). The question then arises if there does not exist a paradox from the start if we introduce these new local gauge principles.

The issue is not settled, there is still hope. The argument goes about as follows [65]). It is admitted that the local gauge principle leads one to introduce a massless field into the dynamics. This means however a massless *bare* field and one must further ask whether this field is observable in any way. In the case of electromagnetism the mass of the dressed photon remains zero. It is not obvious, however, whether this were to remain true if we would study the same mathematical problem for different values of the (bare) charge. Consider for example the energy of positronium in the "vector" state (3S), and imagine you can increase the coupling constant. One can suppose (not prove so far) that as a result this state may get lighter and lighter till it reaches zero total mass. At that stage a degeneracy occurs with the zero photon mass itself. Beyond this it may now come to pass that the zero mass spectral state of the total (electron, photon) system disappears.

This, crudely, is the line of argument by which one hopes to eliminate the paradox and hopes to relate the conservation of baryons (for example) to a mass bearing vector field. One-dimensional calculations can be made to illustrate the point[66]). They are neither free of controversy nor necessarily convincing. For one thing, the "charge" is of dimension L^{-1} in one dimension, so that a length is introduced from the start even for a massless field.

Whatever may be the answer, such investigations may turn out to be of great importance. Their philosophy is that there may exist exact symmetries in a Lagrangian which are masked by dynamical features, and effectively look like broken symmetries. Such dynamical views of broken symmetries have especially been advocated by Heisenberg, they may be related to the idea of "spontaneous breakdown".

This concludes a general round up of invariance principles. It is not completely the author's fault if toward the later part things began to seem vague. They are vague. The same can be said for the following list of questions which brings this review to its open end.

1) What is the relation between gauge invariance on the one hand, mass and *quantized* charge on the other? Are they compatible?

2) Can one reconcile such fundamental notions as charge independence and electromagnetism better than saying that the latter breaks the former?

3) More generally, how can we understand broken symmetries?

4) The *CPT*-theorem ties with space-time an operation (C) which at first sight seems to have nothing to do with space-time. All isotopic spin, hypercharge, baryon conservation, etc. properties are so far unrelated to space time. Are there further relations between space-time and intrinsic symmetries? Will we eventually be able to integrate properties such as isotopic spin with space-time properties – like the Pauli spin became integrated through the Dirac equation?

5) One invariance remains to be mentioned, μ–e universality. μ and e can be substituted for each other in all interactions, so it seems. They are identical apart from mass, or so it seems. What is the μ-meson trying to tell us?

Footnotes and references

1) P. A. M. Dirac, Rev. Mod. Phys. **21**, 393 (1949).
2) E. P. Wigner, Proc. Am. Phil. Soc. **93**, 521 (1949). Several of the present comments on initial conditions are originally given in this paper.
3) G. Hamel, Math. Ann. **59**, 416 (1904) and also Z. Math. Physik **50**, 1 (1904).
4) G. Herglotz, Ann. Physik [4] **36**, 493 (1911).
5) A. Fokker, Proc. Koninkl. Ned. Akad. Wetensch. Amsterdam **19**, 968 (1917).
6) E. Noether, Göttinger Nachr. (1918) p. 235.
7) F. Klein, Göttinger Nachr. (1918) p. 71.
8) See, e.g., L. Rosenfeld, Sur le tenseur d'impulsion-énergie, Acad. Roy. Belg. **18** (6) (1940). Also F. J. Belinfante, Physica **6**, 887 (1939), W. Pauli, Rev. Mod. Phys. **13**, 203 (1941).
9) See, e.g., G. Wentzel, *Quantum Theory of Fields* (Interscience, New York, 1949).
10) See, for example, E. P. Wigner, Invariant quantum mechanical equations of motion, in: *Theoretical Physics* (International Atomic Energy Agency, Vienna, 1963).
11) E. P. Wigner, Z. Physik **40**, 492, 883 (1926); **43**, 624 (1927).
12) A. Pais, Ann. Phys. (N.Y.) **9**, 548 (1960); **22**, 274 (1963).
13) In this connection it is instructive to read the preface of E. Condon and G. Shortley, *The Theory of Atomic Spectra* (Cambridge Univ. Press, 1951), and to compare the preface of the second edition of Wigner's book, *Group Theory* (Academic Press, New York, 1959), with that of the first edition.
14) H. Weyl, *The Theory of Groups and Quantum Mechanics* (Dutton and Co., New York, 1932).
15) G. Racah, Phys. Rev. **61**, 186 (1941); **62**, 438 (1942); **63**, 367 (1943); **76**, 1352 (1949).
16) See, e.g., A. de Shalit and I. Talmi, *Nuclear Shell Theory* (Academic Press, New York, 1963).
17) Kramers communicated his ideas at the Shelter Island Conference, 1947.
18) The complete discussion of the unitary representations has been given by E. P. Wigner, Ann. Math. **40**, 149 (1939). See also ref. 10.
19) A. Pais and S. Treiman, Phys. Rev. **105**, 1616 (1957).
20) O. Laporte, Z. Physik **23**, 135 (1924).
21) E. P. Wigner, Göttinger Nachr. (1928) p. 374.
22) G. Wick, A. Wightman and E. Wigner, Phys. Rev. **88**, 101 (1952). See also G. Feinberg and S. Weinberg, Nuovo Cimento **14**, 571 (1959).
23) J. R. Oppenheimer, Phys. Rev. **35**, 562 (1930).
24) I. Tamm, Z. Physik **62**, 545 (1930).
25) See ref. 14, p. 263.
26) H. A. Kramers, Proc. Acad. Sci. Amsterdam **40**, 814 (1937); *Collected Scientific Papers* (North-Holland Publ. Co., Amsterdam, 1956) p. 697.
27) E. P. Wigner, Göttinger Nachr. (1932) p. 546.
28) H. A. Kramers, Proc. Acad. Sci. Amsterdam **33**, 959 (1930); *Collected Scientific Papers*, p. 522.
29) The difference between time reversal and detailed balancing considerations is nicely illustrated in J. Blatt and V. Weisskopf, *Theoretical Nuclear Physics* (John Wiley, New York, 1952) p. 531.

30) T. D. Lee and C. N. Yang, Phys. Rev. **104**, 254 (1956).
31) L. D. Landau, Zh. Eksperim. i Teor. Fiz. **32**, 405 (1957); translation in: Nucl. Phys. **3**, 127 (1957). See also ref. 22, footnote 9.
32) M. Gell-Mann and A. Pais, Phys. Rev. **97**, 1387 (1955).
33) See refs. 29, 30 and A. Salam, Nuovo Cimento **5**, 299 (1957).
34) For the early developments concerning the *CPT*-theorem see W. Pauli, in: *Niels Bohr and the Development of Physics* (McGraw-Hill, New York, 1955).
35) R. Jost, Helv. Phys. Acta **30**, 409 (1957), als his contribution to *Theoretical Physics in the Twentieth Century* (Interscience, New York, 1960). See furthermore G. Lüders, Ann. Phys. (N.Y.) **2**, 1 (1957).
36) Discussed by Pauli, ref. 34.
37) T. D. Lee, R. Oehme and C. N. Yang, Phys. Rev. **106**, 340 (1957); G. Lüders and B. Zumino, Phys. Rev. **107**, 385 (1957).
38) J. H. Christenson, J. W. Cronin, V. L. Fitch and R. Turlay, Phys. Rev. Letters **13**, 138 (1964).
39) J. Bernstein, G. Feinberg and T. D. Lee, Phys. Rev. **139**, B 1650 (1965).
40) See, e.g., T. D. Lee, in: *Proceedings of the 1965 Oxford International Conference on Elementary Particles* (Rutherford High Energy Laboratory, Harwell, England 1966); N. P. Chang, Phys. Rev. Letters **16**, 337 (1966).
41) W. Heisenberg, Z. Physik **77**, 1 (1932); B. Cassen and E. Condon, Phys. Rev. **50**, 846 (1936).
42) N. Kemmer, Proc. Cambridge Phil. Soc. **34**, 354 (1938).
43) K. Case, R. Karplus and C. N. Yang, Phys. Rev. **101**, 874 (1956).
44) *Proc. 2nd Rochester Conference, January 1952*, especially contributions by E. Fermi and K. Brueckner.
45) R. Jost and A. Pais, Phys. Rev. **87**, 871 (1952).
46) L. Michel, Nuovo Cimento **10**, 319 (1953).
47) T. D. Lee and C. N. Yang, Nuov. Cimento **3**, 749 (1956).
48) M. Gell-Mann, Phys. Rev. **92**, 833 (1953); T. Nakano and K. Nishijima, Progr. Theoret. Phys. (Kyoto) **10**, 581 (1953).
49) A. Pais, Phys. Rev. **86**, 663 (1952).
50) A. Pais, in: *Proc. Kyoto-Tokyo Conference, 1953*, p. 156.
51) See, e.g., R. Behrends et al., Rev. Mod. Phys. **34**, 1 (1962).
52) M. H. Alston et al., Phys. Rev. Letters **5**, 520 (1960).
53) See M. Gell-Mann and Y. Ne'eman, *The Eightfold Way* (W. A. Benjamin Publishers, New York, 1964).
54) E. P. Wigner, Phys. Rev. **51**, 105 (1937).
55) For a review see A. Pais, Rev. Mod. Phys. **38**, 215 (1966).
56) M. Gell-Mann and A. Pais, in: *Proc. Glasgow Conference, 1954* (Pergamon Press, London).
57) G. Feinberg and A. Pais, Phys. Rev. **131**, 2724 (1963).
58) J. M. Gaillard et al., Phys. Rev. Letters **18**, 20 (1967); J. W. Cronin et al., Phys. Rev. Letters **18**, 25 (1967).
59) The corresponding question for angular momentum in *three* dimensions is discussed by W. Pauli, Helv. Phys. Acta **12**, 147 (1939).
60) See the discussion by G. Feinberg and M. Goldhaber, Proc. Natl. Acad. Sci. (U.S.) **45**, 1301 (1959).

61) E. C. G. Stückelberg, Helv. Phys. Acta **11**, 299 (1938), who called it "Erhaltungssatz der schweren Ladung".
62) M. Gell-Mann and R. Feynman, Phys. Rev. **109**, 193 (1958).
63) G. Danby et al., Phys. Rev. Letters **9**, 36 (1962).
64) This new trend started with the work of C. N. Yang and R. Mills, Phys. Rev. **96**, 191 (1954).
65) J. Schwinger in: *Theoretical Physics* (cf. ref. 10) p. 89; also Phys. Rev. **125**, 397 (1962); **128**, 2425 (1962).
66) Ref. 65 and D. G. Boulware and W. Gilbert, Phys. Rev. **126**, 1563 (1963); L. S. Brown, Nuovo Cimento **29**, 617 (1963); B. Zumino, Phys. Letters **10**, 224 (1964).

Spectroscopic and group theoretical methods in physics
© North-Holland Publ. Co., Amsterdam, 1968

THE ROLE OF LIE GROUPS IN STRONG INTERACTION PHYSICS*

Y. NE'EMAN
Physics Department, Tel-Aviv University, Tel-Aviv, Israel

1. Introduction

RACAH TEACHES GROUPS TO "GLOBAL" SYMMETRY SEEKERS

In the Spring of 1951 Giulio Racah was residing at Princeton. For the Spring Term of the Institute for Advanced Study, he delivered a series of seminar lectures on Group Theory and Spectroscopy[1]). The audience included a large number of young physicists who were to take a leading part in the subsequent development of Physics during the 1950's and the 1960's. Two of the participants took the notes and prepared the material for publication. Gell-Mann, Salam and others were interested in Group Theory and were indeed to apply it extensively to problems in Particle Physics. We know now that the material of the first three to four lectures contained in fact all the necessary *tools* for the formulation of a symmetry theory of hadrons and the strong interactions, together with a basic understanding of the way in which hadrons interact with leptons and photons through weak and electromagnetic forces. However this is hindsight. As far as Racah was concerned this material was just an introduction to his physical description of atomic spectroscopy. The audience must have been totally unprepared, so that much of the mathematical discussion was not assimilated. Indeed the years 1954 to 1960 witnessed a frantic search for a "global" symmetry; the search was conducted with a "poor man's group theory". This included only rotation groups, going into higher dimensionality all the time (the later models used rotations in nine dimensions). Unitary groups, which held the key to the phenomenological observations, were not used before 1959, although they

* Research sponsored by the Air Force Office of Scientific Research, Office of Aerospace Research, United States Air Force, under AFOSR grant number AF EOAR 66-39, through the European Office of Aerospace Research.

had been prominent in Racah's mathematical treatment. Racah himself continued to be extensively active in the study of atomic physics; his only involvement in the search for an internal symmetry was related to the discovery of strangeness. With the identification of this quantum number by Gell-Mann, Nakano and Nishijima[2]), all the necessary evidence for the further development of the symmetry scheme was in. However Racah himself raised some doubts[3]) as to the importance of following the Lie Group line, since, as he pointed out, strangeness (or hypercharge Y) could still be a multiplicative quantum number rather than an additive one. The irony of the situation extends to the fact that when I came to deal with the problem of a hadron overall internal symmetry, I had to learn my group theory out of translations of Russian texts by Dynkin[4]) and others, whereas I could have had all my algebra "back at home", so to say.

FINALLY, IT IS SU(3), INTRODUCED VIA A YANG–MILLS LAGRANGIAN

We now know that SU(3) (U(3) if we adjoin the baryon number operator B) represents the searched-for "global" symmetry, provided we construct our assignments starting from the identification of the eight $j=\frac{1}{2}^+$ metastable baryons as a (2, 1, 0) octet[5]). The weights in this notation are

$$h_1 = I_z + \tfrac{1}{2}Y + B\,, \qquad h_2 = -\,I_z + \tfrac{1}{2}Y + B\,, \qquad h_3 = -\,Y + B\,. \tag{1}$$

To introduce SU(3) as a strong interaction symmetry, a Lagrangian model was used. In particular, the Yang–Mills method was applied, so that a coupling of 8 (or 9 for U(3)) $J=1^-$ mesons V^i_μ to the set of current-densities j^μ_i of the SU(3) generators was given a fundamental role,

$$\mathscr{L}_{\text{int}} = g V^i_\mu j^\mu_i\,, \tag{2}$$

where j^μ_i is constructed out of the "basic" fermion fields (the **8** of $J=\frac{1}{2}$ baryons at the beginning, and then the 3 quark triplet which provided a "simpler" model) and of the vector mesons themselves. In the limit of SU(3) conservation

$$\partial_\mu j^\mu_i = 0\,. \tag{3}$$

Such a presentation could not be considered as a useful one, mainly because of the approximate nature of the symmetry. The Lagrangian formulation provides no dynamical picture, since

a) quantized fields yield off-mass shell S-matrix elements and the Field Theory formalism is not yet adequate to deal with these;

b) in particular, massive vector mesons (other than a singlet) yield non-renormalizable theories;

c) the strong coupling does not allow the use of the perturbation expansion;
d) the nucleons and other metastable particles can no more be considered as elementary – while quarks, which could be elementary, may not exist;
e) the unknown factor which breaks SU(3) may in itself represent a strong coupling, so that nothing much could be said about the properties of the S-matrix. Even though we do know that the Hamiltonian density behaves like a scalar $\mathscr{H}_0$ plus a smaller 8th component $\mathscr{H}_8$

$$-\theta^{00} = \mathscr{H}_0 + \mathscr{H}_8 \tag{4}$$

its exponentiated matrix elements may yield any tensors belonging to the product $8 \times 8 \times 8 \times 8$ ....

Weakly-coupled currents generate an exact SU(3) algebra

This is why it was suggested[6]) by Gell-Mann that a better foundation for SU(3) would be provided by a definition in terms of the electromagnetic and atonous (weak) interactions. The small couplings of the hadron currents to photons or lepton-currents enable us to evaluate the matrix-elements (A, B are hadron states) on and off mass shell,

$$\langle \mathrm{A} | j_i^\mu | \mathrm{B} \rangle \tag{5}$$

and analytically continue them. The SU(3) generators are then defined as

$$G_i = \int \mathrm{d}^3 x \, j_i^0 \,. \tag{6}$$

This approach – and its extension to $[\mathrm{SU}(3) \times \mathrm{SU}(3)]_{\gamma 5}$ for vector and axial vector charges[6, 7]) – was brilliantly vindicated by the success[8]) of the Adler–Weisberger sum rule for $G_\mathrm{A}/G_\mathrm{V}$, the renormalization of the axial-vector β-decay coupling.

In the application of current-generated algebras, nothing is postulated as to the strong interactions symmetry features. The methods of Fubini and Furlan[9]) are used to estimate the "leakage" of SU(3) or $[\mathrm{SU}(3) \times \mathrm{SU}(3)]_{\gamma 5}$ transitions, due to the fact that the generators indeed do not commute with the strong-interaction Hamiltonian (except for the G_{1-3} I-spin algebra, $G_8 \sim Y$ and $G_0 \sim B$).

...and regulate some strong couplings at low energy

Some implications can nevertheless be derived for low-energy strong couplings. By assuming a pole-dominance for j_i^μ, Gell-Mann reproduced approximately the universal couplings of the $J=1^-$ mesons[6]). A similar assumption with respect to the $\partial_\mu a_i^\mu$ (the divergences of the axial vector current densities) which are assumed to be dominated by 0^- mesons, yields the Goldberger–Treiman relation. This is also an approximate universality-like condition on couplings, this time relating them to weak interaction parameters. Further along the way, a direct postulation of superconvergence for some strong amplitudes[10]) promises to add some such conditions.

In the following pages we shall describe a recent attempt[11]) to tackle the strong interactions directly via an algebraic formulation. It is postulated in terms of the Regge-picture of high-energy scattering. The entire set of forward-scattering experiments is correctly described. It is possible that a derivation of our basic ansatz from the algebra of electromagnetic and atonous (weak) currents exists, and that we have yet one more example of such an approximate universality requirement. However, the factorizability of Regge residues, and the relative (hopefully) simple picture of high-energy scattering allows us to conjecture that we may have here a real *exact* definition of the strong-interaction algebra. This seems to be isomorphic in part to the algebra of currents, but is not identical with it. Indeed, the study of the connections between the two systems may in itself provide much insight.

In the following pages, we first review the complex-J formalism and its problematics, as a physical parametrization (and nucleus of a theory) of high energy phenomenology. We then present our algebraic approach and study the existing applications. We sketch the possible relevance to some of the difficult points arising from the phenomenology. Finally, we mention possible relationships to non-strong currents.

2. High energy scattering and the complex J plane

Regge poles represent bound states

For a spherically-symmetric potential, the time-independent Schrödinger wave function at large distances $r \to \infty$ takes the form[12])

$$\psi(x) \underset{r\to\infty}{\sim} e^{ikz} + \frac{e^{ikr}}{r} f(k^2, \cos\theta) \tag{7}$$

with a partial-wave expansion,

$$f(k^2, \cos\theta) = \sum_{l=0}^{\infty} (2l+1)\, a_l(k^2)\, P_l(\cos\theta) \tag{8}$$

and

$$a_l(k^2) = \frac{1}{k} e^{i\delta_l} \sin\delta_l , \tag{9}$$

z is chosen in the direction of the incoming beam; k is the plane wave momentum we pick, θ is the scattering angle, δ_l is the phase shift. Bound states appear as poles in the scattering amplitude $f(k^2, \cos\theta)$ at $k^2 = B$,

$$f(k^2, \cos\theta) = (2l+1)\frac{N}{k^2+B}P_l(\cos\theta) + \text{regular function}. \tag{10}$$

Using the Sommerfeld–Watson formula, the expansion (8) becomes,

$$f(k^2, \cos\theta) = \frac{i}{2}\int_{-\frac{1}{2}-i\infty}^{-\frac{1}{2}+i\infty}\frac{(2l+1)\,a_l(k^2)\,P_l(-\cos\theta)\,dl}{\sin\pi l} + \\ + \sum_i \frac{\beta_i(k^2)\,P_{\alpha_i(k^2)}(-\cos\theta)}{\sin\pi\alpha_i(k^2)}, \tag{11}$$

where

$$\beta_i(k^2) = \int_{\alpha_i}(2l+1)\,a_l(k^2)\,dl. \tag{12}$$

There are arguments allowing us to discard the first term in (11), the "background integral". The other terms can be rewritten near an integer value $l(k_l^2)$ of $\alpha(k^2)$

$$\frac{\beta_i(k^2)\,P_{\alpha_i(k^2)}(-\cos\theta)}{\sin\pi\alpha_i(k^2)} = (2l+1)\left\{\beta_i(k^2)/(2l+1)\,\pi\left(\frac{\partial\alpha}{\partial k^2}\right)_{k_l^2}\right\}\times \\ \times\frac{1}{(k^2-k_l^2)}P_l(\cos\theta) + \text{regular function}, \tag{13}$$

and we see by comparing with (10) that it represents a bound state (or resonance if l has a small complex piece) pole in $f(k^2, \cos\theta)$. This expansion is very suitable for asymptotic values of $(\cos\theta)\to\infty$, since

$$P_{\alpha_i}(z) \underset{z\to\infty}{\to} z^{\alpha_i}. \tag{14}$$

...AND ARE ASSUMED TO DOMINATE HIGH ENERGY SCATTERING IN THE CROSSED CHANNEL

In a relativistic amplitude with Mandelstam variables s, t, u

$$s = (p_1+p_2)^2, \qquad t = (p_1-p_1')^2, \qquad u = (p_1-p_2')^2, \\ s+t+u = m_1^2+m_2^2+m_1'^2+m_2'^2; \tag{15}$$

$s = (p_1^0+p_2^0)^2_{\text{c.m.}}$ is the total-energy squared in the center-of-mass system; for elastic scattering, $-t=-(p_1-p_1')^2=\Delta^2$ is the squared momentum transfer. This is the s-channel; in the t-channel, the roles are inverted. For equal-mass particles, we find in the t-channel

$$t = 4(k^2 + m^2), \quad s = -2k^2(1 - \cos\theta), \quad u = -2k^2(1 + \cos\theta), \tag{16}$$

where k and θ are the t-channel c.m. momentum and scattering angle. If we thus study the behavior of the scattering amplitude for large $\cos\theta$ in this channel, holding t itself, we get to the $s\to\infty$ region, i.e. the high-energy region in the s-channel. Assuming Regge behavior then implies for the relativistic amplitude $A(s, t)$

$$A(s, t) \underset{s\to\infty}{\sim} \sum_i \beta_i(t)\, s^{\alpha_i(t)}, \qquad A(s, t, u) = s^{\frac{1}{2}} f(q^2, \Delta^2), \tag{17}$$

where $A(s, t, u)$ has been chosen so that we may use the simplest set of crossing relations,

$$A_u(u, t) = A_s^*(s, t). \tag{18}$$

We also replace the s and u variables by ν and ω, with

$$\nu = s + \tfrac{1}{2}t - m_1^2 - m_2^2, \qquad \omega = u + \tfrac{1}{2}t - m_1^2 - m_2^2. \tag{19}$$

This choice may be shown to yield the simplest crossing form-invariance. Now the optical theorem in the s-channel connects the total cross-section σ_T with the forward scattering amplitude (since $t=-2q^2(1-\cos\theta)$ in the s channel, this is $t=0$)

$$\sigma_T(s) = \frac{4\pi}{qs^{\frac{1}{2}}} \operatorname{Im} A(s, t)_{t=0} \underset{s\to\infty}{\longrightarrow} \frac{8\pi}{s} \operatorname{Im} A(s, t)_{t=0}; \tag{20}$$

on the other hand, the differential cross-section

$$\frac{d\sigma}{d\Omega} = \frac{1}{s}|A(s, t)|^2, \qquad \frac{d\sigma}{dt} = \frac{4\pi}{s^2}|A(s, t)|^2 \quad \text{as} \quad d\Omega = \frac{4\pi}{s}\, dt, \tag{21}$$

and at $t=0$, we have

$$\left.\frac{d\sigma}{d\Omega}\right|_{\theta=0} = \frac{1}{s}\left[(\operatorname{Re} A(s, 0))^2 + (\operatorname{Im} A(s, 0))^2\right],$$

and a ratio

$$X(s, 0) = \frac{\operatorname{Re} A(s, 0)}{\operatorname{Im} A(s, 0)} = \left[\sum_l (2l + 1) \operatorname{Re} A_l(s)\right] \frac{4\pi s^{\frac{1}{2}}}{q\sigma_T}. \tag{22}$$

THE FROISSART BOUND AND THE POMERANCHUK TRAJECTORY PROVIDE A SIMPLE PICTURE

It can be shown that there should exist at least a bound

$$\sigma_{\mathrm{T}}(\nu) \underset{\nu\to\infty}{\leqslant} C \log^2 \nu\,, \qquad C \text{ a constant}\,, \tag{23}$$

and since $s=4(q^2+m^2)$, $s^{\frac{1}{2}} \sim q$, so that from (20) we find

$$A(\nu, 0) \underset{\nu\to\infty}{\leqslant} C\nu \log^2 \nu\,, \tag{24}$$

where we have also assumed that $X(\nu, 0)_{\nu\to\infty} < 1$. Experimentally, $X(\nu, 0)_{\nu\to\infty} \ll 1$.

From the experimental fact that

$$\sigma_{\mathrm{T}}(\nu)_{\nu\to\infty} \to C\,, \tag{25}$$

we infer that the bound (23) is too high. Thus

$$A(\nu, 0) \underset{\nu\to\infty}{\leqslant} C\nu\,, \tag{26}$$

yielding a finite cross-section at $\nu\to\infty$, which could not be achieved in perturbation theory especially in connection with high-spin exchanges.

For varying t we may use the expansion[13])

$$A(\nu, t) \underset{\nu\to\infty}{=} \sum C_{ijk}(t)\, \nu^{\alpha_i(t)} (\log \nu)^{\bar{\alpha}_j(t)} (\log\log \nu)^{\bar{\bar{\alpha}}_k(t)}\,, \tag{27}$$

where from (26)

$$\alpha_i(0) \leqslant 1\,, \qquad \bar{\alpha}_j(0) \leqslant 0\,, \qquad \bar{\bar{\alpha}}_k(0) \leqslant 0\,, \tag{28}$$

the $\bar{\alpha}_j$ and $\bar{\bar{\alpha}}_k$ bounds being due to the fact that a $\nu\alpha_i^{(0)}$ term with $\alpha_i(0) \sim 1$ is indeed observed (the Pomeranchuk pole). The $\bar{\alpha}_j \equiv 0$ and $\bar{\bar{\alpha}}_k \equiv 0$ terms in the expansion (27) thus reduce to a Regge pole behavior as in (14) and (17).

... WHICH MAY BE MARRED BY CUTS IN THE COMPLEX J PLANE

Mandelstam[14]) has shown that $\bar{\alpha}_j = -1, -2, -3, \ldots$ terms may indeed exist and represent cuts in the complex J plane; the cuts are due to the exchange of two or more Regge pole trajectories $\alpha_{\mathrm{A}}(t)$, $\alpha_{\mathrm{B}}(t)$ with relative orbital $L=1, 2, \ldots$. Thus the most effective poles[15]) at large ν will contribute terms going as

$$\nu^{-\alpha_{\mathrm{cut}}(t)} (\log \nu)^{-1}\,, \tag{29}$$

with

$$\alpha_{\mathrm{cut}}(t) = \mathrm{Max}\left[\alpha_{\mathrm{A}}(t_{\mathrm{A}}) + \alpha_{\mathrm{B}}(t_{\mathrm{B}}) - 1\right], \tag{30}$$

where $\sqrt{|t_A|}+\sqrt{|t_B|}\geqslant\sqrt{|t|}$, $t_A, t_B\leqslant 0$, so that

$$\alpha_{cut}(0) = \alpha_A(0) + \alpha_B(0) - 1\,, \tag{31}$$

and if we assume linear

$$\alpha_i(t) = \alpha_i(0) + (\alpha_i)'_{t=0}t\,, \tag{32}$$

we get at $t=0$

$$(\alpha_{cut})' = \frac{(\alpha_A)'(\alpha_B)'}{(\alpha_A)' + (\alpha_B)'}\,, \tag{33}$$

so that $(\alpha_{cut})' <$ either $(\alpha_A)'$ or $(\alpha_B)'$; for A=B:

$$(\alpha_{cut})' = \tfrac{1}{2}(\alpha_A)'\,, \tag{34}$$

i.e. cuts dominate at large negative t. As to the intercept $\alpha_{cut}(0)$, we should really include the ν dependence when comparing with the pole trajectories. We get

$$\alpha_{eff}(\nu, t) = \alpha_{cut}(0) - (\log \nu/\nu_0)^{-1}\,. \tag{35}$$

TRAJECTORIES CARRY SIGNATURES

The $C_{ijk}(t)$ contain the pole term, as in (13). Because of the features of exchange-forces, it has been shown that they contain a signature term,

$$\zeta[\alpha_i^{\pm}(t)] = \frac{1 \pm \exp[-i\pi(\alpha_i^{\pm}(t) - \xi)]}{\sin\pi(\alpha_i^{\pm}(t) - \xi)} \tag{36}$$

($\xi=0$ for meson, $=\frac{1}{2}$ for baryon trajectories) so that the pole occurs for either even (ζ^+) or odd (ζ^-) integer values in $\alpha_i^{\pm}(t)$. Explicit evaluation of $C_i(t)$ also reveals a term

$$G[\alpha_i^{\pm}(t)] = \frac{\Gamma(\alpha_i^{\pm}(t) + \frac{3}{2})}{\Gamma(\alpha_i^{\pm}(t) + 1)}\,, \tag{37}$$

so that

$$A(\nu, t) = \sum_i \beta_i(t)\, G[\alpha_i(t)]\, \zeta[\alpha_i(t)] \left(\frac{\nu}{\nu_0}\right)^{\alpha_i(t)-\Sigma} + \text{"cut" terms}\,, \tag{38}$$

where Σ is the number of units of helicity-flip for the various independent invariant amplitudes.

...THEIR RESIDUES FACTORIZE

It has been proved [16]) that in most cases, the $\beta_i(t)$ factorizes into the product of two vertex-strengths $\gamma_i(t)$ representing a "form factor" coupling the

$\alpha_i(t)$ trajectory to the incoming and outgoing particles in the t-channel crossed picture,

$$\beta_i\{A + B \to C + D, t\} = \gamma_i^{A\bar{C}}(t)\,\gamma_i^{\bar{B}D}(t)\,. \tag{39}$$

SPINS MULTIPLY AMPLITUDES

In N–N scattering, there are 5 invariant amplitudes for each I-spin; however, at $t=0$ only 3 are independent. For N–π scattering, there is only one complex amplitude. We can replace the Dirac decomposition in $\pi_A + N_B \to \pi_C + N_D$,

$$(2\pi)^{-1} A(s,t) = \bar{u}_D\left[A_1(s,t) + \tfrac{1}{2}\mathrm{i}\gamma_\mu (p_A^\mu + p_B^\mu)\,A_2(s,t)\right] u_B \tag{40}$$

by Pauli spinors χ

$$(2\pi)^{-1} A(s,t) = \bar{\chi}_D\left[g(s,t) + \mathrm{i}\,\frac{\sigma\cdot(k_A \wedge k_C)}{|k_A \wedge k_C|}\,h(s,t)\right]\chi_B\,, \tag{41}$$

with asymptotic connections for $s \to \infty$

$$g \to \frac{s}{16\pi}\,A_2\,, \qquad h \to \frac{(-t)^{\frac{1}{2}}}{8\pi}\,A_1\,. \tag{42}$$

The polarization of D for unpolarized B is

$$\left\langle \bar{\chi}_D\,\frac{\sigma\cdot(k_A \wedge k_C)}{|k_A \wedge k_C|}\,\chi_D \right\rangle = \frac{2\,\mathrm{Im}(gh^*)}{|g|^2 + |h|^2}\,, \tag{43}$$

which vanishes if g and h have the same phase.

THE DIFFRACTION PEAK

Replacing $A(s,t)$ in (21) by (38) we can study the model's predictions for the diffraction peak. Assuming one dominant Pomeranchuk pole with $\alpha_P(0) \sim 1$, and $(\alpha_P)' \sim \frac{2}{3}$ (if indeed the f^0(1250 MeV, 2^+) meson is a pole on this trajectory) we find

$$\frac{d\sigma}{dt} \sim s^{(2+\frac{4}{3}t)-2}\,|C(t)|^2 \sim |C(t)|^2\,e^{(\frac{4}{3}\log s)t}\,, \tag{44}$$

which gives an exponential fall-off for the diffraction peak at fixed s and negative t (i.e. the s-channel). On the other hand,

$$\log\left(\frac{d\sigma}{dt}\right) \approx \log|C(t)|^2 - \tfrac{4}{3}|t|\log s \tag{45}$$

implies a shrinkage of the diffraction peak. The shape of the diffraction peak for fixed s is indeed experimentally observed.

... DOESN'T ALWAYS SHRINK

However, the shrinkage in s for fixed t is only seen in pp, K^+p, with a slower rate. It is not seen in $\pi^{\pm}p$, K^-p.

More recently, the shrinkage has indeed been observed[17]) in $\pi^- p \to \pi^0 n$. This is a reaction where only the odd-signature $I=1$ ρ-trajectory is allowed. It has $\alpha_\rho(0) \sim 0.5$, and $\alpha'_\rho(0) \sim 1.0$ so that

$$\log\left(\frac{d\sigma}{dt}\right) \approx \log|C_\rho(t)|^2 - (2|t|+1)\log s. \tag{46}$$

Note that the existence of cuts at $t<0$ would yield slower shrinkage rates.

The mentioned observed failure in the original prediction of general shrinkage[18]) has been interpreted as a flatness $(\alpha_P(t))'=0$ of the Pomeranchuk trajectory. The exponential fall-off in t for fixed s has then to be extracted artificially from the residue $\beta(t)$ itself. This also means that the f^0(1250 MeV; 2^+) meson does not represent a pole on this trajectory. Moreover, an additional P′ trajectory was introduced[19]), to cope with the observed cross-sections. Since then, and after the discovery of $f^{0\prime}$(1500 MeV; 2^+), one has at least three (P, f^0, $P'=f^{0\prime}$) or four (P, P′, f^0, $f^{0\prime}$) even signature isoscalar trajectories. The rest of the $J=2^+$ multiplet – A_2(1320) and K′(1400) – supply isovector and isospinor ($Y=\pm 1$) trajectories. For the odd-signature case, the 1^- nonet (ω(783), ϕ(1019), ρ(765), K*(891)) provide a clean nonet of trajectories.

FITTING σ_T AND $A(\nu, 0)$

The elastic scattering data – in fact total cross-sections σ_T for $\bar{N}N$, NN, πp, Kp – has been fitted[20]) with such a set of 1+9+9 trajectories. Such a fit implies two parameters per trajectory, $\beta_i(0)$ and $\alpha_i(0)$. However, SU(3) connects the factorized residues $\gamma_i^{AB}(0)$. Since one is dealing with elastic scattering, only γ_3 and γ_8 appear in each octet, but the couplings are allowed to take on any F/D admixture. We thus have 7 trajectories coupling to either nucleons or mesons, i.e. 14 coupling parameters, besides the 7 $\alpha_i(0)$ intercepts, altogether 21 parameters for 10 curves.

Similar attempts to fit baryon–baryon charge exchange results (np↔pn, $\bar{p}p \leftrightarrow \bar{n}n$) have been unsatisfactory. Apparently, one has to include the effects of 1^+ and 0^- trajectories as well, since these are allowed here. The requirements due to extra-invariance at $t=0$ connect these two sets of trajectories ("conspiracy"[21])).

The above fits have also attempted to predict X in (22), with rather unsatisfactory results for pp, π^+p. One gets a requirement of $X \to 0$ at a faster rate than is observed. Note that the ratio X (or Re $A(\nu, 0)$) is measured directly in π^-p through the interference between Coulomb and strong-interaction contributions[22]). It can then be checked against the prediction of dispersion relations,

$$\mathrm{Re}\, f(\nu) = \frac{1}{\pi} P \int_{-\infty}^{\infty} \mathrm{d}\nu' \, \frac{\mathrm{Im}\, f(\nu')}{\nu' - \nu} = \frac{1}{4\pi^2} P \int_{-\infty}^{\infty} \mathrm{d}\nu' \, q \, \frac{\sigma_{\mathrm{T}}(\nu')}{\nu' - \nu}, \tag{47}$$

where one makes some plausible assumptions with respect to the very high-energy tail of $\sigma_{\mathrm{T}}(\nu)$. The results of such a check are good.

Dips and maxima occur in $(\mathrm{d}\sigma/\mathrm{d}t)(t)$ for fixed s

The amplitude $h(s, t)$ in (41) does not contribute at $t=0$. $g(s, t)$ contains the kinematical factor $(1 - t/4M_{\mathrm{N}}^2)$ and survives at $t=0$, whereas in $h(s, t)$ we get

$$\frac{t}{4M_{\mathrm{N}}^2}\left(s - \frac{s + p_{\mathrm{lab}}^2}{1 - t/4M_{\mathrm{N}}^2}\right)$$

as kinematical factor and therefore have no spin-flip contribution in forward scattering.

One can therefore assume that the sharp rise of $\mathrm{d}\sigma/\mathrm{d}t$ in $\pi^-\mathrm{p} \to \pi^0\mathrm{n}$ is due to the spin-flip amplitude $h(s, t)$. Because of the quantum numbers, only the ρ-meson odd signature trajectory is allowed in the t-channel here. It was thus also possible to look for further effects due to the features of that trajectory. On the one hand, because of the $\xi=1$ in the spin-flip amplitude, its partial-wave expansions correspond to $[P_l(\cos\theta)]'$, yielding an asymptotic form $\alpha\nu^{\alpha-1}$, as against $P_l(\cos\theta)$ and its ν^{α} limit for the $g(s, t)$ amplitude. Thus $h(s, t)$ vanishes at $\alpha=0$; the σ_{T} fit yields $\alpha_\rho(0) \simeq 0.5$, and if we connect this point with the ρ pole $\alpha_\rho(0.765^2 \simeq 0.6) = 1$ and assume a straight line in the (Re α, t) plane, we find $\alpha(-0.6)=0$. This then explains the dip at $t=-0.6$, supposedly due to the vanishing of h at that point. Noting that similar kinematical zeros appear in most even and odd trajectories, Frautschi predicted dips in several other differential cross sections around $t \sim -0.5$. Moreover, study of backward $\pi^+\mathrm{p} \to \pi^+\mathrm{p}$ scattering displays a dip at $u=-0.2$ $(\mathrm{GeV/c})^2$ in $\mathrm{d}\sigma/\mathrm{d}u$, which does not appear in $\pi^-\mathrm{p} \to \pi^-\mathrm{p}$. This can be explained by the appearance of the nucleon trajectory in the u-channel for π^+p only (the $\Delta(1238; \frac{3}{2}^+)$ trajectory appears in both). The N$(940; \frac{1}{2}^+)$ spinor trajectory has a kinematical factor $(2\alpha+1)$ and therefore should vanish at $\alpha(u) = -\frac{1}{2}$, which fits the $u=-0.2$ dip. Note however that the extension of the Regge formalism to backward scattering of particles with unequal masses requires the further postulation of families[24] of trajectories ("daughters") at intervals $\Delta\alpha(0)=1$ and with alternating parities. This then strengthens the previous finding with respect to "conspiracy". The picture is very much the same as in the non-relativistic classical problems[25] of hydrogen, the oscillator etc. There, the SO(1, 3) unitary infinite ladder-representation, constituted by the sequence of rotational excitations corresponding to a given number of nodes of the radial wave function, is embedded in a representation of SO(2, 3) or SU(1, 3) containing a series of such ladders.

If the Pomeranchuk trajectory is flat, the dips in most $d\sigma/dt$ should vanish beyond $\nu \sim 10$–12 GeV. If dips are still seen at large ν, we have an indication that α_P, which should dominate these regions, also has a kinematical zero and thus intersects the $\alpha=0$ axis, i.e. it is not flat.

… AND POLARIZATION IN πN CHARGE EXCHANGE

If the above picture of $\pi^- p \to \pi^0 n$ dominated singly by the ρ-trajectory were true, we should find no polarization since $g(s, t)$ and $h(s, t)$ have the same phase and $\mathrm{Im}(gh^*)=0$ in (43). However, $\mathscr{P}\neq 0$ and reaches $\sim 20\%$ at 6 GeV/c and $\sim 15\%$ at 11 GeV/c. This could be due to a cut corresponding to the exchange of the ρ and P trajectories together. Using (33) and (35), Chiu and Finkelstein[26] have been able to reproduce the polarization data, and to refit the $d\sigma/dt$ dip, including the cut there too. In addition, they have also refit the cross-over point issue, which we shall discuss in the following paragraphs. For the behavior of the polarization with energy, they find that the $\alpha_\rho(t)$ and $\alpha_{\mathrm{cut}}^{\mathrm{eff}}(t)$ intersect at a ν-dependent point t_0 in negative t, $\alpha_\rho(t_0)-\alpha_{\mathrm{cut}}^{\mathrm{eff}}(t_0)=0$. $\mathscr{P}(t_0)=0$; for $0\leqslant|t|\leqslant t_0$, $\mathscr{P}$ will diminish with rising ν. In the region $t_0\leqslant|t|$, $\mathscr{P}$ will rise with ν.

CROSS-OVER POINTS

All differential cross sections display this feature. Plotting for instance

$$\delta(\bar{p}p) = \frac{d\sigma}{dt}(\bar{p}p \to \bar{p}p) - \frac{d\sigma}{dt}(pp \to pp), \tag{48}$$

we find $\delta(t)$ changes sign, going through $\delta(-0.15\ (\mathrm{GeV/c})^2)=0$. δ can only be given by

$$\mathrm{Re}\left\{(\zeta^+)^*\zeta^-\beta^+\beta^-\nu^{\alpha^+ +\alpha^- -2}\right\}, \tag{49}$$

where $\pm$ denote even and odd signatures, since the interference term between these is the only one to change sign under $p\to\bar{p}$. A similar cross-over point occurs in

$$\delta(\pi^-\mathrm{p}) = \frac{\mathrm{d}\sigma}{\mathrm{d}t}(\pi^-\mathrm{p}\to\pi^-\mathrm{p}) - \frac{\mathrm{d}\sigma}{\mathrm{d}t}(\pi^+\mathrm{p}\to\pi^+\mathrm{p}) \tag{50}$$

at $t=-0.05$. In this case we have again only the ρ trajectory – and the ρP cut – contributing. The simplest explanation would make $g(s,t)$ change sign at the cross over point, with the cut compensating for the negative $g(t)$ at the -0.6 dip in $\mathrm{d}\sigma/\mathrm{d}t$. There are also other possibilities, and the entire issue is still rather speculative.

"ONION" STRUCTURE

Experiments[27]) at $\theta=90°$ (i.e. $t=0$ at $s=4M_\mathrm{N}^2$, and $t=-2M_\mathrm{N}^2$ at $s=8M_\mathrm{N}^2$) in N–N scattering reveal a sharp break in $(\mathrm{d}\sigma/\mathrm{d}t)\,(q^2)$, $q^2=\frac{1}{4}s-M_\mathrm{N}^2$. This can be explained[28]) by a kinematical zero in the P amplitude at $\alpha_\mathrm{P}(t_0)=-1$, where the contribution of the double P cut is suddenly "exposed". If the cut's residue at $t=0$ is small, it won't be felt up to t_0. With rising ν or k^2, the cut will dominate at large $|t|$, since its trajectory is more flat and tops the P trajectory. For this conjecture to hold, $\alpha_\mathrm{P}(t)$ should again have a marked slope, although it is perhaps still only half as steep as the other boson trajectories, whose intercepts all lie around $\alpha(0)=0.5$ with poles at $t\sim0.6$–1.1 (for $\alpha=1^-$) and 1.5–2.2 (for $\alpha=2^+$).

3. The CHN algebra

THE UNIVERSALITY POSTULATE AND β

The CHN algebra identifies the $t=0$ (forward scattering) values of the vertex strengths (39) with the eigenvalues of an algebra, just as in the case of the electric charge in quantum electrodynamics ($i=0, 1, \ldots, 8$ is the U(3) index),

$$\delta^3(\boldsymbol{p}_\mathrm{A}-\boldsymbol{p}_\mathrm{B})\,\gamma^{\mathrm{AB}}_{s,v;i}(0) = \langle \mathrm{A}|\textstyle\int \mathscr{D}(s,v;\lambda^i;\boldsymbol{x},0)\,\mathrm{d}^3x\,|\mathrm{B}\rangle\,; \tag{51}$$

$(\boldsymbol{x},0)$ is a density isomorphic to the quark bilinears

$$\begin{aligned} &\tfrac{1}{2}\mathrm{q}^+\beta\lambda^i\mathrm{q} \quad &&\text{for}\quad (s;\lambda^i;\boldsymbol{x},0)\,,\\ &\tfrac{1}{2}\mathrm{q}^+\lambda^i\mathrm{q} \quad &&\text{for}\quad (v;\lambda^i;\boldsymbol{x},0)\,. \end{aligned} \tag{52}$$

The space-integrals $S^i=\int\mathscr{D}(s;\lambda^i)\,\mathrm{d}^3x$ and $V^i=\int\mathscr{D}(v;\lambda^i)\,\mathrm{d}^3x$ thus generate the algebra of $[\mathrm{U}(3)\times\mathrm{U}(3)]_\beta$. It is the *universality* of such a coupling to Regge trajectories, together with the nature of the β operator and its derived generators S^i, which is at the origin of the "additivity of quark–quark amplitudes" which was noticed and applied by various workers.

When going from a quark (1, 0, 0) representation of U(3) to an antiquark (0, 0, −1), the eigenvalues of the baryon number generator λ^0 change sign, just as the entire matrix representation λ^i becomes $-\lambda^{i\sim}$ in this passage from a contravariant to a covariant representation. However, this sign change cancels in the presence of the β operator, this β being either the Dirac β, whose eigenvalues reproduce the intrinsic relative parities of particle and antiparticle – or any other operator defined so that it yields an additional minus sign in going from 3 to 3*.

In this case, the generator $\beta\lambda^0$ for instance counts

$$N_\beta = \{\mathcal{N}(3) + \mathcal{N}(3^*)\}. \tag{53}$$

where $\mathcal{N}$ is the "number of" 3 or 3* representation spaces, whereas

$$B = \tfrac{1}{3}\{(3) - (3^*)\}. \tag{54}$$

The amplitude for small t is then given by

$$A^{\mathrm{CD}}_{\mathrm{AB}}(\nu, t) = -\sum_{i=0}^{8}\left\{\gamma^{\mathrm{AC}}_{s;i}(t)\,\gamma^{\mathrm{BD}}_{s;i}(t)\,G[\alpha^s_i(t)]\,\zeta[\alpha^s_i(t)]\left(\frac{\nu}{\nu_0}\right)^{\alpha^s_i(t)} + \right.$$

$$\left. + \gamma^{\mathrm{AC}}_{v;i}(t)\,\gamma^{\mathrm{BD}}_{v;i}(t)\,G[\alpha^v_i(t)]\,\zeta[\alpha^v_i(t)]\left(\frac{\nu}{\nu_0}\right)^{\alpha^v_i(t)}\right\}, \tag{55}$$

where $\alpha^s_i \equiv \alpha^+_i$, $\alpha^v_i \equiv \alpha^-_i$. The overall sign is fixed by the requirement of a positive $\sigma_{\mathrm{T}}(\nu\to\infty)$; the relative sign corresponds to the provision of attraction or repulsion between like particles when exchanging even or odd spin particles respectively. For backward scattering, one has to use the u-channel Regge trajectories and poles, and modify (55) accordingly. For sizable negative t, spin-flip amplitudes come in and one has again to rewrite (55) taking appropriate care of the transformation properties of the $\mathscr{D}(\boldsymbol{x}, 0)$. It will look like a product of two matrix elements whose invariantly reduced form factors contribute to the various invariants in the separated amplitude.

Applying this approach to forward πp elastic scattering, and assuming that only the $\mathscr{D}(s; \lambda^0)$ trajectory (vacuum-like, i.e. the Pomeranchuk trajectory) contributes in the asymptotic region, we get the Levin–Frankfurt ratio

$$\frac{\sigma_{\pi\mathrm{p}}}{\sigma_{\mathrm{pp}}} = \frac{\mathrm{Im}\,A_{\pi\mathrm{p}}(s, 0)}{\mathrm{Im}\,A_{\mathrm{pp}}(s, 0)} = \frac{\gamma^{\pi\pi}_{s,0}(0)\,\gamma^{\mathrm{pp}}_{s,0}(0)}{\gamma^{\mathrm{pp}}_{s,0}(0)\,\gamma^{\mathrm{pp}}_{s,0}(0)} = \frac{2}{3}. \tag{56}$$

Baryons and mesons transform under this $[\mathrm{U}(3)\times\mathrm{U}(3)]_\beta$ algebra according to the corresponding sub-multiplets of the $[\mathrm{U}(6)\times\mathrm{U}(6)]_\beta$ rest-assignments [30])

(56,1) and (6,6*). It may be more fitting, however, to use $U(3)^+ \times U(3)^-$ representations defined by the highest weight system $[(h_1^+, h_2^+, h_3^+), (h_1^-, h_2^-, h_3^-)]$ where the $U(\beta)^\pm$ weights are given by the $\frac{1}{2}(1 \pm \beta)$ projections of the definitions in equation (1). This gives us

$$B = \tfrac{1}{3} \sum_{n=1}^{3} (h_n^+ + h_n^-), \tag{57}$$

$$N_\beta = \sum_{n=1}^{3} (h_n^+ - h_n^-). \tag{58}$$

Up to this point we have been using (51) between states at rest, which would imply different frames for the two vertices when space-integrating. It may be that a complete theory would require us to treat both vertices simultaneously, and that the same classification of states cannot be maintained as far as the S^i part of $[U(3) \times U(3)]_\beta$ goes (the V^i have Lorentz-invariant vector's zero component). The effect will be the allowed appearance of a D-type coupling at the baryon or antibaryon $\gamma_i^s(0)$ vertices. All $\gamma_i^v(0)$ vertices are of F type, being universal, and the meson $\gamma_i^s(0)$ is of pure D-type because of charge-conjugation invariancc. The actual amount of D-admixture should be energy-dependent, since we would require no D-coupling at rest ($t=u=0$). On the other hand, with the entire Regge formalism coming into its own at large ν only, it may be plausible to use a fixed parameter for present fits[31]. Also, γ_i cannot be ν-dependent in Reggeism.

TOTAL CROSS SECTIONS AND QUARK MODEL RESULTS

Table 1 of ref. 11 reproduces the predictions of (55) for the scattering of available beam particles ($\bar{p}$, p, $\pi^\pm$, $K^\pm$) on nucleons. The table can easily be extended to other targets (given nuclei, or a ratio between several experiments with any nucleus as a common target etc.). It should be remembered that all such predictions (including (56)) are somewhat modified when one allows for the above mentioned F/D ratio in the $\gamma_{s,i}^{AB}(0)$ vertex-strengths. In that case it is the general fit itself[31]) which replaces all such equalities or inequalities.

From the fact that in (55) the multipliers of the $\gamma_{s,i}^{AC}\gamma_{s,i}^{BD}$ and $\gamma_{v,i}^{AC}\gamma_{v,i}^{BD}$ turn out to be positive numbers, we get

$$\left.\begin{aligned} K^-p &> K^-n \\ \pi^-p &> \pi^+p \\ K^-p &> K^+p \\ K^-p &> K^+n \end{aligned}\right\} \tag{59}$$

$$\left.\begin{array}{r} K^-p - K^-n > |K^+p - K^+n| \\ K^+p + K^-p > K^+n + K^-n \\ \bar{p}p > pp \\ \bar{p}p > pn \\ \bar{p}p > \bar{p}n \\ \bar{p}p - pp > \bar{p}n - pn \\ \bar{p}p + pp > \bar{p}n + pn \end{array}\right\} \tag{59}$$

$$\left.\begin{array}{r} K^+p - K^+n = pp - np \\ K^-p - K^-n = \bar{p}p - \bar{p}n \\ 3(\pi^+p + \pi^-p) = \bar{p}n + pn + pp + \bar{p}p \\ (K^+p - K^-p) - (K^+n - K^-n) = \pi^+p - \pi^-p \end{array}\right\} \tag{60}$$

The latter four results were originally derived from quark model considerations[32]) (the above mentioned "additivity" of quark amplitudes) or from dynamical assumptions in a Regge analysis[33]).

Further relations can be derived once we assume some connection between the intercepts $\alpha_{v,i}(0)$, $\alpha_{s,i}(0)$. These bear among themselves the same relationships as the m^2, if we assume linear trajectories. Thus, assuming $\alpha_{v,3}(0) = \alpha_{v,8}(0)$ is equivalent to taking a common mass for the vector meson octet etc. Such an assumption seems good enough in the latter case, and we then get the Johnson–Treiman relations[34]), which are known to derive from SU(3) symmetry and octet exchange with pure F coupling. Another assumption which seems validated is exchange-symmetry[35]) in $I=1$ trajectories, which yields

$$K^+p = K^+n. \tag{61}$$

Extending the symmetry of vector intercepts to $\alpha_{v,0}(0)$ yields the Freund relation

$$\bar{p}p - pp = \tfrac{5}{4}(\bar{p}n - pn) = 5(\pi^-p - \pi^+p). \tag{62}$$

Combining the two plausible approximate symmetries of SU(3) and the above exchange degeneracy yields

$$K^-n = \tfrac{1}{2}(K^-p + K^+p). \tag{63}$$

A good fit has been achieved for the available $\sigma_T(\bar{p}, p, \pi^\pm, K^\pm$ on p, n) and for the corresponding X ratios (or the Re $A(s, 0)$, using only the 18 trajectories covered by the algebra[31])). The stronger assumption of universality adds the following restrictions to the usual SU(3) fits[20]):

a) baryon and meson residues become connected via the $\gamma_{s,0}(0)$ and $\gamma_{s,8}(0)$,
b) the $\gamma_{v,i}(0)$ can only take pure F-coupling,

c) there is no nineteenth trajectory with independent $\alpha_?(0)$ and $\gamma_?$ for the Pomeranchuk trajectory.

The fit yields $F/D_s \sim -1.9$. The ν^α term is already "renormalized" by the energy-dependence appropriate for the F/D ratio, viewed algebraically. One could then check whether the F/D admixture might arise through anything but SU(3) breaking, also induced algebraically via Lorentz transformations.

By the use of 18 trajectories, the CHN algebra in fact renounces the extra freedom of a flat Pomeranchuk. With the present evidence for onion-structure, this may be required anyhow, so that the onion-picture is consistent with CHN rather than with the opposite, "optical" flat P.

To achieve a fit, holding the F/D ratio constant, CHKN[31]) had to abandon $\alpha_{s,0}(0)=1$ for a somewhat lower figure. This predicts the vanishing of all cross-sections at $\nu\to\infty$, at a low rate which is consistent with the cosmic rays data, but will lead to an observable drop of 3 mb in the pp cross-section at the 30–70 GeV/c energies soon to be available at Serpukhov. At the 10^3 GeV/c which will be attained at the CERN storage ring we should be able to witness a 40% drop in all elastic cross-sections, as compared to the 10 GeV/c region.

The Bond factor $(\alpha_{s,0}(0)-1\approx -0.07)$ is probably not essential to the σ_T fit in itself, considering the trajectories beyond (55) However, it is in the spirit of the algebra, since a value of $\alpha=1$ would give the (s, λ^0) density a rather singular role. Having the $q^+\beta q$ singlet at a higher mass or $\alpha(0)$ value is common to $[U(3)\times U(3)]_\beta$ or $[U(6)\times U(6)]_\beta$ assignments (like the $\eta(960,0^-)$), but $\alpha(0)=1$ is a point of high singularity.

Using the above parameters, CHKN get the right ever-falling off behavior for all three "averaged" σ_T,

$$\begin{aligned} S_N &= \tfrac{1}{4}(pp + pn + \bar{p}p + \bar{p}n), \\ S_\pi &= \tfrac{1}{2}(\pi^+p + \pi^-p), \\ S_K &= \tfrac{1}{4}(K^+p + K^-p + K^+n + K^-n). \end{aligned} \tag{64}$$

Note that without the D-coupling in $\gamma_{s,i}$ we would have for these (t_i^s are the multipliers in (55) and are positive)

$$\begin{aligned} S_N &= 6t_0^s + 3t_8^s, \\ S_\pi &= 4t_0^s + 2t_8^s, \\ S_K &= 4t_0^s - t_8^s, \end{aligned} \tag{65}$$

and S_K would reach its limit from below (since $t_0^s \underset{\nu\to\infty}{\to}$ constant). With $t_0^s \underset{\nu\to\infty}{\to} 0$ we get a general fall off for S_K as well.

It is important to note that

$$X \underset{\nu\to\infty}{\rightarrow} -\operatorname{tg}\left[\frac{1-\alpha_0^s(0)}{2}\right] \sim -0.118$$

is now the high energy limit of the X ratio. All real parts have the correct experimental signs.

CHARGE EXCHANGE AND ASSOCIATED PRODUCTION

In these processes the optical theorem is no more available. We can only use $\sigma_T = \int (\mathrm{d}\sigma/\mathrm{d}t)\,\mathrm{d}t$, which implies knowledge of $(\mathrm{d}\sigma/\mathrm{d}t)(t)$. This is not predicted by the theory at the present stage, although it is conceivable that a study of the $t<0$ region with the $\gamma(t)$ fixed as "form-factors" by the tensor properties of the (x, t) will yield some insight. However, all we can do at present is conjecture that the $(\mathrm{d}\sigma/\mathrm{d}t)(t)$ are similar for various processes, which would then enable us to go from our theoretical prediction of $A(\nu, t)$ to $\mathrm{d}\sigma/\mathrm{d}t$ and σ_T directly. Assuming similar structure in $(\mathrm{d}\sigma/\mathrm{d}t)(t)$ would only be plausible within SU(3) multiplets, and we thus loose much of our predictive power as to the comparison between baryon–baryon and meson–baryon processes.

The charge and strangeness exchanges[36]) always involve *either* $I=1$, $Y=0$ or $I=\frac{1}{2}$, $|Y|=1$, i.e. π-like or K-like objects. With $\gamma_{s,i}$ and $\gamma_{v,i}$ we thus have for any process up to two such trajectories. For $\mathrm{d}\sigma/\mathrm{d}t \sim |A|^2$ we then have at most 3 terms, including the interference

$$|A_{AB}^{CD}|^2 = x_i\left[t_i^s/\sin(\tfrac{1}{2}\pi\alpha_i^s)\right]^2 + y_i\left\{t_i^s t_i^v \sin\left[\tfrac{1}{2}\pi(\alpha_i^s - \alpha_i^v)\right]/\sin(\tfrac{1}{2}\pi\alpha_i^s)\cos(\tfrac{1}{2}\pi\alpha_i^v)\right\} + \\ + z_i\left[t_i^v/\cos(\tfrac{1}{2}\pi\alpha_i^v)\right]^2 \qquad (66)$$

(where i is a "π" or "K" like unitary index); the brackets enclose positive numbers; the x_i, y_i, z_i result from our algebra. There are 4 sets of (x, y, z) values for each i, which we denote respectively by (A), (B), (C), (D) and (P), (Q), (R), (S)

$$\begin{aligned}
&(\mathrm{A}):(0, 0, 8) = (\pi^-\mathrm{p} \to \pi^0\mathrm{n}) \quad \text{or} \quad (\pi^+\mathrm{n} \to \pi^0\mathrm{p}),\\
&(\mathrm{B}):(\tfrac{8}{3}, 0, 0) = (\pi^-\mathrm{p} \to \eta\mathrm{n}) \quad \text{or} \quad (\pi^+\mathrm{n} \to {}_{\mathrm{D}}\mathrm{p}) = \tfrac{1}{2}(\pi^-\mathrm{p} \to \chi\mathrm{n}) \quad \text{or}\\
&\qquad \tfrac{1}{2}(\pi^+\mathrm{n} \to \chi\mathrm{p}),\\
&(\mathrm{C}):(4, 8, 4) = (\mathrm{K}^-\mathrm{p} \to \overline{\mathrm{K}}{}^0\mathrm{n}), \qquad (\mathrm{C}') = (\bar{\mathrm{p}}\mathrm{p} \to \mathrm{nn}),\\
&(\mathrm{D}):(4, -8, 4) = (\mathrm{K}^+\mathrm{n} \to \mathrm{K}^0\mathrm{p}), \qquad (\mathrm{D}') = (\mathrm{pn} \to \mathrm{np}),
\end{aligned} \qquad (67)$$

and we get[37])

$$(\mathrm{A}) + 3(\mathrm{B}) = (\mathrm{C}) + (\mathrm{D}), \qquad (6)$$

and just for $t=0$,

$$\left.\frac{d\sigma}{dt}\right|_{t=0}(C) = \left.\frac{d\sigma}{dt}\right|_{t=0}(C') \qquad \text{at equal } \nu\,, \tag{69}$$

$$\left.\frac{d\sigma}{dt}\right|_{t=0}(D) = \left.\frac{d\sigma}{dt}\right|_{t=0}(D') \qquad \text{at equal } \nu\,, \tag{70}$$

the last two equalities do not bring into account that (C′) and (D′) could get additional contributions from axial vector trajectories etc. If we add exchange-symmetry $\alpha^s=\alpha^v$ for $I=1$, the interference term in (66) vanishes and we get[37])

$$(A) + 3(B) = 2(C) = 2(D) \tag{71}$$

and if we put in the observed value $\alpha(0)=\frac{1}{2}$ we find

$$(A) = 3(B) = (C) = (D)\,. \tag{72}$$

For strangeness-exchange we have (we omit I-spin connected processes)

$$\begin{aligned}
&(P) = 2(\pi^-p\to K^0\Sigma^0) = (\pi^-n\to K^0\Sigma^-) = \tfrac{2}{3}(\pi^-p\to K^0\Lambda)\,,\\
&(P') = (\bar{p}p\to \Sigma^+\Sigma^+) = 4(\bar{p}p\to \overline{\Sigma^0}\Sigma^0) = 2(\bar{p}n\to \overline{\Sigma^+}\Sigma^0) =\\
&\quad = \tfrac{2}{3}(\bar{p}n\to \overline{\Sigma^+}\Lambda) = \tfrac{2}{3}(\bar{p}n\to \bar{\Lambda}\Sigma^-) = \tfrac{4}{9}(\bar{p}p\to \bar{\Lambda}\Lambda)\,,\\
&(Q) = (K^-p\to\pi^-\Sigma^+) = 4(K^-p\to\pi^0\Sigma^0) = 2(K^-n\to\pi^-\Sigma^0) =\\
&\quad = \tfrac{2}{3}(K^-n\to\pi^-\Lambda)\,,\\
&(R) = \tfrac{3}{2}(K^-n\to\eta\Sigma^-) = (K^-p\to\eta\Lambda)\,,\\
&(S) = \tfrac{3}{2}(K^-n\to\chi\Sigma^-) = (K^-p\to\chi\Lambda)\,,
\end{aligned} \tag{73}$$

yielding at the same time

$$6(P) + 3(Q) = 4(R) + 4(S)\,,$$

and for $t=0$ with the same omission of axial-vector contributions etc.

$$\left.\frac{d\sigma}{dt}\right|_{t=0}(P) = \left.\frac{d\sigma}{dt}\right|_{t=0}(P')\,. \tag{74}$$

Knowledge of the sign of the phase-difference $\alpha^s(0)-\alpha^v(0)$ for the $|Y|=1$ trajectories yields numerous inequalities. For instance, if the difference is positive,

$$8(R) > 2(P) > (S)\,, \qquad (P) > (Q)\,; \tag{75}$$

such predictions, e.g.

$$(\pi^-p\to K^0\Sigma^0) > 2(K^-p\to\pi^0\Sigma^0) \tag{76}$$

involve measurements that will probably be available in the near future. It is also possible to use the $\alpha(0)$ intercepts predicted for the 4-5-6-7 components of each octet by the Gell-Mann mass rule – or by Schwinger's nonet relation. Combining these estimates with the above relationships, we can make a general fit to the $\mathrm{d}\sigma/\mathrm{d}t|_{t=0}$ (independently of assumptions regarding the $(\mathrm{d}\sigma/\mathrm{d}t)(t)$ relative structures, $\mathrm{d}\sigma/\mathrm{d}t$ (small t) and σ_{T}. Such a table of predictions was presented in ref. 36.

THE SCALAR DENSITIES AND THE ENERGY-MOMENTUM TENSORS

For the vector densities $\mathscr{D}(v, \lambda^i)$ the relationship with the vector currents of electromagnetism and atonous interactions is obvious. It is important however to note that we are really dealing with the residue coupling to the ρ meson, for instance. Thus we should probably think of $\mathscr{D}(v, \lambda^{1-3}; x, t)$ as having the same matrix-elements as $j^{\mu}_{1-3}(x, t)$ except that the ρ-pole itself should be extracted.

As to the scalar $\mathscr{D}(s, \lambda^i)$, the situation is more complicated. These trajectories are dominated by $J=2^+$ poles, and it had been suggested[38]) that such mesons might dominate the matrix-elements of $\theta^{\mu\nu}$, the energy-momentum tensor density. However, with the abandonment of the connection between the Pomeranchuk trajectory and the $J=2^+$ mesons, this idea could have nothing to do with the role of the Pomeranchuk trajectory P in high energy scattering. On the other hand, even if one were ready to renew the link between P and the f^0 $(J=2^+)$, the formalism would imply (in the approximation of very little variation of the couplings between $t=m^2_{\mathrm{f}^0}$ and $t=0$)

$$\frac{\sigma_{\pi\mathrm{p}}}{\sigma_{\mathrm{pp}}} = \frac{m_\pi}{m_\mathrm{p}} \sim \frac{1}{7} \tag{77}$$

instead of the $\frac{2}{3}$ of (56).

With the CHN algebra, we can get a new understanding of this paradox. First, we do have a declared correspondance between P and the f^0 or the $\mathrm{f}^{0'}(1500, 2^+)$ or some mixture of these two states (we do not know for sure how they are situated in the $(\lambda^0; \lambda^8)$ plane. This anyhow implies that we may have a connection with $\theta^{\mu\nu}$.

Secondly, our algebra fixes the quantum numbers of the one surviving "source" in the high energy region. These have to represent a scalar under $[\mathrm{U}(3)\times \mathrm{U}(3)]_\beta$ and should transform like the β generator.

Considering our candidate "charge-density" θ^{00}, we notice that it may contain parts which do not have the above transformation properties, even if we restrict ourselves to the SU(3) invariant piece. In a quark model,

$$\theta^{00} = \tfrac{1}{2}(\bar{q}\gamma^0 \overset{\leftrightarrow}{\partial}{}^0 q) = -\tfrac{1}{2}(q^\dagger \boldsymbol{\alpha}\cdot\overset{\leftrightarrow}{\nabla} q) + m_0 q^\dagger \beta q + \text{interaction terms}. \tag{78}$$

The $\boldsymbol{\alpha}\cdot\nabla$ term does not commute with the entire $[U(3)\times U(3)]_\beta$. Only the $m_0 q^\dagger\beta q$ plus such parts of the interaction term which may have a similar structure have the correct quantum numbers. This part

$$_{(1.1)}\theta_0^{00} = (m_0 + a)\, q^\dagger \beta q = m' q^\dagger \beta q \tag{79}$$

is projected out as the "high energy charge", just as we can project out an isovector or isoscalar piece in the electromagnetic charge density. This as we see yields the ratio of (56), since m' is a constant and β acts as in (53). Note also that m' does not have to be considered as a "quark mass": the interaction terms may contain functions of the 3rd order Casimir operators of $[U(3)\times U(3)]_\beta$ with vanishing contributions for zero-triality representations but important ones for the others.

We can now check our identification by regarding it as a physical prediction: (79) can be measured, since it is the invariant piece of a $[U(3)\times U(3)]_\beta$ or $[U(6)\times U(6)]_\beta$ mass formula. It thus predicts the observed $\frac{2}{3}$ ratio between mean masses of mesons and baryons. The latter fact had been noticed previously[39]) but this now provides a physical derivation – it had never been explained why such averaged masses rather than the actual masses should yield the ratio of $\pi p/pp$.

Note also that using the entire $\theta^{\mu\nu}$ would imply an infinite algebra for the $\theta^{\mu\nu}$ U(3)-rotated densities. The projected $_{(1.1)}\theta_0^{00}$ can be rotated into $_{(1.1)}\theta_i^{00}$ and yields the $[U(3)\times U(3)]_\beta$ algebra.

We can now hope that using the assumption that the $_{(1.1)}\theta_i^{00}$ are dominated by the 2^+ mesons, we may be able to compute various high-energy "renormalization" effects. For example, from

$$\langle p|\,[S_{\tau^+}, S_{\tau^-}]\,|p\rangle = 1 \tag{80}$$

given by the algebra, we may be able to compute the exchange-degeneracy correction,

$$\Lambda = \gamma^{pn}_{s\tau^+}/\gamma^{pn}_{v\tau^+}, \tag{81}$$

i.e. the ratio between the A_2 and ρ charge exchange factorized residues. However, we may encounter difficulties in making such an analysis as we shall probably have to put the commutator between states at rest, since these are "bad" densities in the $\boldsymbol{p}\to\infty$ limit.

Connection with current commutators

Rubinstein and Veneziano[39]) and Fubini[40]) have analyzed the possibility of deriving the algebra of Regge residues from the requirements of convergence and the pole structure of current commutators. An equal-time commutator of axial current densities a^{μ} taken between pion states can be transformed into an equation[41]),

$$\frac{1}{\pi}\int_{0}^{\infty} a(\nu, t)\,\mathrm{d}\nu = F(t) \tag{82}$$

where $F(t)$ is the pion form-factor, and $a(\nu, t)$ is the absorptive part of A^{ij}, a constituent of $T^{ij}_{\mu\nu}$ (P is the averaged momentum, Q is the momentum difference)

$$T^{ij}_{\mu\nu}(\nu, q_1^2, q_2^2, t) = \int \mathrm{d}^4x\, \theta(x_0)\, \mathrm{e}^{\mathrm{i}Qx} \langle \mathrm{p}_2 | [a^i_{\mu}(\tfrac{1}{2}x), a^j_{\nu}(-\tfrac{1}{2}x) | \mathrm{p}_1 \rangle, \tag{83}$$

where

$$T^{ij}_{\mu\nu} = A^{ij}P_{\mu}P_{\nu} + B^{ij}_1 P_{\mu}Q_{\nu} + \dots \quad \text{and} \quad t^{ij}_{\mu\nu} = a^{ij}P_{\mu}P_{\nu} + b^{ij}_1 P_{\mu}Q_{\nu} + \dots . \tag{84}$$

The right-hand side of (82) has a pole at $t=m_{\rho}^2$. From Regge theory, $t_{\mu\nu} \sim \beta(t)\, \nu^{\alpha(t)}$ and $a \sim \beta(t)\, \nu^{\alpha(t)-2}$ which upon integration in (82) would yield the pole. However, the exact expression contains a factor $(\alpha - 1)$ which could have cancelled this pole, and the formalism should provide a mechanism to cancel this factor. The mechanism suggested by Singh[42]) and Bronzan et al.[43]) is a fixed pole introduced by the weak interaction itself, which interaction should be included to first order. This cancellation can be written as a condition relating the residue $\beta(t)$ to the $F(t)$ commutator and reinstates the above origin for the ρ pole. The exact relationship has not yet been studied thoroughly (it is not clear that we can get full universality in this way, for instance), but it seems that we have here an insight showing how the existence of an algebra of factorized residues ("high energy currents") is essential to the existence of the algebra of weak and electromagnetic currents.

Note that we thus have here either one more case of an approximate universality, due to pole dominance of the current algebra form factors – or perhaps the basis for an *exact* statement describing the strong interaction directly.

Cuts and universality

In the $t \neq 0$ calculations in which we introduced cuts due to the exchange of 2 or more Regge trajectories, we had no direct way of fixing the effective residue

$\beta_{\text{cut}}(t)=\int \mathrm{d}J\,\bar{\beta}(J,t)$ of such cuts. However, from the "onion" structure[26]) we get an estimate of this residue; at $t=0$ it should be very weak. The same result is true for any of these cuts, since the fit we get for $t=0$ requires no cuts. Can the fact that $\beta_{\text{cut}}(0)\sim 0$ be explained?

We may conjecture that this is required by the CHN postulate. In quantum electrodynamics, we know that in the static limit $t=u=0$ the entire Coulomb force[44]) is rendered by the first Born term, i.e. the exchange of a single photon. The same is true of gravitation[45]), and should be one more feature of a "universal" coupling. This would then lead us to expect vanishing effects from cuts at $t=0$.

References

1) The lectures were reprinted in 1961 at CERN. They were finally published in 1965 in: *Springer Tracts in Modern Physics*, Vol. 37 (Springer-Verlag, Berlin, 1965).
2) M. Gell-Mann, Phys. Rev. **92**, 833 (1953); T. Nakano and K. Nishijima, Progr. Theoret. Phys. (Kyoto) **10**, 581 (1953).
3) G. Racah, Nucl. Phys. **1**, 302 (1956). It is interesting that the Ω^- report [(V. E. Barnes et al., Phys. Rev. Letters **12**, 204 (1964)] claims to have settled Racah's doubts directly, in addition to its clear-cut validation of the octet version of SU(3). However, it seems that no such direct inference can be made, as $\Omega^- \to n + K^0 + \pi^-$ which would have been allowed by multiplicative strangeness as a strong process is still forbidden by I-spin conservation. However, back in Israel I introduced Racah to the suggested role of SU(3) in hadron physics. He then worked out "in one weekend" (Rehovoth lecture in 1962) the appropriate formula for matrix elements. He lectured on SU(3) at Istanbul (*Group Theoretical Concepts and Methods in Elementary Particle Physics*, Ed. F. Gürsey (Gordon and Breach, New York, 1964) p. 1.
4) E. B. Dynkin, Usp. Mat. Nauk **2** (4) (1947) [Am. Math. Translations Series **1**, (17) (1950)].
5) H. Goldberg and Y. Ne'eman, Nuovo Cimento **27**, 1 (1963). See also Y. Ne'eman, in: *Recent Developments in Particle Physics, Proc. Intern. Pacific Summer School in Physics*, Ed. M. J. Moravcsik (Gordon and Breach, New York, 1966) p. 51.
6) M. Gell-Mann, Phys. Rev. **125**, 1067 (1962); Physics **1**, 63 (1964).
7) M. Gell-Mann and Y. Ne'eman, Ann. Phys. (N.Y.) **30**, 360 (1964).
8) S. Adler, Phys. Rev. Letters **14**, 1051 (1965); W. I. Weisberger, Phys. Rev. Letters **14**, 1047 (1965).
9) S. Fubini and G. Furlan, Physics **1**, 229 (1965).
10) V. de Alfaro, S. Fubini, G. Furlan and G. Rosseti, Phys. Letters **21**, 576 (1965).
11) N. Cabibbo, L. Horwitz and Y. Ne'eman, Phys. Letters **22**, 336 (1966).
12) See for example, R. Omnès and M. Froissart, *Mandelstam Theory and Regge Poles* (Benjamin, New York, 1963).
13) L. Van Hove, in: *High Energy Physics and Elementary Particles* (Trieste, 1965 Seminar) (IAEA, Vienna, 1965) p. 179.
14) S. Mandelstam, Nuovo Cimento **30**, 1148 (1963); D. Amati, S. Fubini and A. Stang

hellini, Phys. Letters **1**, 29 (1962); V. N. Gribov, I. Ya. Pomeranchuk and K. A. Ter-Martirossyan, Phys. Rev. **139**, B184 (1965).
15) C. B. Chiu and J. Finkelstein, Nuovo Cimento **48**, A820 (1967).
16) M. Gell-Mann, Phys. Rev. Letters **8**, 263 (1962); V. N. Gribov and I. Ya Pomeranchuk, Phys. Rev. Letters **8**, 412 (1962). See also G. C. Fox and Elliot Leader, Phys. Rev. Letters **18**, 628 (1967).
17) R. K. Logan, Phys. Rev. Letters **14**, 414 (1965) etc.
18) B. P. Desai, Phys. Rev. Letters **11**, 59 (1963).
19) K. Igi, Phys. Rev. **130**, 820 (1963).
20) R. J. N. Phillips and W. Rarita, Phys. Rev. **139**, B1336 (1965); V. Barger and M. Olsson, Phys. Rev. Letters **15**, 930 (1965); **16**, 545 (1966); Phys. Rev. **146**, 1080 (1966).
21) V. N. Gribov and D. V. Volkov, in: *Proc. 11th Intern. Conf. High Energy Phys.* (CERN, Genève, 1962) p. 552.
22) S. J. Lindenbaum, in: *Proc. Fourth Coral Gables Conf. on Symmetry at High Energy* (1967) p. 122.
23) S. C. Frautschi, Phys. Rev. Letters **17**, 722 (1966).
24) D. Z. Freedman and J. M. Wang, paper submitted to Berkeley Conference (1966).
25) E. Gotsman and Y. Ne'eman, J. Math. Phys. **7**, 634 (1966); Erratum, J. Math. Phys. **7**, 2280 (1966).
26) C. W. Akerlof, R. H. Hieber, A. D. Krisch, K. W. Edwards, L. G. Ratner and K. Ruddick, Phys. Rev. Letters **17**, 1105 (1966).
27) K. Huang, C. E. Jones, and V. L. Teplitz, Phys. Rev. Letters **18**, 146 (1967).
28) E. M. Levin and L. L. Frankfurt, Zh. Eksperim. i Teor. Fiz. Pisma v Redak. **2**, 105 (1965); JETP Letters **2**, 65 (1965).
29) R. F. Dashen and M. Gell-Mann, Phys. Rev. Letters **17**, 142 (1965).
30) N. Cabibbo, L. Horwitz, J. J. J. Kokkedee and Y. Ne'eman, Nuovo Cimento **45**, 275 (1966).
31) H. I. Lipkin and F. Scheck, Phys. Rev. Letters **16**, 71 (1966); P. G. O. Freund, Phys. Rev. Letters **15**, 929 (1965); J. J. J. Kokkedee and L. Van Hove, Nuovo Cim. **42**, 711 (1966).
32) V. Barger and M. H. Rubin, Phys. Rev. **140**, B1365 (1965).
33) K. Johnson and S. B. Treiman, Phys. Rev. Letters **14**, 189 (1965).
34) R. C. Arnold, Phys. Rev. Letters **14**, 627 (1965).
35) Y. Ne'eman and J. D. Reichert, Phys. Rev. Letters **18**, 1226 (1967).
36) Some of the cases included in (68) were derived independently by G. Alexander, H. J. Lipkin and F. Scheck, Phys. Rev. Letters **17**, 412 (1966) from a quark model, and by A. Ahmadzadeh and C. H. Chan, Phys. Letters **22**, 692 (1966) from a combined quark-Regge calculation.
37) M. Gell-Mann, Physics **1**, 63 (1964); P. G. O. Freund, Phys. Letters **2**, 136 (1962); D. H. Sharp and W. G. Wagner, Phys. Rev. **131**, 2226 (1963); H. Pagels, Phys. Rev. **144**, 1250 (1966); R. Delbourgo, A. Salam and J. Strathdee, Trieste report IC/66/115 (1966).
38) Y. Dothan and Y. Ne'eman, in: *Proc. Second Topical Conf. on Resonant Particles, Athens, Ohio (1965)*, p. 26; see also P. G. O. Freund, Phys. Rev. Letters **16**, 291 (1966).
39) H. Rubinstein and G. Veneziano, to be published.
40) S. Fubini, Lectures at Tel-Aviv University "Worskhop in Particle Physics" (1967).

41) S. Fubini, Nuovo Cimento **43**, 1 (1966); see also R. Dashen and M. Gell-Mann, in: *Proc. Third Coral Gables Conf. in Symmetry Principle at High Energy (1966)*.
42) V. Singh, Phys. Rev. Letters **18**, 36 (1967).
43) J. B. Bronzan, I. S. Gerstein, B. W. Lee and F. E. Low, Phys. Rev. Letters **18**, 32 (1967).
44) R. H. Dalitz, Proc. Roy. Soc. (London) A**206**, 509 (1951).
45) S. Weinberg, Phys. Rev. **140**, B516 (1965).
46) Y. Ne'eman, to be published in: *Proc. of the 1967 Rochester Conference*.

Spectroscopic and group theoretical methods in physics
© North-Holland Publ. Co., Amsterdam, 1968

ELECTROMAGNETIC AND WEAK TRANSITIONS AND THEIR ALGEBRAIC REPRESENTATION BY CURRENT COMMUTATORS*

HAIM HARARI**

Stanford Linear Accelerator Center, Stanford University, Stanford, California, U.S.A.

1. Introduction

The commutation relations suggested by Gell-Mann[1]) for the components of the vector and axial vector hadronic currents have led in the last two years to a wide variety of new relations among previously uncorrelated physical quantities. Among these we find the now famous Adler–Weisberger sum rule[2]) for the axial vector coupling constant, sum rules for the magnetic moments of the nucleon[3]), new relations among semileptonic and non-leptonic weak decay rates[4]) and other developments which are all a part of a major step forward in our understanding of both the properties of the weak interactions and the foundations of particle symmetries. Assuming that the algebraic structure of the currents and their charges is really given by Gell-Mann's commutation relations one is immediately led to consider a more ambitious problem: What are the algebraic properties of the observed particles and resonances, and how do they behave under the operation of the weak and electromagnetic currents and charges? If the vector and axial vector charges (or currents) form a given closed algebra, we can represent their matrix elements between particle states by arbitrarily large matrices satisfying the required commutation relations. The particle states will then transform under the operations of the algebra according to arbitrarily complicated representations. Every such representation will be, in general, a combination of a large number of irreducible representations of the algebra,

* Work supported by the U.S. Atomic Energy Commission.
** On leave of absence from the Weizman Institute, Rehovoth, Israel.

and a particle state will be specified by the relevant combination of representations and by the mixing coefficients which determine the components of the particle's state vector along the directions of base vectors corresponding to each of the involved irreducible representations.

Once we know the transformation properties of a given set of particles we can, in principle, compute the weak and electromagnetic properties of these particles with no additional information. In particular, we can then determine axial vector transition rates (which are related by PCAC to pionic decays) and electromagnetic matrix elements such as magnetic moments or photoproduction amplitudes. If the low-lying baryons and mesons happen to belong to extremely complicated representations of the algebra, such a procedure becomes totally useless, since we have to determine a large number of "representation mixing" parameters before we can predict any measurable experimental quantity. On the other hand, if because of some presently unknown (internal or external) dynamical structure, the low-lying particles do correspond to simple representations of the algebra, we may once for all determine the few relevant mixing parameters and then proceed to predict a large number of transition strengths and coupling constants[5]). The latter possibility, if true, may also provide us with a better general understanding of symmetries such as the various versions of SU(3)$\times$SU(3) and SU(6). The situation is, in many respects, similar to that of the atomic and nuclear shell model in which a simple configuration mixing is in some cases sufficient for explaining a relatively large number of independent experimental observations while in some other cases the required configuration mixture is so complicated that it is essentially useless and other theoretical ideas are needed in order to proceed.

In this paper we consider the possibility of finding a simple algebraic representation for the low-lying baryons and mesons. Various models have been recently proposed[6,7,8]) for the classification of baryons into representations of the algebra of *charges*. Here, we do not consider this problem from the point of view of one model or the other, but rather start from a certain set of plausible basic assumptions, and use all the available data for determining all possible solutions for the classification problem, within the framework of our assumptions. We then discuss the relations between these solutions and the mixing schemes proposed in the literature. We might add, at this point, that a final answer to the classification of particles under the algebra of *charges* will probably have to wait for a complete solution of the more difficult problem of finding the representations of the *local algebra of currents*[9]), since this solution may impose additional restrictions on the classification.

Here, we will discuss only the charge algebra and will not go into some of the complicated problems related to the infinite parameter local algebra.

2. The algebra of charges at infinite momentum

We start by considering the vector and axial vector charges, defined as:

$$Q_i(t) = \int V_{0i}(\boldsymbol{x}, t)\, \mathrm{d}^3x, \qquad Q_i^5 = \int A_{0i}(\boldsymbol{x}, t)\, \mathrm{d}^3x, \tag{1}$$

V_0 and A_0 are the time components of the vector and axial vector hadronic currents, respectively, and i is an isotopic (or a unitary) index. We assume[1]) that the operators $Q_i(t)$ and $Q_i^5(t)$ satisfy, at equal times, the commutation relations of an SU(2) × SU(2) (or an SU(3) × SU(3)) algebra, namely:

$$[Q_i, Q_j] = \mathrm{i}c_{ij}^k Q_k^{ij}, \tag{2a}$$

$$[Q_i, Q_j^5] = \mathrm{i}c_{ij}^k Q_k^5, \tag{2b}$$

$$[Q_i^5, Q_j^5] = \mathrm{i}c_{ij}^k Q_k^{ij}. \tag{2c}$$

c_{ij}^k are the structure constants for SU(2) (or SU(3)). By inserting both sides of eq. (2c) between particle states we may obtain a set of *covariant* sum rules, relating the matrix elements of the ordinary vector charge Q_k to sums over matrix elements for axial vector transitions[2]). The complete set of such sum rules allows us, in principle, to determine the strengths of the axial vector transitions between any pair of states. In the case of exact SU(2) (or SU(3)) *symmetry* eq. (2c) is the most crucial piece of the algebra since, in this limit, eq. (2a) is just the definition of the symmetry and eq. (2b) gives the symmetry transformation properties of the axial charges and hence determines only *relative* magnitudes of different axial matrix elements.

We have emphasized that the sum rules obtained in this way are *covariant*. This is true for the complete sum rule, but not for its term-by-term reduction. The contribution of a given single particle state may depend on the particular frame of reference that we choose, and the relative importance of various states in the sum rule may change when we change the momentum of the states between which we insert the commutator. A trivial example of this is the matrix element of the axial charge Q^5 between two single nucleon states with equal momenta $\boldsymbol{p}$. A straight-forward calculation shows that this matrix element (whose square is the single nucleon contribution to the Adler–Weisberger sum rule) is proportional to $|\boldsymbol{p}|/E$ and therefore depends on $\boldsymbol{p}$. This is neither surprising nor disturbing, since the concept of "equal time" commutation relation a priori introduces here an element which is not manifestly covariant, and there is no reason for any stage of the calculation (except the final sum rule) to exhibit explicit covariant characteristics. We therefore conclude that *as long as we are interested only in the final product*, namely the full covariant exact sum rule, the frame of reference in which we do our calculations is, in principle, totally irrelevant and any discussion concerning the merits of one frame or another is a discussion on matters of convenience or, at most, of clarity of presentation. On the other hand, if we address ourselves to the question of *algebraic properties of the particle states*, the particular frame of reference that we choose may be of crucial importance. If a given state transforms, at a given momentum, according to a certain representation of the algebra of charges, this by no means implies that, at some other momentum, the particle will have the same properties. In particular, the classification of states in some frames of reference may be much simpler than in others, and it is possible that only a certain Lorentz frame will qualify for the usefulness criterion that we mentioned in the previous section, namely: only in this frame will the description of single particle states be sufficiently simple so as to enable us to introduce a simple mixture of representations for the low-lying states and to determine most of the relevant transition strengths using a small number of parameters. Here, and only here, the question of "which Lorentz frame should we use?" becomes a matter of principle in the sense that a poor choice may yield a totally useless complicated scheme of mixtures which will avoid any *simple* physical interpretation.

The Lorentz frame which has the best chances of leading to a relatively simple representation for particle states seems to be the frame in which we evaluate the commutators between particle states moving at infinite momentum[5,10]). The infinite momentum frame was first introduced[11]) as a convenient device for deriving exact sum rules which could also be derived in many other ways. At that point, the choice was a question of aesthetics or convenience. In our case, however, we essentially *have* to choose the $|\boldsymbol{p}| = \infty$ frame because of the following simple advantage[5,10]): In the limit of $\boldsymbol{p} \to \infty$ a large number of the most ugly and complicated intermediate states do not contribute to the sum rules. These include both the connected and the disconnected particle–antiparticle pair states which would be particularly difficult to interpret in terms of the representations of the algebra. Only in this frame we may hope that single particle states actually saturate the sum rules and form simple representations. We will, therefore, use the infinite momentum frame and study the properties of $p = \infty$ states under the $SU(2) \times SU(2)$ and $SU(3) \times SU(3)$ algebras of charges.

The irreducible representations of $SU(2) \times SU(2)$ can be characterized by pairs of isospins (I_L, I_R) where $I_{Li} = Q_i + Q_i^5$, $I_{Ri} = Q_i - Q_i^5$. The isopsin content of the representation (I_L, I_R) is given by $|I_L - I_R| \leqslant I \leqslant I_L + I_R$. We may further characterize the representations by two additional isoscalar operators, a vector charge and an axial vector charge, which commute with all the generators of SU(2) × SU(2). In this way we obtain a U(2) × U(2) algebra and the two additional operators may be identified as the hypercharge (or baryon number, since we now discuss *only* non-strange particles) and the z component of the "intrinsic quark spin" S_z. All states in a given SU(2) × SU(2) multiplet must have the same value of S_z, which serves as an additional characterization of the representation.

In general, $S_z \neq J_z$, where J_z is the ordinary total angular momentum (spin) of the state. We therefore define an additional quantum number[5]) – the z-component of the "internal orbital angular momentum" L_z, satisfying:

$$L_z = J_z - S_z\,. \tag{3}$$

In a quark model S_z is the sum of z-components of the intrinsic spins of the quarks, and L_z is the z-component of their total *orbital* angular momentum. We emphasize, however that S_z, L_z and J_z are perfectly well defined, regardless of the existence or relevance of quarks. Both S_z and L_z are separately conserved in all matrix elements, and the states in any given SU(2) × SU(2) representation may have any (common) integral value of L_z.

In the case of SU(3) × SU(3), I_L and I_R are replaced by the dimensionalities of the representations for the left handed and right handed SU(3) groups corresponding to $Q_i \pm Q_i^5$. The vector charges of SU(3) × SU(3) form the $[(8,1)_0 + (1,8)_0,\ L_z = 0]$ representation while the axial charges form the $[(8,1)_0 - (1,8)_0,\ L_z = 0]$ representation, where the S_z values of the representations are given by the lower indices. In order to find the transformation properties of the *moments* of the currents under the algebra of *charges*, we postulate the following cummutation relations between the Fourier components of the charge densities[9]):

$$[F_i(\boldsymbol{q}), F_j(\boldsymbol{q}')] = \mathrm{i}c_{ij}^k F_k(\boldsymbol{q} + \boldsymbol{q}')\,, \tag{4a}$$

$$[F_i(\boldsymbol{q}), F_j^5(\boldsymbol{q}')] = \mathrm{i}c_{ij}^k F_k^5(\boldsymbol{q} + \boldsymbol{q}')\,, \tag{4b}$$

$$[F_i^5(\boldsymbol{q}), F_j^5(\boldsymbol{q}')] = \mathrm{i}c_{ij}^k F_k(\boldsymbol{q} + \boldsymbol{q}')\,, \tag{4c}$$

where

$$F_i(\boldsymbol{q}) = \int V_{0i}(\boldsymbol{x}, t)\, \mathrm{e}^{\mathrm{i}\boldsymbol{q}\cdot\boldsymbol{x}}\, \mathrm{d}^3x, \quad F_i(0) = Q_i\,, \tag{5a}$$

$$F_i^5(\boldsymbol{q}) = \int A_{0i}(\boldsymbol{x}, t)\, \mathrm{e}^{\mathrm{i}\boldsymbol{q}\cdot\boldsymbol{x}}\, \mathrm{d}^3x, \; F_i^5(0) = Q_i^5\,. \tag{5b}$$

Substituting $\boldsymbol{q}'=0$ in eq. (4) we conclude that for all values of q, $F_i(\boldsymbol{q})$ (or $F_i^5(\boldsymbol{q})$) will transform under the algebra of charges like Q_i (or Q_i^5). All moments of V_0 and A_0 will therefore have the transformation properties of generators of the SU(2) × SU(2) or SU(3) × SU(3) algebra. (They are not generators, of course; they only belong to a representation which is equivalent to that of the generators.) They will all have $S_z=0$ but their L_z values may change according to their J_z values which are most easily determined by considering the helicity properties of the appropriate transitions. Thus, for example, it is interesting to determine the transformation properties of the electric dipole operator, whose matrix element between two $p=\infty$ nucleons is equal to the anomalous magnetic moment. This dipole operator

$$D_i = \int \boldsymbol{x} V_{0i}(x, t)\,\mathrm{d}^3x \tag{6}$$

transforms according to the $[(8,1)_0+(1,8)_0,\ L_z=\pm 1]$ representation of the SU(3) × SU(3) algebra, while the corresponding "axial dipole" is in the $[(8,1)_0-(1,8)_0,\ L_z=\pm 1]$ representation.

We are now equipped with the necessary tools for proceeding to the assignment of states to the representations of the algebra and we shall do this in the next section.

3. The low-lying baryons and the SU(2) × SU(2) algebra of charges

Since the nucleon is an $I=\frac{1}{2}$ state it can have components only in those SU(2) × SU(2) representations which satisfy $|I_L-I_R|=\frac{1}{2}$. If the $J_z=+\frac{1}{2}$ component on the nucleon is *purely* in the representation $[(I_L, I_R)_{\frac{1}{2}}, 0]$ (ref. 12) we immediately find:

$$G_\mathrm{A} = \tfrac{2}{3}(k+1)\,, \tag{7}$$

$$G^* = \tfrac{1}{3}\sqrt{(2k-1)(2k+5)}\,, \tag{8}$$

$$G_i^{**} = 0\,, \tag{9}$$

$$\mu_\mathrm{A}(\mathrm{p}) = \mu_\mathrm{A}(\mathrm{n}) = \mu^* = 0\,, \tag{10}$$

where $k=I_L+I_R$, G_A is the axial vector coupling constant in nucleon β-decay, G^* is the matrix element of the axial charge between N and N* (1236) normalized so that the Adler–Weisberger sum rule reads

$$1 = G_\mathrm{A}^2 - G^{*2} + \text{higher contributions.}$$

G_i^{**} is the matrix element of Q_5 between N and any $I=\frac{1}{2}$ resonance N_i^*, $\mu_\mathrm{A}(\mathrm{p}, \mathrm{n})$ are the anomalous magnetic moments of the proton and the neutron, respectively, and μ^* is the matrix element for the magnetic M1 transition between N and N*(1236). From eqs. (7)–(10) it is clear that no irreducible representation can give a satisfactory description of the experimental situation, particularly in view of the predicted vanishing of all magnetic transitions. Moreover, for any given irreducible representation, G^{**} is predicted to vanish while the Adler–Weisberger sum rule indicates that the contributions of higher $I=\frac{1}{2}$ resonances are extremely important. Using the sum rule as a guide we find that the following steps are necessary in order to improve the situation:

(a) The nucleon must have components in representations with both $L_z=0$ and $L_z=\pm 1$. This is a necessary condition for the existence of non-vanishing matrix elements for the dipole operator D_i (eq. (6)) and for predicting $\mu_A \neq 0$, $\mu^* \neq 0$. For simplicity we exclude $|L_z|>1$ values.

(b) The experimental values $G_A \sim 1.2$ and $G^* \sim 1$ correspond in eqs. (7) and (8) to values of $\frac{1}{2}<k<\frac{3}{2}$. A strong mixing of the nucleon with $k>\frac{3}{2}$ representations would lead to unacceptable large values for G_A and G^*. We therefore conclude that at least for the nucleon, most of the mixing occurs with $k \leqslant \frac{3}{2}$ representations. This is consistent with the absence of $I>\frac{3}{2}$ states among the known N* resonances. Such states would probably exist at relatively low energies if representations with $k>\frac{3}{2}$ would have an appreciable contribution to the nucleon state. The restriction $k \leqslant \frac{3}{2}$ also follows from a simple quark picture, if we assume that the nucleon mixes only with three-quark states.

(c) The N*(1236) $I=\frac{3}{2}$ resonance may have components only in $k \geqslant \frac{3}{2}$ representations. G^* is therefore fully contributed by transitions within the $(1, \frac{1}{2})$ and $(\frac{1}{2}, 1)$ representations.

(d) If we study the contributions of the various N* resonances to the Adler–Weisberger sum rule we find that most of the integral in the region above the first resonance is accounted for by several $I=\frac{1}{2}$ resonances such as $p_{11}(1400)$, $d_{13}(1520)$, $s_{11}(1550)$, $d_{15}(1680)$ and $f_{15}(1680)$. There is no evidence for any important contribution of $I=\frac{3}{2}$ states above N*(1236). We therefore propose that, to a good approximation, only one $I=\frac{3}{2}$ state has a non-negligible axial transition to the nucleon and therefore only one of the two representations $(1, \frac{1}{2})$ and $(\frac{1}{2}, 1)$ will contain both the full $J_z=\frac{1}{2}$ component of N*(1236) and a part of the $J_z=\frac{1}{2}$ component of the nucleon. The remainder of the nucleon's wave function will be divided between the only SU(2) × SU(2) representations with $k=\frac{1}{2}$: $(\frac{1}{2}, 0)$ and $(0, \frac{1}{2})$. We can now write:

$$|\mathrm{N}^*(1236), J_z=\tfrac{1}{2}\rangle = |(1, \tfrac{1}{2})_{\frac{1}{2}}, 0\rangle\,, \tag{11}$$

$$|\mathrm{N}, J_z=\tfrac{1}{2}\rangle = \cos\theta\, |(1, \tfrac{1}{2})_{\frac{1}{2}}, 0\rangle + \sin\theta \left[\sin\varphi\, |(0, \tfrac{1}{2}), \text{any } S_z, L_z\rangle + \right. \\ \left. + \cos\varphi\, |(\tfrac{1}{2}, 0), \text{any } S_z, L_z\rangle\right]. \tag{12}$$

With the assignments (11) and (12) we can express G^* and G_A in terms of θ and φ:

$$G^* = \tfrac{4}{3}\cos\theta\,, \tag{13}$$

$$G_A = \tfrac{5}{3}\cos^2\theta + \sin^2\theta\cos 2\varphi\,. \tag{14}$$

Eqs. (13) and (14) lead to two consistency relations which are necessary conditions for the existence of a solution for θ and φ:

$$G^* \leqslant \tfrac{4}{3}\,, \tag{15}$$

$$\tfrac{8}{3}(G_A - 1) \leqslant G^{*2} \leqslant \tfrac{2}{3}(G_A + 1)\,. \tag{16}$$

Using $G_A = 1.18$ the following bounds on G^* are obtained:

$$0.7 \leqslant G^* \leqslant 1.2\,. \tag{17}$$

It is amusing that the various evaluations of G^* based on PCAC and the experimental N* width or its integrated contribution to the πp total cross section, yield values [13]) ranging from 0.8 to 1.05, all of which are consistent with (17).

(e) In order to specify the S_z and L_z values in eq. (12) we now follow the assignments of the quark model [14]). We find that for $J_z = \frac{1}{2}$ and $|L_z| \leqslant 1$ the $(0, \frac{1}{2})$ representation must have $S_z = \frac{1}{2}$, $L_z = 0$ while $(\frac{1}{2}, 0)$ has either $S_z = -\frac{1}{2}$, $L_z = 1$ or $S_z = \frac{3}{2}$, $L_z = -1$. The complete wave function for the nucleon will then be:

$$|\mathrm{N}, J_z = \tfrac{1}{2}\rangle = \cos\theta\,|(1, \tfrac{1}{2})_{\frac{1}{2}}, 0\rangle + \sin\theta\,\{\sin\varphi\,|(0, \tfrac{1}{2})_{\frac{1}{2}}, 0\rangle + \\ + \cos\varphi\,[\cos\psi\,|(\tfrac{1}{2}, 0)_{\frac{3}{2}}, -1\rangle + \sin\psi\,|(\tfrac{1}{2}, 0)_{-\frac{1}{2}}, 1\rangle]\}\,. \tag{18}$$

The matrix elements of the D_i dipole operator (6) may have contributions from:

$$[(1, \tfrac{1}{2})_{\frac{1}{2}}, 0] \overset{M_A}{\leftrightarrow} [(0, \tfrac{1}{2})_{\frac{1}{2}}, -1]\,,$$

$$[(0, \tfrac{1}{2})_{\frac{1}{2}}, 0] \overset{M_B}{\leftrightarrow} [(0, \tfrac{1}{2})_{\frac{1}{2}}, -1]\,,$$

where M_A and M_B are the reduced matrix elements for the transitions. M_A is a pure isovector and contributes to both μ^* and $\mu_A^V = \mu_A(\mathrm{p}) - \mu_A(\mathrm{n})$. M_B has an isoscalar part M_B^0, contributing only to $\mu_A^S = \mu_A(\mathrm{p}) + \mu_A(\mathrm{n})$, and an isovector part M_B^1 contributing only to μ_A^V. The three reduced matrix elements are independent and we can always compute them from the experimental values μ^*, $\mu_A(\mathrm{n})$, $\mu_A(\mathrm{p})$.

The situation can now be summarized in the following way: We are able to express the five experimental quantities G_A, G^*, $\mu_A(p)$, $\mu_A(n)$ and μ^* in terms of the five parameters θ, φ, $M_A \cos\varphi \sin\psi$, $M_B^0 \sin 2\varphi \sin\psi$, $M_B^1 \sin 2\varphi \sin\psi$. The only predictions are the inequalities (15) and (16) which agree with experiment. We can solve our equations for the five parameters and find:

$$\cos\theta = \tfrac{3}{4} G^* , \tag{19}$$

$$\cos^2\varphi = \frac{G_A + 1 - \frac{3}{2} G^{*2}}{2 - \frac{9}{8} G^{*2}} , \tag{20}$$

$$M_A^1 \sin\theta \cos\varphi \sin\psi = \mu^* , \tag{21}$$

$$M_B^0 \sin^2\theta \sin 2\varphi \sin\psi = \mu_A^S , \tag{22}$$

$$M_B^1 \sin^2\theta \sin 2\varphi \sin\psi = \mu^* - \frac{\mu_A^V}{\sqrt{2}\cos\theta} , \tag{23}$$

where M_A^1, M_B^0 and M_B^1 are arbitrarily normalized. We notice that both $M_B^0 \sin\varphi$ and $M_B^1 \sin\varphi$ are predicted to be negligible with respect to M_A^1. In the limit $M_B \sin\varphi = 0$ we obtain two relations:

$$\mu_A(p) = -\mu_A(n) , \tag{24}$$

$$\frac{\mu^*}{\mu_A^V} = \frac{1}{\sqrt{2}\cos\theta} = \frac{2\sqrt{2}}{3} G^* . \tag{25}$$

If $M_B = 0$, eq. (25) predicts[15] $G^* = 1.04 \pm 0.02$, in good agreement with experiment[13]. The solutions for θ and φ are:

$$\cos\theta = 0.78 \pm 0.01 ; \qquad \cos\varphi = 0.83 \pm 0.02 . \tag{26}$$

If $\sin\varphi = 0$, eq. (14) gives $\cos\theta = 0.52 \pm 0.03$ which together with eq. (25) leads to: $G^* = 0.69 \pm 0.03$, $\mu^* = 5.14 \pm 0.3$ in very poor agreement with the data ($G^* = 0.8 - 1.05$, $\mu^* = 3.36 \pm 0.05$).

The two solutions ($M_B = 0$ and $\varphi = 0$) represent two simplifying approximations to the real unique solution of eqs. (19)–(23). The $\varphi = 0$ solution has the advantage of a simplified nucleon wave function, but seems to be inconsistent both with the experimental values of G^* and μ^* and with the simple-minded physical intuition which says that the presence of $L_z = \pm 1$ components of a multiplet implies that the $L_z = 0$ component also exists. Although we cannot prove this, we find it very hard to imagine that the transformation of the nucleon state to the infinite momentum frame kills only the $L_z = 0$ component of a certain $L \neq 0$ multiplet.

We prefer the $M_B = 0$ solution which essentially says that the $\langle(\frac{1}{2},0)|D_i|(\frac{1}{2},0)\rangle$ reduced matrix elements vanish. Whether this vanishing results from a selection rule of a higher symmetry or from some dynamical reason we do not know.

The $J_z = \frac{3}{2}$ state of N*(1236) probably belongs to the $[(\frac{3}{2}, 0)_{\frac{3}{2}}, 0]$ representation and the reduced matrix element M_C for the transition $\langle(\frac{3}{2}, 0)_{\frac{3}{2}}, 0|$ $D_i |(\frac{1}{2}, 0)_{\frac{3}{2}}, -1\rangle$ is an additional free parameter which can be determined from the experimental ratio between the M1 and E2 N–N* transitions. Higher $I = \frac{1}{2}$ nucleon resonances may have components in all the representations appearing in the nucleon's wave function (18) and we always have enough freedom to fit all their known vector and axial vector transitions.

4. The baryon classification in SU(3) × SU(3)

We now turn to the SU(3) × SU(3) classification of the N–N* system. Following the approach of section 3 we find:

(a) The nucleon must have both $L_z = 0$ and $L_z \neq 0$ components.

(b) All SU(3) × SU(3) representations which allow $I > \frac{3}{2}$ N*'s are excluded. This leaves us only with the three quark representations.

(c) The $J_z = \frac{1}{2}$ component of N*(1236) is in the (6,3) or (3,6) representations.

(d) Most of the contributions to the Adler–Weisberger sum rule from energies above the decuplet states are of octet and singlet states. There is no evidence for an additional important contribution of a decuplet or any higher SU(3) representation. We therefore assume that only one decuplet has large axial transitions to the nucleon. Consequently:

$$|\text{N}^*(1236), J_z = \tfrac{1}{2}\rangle = |(6,3)_{\frac{1}{2}}, 0\rangle . \tag{27}$$

(e) The SU(3) × SU(3) representations which contain octets and possibly singlets but no higher SU(3) multiplets are $(3,\bar{3})$, $(\bar{3},3)$, (8,1) and (1,8). Using the quark model assignments [14]) and assuming $L_z \leqslant 1$ we are led to the following complete wave function for the nucleon:

$$\begin{aligned}|\text{N}, J_z = \tfrac{1}{2}\rangle = \cos\theta\, |(6,3)_{\frac{1}{2}}, 0\rangle + \sin\theta\, \{\sin\varphi\, |(\bar{3},3)_{\frac{1}{2}}, 0\rangle + \\ + \cos\varphi\, [\cos\psi\, |(8,1)_{\frac{3}{2}}, -1\rangle + \sin\psi\, |(3,\bar{3})_{-\frac{1}{2}}, 1\rangle]\} . \end{aligned}\tag{28}$$

For the N–N* system eqs. (27) and (28) lead to the same results as those obtained from the SU(2) × SU(2) analysis of the previous section. In addition, we now have an expression for the d/f ratio of the axial vector transitions between members of the baryon octet:

$$\alpha = \frac{d}{d+f} = \frac{1 + \tan^2\theta(\cos^2\varphi\sin^2\psi - \sin^2\varphi)}{\frac{5}{3} + \tan^2\theta(\cos^2\varphi - \sin^2\varphi)} . \tag{29}$$

We can solve eq. (29) for the mixing angle ψ which remained undetermined in the SU(2) × SU(2) level. The condition for having a solution for ψ is:

$$\frac{1}{2G_A}(G_A + \tfrac{3}{4}G^{*2} - 1) \leqslant \alpha \leqslant 1 - \frac{3G^{*2}}{8G_A}. \tag{30}$$

For $G_A = 1.18$, $G^* = 0.8$, eq. (30) predicts:

$$0.28 \leqslant \alpha \leqslant 0.79\,, \tag{31}$$

and for $G^* = 1.05$ (ref. 13):

$$0.43 \leqslant \alpha \leqslant 0.66\,. \tag{32}$$

This should be compared with the phenomenological value[16]) $\alpha = 0.665 \pm 0.018$.

For the $M_B = 0$ solution of section 3, eq. (29) gives[17]):

$$\sin\psi = 1.02 \pm 0.06\,. \tag{33}$$

This is consistent with no contribution of the $[(8,1)_{\frac{3}{2}}, -1]$ representation to the nucleon wave function. Whether or not ψ is actually 90° depends on the assignment of the $J_z = \frac{3}{2}$ states of the decuplet. These states would naturally belong to the $[(10,1)_{\frac{3}{2}}, 0]$ representation. As long as $\cos\psi \neq 0$, they can be connected by the dipole operator D_i to the $[(8,1)_{\frac{3}{2}}, -1]$ component of the nucleon with an unknown reduced matrix element M_C which can be fitted to the observed E2:M1 ratio for $\gamma + N \rightarrow N^*$. Alternatively, if $\cos\psi = 0$ (which is consistent with eq. (33)) we have to allow some mixing of $[(6,3)_{\frac{1}{2}}, 1]$ in the $J_z = \frac{3}{2}$ state of N*. Both possibilities are perfectly allowed in the SU(3) × SU(3) limit. Only if we introduce a larger algebra of charges (like $SU(6)_W$) we find that the first possibility ($\cos\psi \neq 0$) is favored, as long as eq. (27) holds.

5. The low-lying mesons

We now proceed to the classification of the low-lying mesons. We first consider SU(2) × SU(2) and non-strange mesons and then generalize the results to SU(3) × SU(3).

Since all known mesons have $I \leqslant 1$, we use only $k \leqslant 1$ representations. For non-strange mesons, even (odd) k corresponds to even (odd) S_z (ref. 14). The complete list of $q\bar{q}$, $k \leqslant 1$ representations for these mesons therefore includes $(0,0)_0$, $(1,0)_0$, $(0,1)_0$, $(\frac{1}{2},\frac{1}{2})_1$, $(\frac{1}{2},\frac{1}{2})_{-1}$. Under charge conjugation $(I_L, I_R)_{S_z} \rightarrow \eta(I_R, I_L)_{S_z}$ where $\eta = \pm 1$. We will therefore always use the combinations $\{(1,0)_0 + (0,1)_0\}$ and $\{(1,0)_0 - (0,1)_0\}$ for $C = -1$ and $C = +1$ states, respectively.

All $J_z = 0$ states are eigenstates of the reflection operator $Y = P\,e^{i\pi J_y}$. For a meson with spin-parity J^P, the $J_z=0$ state has $Y=P(-1)^J$. Under the operation of Y

$$[(I_L, I_R)_{S_z}, L_z] \to [(I_R, I_L)_{-S_z}, -L_z].$$

The only combinations which appear for $J_z=0$, $Y=\pm 1$ are therefore $[(0,0)_0, 0]$; $[(1,0)_0 \pm (0,1)_0, 0]$; $[(\frac{1}{2},\frac{1}{2})_1, -1] \pm [(\frac{1}{2},\frac{1}{2})_{-1}, 1]$. Notice that the restrictions imposed by the Y operation apply only to $J_z=0$ states while the restrictions following from (C) apply to states with any J_z.

We now add one more simplifying assumption: We assume that the lowest lying pseudoscalar and vector mesons of the $q\bar{q}$ system tend to mix at infinite momentum mostly with $q\bar{q}$ states with $|L_z| \leqslant 1$, while for higher states such as the 2^+ mesons we allow $|L_z| \leqslant 2$. These assumptions affect only the $J_z=1$ state of the vector mesons and the $J_z=2$ state of the 2^+ mesons. Using this assumption, as well as the restrictions implied by isospin, charge conjugation and Y, we now list the most general assignments allowed for the 0^-, 1^- and 2^+ mesons:

$$|\pi, J_z=0\rangle = \frac{\cos\alpha}{\sqrt{2}}\left[|(1,0)_0, 0\rangle - |(0,1)_0, 0\rangle\right] + \\ + \frac{\sin\alpha}{\sqrt{2}}\left[|(\tfrac{1}{2},\tfrac{1}{2})_1, -1\rangle - |(\tfrac{1}{2},\tfrac{1}{2})_{-1}, 1\rangle\right], \tag{34}$$

$$|\rho, J_z=0\rangle = \frac{1}{\sqrt{2}}\cos\beta\left[|(1,0)_0, 0\rangle + |(0,1)_0, 0\rangle\right] + \\ + \frac{1}{\sqrt{2}}\sin\beta\left[|(\tfrac{1}{2},\tfrac{1}{2})_1, -1\rangle + |(\tfrac{1}{2},\tfrac{1}{2})_{-1}, 1\rangle\right], \tag{35}$$

$$|A_2, J_z=0\rangle = \frac{1}{\sqrt{2}}\left[|(\tfrac{1}{2},\tfrac{1}{2})_1, -1\rangle + |(\tfrac{1}{2},\tfrac{1}{2})_{-1}, 1\rangle\right], \tag{36}$$

$$|\rho, J_z=1\rangle = \frac{1}{\sqrt{2}}\cos\gamma\left[|(1,0)_0, 1\rangle + |(0,1)_0, 1\rangle\right] + \\ + \sin\gamma\,|(\tfrac{1}{2},\tfrac{1}{2})_1, 0\rangle, \tag{37}$$

$$|A_2, J_z=1\rangle = \frac{1}{\sqrt{2}}\cos\delta\left[|(1,0)_0, 1\rangle - |(0,1)_0, 1\rangle\right] + \\ + \sin\delta\left\{\cos\varepsilon\,|(\tfrac{1}{2},\tfrac{1}{2})_1, 0\rangle + \sin\varepsilon\,|(\tfrac{1}{2},\tfrac{1}{2})_{-1}, 2\rangle\right\}, \tag{38}$$

$$|A_2, J_z=2\rangle = \frac{1}{\sqrt{2}}\cos\varphi\left[|(1,0)_0, 2\rangle - |(0,1)_0, 2\rangle\right] + \\ + \sin\varphi\,|(\tfrac{1}{2},\tfrac{1}{2})_1, 1\rangle. \tag{39}$$

The assignments of $I=0$ states such as η, ω and f^0 are obtained from eqs. (34)–(39) by replacing (1,0) and (0,1) by (0,0). The φ and f^* are probably in pure $[(0,0)_0, L_z]$ representations where $L_z = J_z$. This immediately forbids the decays $\varphi \to \rho\pi$ and $f^* \to \pi\pi$. Notice that the sum over all particles of the squares of the coefficients of a given irreducible representation need not be normalized to one, since the same representation may occur more than once.

In the SU(3) × SU(3) limit the classification of the low-lying octets is obtained from eqs. (34)–(39) by the substitutions: $(1,0)_0 \to (8,1)_0$; $(0,1)_0 \to (1,8)_0$; $(\frac{1}{2},\frac{1}{2})_1 \to (3,\bar{3})_1$; $(\frac{1}{2},\frac{1}{2})_{-1} \to (\bar{3},3)_{-1}$. SU(3) singlets include $(1,1)_0$ components as well as $(3,\bar{3})_1$ and $(\bar{3},3)_{-1}$.

Using the experimental data on pionic decays of mesons, we can compute the mixing angles α, β, γ and δ. We find:

$$(f^0|Q_5|\pi) = \sin\alpha\,, \tag{40}$$

$$(\rho|Q_5|\pi) = \cos\alpha\cos\beta\,, \tag{41}$$

$$(\omega|Q_5|\rho) = \sin^2\gamma\,, \tag{42}$$

$$(A_2|Q_5|\rho) = \cos\gamma\cos\delta\,, \tag{43}$$

leading to[18] $\sin\alpha = 0.26 \pm 0.03$, $\cos\alpha\cos\beta = 0.52 \pm 0.05$, $\cos\gamma\cos\delta = 0.35 \pm 0.05$, $\sin^2\gamma \sim 0.6$. The obtained SU(3) × SU(3) classification is[19]:

$$|8, J^P = 0^-, J_z = 0\rangle = \frac{0.97}{\sqrt{2}}\left[|(8,1)_0, 0\rangle - |(1,8)_0, 0\rangle\right] + \frac{0.26}{\sqrt{2}}\left[|(3,\bar{3})_1, -1\rangle - |(\bar{3},3)_{-1}, 1\rangle\right], \tag{44}$$

$$|8, J^P = 1^-, J_z = 0\rangle = \frac{0.5}{\sqrt{2}}\left[|(8,1)_0, 0\rangle + |(1,8)_0, 0\rangle\right] + \frac{0.87}{\sqrt{2}}\left[|(3,\bar{3})_1, -1\rangle + |(\bar{3},3)_{-1}, 1\rangle\right], \tag{45}$$

$$|8, J^P = 2^+, J_z = 0\rangle = \frac{1}{\sqrt{2}}\left[|(3,\bar{3})_1, -1\rangle - |(\bar{3},3)_{-1}, 1\rangle\right], \tag{46}$$

$$|8, J^P = 1^-, J_z = 1\rangle = \frac{0.64}{\sqrt{2}}\left[|(8,1)_0, 1\rangle + |(1,8)_0, 1\rangle\right] + 0.77\,|(3,\bar{3})_1, 0\rangle\,, \tag{47}$$

$$|8, J^P = 2^+, J_z = 1\rangle = \frac{0.55}{\sqrt{2}}\left[|(8,1)_0, 1\rangle - |(1,8)_0, 1\rangle\right] + 0.83\left\{\cos\varepsilon\,|(3,\bar{3})_1, 0\rangle + \sin\varepsilon\,|(\bar{3},3)_{-1}, 2\rangle\right\}. \tag{48}$$

The mixing coefficients given in eqs. (44)–(48) should not be taken very seriously. They can be wrong by as much as 20%–40%. We have given them here only in order to indicate the approximate amount of mixing which occurs and to show that, as is the case with the baryons, the pure meson representations are a very poor approximation to the experimental situation. Only when additional data are available, it may be possible to derive relations which do not depend on the mixing angles. An example of such a relation is the prediction:

$$\langle \mathrm{B}, J_z = 0 | \, Q_5 \, | \omega, J_z = 0 \rangle = \sin\beta \sim 0.87 \,, \qquad (49)$$

where B is the meson at 1220 MeV with $I = 1$, $C = -1$ and presumably $J^P = 1^+$. Eqs. (40), (41) and (49) lead in this case to a relation between $\Gamma(\mathrm{f} \to 2\pi)$, $\Gamma(\rho \to 2\pi)$ and the particular helicity amplitude of $\mathrm{B} \to \omega\pi$. This relation can be tested only when the width, the spin-parity and the relative strength of the S-wave and D-wave in the $\omega\pi$ decay mode of the B meson are known.

6. The possibility of a larger algebra of charges: $\mathrm{SU}(6)_\mathrm{W}$

The obvious candidate for an algebra of charges larger than $\mathrm{SU}(3) \times \mathrm{SU}(3)$ is the $\mathrm{SU}(6)_\mathrm{W}$ algebra which includes in addition to the Q_i and Q_i^5 generators, integrated components of tensor currents. In this algebra the baryon classification of eqs. (27) and (28) is most naturally generalized in the following way: We assume that the *decuplet* states are purely in the $[56, W = \frac{3}{2}, L_z = 0]$ representation. The baryon *octet* has components in [20] $[56, W = \frac{1}{2}, L_z = 0]$; $[70, W = \frac{1}{2}, L_z = 0]$; $[70, W = \frac{1}{2}, L_z = \pm 1]$; $[70, W = \frac{3}{2}, L_z = 0]$; $[70, W = \frac{3}{2}, L_z = \pm 1]$. Although it appears to be larger, the number of mixing angles here is identical to that of eq. (28), since the coefficients of the various terms are related by the additional requirement that the $W = \frac{1}{2}$ decuplet in the 70 has vanishing (or negligible) axial transitions to the nucleon.

All meson states will fall into the 35 and 1 representations with $W = 0, 1$ and $L_z = 0, \pm 1, \ldots$. Again, no freedom is lost, and no new information is gained.

We conclude therefore, that the $\mathrm{SU}(6)_\mathrm{W}$ classification seems to be much more complicated but not more useful than the $\mathrm{SU}(3) \times \mathrm{SU}(3)$ description. Since the physical role of the tensor currents is not understood, we prefer to abandon the larger algebra, at this stage, and to return to it if and when better data on the higher baryon and meson resonances are available and allow us to consider the classification of additional states.

7. Comparison of the different models for the baryons

Three different models have been proposed in the last year for the baryon classification. Gatto, Maiani and Preparata[6]) have proposed an SU(6) model in which the 56 and 20 representations are mixed. In the notation of eq. (28) their model corresponds to $\sin\psi = 1$, $\cos\varphi = \sqrt{\frac{2}{3}} = 0.82$, $M_A = 0$, $M_C = 0$. Although the values for ψ and φ are in good agreement with experiment, the vanishing of M_A and M_C is obviously unacceptable[21]).

A second model was proposed by the present author[7]). We have used only the SU(3) × SU(3) algebra, and proposed a scheme corresponding to $\sin\psi = 1$, $\cos\varphi = \sqrt{\frac{2}{3}} = 0.82$, $M_B^1 = M_B^0 = 0$. These values correspond to the $M_B = 0$ solution of section 2, and they agree very well with experiment. Our model, however, suffers from the following disadvantage: If $\sin\psi = 1$, the same motivation that led us to assume *a priori* that $\cos\varphi = \sqrt{\frac{2}{3}}$ should also lead to the unacceptable result $M_C = 0$. We are therefore forced either to allow $\sin\psi \neq 1$ or to regard $\cos\varphi$ as a free parameter which will then be determined by experiment[21]) to be 0.83. We prefer the first possibility since it is consistent with $SU(6)_W$, and allows a simple classification of $|N^*, J_z = \frac{3}{2}\rangle$.

The third model is the model of Gerstein and Lee[8]) who also used only SU(3) × SU(3). Their model corresponds to the $\varphi = 0$ solution that we have discussed in section 3, and it gives rather poor agreement[21]) with the experimental values of G^* and, particularly, μ^*.

Both our model and the Gerstein–Lee model are consistent with a 56–70 mixture in $SU(6)_W$.

8. Discussion

The analysis of the previous sections indicates that the general situation is this:

The low-lying baryons and mesons can be described at $p = \infty$ in terms of relatively simple representations of the SU(2) × SU(2), SU(3) × SU(3) or $SU(6)_W$ charge algebra. These representations correspond to the three-quark states for the baryons and to quark–antiquark states for the mesons. The L_z values which are required for the lowest states indicate that most of the mixing at infinite momentum occurs with $L = 1$ states. The classification of higher baryon and meson resonances seems to involve mixing with still higher states, presumably with higher values of L. A reasonable principle which seems to be consistent with the general experimental picture is that states which correspond at rest to a given value of L, mix at $p = \infty$ mostly with states having $L-1$, L, $L+1$. This suggestion, as well as the possible detailed classification schemes for the higher resonances will be tested only when and if better data on the transitions between *pairs of resonances* become available.

An interesting idea that has not been fully analysed so far is the possibility of approximate relations between different charges. An example of such a relation is the suggestion that the vector meson poles dominate the matrix elements of both the vector currents and the divergence of the tensor current[5,6,22]). If the nucleon is in an irreducible SU(3) × SU(3) representation, the two pole-dominance assumptions are clearly inconsistent since they predict a finite anomalous magnetic moment, while the transformation properties of the dipole operator (eq. (6)) leads to a vanishing moment. On the other hand, in the case of more complicated representations it is not clear whether or not the two assumptions are consistent. It is possible that for *approximate* mixture of states they may peacefully coexist and only lead to two different sets of *approximations* for any given assignment of the particles. This possibility as well as the problem of additional restrictions on the classification under the algebra of charges are still open questions.

Footnotes and references

1) M. Gell-Mann, Phys. Rev. **125**, 1067 (1962); Physics **1**, 63 (1964).
2) S. L. Adler, Phys. Rev. Letters **14**, 1051 (1965); W. I. Weisberger, Phys. Rev. Letters **14**, 1047 (1965).
3) See e.g. S. L. Adler, Phys. Rev. **143**, 1144 (1966); N. Cabibbo and L. A. Radicati, Phys. Letters **19**, 697 (1966); M. A. B. Beg, Phys. Rev. Letters **17**, 333 (1966); S. Fubini, G. Furlan and C. Rossetti, Nuovo Cimento **43**, 161 1(966).
4) See e.g. M. Suzuki, Phys Rev. Letters **15**, 986 (1965); Sugawara, Phys. Rev. Letters **15**, 870 (1965) (Erratum **15**, 997 (1965)).
5) For a detailed discussion of this idea see, e.g., R. F. Dashen and M. Gell-Mann, in: *Proceedings of the Third Coral Gables Conference, January 1966.*
6) R. Gatto, L. Maiani and G. Preparata, Phys. Rev. Letters **16**, 377 (1966); Phys. Letters **21**, 459 (1966); Phys. Rev. Letters **18**, 97 (1967).
7) H. Harari, Phys. Rev. Letters **16**, 964 (1966); Phys. Rev. Letters **17**, 56 (1966).
8) I. S. Gerstein and B. W. Lee, Phys. Rev. Letters **16**, 1060 (1966); Phys. Rev. **152**, 1418 (1966).
9) A detailed discussion is given by M. Gell-Mann, to be published in the proceedings of the Erice summer school, 1966.
10) I. S. Gerstein and B. W. Lee, Phys. Rev. **144**, 1142 (1966).
11) S. Fubini and G. Furlan, Physics **1**, 229 (1964).
12) Throughout the rest of this paper we will use the notation $[(I_L, I_R)_{S_z} L_z]$ or $[(m, n)_{S_z} L_z]$ where m, n are the SU(3) dimensionalities.
13) The determination of G^* from the experimental data suffers from two major ambiguities. One of them is the error introduced by using PCAC (which in the case of G_A

amounts to 10%–15%) and the other is the difficulty in deciding what energy region is actually dominated by the N*. The total error is probably around ±20%. The numbers quoted in the literature so far are 0.85 and 0.99 (Adler, ref. 2, using f_π and G_A respectively), 0.81 and 0.92 (Weisberger, ref. 2), 1 ±0.2 (Harari, ref. 7), 0.84 (Gerstein–Lee, ref. 8), 1.02 (Cheng and C. W. Kim, Phys. Rev., to be published), 1.04 (D. Horn, Phys. Rev. Letters **17**, 778 (1966)). We will assume that the correct value is somewhere between 0.8 and 1.05.

14) We essentially assume that there is only one kind of quark. The $S_z = \frac{1}{2}$ quark then corresponds, say, to the $(\frac{1}{2},0)$ representation of SU(2) × SU(2) and to (3,1) in SU(3) × SU(3), while the $S_z = -\frac{1}{2}$ component is in the $(0,\frac{1}{2})$ or (1,3). If a second kind of quark (of opposite parity) would be required the S_z values would remain completely arbitrary. We assume that this is not the case.
15) We use: $\mu_A{}^V = 3.7$, $\mu^* = 3.36 \pm 0.05$ as obtained by R. H. Dalitz and D. G. Sutherland, Phys. Rev. **146**, 1180 (1966).
16) N. Brene, L. Veje, M. Roos and C. Cronstrom, Phys. Rev. **149**, 1288 (1966).
17) The $\varphi = 0$ solution gives sin $\psi = 0.84$.
18) We have used $\Gamma(f \to \pi\pi) = 120$ MeV, $\Gamma(\rho \to \pi\pi) = 120$ MeV, $\Gamma(A_2 \to \rho\pi) = 80$ MeV and $G_{\rho\omega\pi}$ as given by the model of M. Gell-Mann, D. Sharp and W. G. Wagner, Phys. Rev. Letters **8**, 261 (1962) using $\Gamma(\omega \to \pi\gamma) = 1.2$ MeV.
19) The only attempt to classify the meson states was done by D. Horn, Phys. Rev. Letters **17**, 778 (1966). He presents one possible solution which allows some arbitrary SU(2) × SU(2) representation called $|\alpha\rangle$, in addition to the $q\bar{q}$ states that we consider. Within the $q\bar{q}$ system, however, our assignments are the most general ones.
20) This is the minimal list of representations for the nucleon wave function. In addition, we could use components of the 20 representation with $L_z = 0, \pm 1$ and still be consistent with eq. (28). We could not have only the 56 and 20 representations since this would predict $\mu^* = 0$.
21) A detailed discussion of this point is given in section 3.
22) S. Fubini, G. Segre and J. D. Walecka, Ann. Phys. (N. Y.) **39**, 381 (1966).

Note added in proof

Since writing this paper in January 1967 it became clear that the axial vector and possibly the scalar mesons play an important role in the SU(2) × SU(2) classification of the lowest lying mesons. The $J_z = 0$ component of the A_1 meson seems to be strongly mixed with the pion. This is supported not only by the type of analysis presented here, but also by the recent study of the charge algebra transformation properties of the mass operator. These properties lead, among other things, to supporting evidence for the nucleon classification (eq. (12)) for $\cos^2\theta = 0.6$. (See F. J. Gilman and H. Harari, Phys. Rev. Letters **19**, 723 (1967) and Phys. Rev., to be published.)

Spectroscopic and group theoretical methods in physics
© North-Holland Publ. Co., Amsterdam, 1968

ON THE CONSTRUCTION OF CURRENTS AND IRREDUCIBLE TENSORS OPERATING IN THE SPACE OF ONE-PARTICLE RELATIVISTIC STATES*

HAIM GOLDBERG
Physics Department, Tel-Aviv University, Tel-Aviv, Israel

1) Recently, matrix elements of current densities, as well as of integrated currents, have been subject to thorough investigation. The relevant discussions combine different aspects of the operators involved, which – a priori – may be inconsistent. Namely, it is assumed that the restrictions imposed on the currents – like conservation, PCAC or equal time commutation relations – are compatible with the fact that these currents are represented on the physical Fock space. Since, from the beginning, they were not defined by their action on Fock space, one wonders whether the current algebraic equations may be solved, and if yes, to what extent the solution is unique.

For the sake of better understanding of the situation, one is tempted to study the space Ω of all operators ω which transform one particle state into one particle state, trying to construct currents, as well as some other operators with prescribed transformation properties. To be specific, we shall consider the case where the two particles are identical, with mass m and spin σ; the procedure is applicable – with obvious modifications – to cases of different masses and spins. We shall first discuss the situation disregarding inner degrees of freedom (associated with isospin, SU_3 etc.); these will be introduced later.

2) The space which carries the one-particle irreducible representation $[m\sigma]$ of the connected Poincaré group $\mathscr{P}_+^\uparrow$ is spanned by the states $\{\langle k, \nu|\}$ (with

* Research sponsored by the Air Force Office of Scientific Research, Office of Aerospace Research, United States Air Force, under AFOSR grant number AF EOAR 66-39, through the European Office of Aerospace Research.

$k^2=m^2$, $k_0>0$, $-\sigma<\nu<\sigma$) which fulfil[1])

$$\langle k'\nu'|k\nu\rangle = (2k_0)\,\delta^3(\mathbf{k}-\mathbf{k}')\,\delta(\nu\nu'), \tag{1}$$

$$\langle k\nu|\,U(a,\Lambda) = \mathrm{e}^{\mathrm{i}k\cdot a}\sum_{\mu} D^{\sigma}_{\nu\mu}(R(k,\Lambda))\,\langle\Lambda^{-1}k,\mu|\,. \tag{2}$$

ν is the eigenvalue of $S_3(k)$ (ref. 2), $U(a,\Lambda)$ the unitary irreducible representation of the element $\{a,\Lambda\}\ \varepsilon\mathscr{P}^{\uparrow}_{+}$, and

$$R(k,\Lambda) = L(k)\,\Lambda L^{-1}(\Lambda^{-1}k) \tag{3}$$

is a spatial rotation ($L(x)$ is the pure Lorentz transformation which carries the timelike 4-momentum x to its rest frame).

An alternative (non-unitary) basis $\{_D\langle k,\alpha|\}$ for $[m\sigma]$ is obtained by the definition[3])

$$_D\langle k\alpha| = \sum_{\nu} D^{(\sigma,0)}_{\alpha\nu}(L^{-1}(k))\,\langle k\nu|\,, \tag{4}$$

where $D^{(\sigma,0)}(L^{-1}(k))$ is the $(\sigma,0)$ representation of $L^{-1}(k)$. These new states fulfil

$$_D\langle k'\alpha'|k\alpha\rangle_D = (2k_0)\,\delta^3(\mathbf{k}-\mathbf{k}')\sum_{\beta} D^{(\sigma,0)}_{\alpha'\beta}(L^{-1}(k'))\,D^{(\sigma,0)*}_{\alpha\beta}(L^{-1}(k)), \tag{5}$$

$$_D\langle k\alpha|U(a,\Lambda) = \mathrm{e}^{\mathrm{i}k\cdot a}\sum_{\beta} D^{(\sigma,0)}_{\alpha\beta}(\Lambda)\,{}_D\langle\Lambda^{-1}k,\beta|\,. \tag{6}$$

Eq. (5) is a special case of relation (1-57) of ref. 4. In the subsequent, only the basis defined by (4) will be discussed; the subindex D, however, will be omitted.

3) The matrix element $\langle k'\alpha'|\,\omega\,|k\alpha\rangle$ is a bilinear functional for pairs of test functions defined over the hyperboloid $k^2=m^2$, $k_0>0$. Accordingly, a natural basis for Ω is the set $\{Q(q\gamma,p\beta)\}=\{|q\gamma\rangle\,\langle p\beta|\}$, where p and q are 4-momenta fulfilling $p^2=q^2=m^2$; $p_0, q_0>0$, and β, γ assume the values $\sigma,\sigma-1,\ldots,-\sigma$. One has

$$\omega = \sum_{\beta\gamma}\int (2p_0)^{-1}(2q_0)^{-1}\,\mathrm{d}^3p\,\mathrm{d}^3q\;\omega(q\gamma,p\beta)\,Q(q\gamma,p\beta), \tag{7}$$

where $\omega(q\gamma,p\beta)$ are bilinear functionals. The following relations hold

$$\begin{aligned}\langle k'\alpha'|\,Q(q\gamma,p\beta)\,|k\alpha\rangle &=\\ =(2p_0)(2q_0)\,\delta^3(\mathbf{p}-\mathbf{k})\,\delta^3(\mathbf{q}-\mathbf{k}')&\sum_{\delta,\varepsilon} D^{(\sigma,0)}_{\beta\delta}(L^{-1}(p))\,D^{(\sigma,0)*}_{\alpha\delta}(L^{-1}(p))\times\\ \times D^{(\sigma,0)}_{\alpha'\varepsilon}(L^{-1}(q))\,D^{(\sigma,0)*}_{\gamma\varepsilon}(L^{-1}(q)),&\end{aligned} \tag{8}$$

$$U^{\dagger}(a,\Lambda)\,Q(q\gamma,p\beta)\,U(a,\Lambda)= \\ = \mathrm{e}^{\mathrm{i}(p-q)\cdot a}\sum_{\beta'\gamma'} D^{(\sigma,0)}_{\beta\beta'}(\Lambda)\,D^{(\sigma,0)*}_{\gamma\gamma'}(\Lambda)\,Q(\Lambda^{-1}q\gamma',\Lambda^{-1}p\beta'). \tag{9}$$

Rather than specifying an operator Q by the 4-vectors p and q, one may change variables and use the 4-vectors r, u defined by

$$r=p-q, \qquad u=[2(m^2+(p\cdot q))]^{-\frac{1}{2}}(p+q), \tag{10}$$

and write $Q(q\gamma,q\beta)=Q(ru;\gamma\beta)$; r and u fulfil

$$u^2=1, \qquad r\cdot u=0, \qquad u_0>0. \tag{11}$$

The 4-vector u may be considered as the representative of the unimodular 2×2 matrix $A(u)=u_0+\boldsymbol{u}\cdot\boldsymbol{\sigma}\,\varepsilon\,SL(2,c)$, or of the corresponding Lorentz transformation $\Lambda(u)=\Lambda(A(u))$. Accordingly, one defines $D^{(l,0)}(u)$ as the $(l,0)$ representation of $A(u)$ (ref. 5). When $u\to\Lambda u$,

$$D^{(l,0)}(A(u))\to D^{(l,0)}(A(\Lambda u))=D^{(l,0)}(A(\Lambda)(u_0+\boldsymbol{u}\cdot\boldsymbol{\sigma})A^{\dagger}(\Lambda))= \\ = D^{(l,0)}(A(\Lambda))\,D^{(l,0)}(u)\,D^{(l,0)\dagger}(A(\Lambda)). \tag{12}$$

A set of operators $\{R(r;l;j_2n_2,j_1n_1)\}$ may now be defined by the relation

$$R(r;l;j_2n_2,j_1n_1)= \\ = \sum_{\beta\gamma m_1m_2}\int \mathrm{d}^4u\,\theta(u_0)\,\delta(u^2-1)\,\delta(r\cdot u)\,D^{(l,0)}_{m_1m_2}(u)\,Q(ru;\gamma\beta)\times \\ \times(\sigma\gamma lm_2|j_2n_2)(\sigma\beta lm_1|j_1n_1). \tag{13}$$

It follows that

$$U^{\dagger}(a,\Lambda)\,R(r;l;j_2n_2,j_1n_1)\,U(a,\Lambda)= \\ = \mathrm{e}^{\mathrm{i}r\cdot a}\sum_{n_1'n_2'} D^{(j_20)*}_{n_2n_2'}(\Lambda)\,D^{(j_10)}_{n_1n_1'}(\Lambda)\,R(\Lambda^{-1}r;l;j_2n_2'j_1n_1'). \tag{14}$$

Eq. (14) establishes the R as "tensor operators", and enables one to define the tensor densities ($\rho=r^2\leqslant0$)

$$t^{(f)}(x;j_2n_2,j_1n_1)=\sum_{l}\int_{\rho\leqslant0}\mathrm{d}^4r\,\mathrm{e}^{-\mathrm{i}r\cdot x}f(\rho,l)\,R(r;l;j_2n_2,j_1n_1), \tag{15}$$

where the $f(\rho,l)$ are arbitrary functions of ρ. The effect of $\{a,\Lambda\}\,\varepsilon\,\mathscr{P}^{\uparrow}_{+}$ on the $t^{(f)}$ is

$$t^{(f)}(x;j_2n_2,j_1n_1)\to\sum_{n_2'n_1'}D^{(j_2,0)*}_{n_2n_2'}(\Lambda)D^{(j_10)}_{n_1n_1'}(\Lambda)\,t^{(f)}(\Lambda^{-1}(x-a);j_2n_2',j_1n_1'). \tag{16}$$

The definitions imply

$$\langle k'\alpha'|\, R(r;\, l;\, j_2 n_2,\, j_1 n_1)\, |k\alpha\rangle =$$
$$= \sum D^{(\sigma,0)}_{\alpha'\delta}(L^{-1}(k'))\, D^{(\sigma,0)*}_{\gamma\delta}(L^{-1}(k'))\, D^{(\sigma,0)}_{\beta\varepsilon}(L^{-1}(k))\, D^{(\sigma,0)*}_{\alpha\varepsilon}(L^{-1}(k)) \times$$
$$\times D^{(l,0)}_{m_1 m_2}(\{2[m^2 + (k\cdot k')]\}^{-\frac{1}{2}}(k+k'))(\sigma\gamma l m_2|j_2 n_2)(\sigma\beta l m_1|j_1 n_1)\, 4k'_0 \times$$
$$\times \delta^3(\boldsymbol{k} - \boldsymbol{k}' - \boldsymbol{r})\, \delta((r-k)^2 - m^2), \tag{17}$$

$$\langle k'\alpha'|\, t^{(f)}(x;\, j_2 n_2, j_1 n_1)\, |k\alpha\rangle =$$
$$= \sum D^{(\sigma,0)}_{\alpha'\delta}(L^{-1}(k'))\, D^{(\sigma,0)*}_{\gamma\delta}(L^{-1}(k'))\, D^{(\sigma,0)}_{\beta\varepsilon}(L^{-1}(k))\, D^{(\sigma,0)*}_{\alpha\varepsilon}(L^{-1}(k)) \times$$
$$\times D^{(l,0)}_{m_1 m_2}(\{2[m^2 + (k\cdot k')]\}^{-\frac{1}{2}}(k+k'))\,(\sigma\gamma l m_2|j_2 n_2) \times$$
$$\times (\sigma\beta l m_1|j_1 n_1)\, \mathrm{e}^{\mathrm{i}(k'-k)\cdot x} f((k-k')^2, l). \tag{18}$$

The sum in (17) is over $\beta\gamma\delta\varepsilon m_1 m_2$, and in (18) over $\beta\gamma\delta\varepsilon m_1 m_2 l$.

Note that the R are not the most general "tensor operators". Instead of $\delta(u^2-1)\,\delta(u\cdot r)$, it is possible to insert any combination (with a finite number of summands) of $\delta^{(M)}(u^2-1)\,\delta^{(N)}(u\cdot r - \phi(\rho))$, where $\delta^{(M)}$ and $\delta^{(N)}$ are derivatives of the Mth and Nth order respectively of the δ-function, and $\phi(\rho)$ is an arbitrary function of ρ. We set $M=N=0$ for simplicity, and $\phi(\rho)=0$ in order to get divergenceless tensors.

4) Relation (8) implies

$$Q(a\alpha, b\beta)\, Q(c\gamma, d\delta) =$$
$$= (2b_0)\, \delta^3(\boldsymbol{b} - \boldsymbol{c}) \sum_{\varepsilon} D^{(\sigma,0)}_{\beta\varepsilon}(L^{-1}(b))\, D^{(\sigma,0)*}_{\gamma\varepsilon}(L^{-1}(c))\, Q(a\alpha, d\delta). \tag{19}$$

Eq. (19) makes it possible to calculate products of the form

$$t^{(f)}(x;\, l_2 m_2,\, l_1 m_1)\, t^{(g)}(y; j_2 n_2, j_1 n_1). \tag{20}$$

Current algebra involves currents of the form

$$j_0^{(f)}(x) = \tfrac{1}{2}\{t^{(f)}(x;\, \tfrac{1}{2}\tfrac{1}{2}, \tfrac{1}{2}\tfrac{1}{2}) + t^{(f)}(x;\, \tfrac{1}{2} - \tfrac{1}{2}, \tfrac{1}{2} - \tfrac{1}{2})\}, \tag{21}$$

and for the sake of simplicity we shall assume $\sigma=0$; the general spin case is treated in exactly the same way. Direct calculation yields

$$[j_0^{(f)}(x), j_0^{(f)}(y)] = 4 \int\limits_{\rho,\sigma\leqslant 0} \mathrm{d}^4 w\, \mathrm{d}^4 r\, \mathrm{d}^4 s\, [(4m^2 - \rho)(4m^2 - \sigma)]^{-\frac{1}{2}} \times$$
$$\times f(\rho) f(\sigma)\, \theta(w_0)\, \delta(w^2-1)\, \delta(w\cdot(r+s))\, Q(r+s, w)\, \mathrm{e}^{-\mathrm{i}(r\cdot x + s\cdot y)} \times$$
$$\times \{\delta(r\cdot[4m^2 - \rho]^{-\frac{1}{2}}[(4m^2 - (r+s)^2)^{\frac{1}{2}} w + s]) \times$$
$$\times [(4m^2 - (r+s)^2)^{\frac{1}{2}} w_0 + s_0]\, [(4m^2 - (r+s)^2)^{\frac{1}{2}} w_0 - r_0] +$$
$$- \delta(r\cdot[4m^2 - \rho]^{-\frac{1}{2}}[(4m^2 - (r+s)^2)^{\frac{1}{2}} w - s]) \times$$
$$\times [(4m^2 - (r+s)^2)^{\frac{1}{2}} w_0 - s_0]\, [(4m^2 - (r+s)^2)^{\frac{1}{2}} w_0 + r_0]\}. \tag{22}$$

The requirement that the r.h.s. of (22) be equal to $j_0^{(f)}(x)\,\delta^3(\boldsymbol{x}-\boldsymbol{y})$ in case $x_0=y_0$ imposes the following integral equation for the function f

$$\begin{aligned}4w_0 f((r+s)^2) = \int \mathrm{d}(r_0-s_0)\,[(4m^2-\rho)\,(4m^2-\sigma)]^{-\frac{1}{2}} f(\rho) f(\sigma)\,\times \\ \times \{\delta(r\cdot[4m^2-\rho]^{-\frac{1}{2}}[(4m^2-(r+s)^2)^{\frac{1}{2}}w+s])\,\times \\ \times [(4m^2-(r+s)^2)^{\frac{1}{2}}w_0+s_0]\,[(4m^2-(r+s)^2)^{\frac{1}{2}}w_0-r_0]\,+ \\ -\,\delta(r\cdot[4m^2-\rho]^{-\frac{1}{2}}[(4m^2-(r+s)^2)^{\frac{1}{2}}w-s])\,\times \\ \times [(4m^2-(r+s)^2)^{\frac{1}{2}}w_0-s_0]\,[(4m^2-(r+s)^2)^{\frac{1}{2}}w_0+r_0]\}\,. \end{aligned} \tag{23}$$

Change variables by defining $A=\sqrt{\frac{1}{2}}(r+s)$, $B=\sqrt{\frac{1}{2}}(r-s)$. A necessary condition for the solubility of (23) is, that the integral on the r.h.s. be independent of $\boldsymbol{B}$. Since this is not the case, we conclude that $j_0^{(f)}(x)$ are non-local operators.

5) To introduce SU_3 indices, one starts with the space $\{\langle k\alpha; i|\}$, where i specifies some vector belonging to an irreducible representation $(\lambda\mu)$ of SU_3. (i stands for $Y_i T_i T_{zi}$). The analogue of (5) reads

$$\langle k'\alpha' i'|k\alpha i\rangle = (2k_0)\,\delta^3(\boldsymbol{k}-\boldsymbol{k}')\,\delta(ii')\sum_{\beta} D^{(\sigma,0)}_{\alpha'\beta}(L^{-1}(k'))\,D^{(\sigma,0)*}_{\alpha\beta}(L^{-1}(k))\,. \tag{24}$$

Define

$$Q(q\gamma i'; p\beta i) = |q\gamma i'\rangle\,\langle p\beta i|\,. \tag{25}$$

One defines the operators $R(r; l; j_2 n_2, j_1 n_1; i'i)$ and $t^{(f)}(x; j_2 n_2, j_1 n_1; i'i)$ similarly to (13) and (15). Note that the index i' transforms under SU_3 according to the representation $(\mu\lambda)$, which is contravariant to $(\lambda\mu)$. Accordingly, one uses the Clebsch–Gordan coefficients of $(\lambda\mu)\times(\mu\lambda)$ to construct irreducible SU_3-tensors.

Acknowledgement

The author would like to thank E. Gotsman, C. Itzykson, M. Jacob and Y. Ne'eman for helpful and stimulating discussions.

References

1) See, e.g., A. J. MacFarlane, Rev. Mod. Phys. **34**, 41 (1962).
2) $S_3(k)=m^{-1}W_3-k_3[m(m+k_0)]^{-1}W_0$, where $W_\alpha=\frac{1}{2}\varepsilon_{\alpha\beta\gamma\delta}P^\beta M^{\gamma\delta}$ (here P^β and $M^{\gamma\delta}$ are the generators of the Poincaré group).

3) See A. O. Barut, I. Muzinich and D. N. Williams, Phys. Rev. **130**, 442 (1963).

4) R. F. Streater and A. S. Wightman: *CPT, Spin and Statistics and All That* (Benjamin, New York, 1964).

5) Denote $u = (u_0, \sqrt{u_0^2 - 1}\,\boldsymbol{e})$ where $\boldsymbol{e}$ is a spatial unit vector parallel to the spatial component of u. Then

$$D_{mn}{}^{j}(u) = \sum_{n'LM} (-)^{n-n'} \left(\frac{4\pi}{2L+1}\right)^{\frac{1}{2}} (jmj-n|LM)(jn'j-n'|L0)\, Y_M{}^L(\boldsymbol{e})\, \{u_0 + (u_0^2-1)^{\frac{1}{2}}\}^{2n'}.$$

Evidently, $D_{mn}{}^{j}(u)$ are algebraic functions of the components of u.

Spectroscopic and group theoretical methods in physics
© North-Holland Publ. Co., Amsterdam, 1968

THE USE OF EFFECTIVE-INTERACTIONS IN THEORETICAL CALCULATIONS OF TRANSITION ELEMENTS SPECTRA

Y. SHADMI*

Department of Theoretical Physics,
The Hebrew University,
Jerusalem, Israel

1. Introduction

G. Racah was the one who, in addition to many deeper ideas, also introduced the idea of "effective-interactions" (first called by him "model-interactions") to theoretical atomic spectroscopy. His contributions to the development of this idea were reported in various papers[1–4]; and his ideas and reactions may also be found in papers of other physicists which were sent to him while they were still being written.

Racah, himself, used to claim that the idea of effective-interactions in atomic spectroscopy is very old and could be traced to a paper by Bacher and Goudsmit[5]) published in 1934. They showed that it is possible to express the terms of an l^n configuration as linear combinations of the terms of l^2 in such a way that the perturbation of l^n by all the configurations differing from it by the states of two electrons and lying far from it can be accounted for by suitable modifications of the terms of l^2. These modifications are independent of n. They also showed that if the far-lying perturbing configuration differs from l^n by the state of one electron only, its effect can be described by expressing the terms of l^n as linear combinations of the terms of l^3 and modifying the values of these terms. In our language, this means that the first mentioned perturbations can be described by two-body effective-interactions, while the description of the second mentioned perturbations also requires three-body effective-interactions. These effective-inter-

* My collaborators in various parts of the research described in this paper were my students, E. Caspi, A. Schwimmer and J. Oreg.

actions "act" within the configuration l^n, and they actually appear as correction-terms added to that part of the matrix of the electrostatic Hamiltonian which belongs to l^n.

The first correction-term of this kind for the configurations d^n was the $L(L+1)$ correction introduced by Trees[6–7] in 1951, in the configuration $3d^5 4s$ of the iso-electronic spectra of Mn II and Fe III. Trees introduced this correction empirically, but in 1952, Racah (by using the above-mentioned ideas of Bacher and Goudsmit) showed that the $\alpha L(L+1)$ and the βQ corrections form a complete set of two-body effective-interactions for the d^n configurations[1]. This is due to the fact that, together with the three Slater integrals $F_0(d^2)$, $F_2(d^2)$, and $F_4(d^2)$, they form a set of five independent parameters which can represent the five terms of d^2.

In his M.Sc. thesis written under Racah's supervision in 1956, N. Sack[8]) introduced two-body effective-interactions between a 3d and a 4p electron into the configurations $3d^2 4p$ of Ti II, and $3d^8 4p$ of Ni II. These effective-interactions were represented by correction-terms of the type $\Lambda L(L+1)$ and $\sigma S(S+1)$. Here, S and L refer to the terms themselves, and not to the d^n core. Since the six terms of a dp configuration are expressed as linear combinations of four Slater parameters (namely F_0, F_2, G_1, G_3), it is evident that the addition of the two above mentioned independent corrections forms a complete set of two-body effective-interactions. Λ and σ are the parameters of these two corrections. However, at that time, these corrections were not very useful. Some years later, Racah and Spector[9] again tried to use the Sack correction for the configurations $d^n p$ in all second spectra of the iron group, but the mean error was not essentially reduced by these corrections.

In this paper, I intend to summarize how we at the Hebrew University used various effective-interactions in order to improve the fit between theory and experiment in atomic spectroscopy.

2. The configurations $(d+s)^n$

Let me denote, first, that the symbol $(d+s)^n$ is an abbreviation for the three configurations $d^n + d^{n-1}s + d^{n-2}s^2$.

For configurations of the type $3d^n$, the developments mentioned in the introduction, and further contributions by Rajnak and Wybourne[10], Stein[11], Judd[12] and Feneuille[13], led to the final conclusion that in order to completely describe the second-order perturbations of a d^n configuration by configurations lying far from it, one needs to improve the Slater approximation by adding two parameters of two-body effective-interactions (usually

α and β are used for this purpose), and two parameters of three-body interactions. The three-body parameters which we use are designated by T and Tx. Here, we shall just mention briefly that α is the coefficient of the $L(L+1)$ correction, β is the coefficient of the Q-correction (where Q is the seniority operator[14]) and T is a three-body interaction parameter which represents the perturbation of the configuration $3s^2 3d^n$ by the configuration $3s3d^{n+1}$. (Naturally, T can, fully or partially, "absorb" many other perturbations.) Tx is an additional independent three-body interaction parameter which makes the set of effective-interaction parameters complete. Formally, it is one of the three parameters which represent the perturbation of $3d^n$ by any configuration of the type $3d^{n-1}n'd$. More detailed definitions of the above mentioned parameters are given in previous papers of mine[15–16]. Now, let me summarize the effect of using all of the above mentioned corrections in the second and third spectra of the iron group. In table 1,

TABLE 1

No.	Effective-interaction parameters included in the calculation	Fe II group: Total number of free parameters	Fe II group: Mean error (cm^{-1})	Fe III group: Total number of free parameters	Fe III group: Mean error (cm^{-1})
1	α	36	± 230	30	± 184
2	α, β	37	± 192	31	± 175
3	α, T	37	± 227	32	± 164
4	α, β, T	39	± 117	33	± 61
5	α, β, T, Tx	42	± 87	35	± 46
6	α, β, Tx	40	± 170	33	± 165
	Configurations included	$3d^n + 3d^{n-1}4s + 3d^{n-2}4s^2$		$3d^n + 3d^{n-1}4s$	
	Number of observed levels	479		322	

we report the effect of the gradual addition of the above mentioned corrections in two systematic calculations; one of all the second spectra, and one of the third spectra of the iron group in which interpolation formulas were used for the interaction parameters. In all the calculations reported in table 1, the Slater approximation is improved by including the spin–orbit interaction. In the second spectra, for each element we calculated the three configurations $3d^n$, $3d^{n-1}4s$ and $3d^{n-2}4s^2$ with the interaction between them. For the third spectra, only the first two of the above mentioned configurations were calculated. We could not take the interaction between them into account because it is so weak that the parameter which represents it could not be determined by the least-squares calculation. In each row of table 1, a different calculation is reported. The difference between these calculations is that different sets of effective-interaction parameters are used in them. In column I, numbers are assigned to the different calculations. The second column reports which effective-interaction parameters are used in each calculation. The rest of the table is divided into two analogous sections: the left-hand section treating the second spectra of the iron group; and the right-hand section giving the analogous information for the third spectra. In each such section, there are two columns, one reporting the total number of free parameters used in each least-squares calculation and the other reporting the resulting mean error.

In the calculations reported in row 1, we use the same approximation which was already used in previous works[17–18]) in which α was the only effective-interaction parameter. The only difference lies in the fact that in the meantime, new experimental material has been accumulated. From rows 2 and 3, we see that the inclusion of β or T, alone, causes only a slight improvement of the approximation, while the results reported in row 4 show what a large improvement of the approximation was achieved by a simultaneous inclusion of the β and T corrections. In row 5, we report the results achieved when the complete set of effective-interaction parameters between 3d electrons, α, β, T and Tx is added to the Hamiltonian. A comparison of row 5 to row 2, where only the two-body effective-interaction is included, shows that the addition of three-body effective-interactions improves the approximation by a factor larger than two for the second spectra, and almost four for the third spectra. The calculation reported in row 6 is analogous to the one reported in row 4, except that the three-body parameter T was replaced by the three-body parameter Tx. Comparison of the mean errors definitely shows how much more important T is than Tx.

In table 2, a comparison of the effectiveness of our approximation for the d^n configuration and $d^{n-1}s$ configuration is reported. For that purpose, we repeated some of the calculations already reported in table 1. Every such least-squares calculation was performed twice; the first time when only the observed levels belonging to all of the d^n configurations were fitted to the calculated ones; and a second time when only the observed levels belonging to all of the $d^{n-1}s$ configurations were fitted to the calculated ones. Of course, in each case, the parameters of the configurations to which no observed levels were fitted were held fixed. The mean errors achieved for each calculation are given in the appropriate columns of table 2. In this

TABLE 2

Effective-interaction parameters included in the calculation	Fe II group Mean error for the obs. levels (cm^{-1})		Fe III group Mean error for the obs. levels (cm^{-1})	
	$3d^n$	$3d^{n-1}4s$	$3d^n$	$3d^{n-1}4s$
α	±223	±235	±233	±136
α, β, T	±126	± 75	± 59	± 60
α, β, T, Tx	± 92	± 60	± 35	± 47
Number of obs. levels	152	280	120	202

case, we obtained opposite results for the second spectra and third spectra: for the second spectra, the mean error of the $d^{n-1}s$ configurations is much smaller than the mean error of the d^n configurations; while in the third spectra, the fit between theory and experiment is much better for the d^n configurations. The result that we expected was the one that we obtained for the third spectra, since the set of effective-interactions which we used is a complete one for the description of a d^n configuration. For a $d^{n-1}s$ configuration, it also gives a complete description of the d^{n-1} core, but we still may have effective-interactions also including an s electron. This difference between the situations in the second and third spectra might be explained by the assumption that effective-interactions are a more efficient manner of representing the perturbations caused to the third spectra of the iron group than they are of those caused to the second spectra. This is a reasonable assumption in the light of the fact that in the third spectra, the perturbing configurations are certainly more distant than they are in the second spectra.

In order to complete the process of describing all the perturbations of the configurations of the type $(d+s)^n$ by far-lying perturbing configurations, one still has to consider that kind of effective interactions which also include s electrons. Since, the configuration ds consists of only two terms, it is fully described by the two Slater parameters $F_0(ds)$ and $G_2(ds)$. Hence, it is evident that no additional two-body effective-interactions with s electrons exist. On the other hand, three-body effective-interactions of such a kind are mathematically possible, and it is very easy to demonstrate that they can really appear in an actual physical Hamiltonian just by considering a possible actual perturbing configuration. By using group-theoretical methods, Feneuille[19]) was able to show that only five linearly independent three-body interaction operators can be added to the electrostatic Hamiltonian of a

$(d+s)^n$ configuration, assuming that all the two-body effective-interactions have already been added to it.

Since in our previous calculations as reported in row 5 of table 1, we already used the two-body effective-interactions represented by α and β, and the three-body interactions represented by T and Tx, we had to build three additional three-body operators. We did it in the following way: following Racah and Stein[20,11]), let us define $u_i^{(k)}$ and $y_i^{(2)}$, which are the one-electron tensorial operators of the order k acting on the coordinates of the ith electron, by their reduced matrices

$$(d \,\|u_i^{(k)}\|\, d) = 1\,, \qquad (d\,\|y_i^{(2)}\|\, s) = 1\,.$$

All the other elements of the reduced matrices are equal to zero. Now we can define the operators

$$U^{(k)} = \sum_i u_i^{(k)}\,, \qquad Y^{(2)} = \sum_i y_i^{(2)}\,.$$

By using the method developed in the above mentioned paper of Racah and Stein[11]), one can easily show that all of the second-order perturbations caused to the $(d+s)^n$ configurations can be represented by a zero-order product of such operators, or by suitable linear combinations of such products. We are not interested in products consisting of $U^{(k)}$'s only, since interactions between only d electrons are already completely described. Thus the operators representing new interactions may be of the forms

$$(U^{(k)} \times Y^{(2)} \times Y^{(2)\dagger})^{(0)} + \text{h.c.} \tag{1}$$

$$(U^{(k)} \times U^{(k')} \times Y^{(2)})^{(0)} + \text{h.c.} \tag{2}$$

$$(U^{(k)} \times Y^{(2)} \times Y^{(2)})^{(0)} + \text{h.c.} \tag{3}$$

The first of these operators acts within the configuration $d^{n-1}s$. The second one contributes to the interaction between d^n and $d^{n-1}s$ or between $d^{n-1}s$ and $d^{n-2}s^2$. The third contributes to the interaction between the configurations d^n and $d^{n-2}s^2$.

An appropriate set of operators of the above mentioned types can be chosen by considering the configuration $(d+s)^3$. A simple counting of the terms of the configuration d^2s and of the non-zero, non-diagonal elements connecting the configurations d^3 and ds^2 shows that we have exactly one independent three-body operator acting within d^2s, and one such operator connecting the configurations d^3 and ds^2. Thus the third independent operator must connect the configurations d^3 and d^2s. It turns out that we have to add to our Hamiltonian one operator of each of the above mentioned types. Since there are no more independent operators, it is unimportant if, in the formulas (1), (2) and (3), we set for k and k' the values 2 or 4. Thus we completed the definition of the operators by arbitrarily choosing for k and k' the value 2. Then we defined three parameters, Px, Py and Pz which are the coefficients of the above mentioned operators numbered as 1, 2 and 3, respectively. In principle, Px, Py and Pz are three additional correction-terms whose numerical values are determined by the usual least-squares calculation method.

In our previously described calculations on the third spectra of the iron group, we could not include even the actual electrostatic interaction between the configurations d^n and $d^{n-1}s$ since it was too weak to be defined by the least-squares calculation. Hence, there is no hope that a much smaller correction of this interaction, represented by the parameter Py, will have any detectable effect. Even in the second spectra of the iron group, where configuration interaction is considerable, it is nevertheless much weaker than the interactions represented by the "internal" parameters of each of the

TABLE 3

	Effective-interaction parameters used in the calculation	α, β, T, Tx	α, β, T, Tx, Px
		$\Delta(\text{cm}^{-1})$	$\Delta(\text{cm}^{-1})$
Second spectra of the iron group	$3d^n + 3d^{n-1}4s + 3d^{n-2}4s^2$: 479 obs. levels	± 86.9	± 84.8
	$3d^n$ only: 152 obs. levels	± 91.9	± 91.9
	$3d^{n-1}4s$ only: 280 obs. levels	± 56.3	± 53.9
Third spectra of the iron group	$3d^n + 3d^{n-1}4s$: 322 obs. levels	± 46.0	± 37.9
	$3d^n$ only: 120 obs. levels	± 35.0	± 35.0
	$3d^{n-1}4s$ only: 202 obs. levels	± 46.5	± 32.1

three configurations d^n, $d^{n-1}s$, and $d^{n-2}s^2$. Thus, it seemed reasonable to introduce first only the new effective-interaction parameter Px which "acts" within the configuration $d^{n-1}s$. In table 3, the results of its introduction are reported separately for the second and for the third spectra of the iron group. For each ionization, we report the total decrease of the mean error; and separately, the decrease of the mean error for the configurations $3d^n$ and $3d^{n-1}4s$. The results given in the first column are those achieved without the new effective-interaction and are thus equal to the 5th calculation reported in table 1. In the second column, we give the results which were obtained when the new effective-interaction parameter Px was included. Comparing the above mentioned columns of table 3, one can see that the addition of the new effective-interaction practically did not improve our approximation in the second spectra. For the third spectra, there is a considerable improvement which is due to a better fit between theory and experiment for the levels belong to the $3d^{n-1}4s$ configurations. For the third spectra, the final mean error for all the $3d^n$ configurations remained $\pm 35\ cm^{-1}$, while for the configurations $3d^{n-1}4s$, it decreased from $\pm 47\ cm^{-1}$ to $\pm 32\ cm^{-1}$, so that now the mean errors for both configurations are practically the same. The ineffectiveness of the new correction-term in the second spectra of the iron group was anticipated from the beginning, since the new correction can mainly improve the configurations of the type $d^{n-1}s$; and we have already pointed out, that in the second spectra of the iron group, our theory gave better results for these configurations than for the d^n configurations even before the new improvement was introduced.

I would like to remark that the effect of all the correction-terms except Px was also tried in the $(d+s)^n$ configurations of the palladium and platinum groups where they did not produce considerable improvements. It should be noted that before introducing the β, T, Tx and Px corrections, the mean errors achieved in some iso-ionized sequences of the palladium and platinum groups were generally smaller than those achieved in the iron group. But now, the situations are reversed. For the platinum group, we have experimental evidence that more perturbing configurations lie very close to the configurations of the type $(d+s)^n$, so that their perturbation cannot be represented by effective-interactions. I have the impression that a similar situation exists in the first and second spectra of the palladium and iron groups. Thus it seems that for the time being, there are no more meaningful effective-interaction correction terms to be added to $(d+s)^n$ configurations. It is impossible to make certain predictions of how the process of improving the theory should be continued. However, my personal feeling is that in most cases, the problem is to develop a method which will enable us to extend the energy matrices by including more interacting configurations in them. This task can not be undertaken by using only the classical Racah methods, since these additional configurations are either completely experimentally unknown or, at best, very few levels belonging to them have been observed. Thus it seems that one of the most interesting problems for the Racah school in theoretical spectroscopy, is to find a method which will enable it to synthesize the benefits of using the one hundred times more accurate semi-empirical method for the configurations which are sufficiently known experimentally with less accurate information for the configurations – which are experimentally unknown – which will have to be obtained by the use of some approximation method for the integration of the radial part of the Schrödinger equation. In the case of the third spectra of the iron group, it may be that the presently used Hamiltonian is already so well approximated that we can try to improve it by the addition of the weaker spin–spin and spin–other–orbit interactions.

Looking at tables 1, 2 and 3, and comparing them, we can see that, in general, the mean error – obtained when all the observed levels of any of the two sequences which we treated was fitted to the calculated levels – is larger than the weighted average of the mean errors obtained separately for the d^n and $d^{n-1}s$ configurations. There are various reasons for this fact:

a) In the complete calculation, each spectrum is given only one additive parameter, while the distances between the centers of the different configurations in that spectrum are determined by interpolation formulas. In the separate calculations, each configuration of every spectrum was given its own additive parameter. Thus, the total number of free parameters in the two separate calculations is larger than the number of free parameters in the complete calculation;

b) for the second spectra, we still have another effect which effectively increases the number of free parameters in the separate calculations. It is true that in a separate calculation, the "internal" parameters of the non-relevant configurations are held fixed; but naturally, the parameters of interaction between the three configurations of the same spectra remain free. The same procedure also applies for the configuration interaction parameters in the second type separate calculation. Thus, in the separate calculations, the same parameters can assume two different sets of optimal values, which they cannot do in the complete calculation;

c) in the second spectra of the iron group, in the complete calculation, we also include 47 levels belonging to the third configuration $3d^{n-2}4s^2$. The accuracy of these levels is generally much worse than the accuracy obtained for the levels of the two lower configurations. Thus, their inclusion in the complete calculation also increases the mean error. Naturally, these levels are not included in the separate calculations performed for each of the two lower configurations.

3. The odd configurations of the type $d^n p$

In principle, for a configuration of the type $d^n p$, two different groups of effective-interaction parameters are necessary:
a) all the effective-interactions which improve the description of the d^n core, and which are identical with the correction-terms fully described in the previous chapter;
b) effective-interactions between d and p electrons.

In his M.Sc. thesis [21]), A. Schwimmer, one of my students, made theoretical calculations on configurations of the type $d^n p$ in iso-electronic spectra in the iron group. He obtained good results for the above mentioned configurations in the third, fourth, fifth and sixth spectra. Since the number of observed parent-terms belonging to the d^n core was rather small (usually 4–6 such parent-terms for each configuration), he used only the parameters A, B, C, α and ζ_d for describing the interaction between the d electrons. In the first stage of these calculations, the d–p interaction was described only by the above mentioned Slater parameters F_2, G_1 and G_3 (F_0 is "absorbed" in the additive parameter A). The mean errors obtained for the various spectra were in the range between 100–200 cm^{-1}. We tried to improve the fit between theory and experiment by introducing into the Hamiltonian the above mentioned Sack corrections which, as we have already shown in the introduction, are two-body effective-interactions between d and p electrons. Contrary to the negative results of Sack [8]) and Spector [9]), in all of the 18 spectra calculated by us, the mean error was reduced by a factor of about three. Thus we were led to one of the following two possible conclusions:
a) that some perturbations which for the second spectra could not be represented successfully by effective-interactions were represented very successfully by such interactions for higher ionizations;
b) that the important perturbations of $d^n p$ configurations in highly ionized atoms are different from those which play the main role in the first and second spectra.

It is also worthwhile mentioning that in the Ph.D. thesis of C. Roth [22]) performed under the supervision of G. Racah, the β and T, as well as the

Sack corrections, were systematically tried in the configurations $d^n p$ and $d^{n-1}sp$ in the first and second spectra of the iron group. However, they did not cause any essential reduction of the mean errors. As in similar cases in the even configurations, already discussed in the previous chapter, here, too, the reason for this situation probably is the presence of perturbing configurations which are not sufficiently distant to be represented by effective interactions.

4. The physical significance of the effective-interaction parameters

Having completed the description of the present situation of the use of effective-interaction parameters in calculating spectra of transition elements, I would like to raise the question of how much physical significance one can attribute to such parameters. From an epistemological point of view, a positive answer to this question is almost self-evident. It is well known that the mean error is so defined that the statistical effect of adding accidental free parameters does not decrease it. Thus, the mere fact that the introduction of the new parameters caused an essential decrease of the mean error is a sufficient demonstration of the statement that *in some way* they represent a relevant physical interaction, and thus that they must have some kind of reality. However, when asking about the physical significance of a new effective-interaction parameter, we give this question a much more restricted meaning, i.e., is it possible to identify one or a small number of perturbing configurations the perturbations of which make the principle contribution to the numerical value of that parameter? If we could give a positive answer to this question, it might also help us to understand the large difference in the relative importance of some effective-interaction parameters (e.g. T and Tx). From the mathematical point of view, this question must not have a definite answer, since once you have a complete set of effective-interactions, you can use them to build up linear combinations which will also constitute such a complete set. However, the relative importance of the "members" of this new set may be entirely different. In spite of this mathematical consideration, it is interesting to point out that for some of the effective-interaction parameters, the uses of which were described in the previous chapters, at least a semi-quantitative positive answer to our question can be given.

For the explanation of the parameters α and β, the discussion was already presented in detail in a previous paper[15]) so that here we shall repeat it very briefly. Trees and Jørgensen[23]) tried to explain α and β as mainly representing the perturbation of a $3s^2 3p^6 3d^n$ configuration by the configuration $3s^2 3p^4 3d^{n+2}$, but the numerical values obtained for α and β in this way were considerably different from what were then believed to be the empirical values of these parameters. The introduction of the T correction caused an abrupt change of the empirical values of α and β, and in my above mentioned paper[15]), correct approximate values for these parameters were obtained by assuming that they mainly represent the perturbations caused by the two configurations $3s^2 3p^4 3d^{n+2}$ and $3s^0 3p^6 3d^{n+2}$.

The algebraic matrix of the parameter T was originally calculated[15]) by assuming that this parameter has to represent the second order perturbation of the configuration $3s^2 3p^6 3d^n$ by the configuration $3s3p^6 3d^{n+1}$. In order to represent this perturbation, the parameter T had to assume a negative value. In principle, it could also represent in the same way perturbations of a $3d^n$ configuration by configurations in which a 2s or 1s electron has jumped to a 3d state. However, these perturbations are no doubt negligible. It is true that a linear combination of T and some two-body interaction parameters can also fully represent the perturbation caused to a $3d^n$ configuration by any configuration of the type $3d^{n-1}n's$, but such a perturbation will contribute a positive number to the value of T. Since in all of our calculations, T is always negative, we may at least conclude that the most important contribution to the value of T comes from the perturbation caused to a $3s^2 3p^6 3d^n$ configuration by a $3s3p^6 3d^{n+1}$ configuration. In this connection, it is interesting to note that the addition of the parameter Tx did not appreciably change the values of the parameters α, β and T.

We may summarize this part of our discussion by stating that the main contributions to the values of the parameters α, β and T are from perturbations caused by configurations characterized by the same set of principle quantum numbers as the perturbed configuration $3s^2 3p^6 3d^n$. The fact that these parameters are larger for the third spectra than for the second spectra also supports this statement.

Now let us discuss in more detail the above mentioned parameters Λ and σ used by Schwimmer for $d^n p$ configurations in various spectra of the iron group. Studying their behavior along an iso-electronic sequence as functions of the atomic number, we find that Λ is fairly constant along the iso-electronic sequence, while σ starts with a zero-value on the left-hand side of the sequence and then increases monotonously. We may explain these facts by examining the main perturbations to a $3d^n 4p$ configuration as systematically described in fig. 1.

Fig. 1 gives a qualitative description of the relative position of these three configurations. We see that on the left, the main perturbation of $3d^n 4p$ is

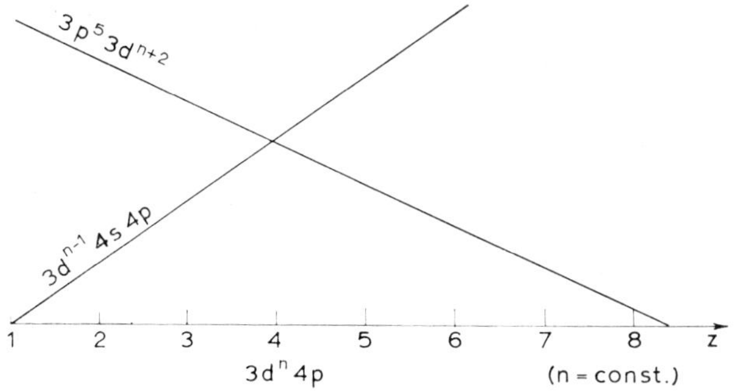

Fig. 1. Relative positions of the main perturbing configurations.

by $3d^{n-1}4s4p$, while on the right, the main perturbation is caused by $3p^5 3d^{n+2}$. We calculated the effective-interactions which represent these perturbations. It turned out that for their description they also need three-body operators, but we calculated only the two-body part of these effective-interactions. The result of this calculation was that the parameter Λ is necessary for the representation of both perturbations, while σ is only necessary for representing the perturbation caused by the configuration $3p^5 d^{n+2}$. When going from left to right, the contribution of $3d^{n-1}4s4p$ to Λ decreases, but the contribution of $3p^5 3d^{n+2}$ to it increases, and so we can have a qualitative understanding of why this parameter can be fairly constant. On the other hand, it is clear that σ should increase monotonously.

Now, it is possible for us to understand why the same corrections were not successful when used in the second spectra of the iron group[8–9]. For such a spectrum, the configuration $3p^5 3d^{n+2}$ is so high that its effect is negligible. On the other hand, the configuration $3d^{n-1}4s4p$ interacts very strongly with $3d^n 4p$. But in the second spectra, these two configurations are so close that their interaction can not be successfully represented by effective-interactions and must be taken into account by diagonalizing the energy matrix common to both configurations.

At the end of this discussion, I would just like to mention that actually even the Slater parameters, when their values are determined by the semi-empirical method, are also to some extent representing effective-interactions. Practically, for any actual far-lying perturbing configuration, one can calculate the contribution of its perturbation to the values of these Slater parameters. This fact may raise doubts as to whether these semi-empirical Slater parameters are actually functionals of an approximate effective central field in which the interacting electrons really move. It may be that some comfort can be drawn from the fact that in all of the various approximations mentioned or reported in our present paper, the changes in the values assumed by any of the Slater parameters used by us never exceeded 10% of their values, and in most cases, this change was even much smaller.

The effective-interactions as we tried to summarize their use in the present paper are a tool for summing up the infinite series of the second-order perturbation theory. For a given Hamiltonian, this tool has two weaknesses:
a) it ignores higher order perturbation terms;
b) it assumes a constant difference between the levels of the perturbing configuration and the levels of the perturbed one, which is a good assumption only if the perturbing configuration lies sufficiently far away.

Both above mentioned weaknesses can be overcome by including more configurations in that part of the matrix which is exactly diagonalized. In this way, effective-interactions will have to represent only perturbations by configurations which lie at such a distance that the assumption that it is the same for all levels is a very good one. Naturally, the same assumption also completely justifies the neglect of higher order perturbations. It seems that for the transition elements, we have more or less come to the point where the possibility of pushing on with the use of effective-interactions is exhausted until other ways of improving the approximations are used. Of course, there is always a possibility that we may arrive at a situation where a more accurate Hamiltonian is necessary.

References

1) G. Racah, Phys. Rev. **85**, 381 (1952).
2) G. Racah, Rydberg Centennial Conference, Acta Univ. Lund **50**, 31 (1955).
3) G. Racah and Y. Shadmi, Phys. Rev. **119**, 156 (1960).
4) G. Racah, J. Quant. Spectry. Radiative Transfer **4**, 617 (1964).
5) R. F. Bacher and S. A. Goudsmit, Phys. Rev. **46**, 948 (1934).
6) R. E. Trees, Phys. Rev. **83**, 756 (1951).
7) R. E. Trees, Phys. Rev. **84**, 1089 (1951).
8) N. Sack, Phys. Rev. **102**, 1302 (1956).
9) G. Racah and N. Spector, Bull. Res. Council Israel **9F**, 75 (1960).
10) K. Rajnak and B. G. Wybourne, Phys. Rev. **132**, 280 (1963).
11) G. Racah and J. Stein, Phys. Rev. **156**, 58 (1967).
12) B. R. Judd, Physica **33**, 174 (1967).
13) S. Feneuille, Compt. Rend. (Paris) **262**, 23 (1966).
14) G. Racah, Phys. Rev. **63**, 367 (1943).
15) Y. Shadmi, Phys. Rev. **139**, A43 (1965).
16) Y. Shadmi, J. Oreg and J. Stein, to be published in J. Opt. Soc. Am.
17) G. Racah and Y. Shadmi, Bull. Res. Council Israel **8F**, 15 (1959).

18) Y. Shadmi, Bull. Res. Council Israel **10F**, 109 (1962).
19) S. Feneuille, Ph.D. Thesis, Laboratoire Aimé Cotton, Orsay (1967).
20) G. Racah, Phys. Rev. **62**, 438 (1942).
21) A. Schwimmer, M.Sc. Thesis, The Hebrew University of Jerusalem (1966).
22) C. Roth, Ph.D. Thesis, The Hebrew University of Jerusalem (1967).
23) R. E. Trees and C. K. Jørgensen, Phys. Rev. **123**, 1278 (1961).

Spectroscopic and group theoretical methods in physics
© *North-Holland Publ. Co., Amsterdam, 1968*

THE RANDOM PHASE APPROXIMATION AND THE SEPARATION OF COLLECTIVE DEGREES OF FREEDOM

ISSACHAR UNNA
Department of Theoretical Physics,
The Hebrew University,
Jerusalem, Israel

1. Introduction

An interesting property of the random phase approximation (RPA) has been pointed out by Thouless and Valatin[1]) some years ago. It is the fact that in the RPA it is easy and straightforward to separate out explicitly any desired degree of freedom. This is, of course, of major importance for degrees of freedom which have some special physical significance. One example is the number degree of freedom in the Bardeen–Cooper–Schrieffer (BCS) treatment of pairing correlations. The separation of the number degree of freedom enables one to eliminate, in the RPA, all those spurious states arising from the variations of the particle number in the BCS method[2]). Another example is the center of mass degree of freedom. The usual shell model Hamiltonian gives rise to excited states which differ from other states only by their different center of mass motion. Of physical interest are only those states corresponding to center of mass in rest. Thus, again, in the frame of the RPA, it is possible to eliminate those spurious states corresponding to excited center of mass motions. Here, however, it is not always possible to eliminate the spurious states completely even in the RPA. This is not a limitation of the method discussed here but rather a basic fact that such an elimination is in general impossible for a Hamiltonian which is not translation invariant[3]). The above two examples were pertaining to degrees of freedom the special significance of which was their being *non-physical*. They had to be eliminated in order to recover the purely physical degrees of freedom of the system.

Even more spectacular may be the application of the method to the separation of collective degrees of freedom such as giant dipole vibrations, quadrupole vibrations, rotations [4]), etc.

The purpose of this note is to outline in generalized form the procedure by which any desired degrees of freedom can be eliminated in the RPA. We shall briefly describe the approximations involved and point out the basic limitations of the procedure having to do with the given form of the Hamiltonian in every case.

2. The random phase approximation

For our purpose, it is most convenient to look upon the random phase approximation as the quasi-boson approximation [5]). For the sake of notations let us review it here briefly. In the following, we shall restrict ourselves to potentials with spherical symmetry. Generalization to other cases is straightforward [4]).

We have a Hamiltonian

$$\mathscr{H} = \sum_{\nu} \varepsilon_\nu a_\nu^\dagger a_\nu + \sum_{\alpha\beta\gamma\delta} v_{\alpha\beta\gamma\delta}\, a_\alpha^\dagger a_\beta^\dagger a_\delta a_\gamma\,, \tag{1}$$

where ε_ν are Hartree–Fock energies, $a_\nu^\dagger$ create the corresponding single particle H–F states and the second term represents additional residual interactions. The Greek letters $\nu, \alpha, \beta, \gamma, \delta$ stand for complete sets of single particle quantum numbers each (say, $n_\alpha\, l_\alpha\, j_\alpha\, m_\alpha\, m_{\tau_\alpha}$)*. Pairing correlations are most easily taken care of (in the Hartree–Fock–Bogoliubov sense [6])) by applying the transformation

$$a_{\nu\, m_\nu} = u_\nu \alpha_{\nu\, m_\nu} + (-1)^{j_\nu - m_\nu} v_\nu \alpha^\dagger_{\nu\, -m_\nu}, \qquad u_\nu^2 + v_\nu^2 = 1\,, \tag{2}$$

where $\alpha^\dagger, \alpha$ are known as the quasi-particle creation and annihilation operators.

The Hamiltonian can now be expressed in terms of quasi-particle pair operators defined by eq. (3)**:

$$\begin{aligned} A_{JM}(\nu\mu) &\equiv \sum_{m_\nu m_\mu} C(j_\nu j_\mu J;\, m_\nu m_\mu M)\, \alpha_{\mu\, m_\mu} \alpha_{\nu\, m_\nu}\,, \\ B_{JM}(\nu\mu) &\equiv \sum_{m_\nu m_\mu} (-1)^{j_\mu - m_\mu} C(j_\nu j_\mu J;\, m_\nu - m_\mu M)\, \alpha^\dagger_{\mu\, m_\mu} \alpha_{\nu\, m_\nu}\,. \end{aligned} \tag{3}$$

* Sometimes, the same notation will be used for the quantum numbers ($n_\alpha l_\alpha j_\alpha$) as will be clear from the context.

** We follow the notation of ref. 7.

The Hamiltonian will take the form

$$\mathscr{H} = C + \sum_{\nu} d_{\nu} [A^{\dagger}_{00}(\nu\nu) + A_{00}(\nu\nu)] + \sum_{\nu} E_{\nu}(2j_{\nu}+1)^{\frac{1}{2}} B_{00}(\nu\nu) + \\ + \sum_{\substack{\nu\mu \\ \nu'\mu' \\ JM}} \{e^{J}_{\nu\mu\nu'\mu'} A^{\dagger}_{JM}(\nu\mu) A_{JM}(\nu'\mu') + f^{J}_{\nu\mu\nu'\mu'}(-1)^{M} A^{\dagger}_{JM}(\nu\mu) A^{\dagger}_{J-M}(\nu'\mu') + \\ + g^{J}_{\nu\mu\nu'\mu'} A^{\dagger}_{JM}(\nu\mu) B_{JM}(\nu'\mu') + h^{J}_{\nu\mu\nu'\mu'} B^{\dagger}_{JM}(\nu\mu) B_{JM}(\nu'\mu') + \\ + \text{Hermitian conjugates}\}, \tag{4}$$

where C, d_{ν}, E_{ν}, $e^{J}_{\nu\mu\nu'\mu'}$, $f^{J}_{\nu\mu\nu'\mu'}$, $g^{J}_{\nu\mu\nu'\mu'}$, $h^{J}_{\nu\mu\nu'\mu'}$ are constant coefficients.

The quasi-boson approximation consists of replacing the pair operators $A, A^{\dagger}$ by new operators $\boldsymbol{A}, \boldsymbol{A}^{\dagger}$, respectively, which satisfy exact boson commutation relations

$$[\boldsymbol{A}_{JM}(\nu\mu), \boldsymbol{A}^{\dagger}_{J'M'}(\nu'\mu')] = \delta_{JJ'}\delta_{MM'}\{\delta_{\nu\nu'}\delta_{\mu\mu'} + (-1)^{j_{\nu}-j_{\mu}+J}\delta_{\nu\mu'}\delta_{\nu'\mu}\}. \tag{5}$$

Terms containing B (or $B^{\dagger}$) operators are neglected with the exception of the linear term, which appears in $\mathscr{H}$ multiplied by a relatively big factor. In the linear term one replaces

$$B_{00}(\nu\nu) = \frac{1}{\sqrt{(2j_{\nu}+1)}} \sum_{\substack{\mu \\ JM}} \mathbf{A}^{\dagger}_{JM}(\nu\mu)\,\mathbf{A}_{JM}(\nu\mu). \tag{6}$$

In recent years it has been stated[7]) that these replacements may be interpreted as a small oscillations approximation, corresponding to the lowest order of an expansion in $(n/\Omega)^{\frac{1}{2}}$, where n is the average number of quasi-particles in the ground state and Ω the number of available quasi-particle states. Such an expansion, if valid, might provide us with a procedure to calculate higher order corrections to the RPA as well as to enable an extension of separation method to be described in the next section.

3. Separation of collective degrees of freedom

Let us denote the collective degree of freedom, to be considered, by $Q^{(k)}_{m}$. This may be a scalar degree of freedom ($k=0$) like $(\hat{N}-\langle\hat{N}\rangle)$ the operator of the particle number deviation. It may be a vector degree of freedom ($k=1$) like

$$\boldsymbol{R} = \sum_{i=1}^{N} r_i \boldsymbol{Y}_1(\theta_i\phi_i),$$

the center of mass coordinate. It may be a tensor degree of freedom like

$$\sum_{i=1}^{N} r_i^2\, Y_{2\mu}(\theta_i \phi_i)\,.$$

It could also be the Euler angles of a symmetry axis, or include tensor properties in spin and isospin space, etc.

In the quasi-boson approximation any single particle operator can be expressed as a linear combination of quasi-boson operators $A_{JM}(\nu\mu)$, $A^{\dagger}_{JM}(\nu\mu)$. This is true, in particular, for any such collective operator

$$Q_m^{(k)} = \sum_{i=1}^{N} q_m^{(k)}(i)\,,$$

$$Q_m^{(k)} = \sum_{\nu\mu} \langle \nu | q_m^{(k)} | \mu \rangle\, a_\nu^{\dagger} a_\mu\,. \tag{7}$$

If $Q_m^{(k)}$ is a Hermitian operator, it takes the following form in terms of the quasi-boson operators

$$Q_m^{(k)} = \sum_{\nu\mu} \left[q_{\nu\mu}^{(k)}\, \mathbf{A}^{\dagger}_{km}(\nu\mu) + q_{\nu\mu}^{(k)*} (-1)^m\, \mathbf{A}_{k-m}(\nu\mu) \right], \tag{8}$$

where

$$q_{\nu\mu}^{(k)} \equiv (2k+1)^{-\frac{1}{2}} \left(j_\nu \| q^{(k)} \| j_\mu \right) u_\nu v_\mu\,. \tag{9}$$

It is convenient to write the canonical conjugate operator $P_m^{(k)}$ as

$$P_m^{(k)} = \mathrm{i} \sum_{\nu\mu} \left[p_{\nu\mu}^{(k)}\, \mathbf{A}^{\dagger}_{k\,m}(\nu\mu) - p_{\nu\mu}^{(k)*} (-1)^m\, \mathbf{A}_{k-m}(\nu\mu) \right], \tag{10}$$

with $\mathrm{i}p_{\nu\mu}^{(k)}$ defined analogously to eq. (9). The q's and p's satisfy the condition

$$\sum_{\nu\mu} \left[q_{\nu\mu}^{(k)*} p_{\nu\mu}^{(k)} + q_{\nu\mu}^{(k)} p_{\nu\mu}^{(k)*} \right] = 1\,. \tag{11}$$

Eqs. (10) and (11) can, indeed, serve as *defining* equations for the conjugate momentum. This is of importance for scalar operators $Q_0^{(0)}$ (e.g. the number deviation). No single particle operator exists which can be identified with $P_0^{(0)}$. Still, eqs. (10) and (11) enable one to define formally such an operator.

For practical purposes, the sums in eqs. (8) and (10) can be considered to have a finite (and usually small) number of terms. Of all states ν, μ, the energies of which are far removed from the Fermi level only those contribute to this sum for which ε_μ is far below and ε_ν far above the Fermi level. However, for such states the reduced matrx elements $(j_\nu \| q^{(k)} \| j_\mu)$, $(j_\nu \| p^{(k)} \| j_\mu)$ become very small due to the small overlap between the wave functions. For the special case $k=0$ (e.g. the number deviation operator) only states ν for which $u_\nu v_\nu \neq 0$, that is, states near the Fermi level, contribute.

The finiteness of the sums (8) and (10) together with the simple boson commutation relations satisfied by A, $A^\dagger$ (eq. (5)) can now be utilized in the following way. We construct a complete set of operators $Q_m^{(k)}(j), P_m^{(k)}(j)$ which replaces the original set of operators $A_{km}(\nu\mu)\, A_{km}^\dagger(\nu\mu)$. The new set of operators is built in such a way that one of them, say $Q_m^{(k)}$ (1), is identified with the operator $Q_m^{(k)}$ (eq. 8)). This, of course, represents the degree of freedom which is of special interest to us. The operators $(-1)^m P_{-m}^{(k)}(j)$ are taken to be the canonical conjugate momenta to $Q_m^{(k)}(j)$

$$[Q_m^{(k)}(j), (-1)^m P_{-m}^{(k)}(j)] = \mathrm{i}\,. \tag{12}$$

One defines the operators in such a way that operators corresponding to different modes of motion commute with each other. Thus, the new set of operators has the following commutation relations

$$[Q_m^{(k)}(j), Q_{m'}^{(k')}(j')] = [P_m^{(k)}(j), P_{m'}^{(k')}(j')] = 0\,, \tag{13}$$

$$[Q_m^{(k)}(j), P_{m'}^{(k')}(j')] = \mathrm{i}(-1)^m\, \delta_{jj'}\, \delta_{kk'}\, \delta_{m,\,-m'}\,, \tag{14}$$

These relations lead directly to equations for the coefficients $q_{\nu\mu}^{(k)}(j), p_{\nu\mu}^{(k)}(j)$ (see eqs. (5), (8) and (10)):

$$\sum_{\nu\mu} [q_{\nu\mu}^{(k)*}(j)\, q_{\nu\mu}^{(k)}(j') - q_{\nu\mu}^{(k)}(j)\, q_{\nu\mu}^{(k)*}(j')] =$$

$$= \sum_{\nu\mu} [p_{\nu\mu}^{(k)*}(j)\, p_{\nu\mu}^{(k)}(j') - p_{\nu\mu}^{(k)}(j)\, p_{\nu\mu}^{(k)*}(j')] = 0\,, \tag{15}$$

$$\sum_{\nu\mu} [q_{\nu\mu}^{(k)*}(j)\, p_{\nu\mu}^{(k)}(j') + q_{\nu\mu}^{(k)}(j)\, p_{\nu\mu}^{(k)*}(j')] = \delta_{jj'}\,. \tag{16}$$

The canonical transformation just described can be inverted to give

$$\mathbf{A}_{k\,m}(\nu\mu) = \sum_j [p_{\nu\mu}^{(k)}(j)(-1)^m Q_{-m}^{(k)}(j) + \mathrm{i}q_{\nu\mu}^{(k)}(j)(-1)^m P_{-m}^{(k)}(j)]\,, \tag{17}$$

$$\mathbf{A}_{k\,m}^\dagger(\nu\mu) = \sum_j [p_{\nu\mu}^{(k)*}(j)\, Q_m^{(k)}(j) - \mathrm{i}q_{\nu\mu}^{(k)*}(j)\, P_m^{(k)}(j)]\,. \tag{18}$$

Expressions (17) and (18) are now inserted into the RPA Hamiltonian (see eq. (4) with subsequent discussion).

The term linear in A and $A^\dagger$ takes now the form

$$\sum_i [s_i Q_0^{(0)}(i) + t_i P_0^{(0)}(i)]\,.$$

Here, s_i, t_i are real coefficients. The physical part of this term should vanish in order to make the BCS ground state stationary with respect to small physical variations. There is however no sense in making the state stationary with respect to non physical variations such as variations in the number of particles. Setting $Q_0^{(0)}(1) \equiv (\hat{N} - N)$, where N is the number of particles in the system treated, we find that $P_0^{(0)}(1)$ does not appear in the linear term. Therefore, the requirements $s_i = t_i = 0$ for $i = 2, 3, \ldots$ together with $\langle 0 | (\hat{N} - N) | 0 \rangle = 0$ provide the correct solution to the BCS problem. The bilinear terms of the Hamiltonian take the simple form

$$\sum_{\substack{jj' \\ km}} [x_{jj'}^{(k)} (-1)^m P_m^{(k)}(j) P_{-m}^{(k)}(j') + y_{jj'}^{(k)} (-1)^m Q_m^{(k)}(j) Q_{-m}^{(k)}(j')] . \tag{19}$$

We see that in general there is coupling between the various modes of motion j, j', etc. In particular the special mode $k = k_0$, $j = 1$ is, in general, coupled to other modes, $j \neq 1$. This coupling can of course not be avoided. One should rather look for a Hamiltonian in which this coupling is small or zero.

In the usual RPA one deliberately looks for the *normal modes* of motion, $Q_m^{(k)}(j)$, $P_m^{(k)}(j)$, so that the interesting part of the Hamiltonian takes the form

$$\sum_{\substack{j \\ km}} \left[\frac{1}{2B_j} (-1)^m P_m^{(k)}(j) P_{-m}^{(k)}(j) + \frac{C_j}{2} (-1)^m Q_m^{(k)}(j) Q_{-m}^{(k)}(j) \right] . \tag{20}$$

Some of these normal modes are usually of special interest, having collective nature. These modes correspond to excitations with especially low or especially high energies. Modes which can always be considered as normal modes are those corresponding to zero excitation energies, namely, the constants of motion. Whenever a certain operator, say $\boldsymbol{P}^{(k_0)}(1)$, is a constant of motion the Hamiltonian can be brought into the form

$$\frac{1}{2B} [\boldsymbol{P}^{(k_0)}(1)]^2 + \sum_{\substack{j, j' \geq 2 \\ km}} (\text{expressions of the form (19)}) . \tag{21}$$

In this case the procedure outlined in the present paper provides a direct method for the calculation of the inertial parameter B. Examples are the total momentum in calculations for nuclear matter, the total angular momentum in non-spherical H–F fields and the number deviation in BCS calculations. In the latter case our procedure leads to the exact term $\lambda' (\hat{N} - N)^2$ which has to be subtracted from the Hamiltonian in addition to the usual $\lambda(\hat{N} - N)$ in order to get spuriousity-free results in the RPA.

When the degrees of freedom which are of special interest are not normal modes of motion, it may still be worthwhile to calculate explicitly the form

(19) of the RPA Hamiltonian. This makes it possible to check whether terms coupling these degrees of freedom to others are small, and approximate separation is still possible[3]).

References

1) D. J. Thouless and J. G. Valatin, Nucl. Phys. **31**, 211 (1962).
2) I. Unna and J. Wenesser, Phys. Rev. **137**, B1455 (1965).
3) H. Nissimov and I. Unna, to be published (1968).
4) J. N. Ginocchio and J. Weneser, Isospin invariance and the pairing force problem, to be published in Phys. Rev.; also E. Marshalek and J. Weneser, Private communication.
5) V. Gillet, in: *Proc. Intern. School Phys. "Enrico Fermi"*, Course XXXVI (1965) (Academic Press, New York, 1967).
6) F. Villars, in: *Proc. Intern. School Phys. "Enrico Fermi"*, Course XXIII (1961) (Academic Press, New York, 1963).
7) S. T. Beliaev and V. G. Zelevinsky, Nucl. Phys. **39**, 582 (1962).

Spectroscopic and group theoretical methods in physics
© *North-Holland Publ. Co., Amsterdam, 1968*

PROPERTIES AND METHODS OF INTERPRETATION OF RARE-EARTH SPECTRA

Z. B. GOLDSCHMIDT
Department of Theoretical Physics, The Hebrew University, Jerusalem, Israel

1. The characteristic structure of rare earth spectra

The rare-earth spectra, especially in low ionizations, are characterized by a high abundance of spectral lines and a high density of energy levels, both even and odd, in which no apparent regularity, such as a multiplet structure, may be discerned. Consequently these spectra are classified as "very complex", and their successful interpretation has only recently been accomplished.

The extreme complexity of these spectra is attributable to two factors, for which a shorthand notation will be introduced:

1) Competition between configurations;
2) Competition between interactions.

1.1. Competition between configurations

By this term we refer to the accumulation of many configurations, both even and odd, at about the same height, thus leading to a high density of energy levels. This competition is due to the well known fact that in the rare-earth spectra the binding energies of the 4f, 5d, 6s and 6p electrons are roughly equal. It may therefore be regarded as the manifestation of a basic *competition between electrons* in these spectra. In order to describe the structure of the rare-earth spectra in terms of the competition between configurations or between electrons, let us assign to each rare-earth, characterized by its atomic number Z, an ordinal number.

$$N = Z - 57\,,$$

that is, $N=0$ for lanthanum ($Z=57$), $N=1$ for cerium ($Z=58$), etc. In this way, the number of electrons outside closed shells will be $N+K$, where K equals 3, 2, 1 or 0 for first, second, third, or fourth spectra respectively.

1.1.1. *First and second spectra*

The characteristic structure of the first and second rare-earth spectra is given in fig. 1. Each spectrum consists of two systems of configurations A and B based on the scores $4f^N$ and $4f^{N+1}$ respectively, where N is the ordinal number defined above. Each system comprises one group of low configurations and two groups of high ones, the parity of the high configurations being opposite to that of the low ones

System A

low – parity of N

$$4f^N(5d+6s)^K \equiv 4f^N5d^K + 4f^N5d^{K-1}6s + 4f^N5d^{K-2}6s^2$$

high I – parity of $N+1$

$$4f^N(5d+6s)^{K-1}6p \equiv 4f^N5d^{K-1}6p + 4f^N5d^{K-2}6s\,6p + 4f^N5d^{K-3}6s^2\,6p$$

high II – parity of $N+1$

$$4f^{N-1}(5d+6s)^{K+1} \equiv 4f^{N-1}5d^{K+1} + 4f^{N-1}5d^K6s + 4f^{N-1}5d^{K-1}6s^2$$

System B

low – parity of $N+1$

$$4f^{N+1}(5d+6s)^{K-1} \equiv 4f^{N+1}5d^{K-1} + 4f^{N+1}5d^{K-2}6s + 4f^{N+1}5d^{K-3}6s^2$$

high I – parity of N

$$4f^{N+1}(5d+6s)^{K-2}6p \equiv 4f^{N+1}5d^{K-2}6p + 4f^{N+1}5d^{K-3}6s\,6p + 4f^{N+1}5d^{K-4}6s^2\,6p$$

high II – parity of N

$$4f^{N+2}(5d+6s)^{K-2} \equiv 4f^{N+2}5d^{K-2} + 4f^{N+2}5d^{K-3}6s + 4f^{N+2}5d^{K-4}6s^2$$

The following facts should be noted:

1) In each system all configurations of the same parity overlap or are close to each other.

2) In each system there exist spectral transitions in the optical region between *high* and *low* configurations. Since the optical transitions which connect the two systems are very few (see next paragraph), each of the systems effectively generates a separate spectrum. The overlap of these two spectra is one of the reasons for the abundance of lines in rare-earth spectra.

3) The low configurations of the systems A and B lie at about the same height, and since they have opposite parities, there exist spectral transitions

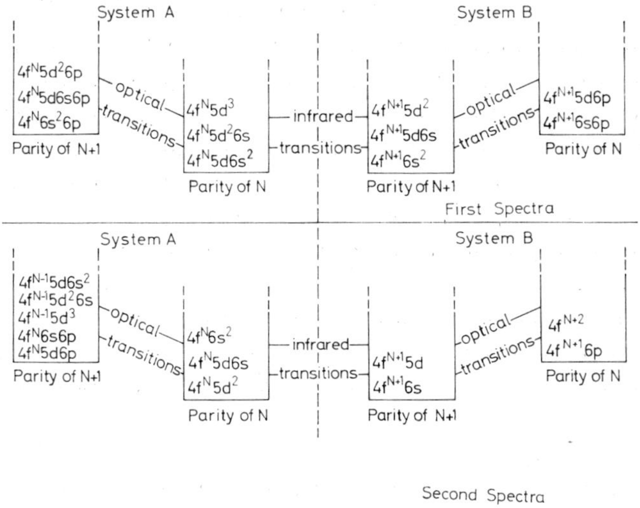

Fig. 1. Characteristic structure of first and second rare-earth spectra.

between them in the infra-red region. The same also holds for the high configurations of A and B. These transitions, which are usually difficult to detect, are very important for determining the relative height of the two systems, and, in particular, for establishing the system which contains the ground level of the ion under investigation.

4) The three competing configurations in each of the six groups "low A", "high I-A", "high II-A", "low B", "high I-B" and "high II-B", are obtained from each other by interchanging 5d and 6s electrons. The overlap of the configurations in each group demonstrates *the competition between the* 5d *and* 6s *electrons.*

5) The group of "low A" configurations is obtained from the group "low B" by replacing a 4f by a 5d electron. The same applies to the groups "high I-A" and "high I-B". Since the low as well as the high I configurations of the two systems lie at about the same height, we deduce *the competition* 4f–5d, 6s. This competition leads to the existence of two stable cores $4f^N$ and $4f^{N+1}$, in such a way that the lowest configurations of the groups $4f^N(5d+6s)^K$ and $4f^{N+1}(5d+6s)^{K-1}$ compete for the title "ground configuration" of the ion. On the other hand, a configuration obtained from $4f^N(5d+6s)^K$ by replacing an additional 4f electron by a 5d or 6s electron is an excited configuration. The same applies to $4f^{N+1}(5d+6s)^{K-1}$ when one of its 5d or 6s electrons is replaced by a 4f electron.

6) The groups of configurations "high I-A" and "high II-A" overlap. This shows that an excitation of a 4f electron from the $4f^N$ core into a 5d or 6s state is energetically equivalent to an excitation of an electron 5d or 6s into 6p. The two groups of configurations differ in the two electrons 4f6p compared with $(5d+6s)^2 \equiv 5d^2+5d6s+6s^2$. We can summarize this situation by stating that *in the high configurations of system* A *there exists a competition between the pairs of electrons* 4f6p, $5d^2$, 5d6s *and* $6s^2$.

7) The groups of configurations "high I-B" and "high II-B" overlap. This shows than an excitation of an electron from a 5d or 6s state into 6p is energetically equivalent to its excitation from the same initial state into a 4f state, thus transforming the $4f^{N+1}$ core into $4f^{N+2}$. *In the high configurations of the system* B *there exists a competition between* 4f *and* 6p *electrons.*

1.1.2. *Third and fourth spectra*

The characteristic structure of the third and fourth spectra is shown in fig. 2. In the third spectra the system A comprises, as before, three groups of configurations

$$\text{System A} \left\{ \begin{array}{ll} \text{low} & 4f^N(5d+6s) \\ \text{high I} & 4f^N 6p \\ \text{high II} & 4f^{N-1}(5d+6s)^2 \end{array} \right\} (K=1)\,.$$

The competitions described above between the separate configurations of the "low A" group on the one hand and between those of the "high A" groups

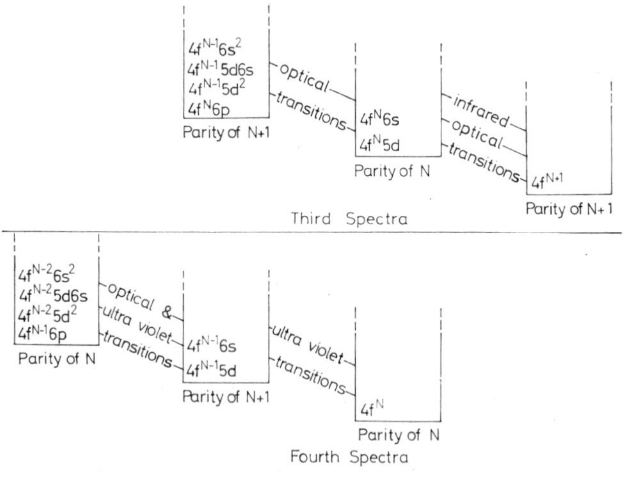

Fig. 2. Characteristic structure of third and fourth rare-earth spectra.

on the other hand, exist also here, although a stabilization of the 5d shell with respect to the 6s is recognized.

The system B degenerates, in the third spectra, into the single configuration $4f^{N+1}$.

Contrary to the situation in the first and second spectra, where the lowest configurations of the A and B systems compete for the title ground configuration, the configuration $4f^{N+1}$ ("low B") in the third spectra is *lower* than $4f^{N}(5d+6s)$ ("low A") by such an amount that most of the transitions between them fall in the optical region*. We can therefore conclude that in the third spectra the two systems A and B have degenerated into one system consisting of three stories with optical transitions between the first and second stories as well as between the second and third ones.

The above mentioned structural differences between the third spectra and those belonging to lower degrees of ionization may be explained as follows: On raising the degree of ionization, the effective charge seen by the electrons outside closed shells increases; this increase is greatest for the internal 4f electrons, smaller for the "half internal" 5d electrons, and smallest for the outer 6s electrons. Consequently in the third spectra the binding energies of these electrons satisfy the inequalities

$$\mathscr{E}_{4f} < \mathscr{E}_{5d} < \mathscr{E}_{6s}\,.$$

In the fourth spectra the system B does not exist at all. The system A has degenerated into two groups of configurations: "low", $4f^{N}$, which forms the ground configuration in each of these spectra, and "high II", $4f^{N-1}(5d+6s)$. These groups constitute the first and second stories of the fourth spectra respectively. A third story comprises the two additional groups of configurations $4f^{N-1}6p$ and $4f^{N-2}(5d+6s)^2$. These three stories are analogous to those of the third spectra with the difference that here $N-1$ takes the place of N in the third spectra. The separations of the stories are greater in the fourth spectra, which indicates a further stabilization of the 4f and 5d shells.

1.1.3. *Configuration interaction* (CI)

The competition between configurations in the rare-earth spectra results is strong interactions between them. Consequently the energy level problem cannot be treated configuration by configuration, but electrostatic interaction *between* configurations must be included in the calculations in ad-

* Gd III, in which $4f^7 5d$ and not $4f^8$ is the ground configuration, forms an exception to this rule, since the half filled shell $4f^7$ is especially stable.

dition to the electrostatic and spin–orbit interactions *within* the configurations. The experience gained in the course of this work shows that CI between *all* configurations of the same parity should be included in the theoretical calculations and it cannot be limited to one system only. For complex configurations this entails the construction of very large matrices and the evaluation of a large number of radial integrals, also referred to as parameters, which represent the various interactions.

1.2. Competition between interactions

The relative strengths of the various interactions determine the special characteristics of the spectrum under consideration, such as the structure of the energy level scheme, the composition of the eigenstates, the values of the g-factors, intensities, and selection rules. In particular, the existence of a coupling depends on some of the interactions being much stronger than the remaining ones. It is a characteristic property of many-earth spectra, that a large number of interactions, CI included, are of the same order of magnitude. In such cases it may become impossible to define a coupling and/or to characterize the levels according to configuration quantum numbers. This is referred to as "competition between interactions". This competition explains the lack of apparent regularity in the energy level structure, and the breakdown of the selection rules for the spectral transitions; this is an additional reason for the extreme richness in spectral lines of rare-earth spectra.

1.2.1. *Classification of the various interactions*

For each spectrum under investigation, and for each parity, a table containing the parameters representing the various interactions within and between configurations should be constructed. As an example tables 1 and 2 are given, which contain the electrostatic parameters of the odd and even configurations of Ce II ($N=1$, $K=2$) respectively. The following parameters are used: The internal parameters of each configuration are the usual Slater parameters renormalized by Condon and Shortley[1]). For equivalent electrons the linear combinations E^i and A, B, C of Slater parameters defined by Racah[2,3]) are used. The spin–orbit parameters ζ_{nl}, not included in the tables, are also those defined by Condon and Shortley[1]). The parameters which represent CI are again Slater parameters normalized so as to eliminate all denominators from two-particle matrix elements. They are defined as follows:

$$H = \frac{R^2(\mathrm{dd}, \mathrm{ds})}{35},$$

$$J = \frac{R^2(\mathrm{dp, sp})}{5}, \qquad K = \frac{R^1(\mathrm{dp, ps})}{3},$$

$$L_2 = \frac{R^2(\mathrm{ff, fp})}{525}, \qquad L_4 = \frac{R^4(\mathrm{ff, fp})}{693},$$

$$M = \frac{R^2(\mathrm{fd, fs})}{15}, \qquad N = \frac{R^3(\mathrm{fd, sf})}{21} = \frac{R^3(\mathrm{ff, ds})}{21},$$

$$R_1 = \frac{R^1(\mathrm{fp, dd})}{35} = \frac{R^1(\mathrm{fd, dp})}{35}, \qquad R_3 = \frac{R^3(\mathrm{fp, dd})}{735} = \frac{R^3(\mathrm{fd, dp})}{735},$$

$$R_2 = \frac{R^2(\mathrm{fd, pd})}{245}, \qquad R_4 = \frac{R^4(\mathrm{fd, pd})}{441},$$

$$T_1 = \frac{R^1(\mathrm{fp, ds})}{5} = \frac{R^1(\mathrm{fs, dp})}{5}, \qquad T_3 = \frac{R^3(\mathrm{fp, sd})}{35} = \frac{R^3(\mathrm{fd, sp})}{35},$$

$$T_2 = \frac{R^2(\mathrm{fs, pd})}{35} = \frac{R^2(\mathrm{fd, ps})}{35}.$$

In the $4f^n$ configurations effective two-body interactions are included, which represent, to second-order of perturbation theory, the electrostatic CI with distant configurations differing from $4f^n$ in the quantum numbers of two electrons[4–6]. These interactions are represented in the Hamiltonian by

$$L(L+1)\,\alpha + Q\beta + 12g(U)\,\gamma,$$

where Q is the seniority operator defined by Racah[7]) and $g(U)$ are the eigenvalues of the Casimir operator of the special group G_2. In configurations containing 4f and 5d electrons, effective two-body interactions represented by $(l_f, l_d)\cdot El + (s_f, s_d)\cdot Es$ are included[8]).

It is interesting to point out the correspondence between the various CI parameters and the competitions between electrons mentioned in section 1.1.1 above.

1) The competition between the 5d and 6s electrons. This involves the parameters H(dd, ds), G_2(dd, ss), M(fd, fs), N(fd, sf), J(dp, sp), K(dp, ps).
2) The competition 4f–5d, 6s involves G_1, G_3, G_5 (ff, dd), N(ff, ds), G_3 (ff, ss).
3) The competition between the 4f6p and $(5d+6s)^2$ pairs is represented by R_1, R_3 (fp, dd) and T_1, T_3 (fp, ds).
4) The competition 4f–6p is represented by L_2, L_4 (ff, fp), R_1, R_3 (fd, dp), R_2, R_4 (fd, pd), T_1 (fs, dp), T_2 (fs, pd), T_2 (fd, ps), T_3 (fd, sp).

TABLE 1

Parameters for the even configurations of Ce II

	$4f^2 5d$	$4f^2 6s$	$4f5d6p$	$4f6s6p$	$5d^3$	$5d^2 6s$	$5d6s^2$
$4f^2 5d$	E^0, E^1, E^2, E^3(ff) F_2, F_4, G_1, G_3, G_5(fd)						
$4f^2 6s$	M, N(fd, fs)	E^0, E^1, E^2, E^3(ff) G_3(fs)					
$4f5d6p$	L_2, L_4(f^2, fp) R_1, R_3, R_2, R_4(fd, dp)	$T_1 T_2$(fs, dp)	$F_0, F_2, F_4, G_1, G_3, G_5$(fd) F_2, G_2, G_4(fp) F_2, G_1, G_3(dp)				
$4f6s6p$	T_3, T_2(fd, sp)	L_2, L_4(f^2,fp)	J, K(dp, sp) M, N(fd, fs)	F_0, G_3(fs) F_2, G_2, G_4(fp) G_1(sp)			
$5d^3$	G_1, G_3, G_5(f^2, d^2)	–	R_1, R_3(fp, d^2)	–	A, B, C(dd)		
$5d^2 6s$	N(f^2, ds)	G_1, G_3, G_5(f^2, d^2)	T_1, T_3(fp, ds)	R_1, R_3(fp, d^2)	H(d^2, ds)	A, B, C(dd) G_2(ds)	
$5d6s^2$	G_3(f^2, s^2)	N(f^2, ds)	–	T_1, T_3(fp, ds)	G_2(d^2, s^2)	H(d^2, ds)	A

TABLE 2

Parameters for the odd configurations of Ce II

	$4f^3$	$4f^2 6p$	$4f 5d^2$	$4f 5d 6s$	$4f 6s^2$
$4f^3$	E^0, E^1, E^2, E^3(ff)				
$4f^2 6p$	L_2, L_4(f^2, fp)	$E^0, E^1, E^2\ E^3$ (ff) F_2, G_2, G_4(fp)			
$4f 5d^2$	G_1, G_3, G_5(f^2, d^2)	R_1, R_3(fp, d^2)	A, B, C (dd) F_2, F_4, G_1, G_3, G_5(fd)		
$4f 5d 6s$	N (f^2, ds)	T_1, T_3 (fp, ds)	H (d^2, ds) M, N (fd, fs)	$F_0, F_2, F_4, G_1, G_3, G_5$(fd) G_3(fs) G_2(ds)	
$4f 6s^2$	G_3(f^2, s^2)		G_2(d^2, s^2)	M, N (fd, fs)	F_0

1.2.2. *The heart of the matter*

The two main problems connected with the interpretation of rare-earth spectra are:

1) Evaluation of the strengths of the various interactions *within* the configurations. This enables the establishment of the *couplings* in the individual configurations, that is the choice of the most appropriate coupling scheme for characterizing the states of these configurations.

2) Evaluation of the strengths of the various CI and the repulsions they induce on the energy levels. This helps in understanding the deviations of the energy level schemes from the characteristic structure of the individual configurations.

2. Methods of interpretation of rare-earth spectra

The interpretation of a given spectrum is achieved by calculating its energy levels. For this purpose, energy matrices are constructed which include all the relevant interactions within and between configurations, and these are subsequently diagonalized. It is a tradition in theoretical spectroscopy to calculate exactly only the angular part of the energy matrices, whereas the radial integrals are regarded as adjustable parameters.

For simple spectra these parameters are evaluated by a direct comparison of the theoretical formulas for the energy levels with their experimental values. Since in most cases the number of parameters is much smaller than the number of levels, the energy level calculation is based on an iterative diagonalization–least-squares process. This process comprises four parts:

1) Approximate evaluation of the various interaction parameters.

2) Diagonalization of the energy matrices. The results of the diagonalization include, in addition to the calculated values of the energy levels, also their g-factors, the components of their eigenvectors in any desired coupling scheme, and their derivatives with respect to the parameters.

3) Comparison of the theoretical results with experimental data. This is based on the heights of the levels, their "names" and their g-factors.

4) Improvement of the initial values of the parameters, and of the fit between the calculated and observed levels, by means of a least-squares calculation.

For complex spectra, like those of the rare-earths, the situation is completely different, since in these spectra we usually have:

1) High-order energy matrices, which possess many large off-diagonal elements.

2) A dense list of observed energy levels, most of which are not identified by the experimentalist – only their J and g values are given.

These features complicate the evaluation of initial parameters directly from the experimental data of a single spectrum, and lead to uncertainties in the proper fit of experimental levels to calculated ones, thereby preventing the straightforward application of the iterative process.

In order to get complete and meaningful information about the values of the various parameters, it is necessary to carry out simultaneously the interpretation of several neighbouring spectra, both along an isoionic sequence and of different ions of the same element, in such a way that the values of parameters representing the same interactions in the various spectra are continuously compared. This method is based on the fact, known also in simpler spectra, that the values of the parameters change systematically while moving along an isoionic row or along different degrees of ionization of the same element.

For the purpose of obtaining initial values of unknown parameters, it is convenient to start with simple spectra, especially two-electron ones, at both ends of the rare-earths group, since in these spectra the orders of the energy matrices are relatively small, and the identity of the experimental levels is usually certain. Also, in these spectra, a detailed analysis of the role played by the individual interactions can be performed, which facilitates the interpretation of more complex spectra.

However, the information about the values of the parameters obtained from two-electron spectra is incomplete; in particular, the relative phases of the CI parameters cannot be established.

Complete, unambiguous and reliable information concerning *all* parameters relevant to rare-earth spectra can be gained through the interpretation of three electron spectra. In the first stage of this interpretation, initial values of the parameters are established, both by using the results of the interpretation of all available two-electron neighbouring spectra, and by direct comparison of the theoretical formulas of "isolated levels" of the investigated three-electron spectrum to their experimental values. Several diagonalizations are then performed, using various possible values for the still doubtful parameters. The results of these diagonalizations are compared with the experimental data. This comparison is best done in several steps, starting with extreme J values, for which the density of energy levels is relatively low, so that many of them may be regarded as isolated; in addition, the number of competing interactions (parameters) for these levels is comparatively small since they belong to only a part of the competing configurations. The proper choise of initial values for many of the parameters guarantees in advance a proper fit between many observed levels and calculated ones. Ambiguities in the fit are resolved by means of additional criteria such as observed g-factors. Of special use are g-factors having extreme values, since their corresponding calculated values can easily be traced in the various stages of the calculations. In cases of disagreement between calculated and observed levels and/or their g-factors, examination of the derivatives of these levels with respect to the various parameters often points out the parameters responsible for this discrepancy, and also leads to the establishment of improved values for these parameters. In this way the correct values of all doubtfull parameters which enter into the determination of extreme J energy levels are determined. After a satisfactory fit for most levels included in the first step of the calculations has been obtained, the process is repeated for intermediate J values, until a rough, but over-all, fit of all levels has been achieved. This fit is subsequently improved, and still better values for the parameters are obtained, by a straight-forward application of the iterative diagonalization–least-squares process.

Two points should be particularly stressed:

1) In each stage of the calculations, conclusions concerning corrected values for the various parameters should be reached only after comparing these corrected values with those of the corresponding parameters in neighbouring spectra.

2) In order to achieve a good agreement between all calculated and observed levels, in particular in intermediate J values, it is always necessary to include CI with all neigh bouring configurations, and often also effective interactions, which represent CI with distant configurations.

3. Results

The application of the methods described above resulted in a complete understanding of many third, second and first rare-earth spectra. These are listed in table 3, which also enumerates the configurations investigated in each spectrum.

In all these spectra, a very good agreement between theory and experiment has been achieved, and consistent values for the parameters representing the various interactions within and between configurations have been obtained. The stage has been reached where it is possible to make detailed predictions about the structure of rare-earth spectra, even in those cases where the experimental data are still very poor.

TABLE 3

List of investigated rare-earth spectra

Ion	Groups of configurations	Found experimentally by ref.	Theoretically investigated by ref.
Pr IV	$4f^2$, $4f6p$, $4f5d$, $4f6s$	9	9, 10, 11, 12, 13
Ce III	$4f^2+4f6p+5d^2+5d6s$, $4f5d+4f6s$	14, 15	16, 10, 17, 8
Pr III	$4f^3$, $4f^25d+4f^26s$, $4f^26p$	18	5, 10, 51
Gd III	$4f^7(^8S)\,6s$, $4f^7(^8S)\,5d$, $4f^7(^8S)\,6p$	19	19
Yb III	$4f^{13}6s$, $4f^{13}5d$, $4f^{13}6p$	20	20, 21
La II	$5d^2+5d6s+6s^2+4f6p+4f^2+6p^2$, $4f5d+4f6s+5d6p+6s6p$	22	16, 17, 10
Ce II	$4f^25d+4f^26s+4f5d6p+4f6s6p+5d^3+5d^26s+5d6s^2$, $4f5d^2+4f5d6s+4f6s^2$, $4f^26p$, $4f^3$	23	10
Pr II	$4f^3(^4I)\,6s$	24	25
Nd II	$4f^4(^5I)\,6s$	26	25
Gd II	$4f^7(^8S)\,5d^2+4f^7(^8S)\,5d6s+4f^7(^8S)\,6s^2$, $4f^7(^8S)\,5d6p+4f^7(^8S)\,6s6p$	27	28, 29, 30
Er II	$4f^{12}6s$	31	32, 33
Yb II	$4f^{13}5d^2+4f^{13}5d6s+4f^{13}6s^2$, $4f^{13}5d6p+4f^{13}6s6p$	34	35
Lu II	$5d^2+5d6s+6s^2$, $5d6p+6s6p$	36	10, 8
Hf II	$5d^3+5d^26s+5d6s^2$, $5d^26p+5d6s6p+6s^26p$	37	38, 39
Ce I	$4f5d^3+4f5d^26s+4f5d6s^2+4f^26s6p+4f^25d6p$, $4f^25d^2+4f^25d6s+4f^26s^2+4f5d^26p+4f5d6s6p+4f6s^26p$	40	41, 42
Er I	$4f^{12}6s^2$, $4f^{11}5d6s^2+4f^{12}6s6p$	43	44, 45, 46
Tm I	$4f^{13}6s6p+4f^{12}5d6s^2$	47	47

4. The configurations $4f^n$, $4f^{n-1}6s$, $4f^{n-1}6p$ and $4f^{n-1}5d$; competition between internal interactions; couplings

In this section we summarize the results of a systematic investigation of several types of configurations characteristic to rare-earth spectra, which, in the first approximation, may be considered as "isolated", and therefore treated separately. These results include information concerning the strengths of various interactions within the investigated configurations, and their effects on the energy level schemes. Couplings in the various configurations are defined, and correlated in each case with the strong interactions, and finer structural details of the energy level schemes are discussed in terms of the weak interactions.

4.1. The $4f^n$ configurations

The $4f^n$ configuration forms the ground configuration of the third and fourth rare-earth spectra. Since in these spectra the $4f^n$ configuration lies much lower than other configurations of the same parity (see section 1.1.1), it can, in the first approximation, be treated separately. The CI with distant configurations is taken account of in the theoretical calculations by means of the two-body effective parameters α, β, and γ*. Several $4f^n6s^2$ configurations in first rare-earth spectra were also treated in the same manner.

The systematic study of the $4f^n$ configurations resulted in information concerning the strength of the interactions between the 4f electrons, that is, it provided quantitative information on the values and their mode of change along the rare-earth series of the electrostatic parameters E^1, E^2, E^3(4f, 4f), and the spin–orbit parameter ζ_{4f}. Values for the effective parameters α, β and γ were only obtained for the left side of the rare-earth group, since the experimental data on the right side are poor. The values obtained for the parameters in all the investigated $4f^n$ and $4f^n6s^2$ configurations are given in table 4. If we measure the strength of an interaction within a configuration by the magnitudes of the splittings it induces on the levels of the previous approximation, it is clear, from inspection of table 4 and the theoretical formulas for the electrostatic and spin–orbit interactions, that the first interaction is stronger in the $4f^n$ configurations than the second one. On moving from the left side of the rare-earth group to its right side, the parameters representing both interactions increase, but the increase of ζ_{4f} is much greater than that of the electrostatic parameters E^i. These facts allow to determine the nature of the coupling in the $4f^n$ configurations: it is near to Russell–Saunders on the extreme left side of the rare-earth group, and approaches intermediate coupling on moving to the middle and to the right side of the group. Both the Grotrian diagrams of the various configurations and the calculated compositions of the eigenvectors confirm this conclusion.

The detailed understanding of the spectroscopic properties of the $4f^n$ configurations greatly facilitates the theoretical interpretation of the more com-

* In Pr III $4f^3$ three-body effective interactions were also included in the calculations[10,12]. These interactions represent, to second order in perturbation theory, the CI with all distant configurations differing from $4f^3$ in the quantum numbers of one electron.

TABLE 4

Parameters for the $4f^n$ and $4f^n 6s^2$ configurations in rare-earth spectra

Ion	Configuration	Ref.	E^1	E^2	E^3	α	β	γ	ζ_{4f}
Ce IV	4f	54							644
Pr IV	$4f^2$		5011	23.15	488	24	0	−49	760
Yb IV	$4f^{13}$	20							2883
La III	4f	55							429
Ce III	$4f^2$		3814	18.49	396	37.8	−950	−60	545
Pr III	$4f^3$		4246	19.95	410	31.4	−834	−68	663
Nd I	$4f^4(^5I)\, 6s^2$	49							777
Sm I	$4f^6(^7F)\, 6s^2$	49							1062
Er I	$4f^{12}\, 6s^2$		6307	30.26	606	0	0	0	2237
Tm I	$4f^{13}\, 6s^2$	50							2506

plicated configurations $4f^{n-1}n'l'$, $4f^{n-2}n'l'n''l''$ and $4f^{n-3}n'l'n''l''n'''l'''$ in free ions, and of the configurations $4f^n$ of rare-earth ions in crystals.

Recently, calculations of the $4f^n$ configurations have been conducted, in which additional magnetic interactions such as spin–spin and spin–other-orbit were included[11,12,13]). These will be discussed elsewhere.

4.2. The $4f^{n-1}6s$ configurations

The $4f^{n-1}6s$ configurations are the simplest of the $4f^{n-1}n'l'$ ($n'l'=5d$, 6s, 6p,...) configurations, which are common in the rare-earth spectra. Levels belonging to $4f^{n-1}6s$ configurations were experimentally identified in various rare-earth ions, as shown in table 3. A systematical study of these configurations has been made in this work. This study provided us with quantitative information on the values, and mode of change along the rare-earth series, of the $4f^{n-1}$ core parameters, and of the parameter $G_3(4f, 6s)$, which represents the electrostatic (exchange) interaction 4f–6s. The strength of the exchange interaction 4f–6s depends on the amount of overlap of the corresponding eigenfunctions. Since the 4f is an internal electron, whereas the 6s is an external one, this overlap is small, resulting in a weak 4f–6s interaction. The relative strengths of the various interactions are as follows:

$$\begin{aligned}&\text{electrostatic interaction of the } f^{n-1} \text{ core represented by } E^i, \alpha, \beta, \gamma >\\ &\quad > \text{spin–orbit interaction of the } 4f^{n-1} \text{ core represented by } \zeta_{4f} \gg\\ &\quad \gg \text{electrostatic 4f–6s interaction represented by } G_3(4f, 6s),\end{aligned}$$

thus leading to the immediate conclusion that in the $4f^{n-1}6s$ configurations there exists a $J_1 j$ coupling, where J_1 denotes the total angular momentum of the core, and j $(=\frac{1}{2})$ is the total angular momentum of the 6s electron. In this coupling, the core electrons are first coupled by the two stronger interactions to form states characterized by $S_1L_1J_1$. The electrostatic interaction 4f–6s then couples J_1 and j to form states of the ion characterized by the total angular momentum $J=J_1\pm j=J_1\pm\frac{1}{2}$. The jJ_1 coupling is reflected in the energy level structure of the $4f^{n-1}6s$ configurations in the following way: the levels are grouped into pairs, where each pair, characterized by $S_1L_1J_1$, consists of two adjacent levels having the consecutive J values $J=J_1\pm\frac{1}{2}$. The small separations between the levels belonging to each pair are an indication of the weakness of the 4f–6s interaction. A typical example of a Grotrian diagram of a $4f^{n-1}6s$ configuration is that of PrIII $4f^2 6s$ given in fig. 3.

A close examination of the above-mentioned Grotrian diagram, and also that of NdII $4f^4(^5I)6s$ given in fig. 4, shows that the pair structure exhibits

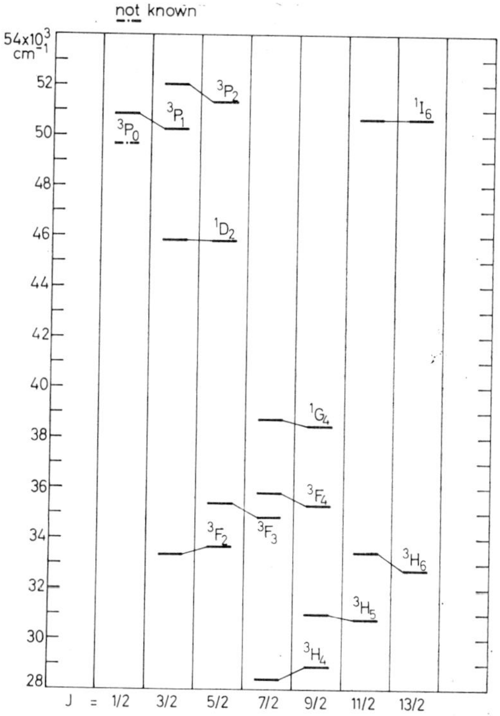

Fig. 3. Grotrian diagram of Pr III. $4f^2$ 6s.

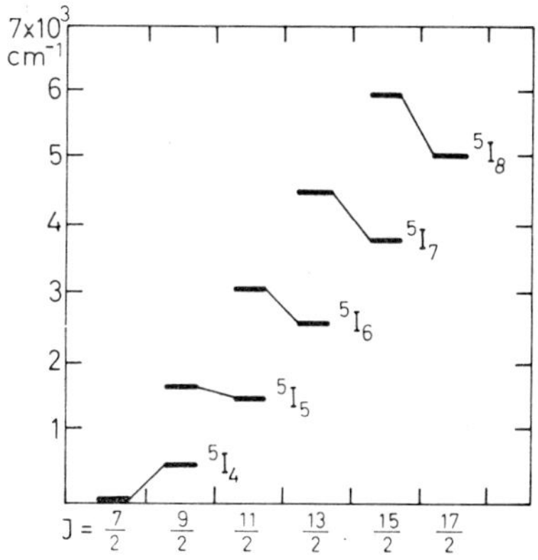

Fig. 4. Grotrian diagram of Nd II $4f^4(5I)$ 6s.

a definite regularity: for each term S_1L_1 of the core $4f^{n-1}$ with $S_1 \neq 0$, the pair arising from $J_1 = S_1 + L_1$ is inverted; as J_1 decreases, the splittings of the pairs belonging to the same S_1L_1 core term become smaller, until, for a certain J_1 value, the pairs become normal. The pair arising from the core level $J_1 = L_1 - S_1$ is normal in both spectra shown here.

The regularity of the pair structure can be explained by studying the formula for the exchange interaction 4f–6s in the $J_1 j$ coupling scheme. For $J_1' = J_1$ we obtain (disregarding terms depending on $n-1$)[48]):

$$(4f^{n-1}(\alpha S_1 L_1 J_1), 6sj; JM\,|H_{\text{exch}}|\,4f^{n-1}(\alpha S_1 L_1 J_1), 6sj; JM) =$$
$$= \pm\, \delta(\alpha, \alpha')\, \delta(S_1, S_1')\, \delta(L_1, L_1') \times$$
$$\times \frac{L_1(L_1+1) - S_1(S_1+1) - J_1(J_1+1)}{2J+1}\, G_3(4f, 6s),$$

where the $\pm$ signs correspond to $J = J_1 \pm \frac{1}{2}$ respectively. The matrix elements not diagonal in J_1 may be neglected for the case of $J_1 j$ coupling. From this formula we get for the theoretical splitting of the pair $S_1 L_1 J_1$

$$\Delta T_{J_1} = T_{J_1+\frac{1}{2}} - T_{J_1-\frac{1}{2}} =$$
$$= \frac{2J_1+1}{2J_1(J_1+1)} [L_1(L_1+1) - S_1(S_1+1) - J_1(J_1+1)]\, G_3(4f, 6s). \quad (1)$$

Since $G_3(4f, 6s)$ is always positive[3]), the property of a pair to be normal or inverted depends on the sign of the brackets:

$$[\ldots] > 0 \quad \text{normal pair},$$
$$[\ldots] < 0 \quad \text{inverted pair}.$$

For the extreme J_1 values belonging to a core term $\alpha S_1 L_1$ one obtains:

1) $$J_1 = L_1 + S_1 \quad (S_1 \neq 0),$$
$$[L_1(L_1+1) - S_1(S_1+1) - J_1(J_1+1)] = -\,2S_1(S_1 + L_1 + 1) < 0,$$
Inverted pair.

2) $$J_1 = L_1 - S_1 \quad (S_1 \neq 0,\ L_1 \geqslant S_1),$$
$$[L_1(L_1+1) - S_1(S_1+1) - J_1(J_1+1)] = 2S_1(L_1 - S_1).$$

a) $L_1 > S_1$,
$$2S_1(L_1 - S_1) > 0,$$
Normal pair.

b) $L_1 = S_1$.

In this case $J_1 = L_1 - S_1 = 0$, and J assumes the single value $J = \frac{1}{2}$.

3) $$J_1 = S_1 - L_1, \quad (S_1 \neq 0, \quad S_1 > L_1),$$
$$[L_1(L_1+1) - S_1(S_1+1) - J_1(J_1+1)] = -2(S_1 - L_1)(S_1+1) < 0,$$
Inverted pair.

For the configurations 4f6s, $4f^{13}$6s, $4f^2$6s and $4f^{12}$6s the theory predicts only the pairs characterized by $J_1 = L_1 - S_1$ to be normal, with all the other pairs inverted. A glance at fig. 3 shows that experiment confirms the theory for Pr III $4f^2$6s. For Nd II $4f^4(^5I)$ 6s the theory predicts the pairs

$$J_1 = L_1 - S_1 = 4, \qquad J_1 = L_1 - S_1 + 1 = 5$$

to be normal. A glance at fig. 4 shows that the pair $^5I_4$ is indeed normal, whereas the pair $^5I_5$ is inverted, the last phenomenon resulting from the effect of electrostatic matrix elements not diagonal in J_1*.

For the core singlet terms, $S_1 = 0$, $J_1 = L_1$, formula (1) gives $\Delta T_{J_1} = 0$, that is, pairs arising from singlet parent terms should have zero splitting. Looking at fig. 3, we see that the splittings of the pairs $^1D_2$ and $^1I_6$ are approximately zero, which confirms the theory. The finite splitting of the pair $^1G_4$ reflects the strong admixture of the core levels $^1G_4$ and $^3F_4$ due to the spin–orbit interaction of the 4f electrons.

The values of the parameters obtained in the calculations of the various $4f^{n-1}$ 6s configurations are given in table 5.

4.3. The $4f^{n-1}$6p configurations

The systematic study of the $4f^{n-1}$6p configurations, provided quantitative information on the parameters F_2(4f, 6p), G_2(4f, 6p) and G_4(4f, 6p) which represent the electrostatic 4f–6p interaction, on the spin–orbit parameter ζ_p, and yielded additional values for the $4f^{n-1}$ core parameters mentioned above. Since 4f is an internal electron, whereas 6p is an external one, the electrostatic 4f–6p interaction is very weak, especially the exchange part which is represented by G_2(4f, 6p) and G_4(4f, 6p).

The relations between the various interactions are as follows:

Electrostatic interaction of the $4f^{n-1}$ core represented by E^i, α, β, $\gamma >$
$>$ spin–orbit interaction of the $4f^{n-1}$ core represented by $\zeta_{4f} \gg$
$\gg$ electrostatic interaction 4f–6p represented by F_2, G_2, $G_4 \ll$
$\ll$ spin–orbit interaction of 6p represented by ζ_{6p},

* In Pm II $4f^5(^6H)$ 6s and Sm II $4f^6(^7F)$ 6s there is also a breakdown of $J_1 j$ coupling, because of the off-diagonal matrix elements of the 4f–6s electrostatic interaction mixing core levels of different J_1 [52, 53]).

TABLE 5

Parameters for the $4f^{n-1}6s$ configurations in rare-earth spectra

Ion	Configuration	Ref.	E^1	E^2	E^3	α	β	γ	ζ_{4f}	$G_3(4f, 6s)$
Pr IV	4f 6s								861	384
Ce III	4f 6s								635	298
Pr III	$4f^2 6s$		4954	22.8	481	24	0	−52	757	305
Gd III	$4f^7(^8S)$ 6s									294
Yb III	$4f^{13} 6s$								2914	337
La II	4f 6s								402	151
Ce II	$4f^2 6s$		3660	17.8 (fixed)	360	28 (fixed)	0	−60 (fixed)	535	176
Pr II	$4f^3(^4I)$ 6s									190
Nd II	$4f^4(^5I)$ 6s									203
Er II	$4f^{12} 6s$		6437	30	593	0	0	0	2236	211
Tm II	$4f^{13} 6s$	50							2506	212

thus leading to the conclusion that in the $4f^{n-1}6p$ configurations there also exists a $J_1 j$ coupling. Since the total angular momentum j of the 6p electron can assume the two values

$$j = \tfrac{1}{2}, \tfrac{3}{2},$$

each level of the $4f^{n-1}$ core characterized by $\alpha S_1 L_1 J_1$ splits, due to the 4f–6p electrostatic interaction, into two groups of levels; one group comprises a pair of adjacent levels (doublet) with the consecutive J values

$$J = J_1 \pm \tfrac{1}{2},$$

whereas the second group comprises four adjacent levels (quartet) with the consecutive J values

$$J = J_1 \pm \tfrac{3}{2}, \quad J_1 \pm \tfrac{1}{2}.$$

The small separations between the levels belonging to each group indicate the weakness of the 4f–6p interaction. A typical example of an energy level diagram of a $4f^{n-1}6p$ configuration is that of Pr III $4f^2 6p$ given in fig. 5.

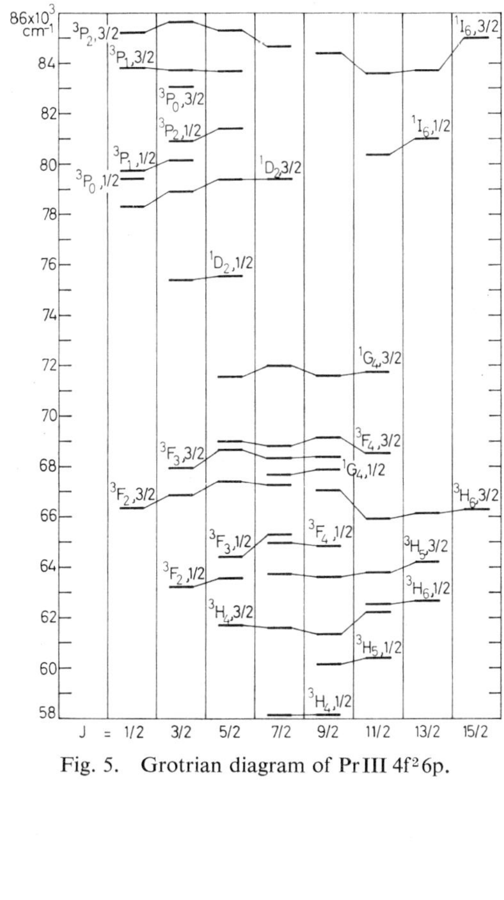

Fig. 5. Grotrian diagram of Pr III $4f^2 6p$.

In this case too we investigated the regularities in the structure of the doublets and the quartets. Since the exchange interaction 4f–6p is very weak, the structure of these groups should mainly be determined by the direct 4f–6p interaction, which is a quadrupole interaction represented by F_2 (4f, 6p). The angular part of this interaction in the $J_1 j$ coupling scheme is given by

$$Q = (4\mathrm{f}^{n-1}(\alpha S_1 L_1 J_1), 6\mathrm{p}j; JM | \sum_{i>j=1}^{n} C_i^{(2)} \cdot C_j^{(2)} | 4\mathrm{f}^{n-1}(\alpha S_1 L_1 J_1), 6\mathrm{p}j; JM) =$$

$$= (n-1) \times$$

$$\times (4\mathrm{f}^{n-1}(\alpha S_1 L_1 J_1), 6\mathrm{p}j; JM | C_{n-1}^{(2)} \cdot C_n^{(2)} | 4\mathrm{f}^{n-1}(\alpha S_1 L_1 J_1), 6\mathrm{p}j; JM) =$$

$$= (n-1)(-1)^{j+J_1+J} (\mathrm{f}^{n-1}\alpha S_1 L_1 J_1 \| C^{(2)} \| \mathrm{f}^{n-1}\alpha S_1 L_1 J_1)(\mathrm{p}j \| C^{(2)} \| \mathrm{p}j) \times$$

$$\times \bar{W} \begin{pmatrix} J_1 & J_1 & 2 \\ j & j & J \end{pmatrix}.$$

1) For $j = \frac{1}{2}$ we have

$$\bar{W} \begin{pmatrix} J_1 & J_1 & 2 \\ \frac{1}{2} & \frac{1}{2} & J \end{pmatrix} = 0, \quad \text{hence} \quad Q = 0.$$

We may therefore conclude that the splittings of the doublets should be very small, see for instance the doublets $^3H_{4,5,6}$, $^1D_2$ in fig. 5. When larger splittings occur, they are caused either by the exchange interaction 4f–6p, or, when there is a breakdown in the $J_1 j$ coupling, by matrix elements of the direct 4f–6p interaction not diagonal in J_1 and/or in j; the splittings may also be due to CI effects.

2) For $j = \frac{3}{2}$ we obtain

i) $$(\mathrm{p}\tfrac{3}{2} \| C^{(2)} \| \mathrm{p}\tfrac{3}{2}) = \frac{2}{\sqrt{5}}.$$

ii) $$(n-1)(\mathrm{f}^{n-1}\alpha S_1 L_1 J_1 \| C^{(2)} \| \mathrm{f}^{n-1}\alpha S_1 L_1 J_1) =$$

$$= (n-1)(\mathrm{f} \| C^{(2)} \| \mathrm{f})(\mathrm{f}^{n-1}\alpha S_1 L_1 J_1 \| u^{(2)} \| \mathrm{f}^{n-1}\alpha S_1 L_1 J_1) =$$

$$= (\mathrm{f} \| C^{(2)} \| \mathrm{f})(\mathrm{f}^{n-1}\alpha S_1 L_1 J_1 \| u^{(2)} \| \mathrm{f}^{n-1}\alpha S_1 L_1 J_1),$$

where $u^{(2)}$ is a tensorial operator of degree two introduced by Racah [3]) and defined by its reduced matrix element.

$$(nl \| u^{(2)} \| n'l') = \delta(n, n')\,\delta(l, l'),$$

$$u^{(2)} = \sum_{i=1}^{n-1} u_i^{(2)},$$

and $(\mathrm{f}\|C^{(2)}\|\,\mathrm{f})$ is a positive number.

iii) $$(-1)^{\frac{3}{2}+J_1+J}\,\bar{W}\begin{pmatrix} J_1 & J_1 & 2 \\ \frac{3}{2} & \frac{3}{2} & J \end{pmatrix} =$$
$$= A(J_1)\,[K(K+1) - 5J_1(J_1+1)] = A(J_1)\,N(J),$$

where
$$K = J(J+1) - J_1(J_1+1) - \tfrac{15}{4},$$

and
$$A(J_1) = \frac{1}{2\sqrt{[5(2J_1-1)\,2J_1(2J_1+1)(2J_1+2)(2J_1+3)]}}.$$

We therefore get for the quadrupole interaction the expression

$$Q = B\cdot A(J_1)\cdot N(J)\,(\mathrm{f}^{n-1}\,\alpha S_1L_1J_1\,\|U^{(2)}\|\,\mathrm{f}^{n-1}\,\alpha S_1L_1J_1),$$

where B and $A(J_1)$ are positive numbers and $N(J)$ includes all the dependence of Q upon J.

The evaluation of $N(J)$ for all the values of J generated from a particular value of J_1 gives
$$N(J_1+\tfrac{3}{2}) = 2J_1(2J_1-1),$$
$$N(J_1+\tfrac{1}{2}) = -2(J_1+3)(2J_1-1),$$
$$N(J_1-\tfrac{1}{2}) = -2(J_1-2)(2J_1+3),$$
$$N(J_1-\tfrac{3}{2}) = 2(J_1+1)(2J_1+3),$$

with
$$N(J_1+\tfrac{3}{2}) - N(J_1+\tfrac{1}{2}) =$$
$$= N(J_1-\tfrac{3}{2}) - N(J_1-\tfrac{1}{2}) = 2(2J_1-1)(2J_1+3) > 0.$$

Inspection of the last formulas shows that for quartets generated from core levels for which $(\mathrm{f}^{n-1}\alpha S_1L_1J_1\,\|U^{(2)}\|\,\mathrm{f}^{n-1}\alpha S_1L_1J_1)$ is positive, the quadrupole interaction Q is positive when J_1 and j are parallel or antiparallel, and negative when J_1 and j are nearly perpendicular*.

For core levels having negative $(\mathrm{f}^{n-1}\alpha S_1L_1J_1\,\|U^{(2)}\|\,\mathrm{f}^{n-1}\alpha S_1L_1J_1)$, the contributions of the quadrupole interaction Q to the energy levels reverse their sign. These features of Q are reflected in the Grotrian diagrams of the $4\mathrm{f}^{n-1}6\mathrm{p}$ configurations in the following way: quartets of the first kind are bowl shaped, whereas quartets of the second kind are umbrella shaped.

* Quartets are obtained only for $J_1 \geqslant \frac{3}{2}$. The values $J_1 = \frac{3}{2}$, 2 are exceptions to the rule formulated above, since $N(J_1-\frac{1}{2}) > 0$ for $J_1 = \frac{3}{2}$ and $N(J_1-\frac{1}{2}) = 0$ for $J_1 = 2$.

In the 4f6p configurations $(4f\,^2F_{\frac{5}{2},\frac{7}{2}}\|U^{(2)}\|\,4f\,^2F_{\frac{5}{2},\frac{7}{2}})$ is positive for both J_1 values, therefore both quartets are expected to be bowl shaped. This is confirmed by experiment, see the Grotrian diagram of PrIV 4f6p in fig. 6.

In the $4f^{13}6p$ configurations $(4f^{13}\,^2F_{\frac{5}{2},\frac{7}{2}}\|U^{(2)}\|\,4f^{13}\,^2F_{\frac{5}{2},\frac{7}{2}})$ is negative for both J_1 values, therefore both quartets are expected to be umbrella shaped. See the Grotrian diagram of YbIII $4f^{13}6p$ in fig. 7.

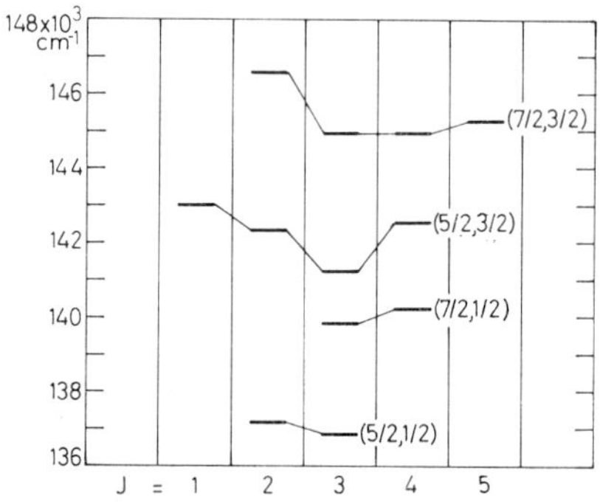

Fig. 6. Grotrian diagram of PrIV 4f6p.

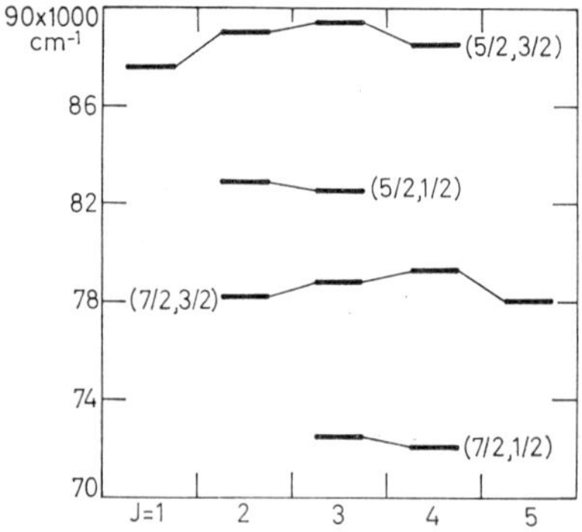

Fig. 7. Grotrian diagram of YbIII $4f^{13}6p$.

In PrIII $4f^2 6p$ (fig. 5) both kinds of quartets occur. The correspondence between the signs of $(f^{n-1}\alpha S_1 L_1 J_1\|U^{(2)}\|\,f^{n-1}\alpha S_1 L_1 J_1)$ and the shapes of the quartets in this configuration is given in table 6.

The values of the parameters obtained in the calculations of the various $4f^{n-1}6p$ configurations are given in table 7.

TABLE 6

Quartet structure in PrIII $4f^2 6p$

Core level	Sign of $(f^{n-1}\alpha S_1L_1J_1 \| U^{(2)} \| f^{n-1}\alpha S_1L_1J_1)$	Quartet Structure
$^3H_4$	+	bowl
$^3H_5$	+	bowl
$^3H_6$	+	bowl
$^1I_6$	+	bowl
$^3P_2$	−	umbrella
$^3F_2$	−	umbrella

4.4. THE $4f^{n-1}5d$ CONFIGURATIONS

Levels belonging to the $4f^{n-1}5d$ configurations were experimentally found in various rare-earth spectra, as shown in table 3. The systematic study of these configurations provided quantitative information on the values, and their mode of change along the rare-earth series, of the following parameters: (1) The $4f^{n-1}$ core parameters. (2) The Slater parameters F_2, F_4, G_1, G_3 and G_5 representing the electrostatic 4f–5d interaction. (3) The spin–orbit parameter ζ_{5d}. Since 4f is an internal electron and 5d is "half" internal, the

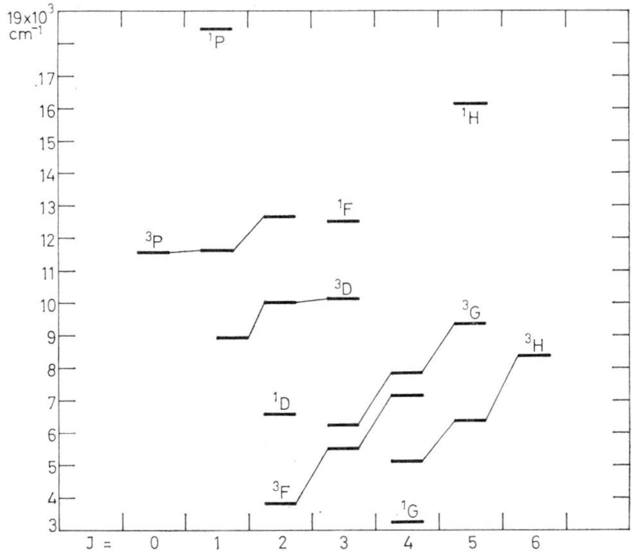

Fig. 8. Grotrian diagram of CeIII 4f5d.

TABLE 7

Parameters for the $4f^{n-1}6p$ configurations in rare-earth spectra

Ion	Configuration	E^1	E^2	E^3	α	β	γ	ζ_{4f}	ζ_{6p}	F_2	G_2	G_4
Pr IV	$4f6p$							864	3244	104	13	14
Ce III	$4f6p$							644	2155	72	5	5
Pr III	$4f^2 6p$	4931	23.13	484	25	-800	-60	755	2422	71	8.5	11
Yb III	$4f^{13} 6p$							2921	4020	81	10	10
La II	$4f6p$							410	1102	85	13	7
Ce II	$4f^2 6p$	3828	18.25	370	28(f)	-700(f)	-60(f)	528	1234	64	12	6

electrostatic interaction between them should be strong. We would therefore expect the coupling in these configurations to be close to Russell–Saunders coupling. This is really the case on the left side of the rare-earth group, as can be inferred from the Grotrian diagram of Ce III 4f 5d given in fig. 8, and from the results of the theoretical calculations of this configuration.

It is instructive to summarize the results of the calculations of more complicated configurations on the left side of the rare-earth group, such as Ce II $4f^2 5d$ (ref. 10) and Pr III $4f^2 5d$ (refs. 5, 10). The most appropriate scheme for characterizing the states of these configurations is

$$4f^2(S_1L_1), 5d, SLJM .$$

Indeed, the results of the calculations demonstrate that most of the terms are each characterized by a single pair SL of quantum numbers; but the quantum numbers S_1L_1 representing the parent terms are usually bad, in consequence of the strong 4f–5d electrostatic interaction. The coupling in these configurations is still referred to as LS coupling, although the states cannot be uniquely described by one set of quantum numbers, i.e. the order in which the various angular momenta are coupled cannot be uniquely specified.

On advancing to the right side of the rare-earth series, the values of the various parameters change in the following manner, as shown in table 8;

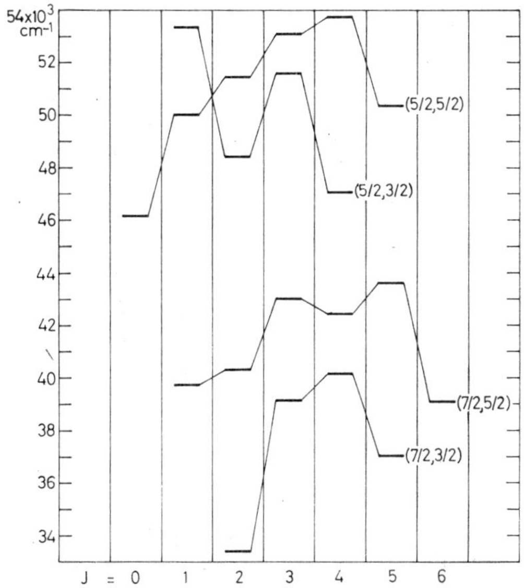

Fig. 9. Grotrian diagram of Yb III $4f^{13} 5d$.

TABLE 8

Parameters for the $4f^{n-1}5d$ configurations in rare-earth spectra

Ion	Configuration	E^1	E^2	E^3	α	β	γ	F_2	F_4	G_1	G_3	G_5	ζ_{4f}	ζ_{5d}
Pr IV								215	26	312	44	6.8	870	1082
Ce III	$4f\,5d$							184	22	311	41	6	635	757
Pr III	$4f^2\,5d$	5278	22.63	481	24	0	−52	183	21	300	37	6	770	721
Yb III	$4f^{13}\,5d$							186	14	193	25	4	2950	1211
Ce II	$4f^2\,5d$	3793	15.23	363	17	−869	−60	153	15	286	32	5	554	325
Er I	$4f^{11}\,5d\,6s^2$	6437	30	593				144	15	104	16	3.2	2383	807

the core parameters, especially ζ_{4f}, increase appreciably; the parameter ζ_{5d} also increases, whereas the parameters representing the electrostatic 4f–5d interaction slightly decrease. These changes lead us to expect an increasing departure from *LS* coupling and, ultimately, an approach to $J_1 j$ coupling on the right side of the series. This trend is greatly assisted by the fact that for $n-1>7$ the dominant parameter G_1 of the 4f–5d interaction contributes only to states generated from $4f^{13}5d(^1P_1)$, and vanishes elsewhere. Thus, in spite of the fact that the 4f–5d parameters remain relatively large, a quite good $J_1 j$ coupling is valid for the $4f^{n-1}5d$ configurations on the right side of the rare-earth group. This is nicely demonstrated in the Grotrian diagram of YbIII $4f^{13}5d$ given in fig. 9: the umbrella shape of the quartets and sextets is due to the quadrupole interaction represented by F_2(4f, 5d), as already proved for the $4f^{n-1}6p$ configurations. The large departure of the quartet $(\frac{5}{2}, \frac{3}{2})$ from the umbrella shape demonstrates the breakdown of the $J_1 j$ coupling in $J=1$, due to the exchange interaction represented by G_1 (4f, 5d).

Recent calculations in the $4f^{n-1}5d$ configurations indicate that the fit between calculated and observed levels improves considerably on the inclusion of effective interactions of the type

$$(\sum_i l_{f_i}, l_d)\cdot El + (\sum_i s_{f_i}, s_d)\cdot Es\,.$$

These lead to a reduction of the mean error by 30%–50%.

5. Groups of interacting configurations; study of CI effects; competition between internal and configuration interactions

In this section the methods of approach to the interpretation of spectra in which several configurations interact are demonstrated by means of relatively simple examples, in which the separate effect of each interaction can be clearly visualized. In particular, the effect of various CI are studied in detail, both by calculating the repulsions they induce on the individual levels and their influence on the compositions of the eigenvectors. It is shown that the inclusion in the theoretical calculations of CI between neighbouring configurations is essential for obtaining "true", and therefore consistent, values for the various interaction parameters.

The examples chosen for discussion are the groups of configurations (d^2+ds+s^2) of LaII, fd+fs of CeIII, and dp+sp of LuII, by means of which the competition between the electrons 5d and 6s is illustrated. In addition, the group of configurations $fp+d^2+ds$ of CeIII is discussed, which illustrates the competition between the pairs of electrons fp, d^2 and ds.

5.1. The configurations $(5d+6s)^2$ of La II

The configurations $5d^2+5d6s+6s^2$ constitute the lowest configurations ("low A") of La II, with $5d^2\,(^3F_2)$ as the ground level. All levels belonging to these configurations, with the exception of $5d^2\,(^1S)$, were experimentally found. The appropriate Grotrian diagram is given in fig. 10. The figure shows that the three configurations overlap; this is a typical example of

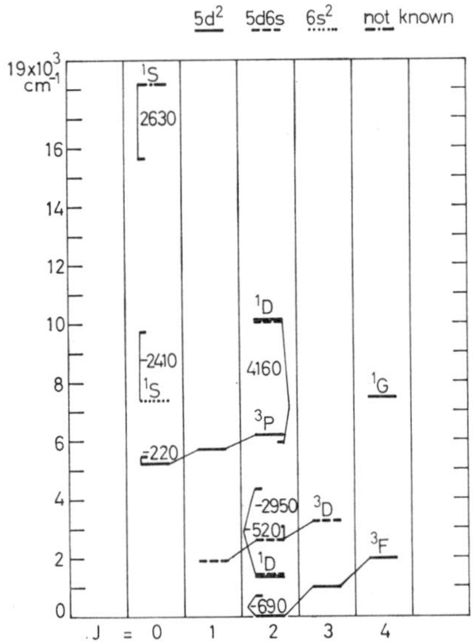

Fig. 10. Grotrian diagram of La II $5d^2+5d6s+6s^2$.

the above-mentioned competition between the 5d and 6s electrons. CI should therefore be included in the energy level calculations. Both the distribution of the levels, and their g-values show that in these configurations the electrons are LS coupled.

The theoretical calculations of these configurations were conducted by Amiel[16]) in 1955, and are reviewed here with the purpose of studying CI effects.

5.1.1. *Evaluation of the radial parameters; results*

The formulas for the electrostatic interaction within and between configurations are given in table 9. The configuration 5d6s, comprising the two terms ^1D and ^3D, is described by the two internal Slater parameters F_0 and

TABLE 9

Formulas of the electrostatic interaction for the configurations d^2+ds+s^2

	$d^2\,{}^1S$	$s^2\,{}^1S$
$d^2\,{}^1S$	$A+14B+7C$	$\sqrt{5}\,G'_2$
$s^2\,{}^1S$	$\sqrt{5}\,G'_2$	F'_0
	$d^2\,{}^1D$	$ds\,{}^1D$
$d^2\,{}^1D$	$A-3B+2C$	$2\sqrt{35}\,H$
$ds\,{}^1D$	$2\sqrt{35}\,H$	F_0+G_2
$d^2\,{}^3P=A+7B$		
$d^2\,{}^3F=A-8B$		$ds\,{}^3D=F_0-G_2$
$d^2\,{}^1G=A+4B+2C$		

G_2. Since the number of parameters equals the number of terms, an exact solution to the electrostatic problem is possible whenever both terms are experimentally known. However, the values of the parameters obtained in this fashion are effective ones, which include the effects of the repulsion by the configuration $5d^2$. The four known terms of the configuration $5d^2$ are described by only three internal parameters A, B and C. If these parameters are evaluated so as to fit the three terms ${}^3P$, ${}^3F$ and ${}^1G$ unperturbed by the configuration 5d 6s, there exists a large deviation between the calculated and observed values of the perturbed term ${}^1D$. This deviation measures the strength of CI and permits the evaluation of the CI parameter H(dd, ds) and the unperturbed position of the term 5d 6s $({}^1D)=F_0+G_2$. This evaluation is achieved through the requirement that the eigenvalues of the electrostatic matrix of ${}^1D$ should be equal to the observed ${}^1D$ terms. The value obtained for the sum F_0+G_2, together with the equation 5d 6s $({}^3D)=F_0-G_2$, give the separate values of F_0 and G_2. F_0' is evaluated assuming that $G_2'=G_2$. The spin–orbit parameters $\zeta_d(5d^2)$ and $\zeta_d'(5d\,6s)$ are directly evaluated from the splittings of the various terms.

The subsequent application of the iterative diagonalization – least-squares procedure then leads to the best fit between calculated and observed levels and also gives the improved values of the parameters representing the various interactions. The final results are given in tables 10 and 11. Inspection of table 10 shows that the agreement between theory and experiment is very

TABLE 10

The configurations $(5d + 6s)^2$ of La II

Configuration	Designation	J	Obs.	Calc.	O−C	g-obs.	g-calc.	Repulsion due to CI	Purity
$5d^2$	^3F	2	0.00	−10	10	0.721	0.727	− 690	82% + $d^2\,{}^1D$ 11%
		3	1016.10	1022	− 6	1.083	1.083		100%
		4	1970.70	1973	− 2	1.248	1.248		99%
	^1D	2	1394.46	1399	− 5	0.977	0.973	−2950	35% + $ds\,{}^1D$ 34% + + $d^2\,{}^3F$ 16%
5d 6s	^3D	1	1895.15	1896	− 1	0.498	0.500		100%
		2	2591.60	2584	8	1.133	1.140	− 520	85% + $d^2\,{}^1D$ 9%
		3	3250.35	3255	− 5	1.334	1.333		100%
$5d^2$	^3P	0	5249.70	5263	−13	$\frac{0}{0}$	$\frac{0}{0}$	− 220	94% + $s^2\,{}^1S$ 3% + + $d^2\,{}^1S$ 3%
		1	5718.12	5717	1	1.497	1.500		100%
		2	6227.42	6216	11	1.481	1.485		97%
$6s^2$	^1S	0	7394.57	7394	1	$\frac{0}{0}$	$\frac{0}{0}$	−2410	83% + $d^2\,{}^1S$ 12%
$5d^2$	^1G	4	7473.32	7472	1	1.000	1.002		99%
5d 6s	^1D	2	10094.86	10095	0	1.005	1.008	4160	53% + $d^2\,{}^1D$ 45%
$5d^2$	^1S	0		18221			$\frac{0}{0}$	2630	85% + $s^2\,{}^1S$ 14%

$G_2(ds) = 1703$, $G_{2_{\mathrm{eff}}}(ds) = -683$ or 3668.

TABLE 11

Parameters for the configurations $(5d+6s)^2$ of La II

Parameter	Value (cm^{-1})
A (d^2)	3775 ± 5
F_0 (ds)	4414 ± 14
$F'_0(s^2)$	8854 ± 29
B (d^2)	313 ± 1
C (d^2)	1200 ± 7
G_2 (ds)	1703 ± 13
H (dd, ds)	361 ± 1
ζ_d (d^2)	498 ± 4
ζ_d (ds)	543 ± 7
Δ	12

$G'_2(d^2, s^2) = G_2(ds)$.

good concerning both the levels and their g-values, the mean error Δ being 12 cm^{-1}. It should be emphasized that although the good agreement was obtained with a number of electrostatic parameters which equals the number of terms, the values obtained for the parameters are in full agreement with the corresponding ones in the neighbouring spectra.

We may therefore conclude that the results have physical significance.

5.1.2. *Discussion*

The effects of CI in this group of configurations may be studied in three ways: (1) by calculating the magnitudes of the repulsions of the interacting levels. (2) by inspecting the composition percentages of the various levels. (3) by comparing the unperturbed value of G_2 (ds) to the effective one $G_{2\text{eff}}$(ds). The results of this analysis are summarized in columns 9, 10 and at the bottom of table 10. It is seen from the table that in consequence of the CI represented by H(dd, ds), the assignments of configurational quantum numbers to the two ^1D's at 1394 cm^{-1} and 10095 cm^{-1} are meaningless. If the low ^1D is assigned 5d 6s (^1D) after Russell and Meggers [22]), we obtain for $G_{2\text{eff}}$(ds) the value

$$G_{2\text{eff}}(\text{ds}) = \tfrac{1}{2}[\text{ds}(^1D)_{\text{obs}} - \text{ds}(^3D)_{\text{obs}}] = -683 \text{ cm}^{-1}.$$

If the high ^1D is assigned 5d 6s (^1D) as suggested by the calculations (the biggest part of ds (^1D) is concentrated in the level 10095 cm^{-1} and most of d^2 (^1D) is concentrated in the low levels 1394 cm^{-1}, 0 cm^{-1} and 2592 cm^{-1}), then

$$G_{2_{\text{eff}}}(\text{ds}) = 3668 \text{ cm}^{-1}.$$

The "true" or unperturbed value of G_2 (ds) is 1703 cm^{-1}. The admixture of $d^2(^1D)$ in the levels 0 cm^{-1} and 2592 cm^{-1} is reflected in their downward repulsions by the level 10095 cm^{-1}, as seen in column 9 of table 10.

5.2. The configurations 4f5d + 4f6s of Ce III

There are 24 levels in these configurations, all of which are experimentally known. The first theoretical calculations of these configurations were conducted by Stern[17]) in 1955. The calculations were performed in intermediate coupling, but without taking CI into account. Stern's results are reproduced in part in tables 12 and 13. The mean quadratic errors obtained were 8.4 cm^{-1} for the fs configuration and 226 cm^{-1} for fd. The small mean error for fs is not surprising, since in this configuration the number of terms equals the number of electrostatic parameters. The large mean error for fd cannot be attributed to CI with fs, which is the only near odd configuration, since the deviations of the $^{1,3}F$ terms which are mainly affected by this interaction are smaller than those of ^1D, ^3G and ^3H. On the other hand, the trend of the deviations

Table 12

Parameters for the odd configurations of Ce III

Parameter	Initial value (Stern[17]))	Final value
F_0 (fd)	9408	8816 ± 65
F'_0(fs)	20814	20810 ± 91
F_2 (fd)	176	184 ± 2
F_4 (fd)	21	21.8 ± 0.6
G_1 (fd)	297	311 ± 3
G_3 (fd)	39	41 ± 1
G_5 (fd)	4.8	5.8 ± 0.2
El	0	11 ± 3
Es	0	325 ± 47
G'_3(fs)	298	299 ± 86
M	0	74 (fixed)
N	0	12 (fixed)
ζ_f (fd)	650	635 ± 19
ζ'_f (fs)	650	635 ± 19
ζ_d (fd)	780	757 ± 43
Δ		95

suggests the introduction of two "effective interaction" parameters *El* and *Es*, whose coefficients are given by $(l_f \cdot l_d)$ and $(s_f \cdot s_d)$ respectively. The inclusion of these parameters reduced the mean error to 116 cm^{-1}. The subsequent introduction of CI hardly affected the calculated values of the levels, but led to extremely small admixtures with fs, which may explain the forbidden $4f6s$–$4f^2$ transitions observed by Sugar[15]). The final results are given in tables 12 and 13.

It may be concluded that in spite of the closeness of the fd and fs configurations, the effective interactions representing CI of fd with distant configurations are much stronger than the direct CI between them. These conclusions were corroborated through the investigations of additional spectra containing 4f and 5d electrons (see table 3).

5.3. The configurations 5d6p + 6s6p of LuII

5.3.1. *Introduction*

The low odd configurations 6s6p and 5d6p of LuII, all the energy levels of which have been experimentally identified, begin at about 27000 cm^{-1} above the ground level $6s^2\,(^1S)$. The Grotrian diagram of these configurations is given in fig. 11. The figure shows that while there is no actual overlap of the two configurations, they are quite close to each other, due to the above mentioned competition between the 6s and 5d electrons. CI must therefore

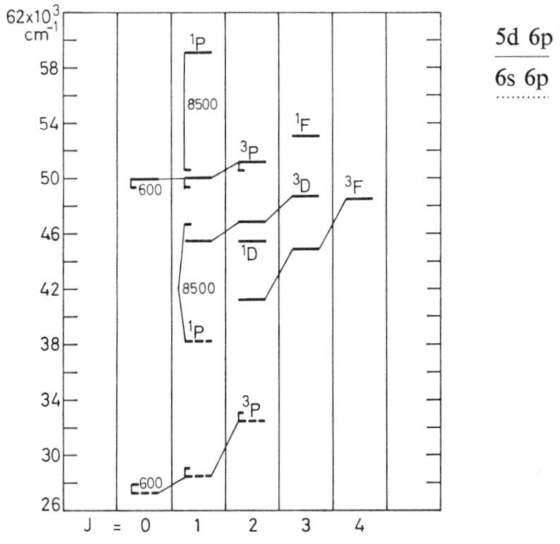

Fig. 11. Grotrian diagram of LuII 5d6p + 6s6p.

TABLE 13

Low odd levels of Ce III

Configuration	Term	J	Obs.	Stern's results [17] Calc.	Stern's results [17] O−C	Calc.	O−C	g-obs.	g-calc.	Purity
4f5d	^1G	4	3277	3451	−174	3329	−52		0.952	65% + ^3H 30%
4f5d	^3F	2	3822	3907	−85	3834	−12		0.772	70% + ^1D 29%
		3	5502	5563	−61	5590	−88		1.044	87% + ^3G 11%
		4	7150	7327	−177	7289	−139		1.195	75% + ^3G 17%
4f5d	^3H	4	5127	5092	35	5080	47		0.879	69% + ^1G 25%
		5	6361	6018	343	6280	81		1.033	100%
		6	8350	8162	188	8337	13		1.167	100%
4f5d	^3G	3	6265	5957	308	6159	106		0.802	84% + ^3F 13%
		4	7837	7748	89	7809	28		1.075	83% + ^3F 13%
		5	9326	9181	145	9313	13		1.197	99%
4f5d	^1D	2	6571	7020	−448	6657	−86		0.915	65% + ^3F 30%
4f5d	^3D	1	8922	8850	72	8816	106		2.000	96%
		2	9900	9949	−49	10000	−100		1.167	96%
		3	10127	10094	33	10070	57		1.214	66% + ^1F 31%
4f5d	^3P	0	11577	11640	−63	11614	−37		$\frac{0}{0}$	100%
		1	11613	11624	−11	11606	7		1.461	94%
		2	12642	12720	−78	12591	51		1.480	96%
4f5d	^1F	3	12501	12636	−135	12391	110		1.106	64% + ^3D 33%
4f5d	^1H	5	16152	16178	−26	16247	−95		1.002	99%
4f5d	^1P	1	18444	18400	44	18455	−11		1.011	94%
4f6s	$(\frac{5}{2}, \frac{1}{2})$	2	19236			19245	−9	0.665	0.667	100%
		3	19464			19466	−2	1.07	1.058	99%
4f6s	$(\frac{7}{2}, \frac{1}{2})$	4	21476			21467	9	1.27	1.250	100%
		3	21849			21849	0	1.035	1.026	99%

be included in the calculations. A second conclusion which may be drawn from the figure is that the Russell–Saunders coupling scheme is the most appropriate one for characterizing the states of these configurations.

5.3.2. *Evaluation of the radial parameters; results*

The formulas for the electrostatic interaction are given in table 14. The parameters representing this interaction are evaluated in a similar fashion to that described in section 5.1. Although there is more than one solution for J and K, because only the squares of their sum and their difference are determined by the formulas, information obtained from other spectra shows that J and K have the same sign, and satisfy the condition $|K|>|J|$. The spin–orbit parameters $\zeta_d(\mathrm{dp})$, $\zeta_p(\mathrm{dp})$ and $\zeta'_p(\mathrm{sp})$ were directly evaluated from the splittings of the various terms. The subsequent application of the iterative diagonalization–least-squares procedure led to a very good agreement between theory and experiment, the mean error Δ being 56 cm^{-1}. The observed and calculated levels, as well as their composition percentages and the calculated g-values are given in table 15. No measured g-values are available. The values obtained for the parameters in table 16 are in full agreement with the corresponding ones in the neighbouring spectra of YbII $f^{13}dp+f^{13}sp$ (ref. 35) and HfII $d^2p+dsp+s^2p$ (ref. 39).

5.3.3. *Discussion*

The effects of CI in this spectrum are summarized in table 17. The second column of this table lists the numerical values of the CI matrix elements for

TABLE 14

Formulas of the electrostatic interaction for the configurations dp + sp

	dp ^1P	sp ^1P
dp^1P	$F_0+7F_2+G_1+21G_3$	$(J+K)\sqrt{2}$
sp^1P	$(J+K)\sqrt{2}$	$F'_0+G'_1$
	dp ^3P	sp ^3P
dp^3P	$F_0+7F_2-G_1-21G_3$	$(J-K)\sqrt{2}$
sp^3P	$(J-K)\sqrt{2}$	$F'_0-G'_1$

$$\mathrm{dp}\,^1D=F_0-7F_2-3G_1+7G_3$$
$$\mathrm{dp}\,^3D=F_0-7F_2+3G_1-7G_3$$
$$\mathrm{dp}\,^1F=F_0+2F_2+6G_1+G_3$$
$$\mathrm{dp}\,^3F=F_0+2F_2-6G_1-G_3$$

TABLE 15

Low odd levels of Lu II

Configuration	Designation	J	Obs.	Calc.	O−C	g-calc.	Purity
6s 6p	^3P	0	27264	27284	−20	$\frac{0}{0}$	99 %
		1	28503	28481	22	1.475	94 %
		2	32453	32454	− 1	1.500	98 %
6s 6p	^1P	1	38223	38228	− 5	1.009	56 % + dp ^1P 34 %
5d 6p	^3F	2	41225	41271	−46	0.773	70 % + ^1D 27 %
		3	44919	44902	17	1.097	93 %
		4	48537	48553	−16	1.250	100 %
5d 6p	^1D	2	45458	45386	72	0.988	60 % + ^3F 24 % + ^3P 12 %
5d 6p	^3D	1	45532	45505	27	0.576	89 %
		2	46904	46945	−41	1.146	87 %
		3	48733	48750	−17	1.270	79 % + ^1F 14 %
5d 6p	^3P	0	49963	49965	− 2	$\frac{0}{0}$	99 %
		1	50049	50002	47	1.429	90 %
		2	51202	51246	−44	1.427	82 % + ^1D 9 %
5d 6p	^1F	3	53079	53069	10	1.050	85 % + ^3D 15 %
5d 6p	^1P	1	59122	59127	− 5	1.011	64 % + sp ^1P 30 %

TABLE 16

Parameters for the odd configurations of Lu II

Parameter	Value
F_0 (dp)	48550 ± 30
F'_0(sp)	37961 ± 107
F_2 (dp)	320 ± 8
G_1 (dp)	529 ± 7
G_3 (dp)	15 ± 6
G'_1 (sp)	6958 ± 164
J (dp, sp)	2579 ± 211
K (dp, ps)	4176 ± 197
ζ_d (dp)	1100 ± 32
ζ_p (dp)	2907 ± 70
ζ'_p (sp)	3493 ± 54
Δ	56

TABLE 17

CI effects in the odd configurations of Lu II

Term	CI matrix element (cm^{-1})	Individual repulsions (cm^{-1})	Admixture (%)
^1P	$(J+K)\sqrt{2} = 9552$	8500	30–34
^3P	$(K-J)\sqrt{2} = 2582$	600	1–2

$G'_1 = 6958$, $G'_{1\,\mathrm{eff}} = \frac{1}{2}(\mathrm{sp}\ ^1P_{\mathrm{obs}} - \mathrm{sp}\ ^3P_{\mathrm{obs}}) = 3832$.

the two interacting pairs of terms. The interaction between the ^1P's is much stronger than that between the ^3P's, and this fact is reflected in all the columns of the table. The repulsions of the individual terms cited in column 3 were calculated by multiplying the numerical values of the parameters J and K by the derivatives of the investigated levels with respect to these parameters. The big difference between the magnitudes of the repulsions of the ^1P's and the ^3P's causes the serious discrepancy between G'_1 and $G'_{1\mathrm{eff}}$: since the sp configuration is lower than dp, the greater downward repulsion of ^1P leads to a $G'_{1\mathrm{eff}}$ smaller than G'_1. Column 4 shows that the admixture of the two ^1P levels is quite big whereas the admixture of the ^3P's is much smaller.

5.4. THE CONFIGURATIONS $4f6p + 5d^2 + 5d6s$ OF Ce III

5.4.1. *Introduction*

There are 25 levels belonging to these configurations, all of which, excepting the d^2 (^1S), are experimentally known. Their Grotrian diagram is given in fig. 12. Inspection of this diagram shows that the configurations 4f6p and $5d^2$ overlap and that the configuration 5d6s is located about 9000 cm^{-1} above them. This is a typical example of the competition between the $4f6p + 5d^2 + 5d6s$ pairs of electrons. The diagram also shows that in the $5d^2$ and 5d6s configurations the electrons are *LS* coupled, whereas the structure of the 4f6p configuration is characteristic of *jj* coupling. The twelve levels

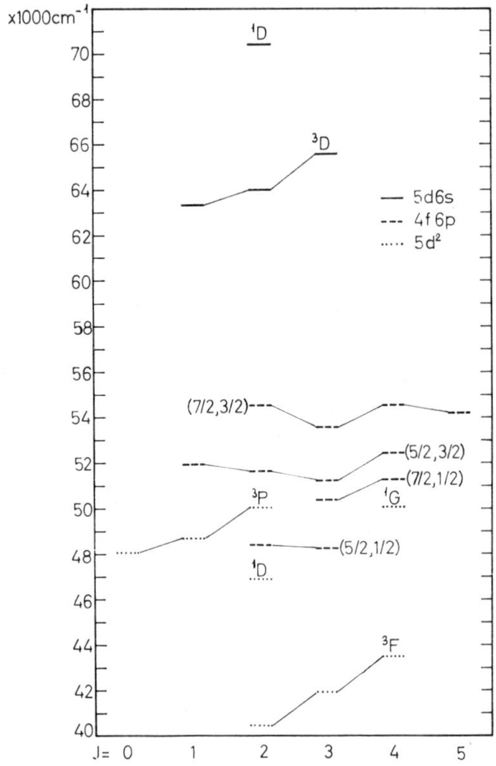

Fig. 12. Grotrian diagram of Ce III $4f6p + 5d^2 + 5d6s$.

belonging to the last configuration are clearly separated into four groups: two doublets characterized by $f_{\frac{5}{2}}p_{\frac{1}{2}}$ and $f_{\frac{7}{2}}p_{\frac{1}{2}}$ respectively, and two quartets characterized by $f_{\frac{5}{2}}p_{\frac{3}{2}}$ and $f_{\frac{7}{2}}p_{\frac{3}{2}}$. The lower quartet is bowl shaped as predicted by the theory, while in the higher quartet the level $(f_{\frac{7}{2}}p_{\frac{3}{2}})_4$ at 54549.34 cm^{-1} is too high. On considering the doublets we note that the splitting of the pair $f_{\frac{5}{2}}p_{\frac{1}{2}}$ is small as expected, whereas the splitting of $f_{\frac{7}{2}}p_{\frac{1}{2}}$ is quite big. These departures from *jj* coupling will be explained later. The spin–orbit parameters ζ_f and ζ_p are directly evaluated from the separations between the four groups of levels: The mean separation of the two doublets, as well as that of the quartets, equals $\frac{7}{2}\zeta_f$; the mean separation of a quartet and a doublet possessing the same value of j_f equals $\frac{3}{2}\zeta_p$.

5.4.2. *Evaluation of the electrostatic parameters; results*

The electrostatic parameters to be evaluated are given in table 18. Initial values for the internal parameters were obtained by linear interpolation or

TABLE 18

Parameters for the even configurations of Ce III

	4f6p	5d²	5d6s
4f6p	F_0, F_2, G_2, G_4(fp)		
5d²	R_1, R_3(fp, d²)	A, B, C (dd)	
5d6s	T_1, T_3(fp, ds)	H (d², ds)	F_0, G_2(ds)

TABLE 19

Parameters for the configurations 4f6p + 5d² + 5d6s of Ce III

Parameter	Initial value	Final value
F_0 (fp)	51989	52001 ± 62
A (d²)	46026	46027 ± 67
F_0 (ds)	66367	66388 ± 96
F_2 (fp)	70	72 ± 6
G_2(fp)	13	14 ± 5
G_4(fp)	6	5 ± 1.5
B (d²)	440	442 ± 3
C (d²)	1450	2006 ± 111
G_2(ds)	2100	2225 ± 141
H (dd, ds)	400	452 ± 37
R_1 (fp, dd)	90	89 ± 3
R_3(fp, dd)	0	0(fixed)
T_1 (fp, ds)	1260	1071 ± 146
T_3 (fp, sd)	0	0(fixed)
ζ_f (fp)	648	644 ± 10
ζ_p (fp)	2160	2155 ± 33
ζ_d (d²)	835	837 ± 14
ζ_d (ds)	900	927 ± 28
Δ		47

TABLE 20

The configurations $4f6p + 5d^2 + 5d6s$ of Ce III

Configuration	Designation	J	Obs.	Calc.	O−C	g-obs.	g-calc.	Purity
$5d^2$	^3F	2	40440	40442	−2		0.679	95%
		3	41939	41938	1		1.083	98%
		4	43517	43515	2		1.247	97%
$5d^2$	^1D	2	46890	46893	−3		1.062	71% + $d^2\ ^3P$ 15%
$5d^2$	^3P	0	48076	48055	−21		$\frac{0}{0}$	99%
		1	48674	48704	−30		1.500	100%
		2	50044	50033	11		1.404	82% + $d^2\ ^1D$ 14%
4f6p	$f_{5/2}\,p_{1/2}$	2	48405	48371	34	0.85	0.813	89%
		3	48267	48316	−49	0.87	0.870	97%
$5d^2$	^1G	4	50058	50068	−10	1.06	1.047	36% + fp ^1G 41% + fp ^1F 15%
4f6p	$f_{7/2}\,p_{1/2}$	3	50375	50377	−2	1.16	1.150	91%
		4	51289	51234	55	1.09?	1.078	41% + $f_{5/2}\,p_{3/2}$ 32% + $d^2\ ^1G$ 20%
4f6p	$f_{5/2}\,p_{3/2}$	1	51932	51927	5	0.40	0.500	95%
		2	51641	51661	−20	0.99	1.002	91%
		3	51262	51219	43	0.92?	0.942	92%
		4	52441	52502	−61	1.135	1.132	45% + $f_{7/2}\,p_{3/2}$ 38% + $d^2\ ^1G$ 16%
4f6p	$f_{7/2}\,p_{3/2}$	2	54556	54560	−4	1.08	1.040	93%
		3	53616	53615	1	1.24	1.204	94%
		4	54549	54541	8	1.05	1.046	53% + $d^2\ ^1G$ 27% + $f_{5/2}\,p_{3/2}$ 12%
		5	54194	54193	1	1.21	1.200	100%
5d6s	^3D	1	63335	63302	33		0.500	95%
		2	64011	64056	−45		1.162	93%
		3	65559	65548	11		1.333	96%
5d6s	^1D	2	70433	70432	1		1.005	90%

extrapolation from neighbouring spectra. The parameters of fp were interpolated from f^2p of Ce II (ref. 10) and Pr III (ref. 10). The parameters of d^2+ds were extrapolated from the configurations $(d+s)^n$ in La II ($n=2$) and Ce II ($n=3$) (ref. 10). These initial parameters were introduced into the theoretical formulas and the deviations between the calculated and observed levels were then examined. The relative heights of the configurations and the numerical values of the CI parameters were then chosen so as to minimize these deviations. The initial parameters which served for the first diagonalization of the energy matrices are given in table 19 under the heading "initial value". The least squares calculation which followed gave a mean error of 47 cm^{-1}. The values of the parameters improved by the least-squares are given under the heading "final value". A comparison of the two columns shows that the parameters hardly changed, except for the parameter C of d^2 which increased appreciably. No information concerning this parameter is available from other third rare-earths spectra. On allowing R_3 and T_3 to change freely they assumed the values 1.4 ± 3.6 and -12 ± 198 respectively, which justifies fixing them on zero. A comparison of calculated and observed values for the levels and their g-values* is given in table 20. The table also includes the composition percentages of the levels with respect to the appropriate coupling schemes.

5.4.3. *Discussion*

Excellent agreement between theory and experiment was obtained by using interpolative values of the parameters. This confirms our assumption on the systematic behaviour of the various parameters.

The results of the calculations confirm our earlier deductions concerning the validity of the Russell–Saunders coupling scheme for d^2 and ds. The deviations from *jj* coupling encountered in the configuration fp may best be explained by means of table 21, which lists the composition percentages of the levels of this configuration in the *LS* and *jj* coupling schemes. The table also includes results obtained in a diagonalization in which CI was completely neglected. A comparison of columns 1 and 2 clearly shows the superiority of the *jj* coupling scheme for all the levels of fp with $J \neq 4$: the greatest components of the eigenvectors always exceed 89% and are in all cases much larger than the components in *LS*. As long as CI is neglected, the same also holds for $J=4$, as shown in column 3 of the table. The inclusion of CI changes the situation completely for the $J=4$ levels: the magnitudes of the

* Observed g-values are those given by Russell et al.[14]).

TABLE 21

Composition percentages of levels belonging to the 4f6p configuration in Ce III

Level (cm^{-1})	J	Composition percentages in LS		Composition percentages in jj		Composition percentages in jj without CI	
51932.34	1	95.3	^3D	95.3	$(\frac{5}{2}, \frac{3}{2})$		
48404.86	2	64.7	^3F	89.1	$(\frac{5}{2}, \frac{1}{2})$		
		17.2	^1D				
		12.8	^3D				
51460.68	2	54.2	^3D	90.7	$(\frac{5}{2}, \frac{3}{2})$		
		27.8	^3F				
		13.3	^1D				
54556.48	2	63.0	^1D	93.3	$(\frac{7}{2}, \frac{3}{2})$		
		27.9	^3D				
48267.00	3	57.4	^3G	96.8	$(\frac{5}{2}, \frac{1}{2})$		
		30.5	^1F				
		10.4	^3F				
50375.00	3	54.4	^3F	90.6	$(\frac{7}{2}, \frac{1}{2})$		
		30.8	^3D				
		13.0	^1F				
51262.21	3	40.8	^3G	91.5	$(\frac{5}{2}, \frac{3}{2})$		
		27.9	^1F				
		23.5	^3F				
53615.98	3	57.1	^3D	94.9	$(\frac{7}{2}, \frac{3}{2})$		
		28.5	^1F				
		10.1	^3F				
50057.60	4	35.8	$d^2\ ^1G$	35.8	$d^2\ ^1G$	99	$d^2\ ^1G$
		41.4	^1G	51.5	$(\frac{7}{2}, \frac{1}{2})$		
		15.4	^3F	10.6	$(\frac{5}{2}, \frac{3}{2})$		
51289.38	4	58.9	^3G	40.6	$(\frac{7}{2}, \frac{1}{2})$	95	$(\frac{7}{2}, \frac{1}{2})$
		19.5	^3F	32.4	$(\frac{5}{2}, \frac{3}{2})$		
		19.6	$d^2\ ^1G$	19.6	$d^2\ ^1G$		
52440.96	4	45.8	^3F	44.9	$(\frac{5}{2}, \frac{3}{2})$	96	$(\frac{5}{2}, \frac{3}{2})$
		35.1	^3G	38.4	$(\frac{7}{2}, \frac{3}{2})$		
		16.2	$d^2\ ^1G$	16.2	$d^2\ ^1G$		
54549.34	4	53.8	^1G	53.3	$(\frac{7}{2}, \frac{3}{2})$	91	$(\frac{7}{2}, \frac{3}{2})$
		27.3	$d^2\ ^1G$	27.3	$d^2\ ^1G$		
		17.7	^3F	12.0	$(\frac{5}{2}, \frac{3}{2})$		
54193.84	5	100	^3G	100	$(\frac{7}{2}, \frac{3}{2})$	100	$(\frac{7}{2}, \frac{3}{2})$

TABLE 22

CI effects in the low even configurations of Ce III

Pairs of repulsing terms	CI responsible for repulsion	Individual repulsions (cm^{-1})	Admixture (%)
fp ^1D–ds ^1D	T_1(fp, ds)	650	1
fp ^3D–ds ^3D	T_1(fp, ds)	750	4
d^2 ^1D–ds ^1D	H (dd, ds)	2100	5.5
fp ^1D–d^2 ^1D	R_1(fp, dd)	130	3.8
fp ^3F–d^2 ^3F	R_1(fp, dd)	250	1.5
fp ^1G–d^2 ^1G	R_1(fp, dd)	1400	27–41

biggest components in *jj* coupling now vary between 40% and 53%, and in two cases they are even smaller than those in *LS*. This clearly indicates a *breakdown of jj coupling* due to *electrostatic configuration interaction.* The interaction responsible for this breakdown is the CI between fp and d^2, which is particularly strong for the ^1G terms. In consequence of this interaction, the assignments of configurational quantum numbers to the two levels 50057.60 and 54549.34, both of which contain about 80% of ^1G, become meaningless. As shown in table 22, the upward repulsion of the level 54549.34, which contains the highest percentage of $(f_{\frac{7}{2}}p_{\frac{3}{2}})_4$, amounts to 1400 cm^{-1}. The distortion of the quartet $f_{\frac{7}{2}}p_{\frac{3}{2}}$ from the bowl structure is thus proved to be attributable to CI. The overall effects of CI in this group of configurations are summarized in table 22. In particular, the interactions mainly responsible for the mutual repulsions of various pairs of terms are emphasized.

The calculations show that the splitting of the $f_{\frac{7}{2}}p_{\frac{1}{2}}$ doublet is due to electrostatic interaction within the fp configuration. As a result of this interaction, the level $(f_{\frac{7}{2}}p_{\frac{1}{2}})_3$ is not pure but contains about 10% of $p_{\frac{3}{2}}$. The quadrupole moment thus acquired by the p-electron causes the splitting of this doublet.

Acknowledgement

I would like to thank Dr. N. Zeldes and my husband, Dr. Z. H. Goldschmidt for reading the manuscript and for many helpful comments.

References

1) E. U. Condon and G. H. Shortley, *The Theory of Atomic Spectra* (Cambridge University Press, Cambridge, 1935).

2) G. Racah, Phys. Rev. **76**, 1352 (1949).
3) G. Racah, Phys. Rev. **62**, 438 (1942).
4) Z. B. Goldschmidt, unpublished material (1961).
5) R. E. Trees, J. Opt. Soc. Am. **54**, 651 (1964).
6) K. Rajnak and B. G. Wybourne, Phys. Rev. **132**, 280 (1963).
7) G. Racah, Phys. Rev. **63**, 367 (1943).
8) Z. B. Goldschmidt, *La Structure Hyperfine Magnétique des Atomes et des Molécules* (C.N.R.S., Paris, 1966).
9) J. Sugar, J. Opt. Soc. Am. **55**, 1058 (1965).
10) Z. B. Goldschmidt, unpublished material.
11) Z. B. Goldschmidt and A. Pasternak, unpublished material.
12) Z. H. Goldschmidt, private communication.
13) B. R. Judd, H. M. Crosswhite and Hannah Crosswhite, Results presented at the Atomic Spectroscopy Symposium, N.B.S. Gaithersburg, Maryland (September 1967) and private communication.
14) H. N. Russell, A. B. King and R. J. Lang, Phys. Rev. **52**, 456 (1937).
15) J. Sugar, J. Opt. Soc. Am. **55**, 33 (1965).
16) S. Amiel, M.Sc. Thesis (1955).
17) D. Stern, M.Sc. Thesis (1955).
18) J. Sugar, J. Opt. Soc. Am. **53**, 831 (1963).
19) W. R. Callahan, J. Opt. Soc. Am. **53**, 695 (1963).
20) B. W. Bryant, J. Opt. Soc. Am. **55**, 771 (1965).
21) Z. B. Goldschmidt and S. Nir, unpublished material.
22) H. N. Russell and W. F. Meggers, Natl. Bur. Std. J. Res. **9**, 625 (1932).
23) G. R. Harrison, W. F. Albertson and N. F. Hosford, J. Opt. Soc. Am. **32**, 439 (1941).
24) N. Rosen, G. R. Harrison and J. R. McNally, Jr., Phys. Rev. **61**, 167 (1942).
25) G. Racah, Z. B. Goldschmidt and A. Lonka, unpublished material.
26) P. Schuurmans, Physica **11**, 419 (1946).
27) H. N. Russell, J. Opt. Soc. Am. **40**, 550 (1950).
28) N. Zeldes, Phys. Rev. **90**, 413 (1953).
29) Z. B. Goldschmidt and S. Nir, to be published.
30) G. Smith and B. G. Wybourne, J. Opt. Soc. Am. **55**, 1278 (1965).
31) J. R. McNally and K. L. Van der Sluis, J. Opt. Soc. Am. **49**, 200 (1959).
32) Z. B. Goldschmidt, J. Opt. Soc. Am. **53**, 594 (1963).
33) B. R. Judd and L. C. Marquet, J. Opt. Soc. Am. **52**, 504 (1962).
34) W. F. Meggers, private communication (1965), and Natl. Bur. Std. J. Res. **71 A**, 396 (1967).
35) G. Racah, Z. B. Goldschmidt and Y. Bordarier, unpublished material.
36) L. F. H. Bovey and R. W. B. Pearse, AERE c/R 1976, 19 pp. (1956).
37) W. F. Meggers, unpublished material (1957).
38) M. Gehatia, Phys. Rev. **94**, 618 (1954).
39) Z. B. Goldschmidt and Y. Bordarier, unpublished material.
40) W. C. Martin, private communication.
41) Z. B. Goldschmidt and D. Salomon, unpublished material.
42) Z. B. Goldschmidt, unpublished material.
43) L. C. Marquet, Ph. D. Thesis, University of California, Berkeley (1964).
44) G. Racah, Z. B. Goldschmidt and S. Toaff, J. Opt. Soc. Am. **56**, 407 (1966).

45) L. C. Marquet and S. P. Davis, J. Opt. Soc. Am. **55**, 471 (1965).
46) L. C. Marquet and W. E. Behring, J. Opt. Soc. Am. **55**, 576 (1965).
47) P. Camus, J. Phys. (Paris) **27**, 717 (1966).
48) B. R. Judd, Phys. Rev. **125**, 613 (1962).
49) J. G. Conway and B. G. Wybourne, Phys. Rev. **130**, 2325 (1963).
50) W. F. Meggers, J. Opt. Soc. Am. **31**, 157 (1941).
51) N. Pelletier-Allard, private communication.
52) J. Reader, private communication.
53) B. G. Wybourne, *Spectroscopic Properties of Rare Earths* (Interscience, New York, 1965).
54) R. Lang, Can. J. Res. A **13**, 1 (1935); A **14**, 127 (1936).
55) J. Sugar and V. Kaufman, J. Opt. Soc. Am. **55**, 1283 (1965).

SUBJECT INDEX